COMPUTING SCIENCE

Third Edition

PETER BISHOP

Nelson

Thomas Nelson and Sons Ltd
Nelson House   Mayfield Road
Walton-on-Thames   Surrey
KT12 5PL   UK

51 York Place
Edinburgh
EH1 3JD   UK

Thomas Nelson (Hong Kong) Ltd
Toppan Building 10/F
22A Westlands Road
Quarry Bay   Hong Kong

Thomas Nelson Australia
102 Dodds Street
South Melbourne
Victoria 3205   Australia

Nelson Canada
1120 Birchmount Road
Scarborough   Ontario
M1K 5G4   Canada

First published by Thomas Nelson and Sons Ltd 1991

ISBN 0-17-448180-2
NPN 9 8 7 6 5 4 3 2 1

Printed in Hong Kong.

Acknowledgement is due to the following for permission to use
photographs.
ATEX: 31.3; Barclays Bank: 1.1; British Steel: 1.2; Chris Ridgers: 2.3; Cray
Research: 9.2; Neil Croft: 34.7; Digital: 15.2; ES2: 11.1, 11.2, 11.3, 11.4, 11.5,
34.4, 34.5, 34.6; Leslie Garland: 14.8; GEC: 31.1; The Guardian: 36.2;
Hewlett Packard: 14.4; Hitachi: 10.2; Hutchinson Library: 36.4; IBM: 1.3,
2.4, 9.1, 11.6, 11.7, 14.5, 35.1, 36.5; Intel: 2.2, 2.6, 13.1; Novosti: 36.3;
PIRA: 14.3; Psion: 2.5; Research Machines: 14.2, 14.6, 15.1, 23.1; John Rose
Associates: 31.2; Rolls Royce: 34.1, 34.2; Science Photo Library: 1.4, 10.3,
11.8, 32.2, 36.1, 2.1; Sun Micro Systems: 14.1; Bob Watkins: 35.2; John
Walmsley: 10.4; Wylfa Nuclear Power Station: 32.1.

Preface

The Computing Common Core document, from which all UK Advanced Level syllabuses in Computing are derived, states the aims of A Level Computing courses as follows:
'Syllabuses in Computing should seek to develop:

- an understanding of the principles of computing
- the application of these principles
- the skills of problem solving in a computing context.'

Computing Science subscribes to these aims. It gives a broad and thorough introduction to Computing Science. It is tailored to meet the requirements of all the examination boards in the United Kingdom which offer courses in Computing or Computing Science at Advanced Level. Almost all the material in the syllabuses for these courses is covered in the book, which contains a number of questions from past examination papers. Also covered are syllabuses of other Commonwealth countries which are equivalent to the UK courses.

In addition, Computing Science has been written with the requirements of the computing industry in mind. The material, while conforming to the examination syllabuses, is also in line with accepted practices in the computing industry. A few topics, notably integrated circuit design, software engineering, artificial intelligence and expert systems are covered because of their significance in the world of computing. It is assumed that in due course these topics will be assimilated into Computing Science syllabuses.

It is realised that a book of this nature is useful for a number of other purposes. These include a reference book for teachers preparing computing courses at GCSE or Advanced level, a textbook for students of Advanced Level and equivalent courses at colleges of further education, and a foundation book for students embarking on computing courses at universities or polytechnics.

Computing Science covers five major subject areas: the principles of computing, the design of computer hardware, the various layers of computer software, the theory and practice of computer applications, and a brief look at the social implications and likely future of computing. Microprocessors are given due, but not undue, attention.

A model computer, the AMC, has been designed to introduce the topics of processor architecture and operation, and low level language. The AMC is tailored specifically to the requirements of the book. It is also an example of the most recent trend in processor architecture – Reduced instruction set computer (Risc) architecture. In the same series as this book there is a software package which enables the AMC to be simulated on a microcomputer.

Many of the topics introduced in general terms are reinforced by case studies, drawn from various sectors of the computing industry. Case studies include processor architecture, high level languages, compilers, operating systems, data communications networks and computer applications.

Some exercise questions in the book are marked ◆. This indicates that they are considerably above the average level of difficulty of the material, and may be omitted without loss of continuity.

The Third Edition

■ The Third Edition retains the aims and objectives of the two previous editions. All the material has been revised to bring it up to date with developments in the computing industry, and changes in syllabuses. The major revisions are to give increased emphasis to computer applications, and to the skill of problem solving in a computing context. The bulk of these changes are in the following chapters:

9 Computer Structure: redrafted to reflect the continuous range in the capacity of computer systems, from laptops to supercomputers, and the emergence of desktop workstations as a significant class of computers.

13 Advanced Processor Features: extensively revised to incorporate Risc architectures and parallel processing.

15 Processor Case Studies: the Research Machines Nimbus PC-186 has been replaced by the Nimbus PC-386.

21 Software Packages: a new chapter reflecting the growing significance of this type of software. Subsequent chapters have been re-numbered.

24 Fourth Generation Languages: retitled to reflect the widespread acceptance of the term, in place of 'software development tools'.

26 Information System Design (previously Chapter 25: Principles of Data Processing): substantially revised to reflect the emphasis on applications and problem-solving in current syllabuses.

29 User Interfacing: a new chapter to cover the increasingly important topic of user interface design.

32 Control Systems: a new chapter to complement the material on data communications, giving coverage to the three aspects of information technology: computing, communications and control.

34 Applications Case Studies: extensively revised with the inclusion of three new case studies: the Rolls Royce advanced integrated manufacturing system, the Solo 1400 Asic design system and the London Underground automated ticketing system.

35 The Computing Industry: updated to reflect current developments and revised to incorporate material from the chapter on Data Processing Personnel in the previous edition.

36 Computing in Perspective: extensively revised to reflect current developments and increasing emphasis in syllabuses.

Past Examination Papers

■ The set of past examination papers from the previous edition has been completely replaced with a selection from recent papers. All past examination paper questions are now in the Revision Exercise (Chapter 37). The following abbreviations are used to identify questions from past examination papers:

AEB   Associated Examining Board
OLE   Oxford Delegacy of Local Examinations
UL   University of London School Examinations Council
JMB   Joint Matriculation Board
UCLES   University of Cambridge Local Examination Syndicate
WJEC   Welsh Joint Education Committee
NIEB   Northern Ireland Examinations Board.

Acknowledgements

I am grateful to a number of people who have given their time, expertise and enthusiasm to help me with various aspects of this book.

From Imperial College, London: Valerie Downes gave advice on the overall structure of the book, and reviewed all the material in detail; Derek Brough helped with the design of the AMC, and with the material on compilers and interpreters; James Jacobsen advised me on databases and Cobol; Martin Cripps gave a second opinion on the AMC design; Meir Lehman provided advice and source material on software engineering; John Darlington advised on functional programming and Richard Ennals provided material on logic programming.

Help with the case studies has come from a number of sources. The following people have provided source material, reviewed drafts of sections and given other helpful advice: William White of Cray Research (UK) Limited for the Cray-2 case study; David Jay and Jeremy Welsh of Research Machines Limited for the RM Nimbus case study; Mr E. Wilson of ICL for the ICL 2900 Series case study and its operating system, VME/B; Tony Hetherington of Prospero Software for the ProPascal case study; Richard Mulholland of Cognos Limited for the Powerhouse software development system; Max Butcher from Rolls Royce for the AIMS case study; the Public Relations department of London Transport for the Automated Ticketing System; Keith Simmonds and John Clarke of CBS Records for the case study on the CBS European manufacturing system; Dr Alan Gadd from the Meteorological Office for the weather forecasting system; Christopher Gare from European Silicon Structures for the Solo 1400 case study.

Thanks are due to the following examination boards, who gave permission to reproduce questions from past examination papers: the Associated Examining Board, the Joint Matriculation Board, the University of London School Examinations Council, the Oxford Delegacy of Local Examinations, the Welsh Joint Education Committee, the Northern Ireland Examinations Board, the Southern Universities Joint Board and the University of Cambridge Local Examinations Syndicate.

My thanks go to Sarah Bishop and Jennifer Davies who helped with the typing and checking of the Third Edition, and to Sheila Maynard of the Association of Computing/IT Teachers, who reviewed the entire draft. The text was entered and edited using the WordStar word processor on a Research Machines Nimbus PC-186 and a Compaq LTE/286, and transferred for printing to a Research Machines 380Z.

Peter Bishop
10th September 1990

Contents

1 Introduction — 1
1.1 Objectives of the Book — 1
1.2 Skills Taught — 1
1.3 An Overview of Computing — 2
1.4 What is a Computer? — 3
1.5 Capabilities and Limitations of Computers — 3
1.6 Conclusion — 4

Principles of Computing

2 Concepts of Computing — 5
2.1 Information and Data — 5
2.2 System — 5
2.3 Computer and Program — 6
2.4 Hardware and Software — 8
2.5 Algorithm — 8
2.6 Module and Interface — 9
2.7 Design and Implementation — 10
2.8 General-Purpose and Dedicated Computers — 10
2.9 The Theory of Computing — 11
2.10 Integrated Circuit Technology — 12
2.11 Conclusion — 12

3 Data — 14
3.1 Binary Coding of Data — 14
3.2 Place Value — 14
3.3 Character Code — 15
3.4 Binary Coded Decimal — 16
3.5 Sign-and-Magnitude Code — 16
3.6 Twos Complement Numbers — 16
3.7 Ones Complement Numbers — 17
3.8 Fractions — 18
3.9 Floating Point Numbers — 19
3.10 Bits, Bytes and Words — 20
3.11 Octal and Hexadecimal Numbers — 20
3.12 Self-Checking Codes: Parity — 21
3.13 Data Encryption — 22
3.14 Analogue Data — 22
3.15 Conclusion — 24

4 Data Structures — 27
4.1 The Concept of Structured Data — 27
4.2 Pointers — 27
4.3 Strings — 28
4.4 Arrays — 28
4.5 Static and Dynamic Data Structures — 28
4.6 Stacks — 29
4.7 Queues — 30
4.8 Lists — 31
4.9 Trees — 33
4.10 Data Types — 34

4.11 Implementation of Data Structures — 34
4.12 Conclusion — 35

5 Computer Arithmetic — 40
5.1 Characteristics of Computer Arithmetic — 40
5.2 Integer Arithmetic — 41
5.3 Floating Point Arithmetic — 44
5.4 Conclusion — 46

6 Boolean Logic — 48
6.1 Two-State Representation of Data — 48
6.2 The Elementary Logic Operations — 48
6.3 Logic Operation Symbols — 51
6.4 Combinations of Logic Operations — 51
6.5 Conclusion — 53

7 Artificial Intelligence — 56
7.1 Notions of Intelligence — 56
7.2 Machine Intelligence — 56
7.3 Knowledge Representation — 57
7.4 Game Playing Programs — 59
7.5 Reasoning Programs — 59
7.6 Natural Language Recognition — 60
7.7 Image Recognition — 61
7.8 Expert Systems — 61
7.9 Conclusion — 61

Computer Hardware

8 Logic Circuits — 63
8.1 Hardware Implementation of Logic Operations — 63
8.2 Control Switches — 64
8.3 Masks — 65
8.4 Decoders — 65
8.5 Addition Units — 67
8.6 Flip-Flops — 68
8.7 Registers — 71
8.8 Uncommitted Logic Arrays — 73
8.9 Conclusion — 73

9 Computer Structure — 76
9.1 The Functional Units of a Computer — 76
9.2 The Seven Classes of Computer System — 77
9.3 A Typical Microcomputer — 79
9.4 A Typical Mid-range Computer — 79
9.5 A Typical Supercomputer — 80
9.6 Conclusion — 81

10 Processor Architecture — 82
10.1 Objectives of a Processor — 82
10.2 The Structure of a Processor — 82
10.3 A Model Computer - the AMC — 83
10.4 The AMC Memory Unit — 84
10.5 Construction of Immediate Access Store — 85

10.6	The AMC Arithmetic and Logic Unit	86
10.7	The AMC Input/Output Unit	88
10.8	The AMC Control Unit	89
10.9	The AMC and Real Processors	91
10.10	Conclusion	91

11 Processor Fabrication 93
11.1	Transistors and Integrated Circuits	93
11.2	Integrated Circuit Design	94
11.3	Integrated Circuit Fabrication	95
11.4	Computer Manufacture	97
11.5	Computer Design	97
11.6	Printed Circuit Board Design	99
11.7	Computer Assembly	99
11.8	Testing, Commissioning and Maintenance	100
11.9	Conclusion	102

12 Processor Operation 103
12.1	Machine Language	103
12.2	Addressing	103
12.3	AMC Machine Language	105
12.4	Example Program 12.1	111
12.5	Stack Manipulation and Subprogram Calls	112
12.6	Example Program 12.2	115
12.7	The Instruction Cycle	116
12.8	Interrupts	118
12.9	Microcode	119
12.10	Conclusion	119

13 Advanced Processor Features 122
13.1	Duplicate Processing Circuits	122
13.2	Distributed Array Processing	122
13.3	Advanced Memory Architecture	123
13.4	Pipelining	123
13.5	Cache Stores	124
13.6	Content-Addressable Memory	125
13.7	Risc Processors	125
13.8	Parallel Computer Architectures	125
13.9	Conclusion	126

14 Peripheral Devices 128
14.1	Terminals	128
14.2	Input Devices	129
14.3	Output Devices	132
14.4	Backing Store	135
14.5	Serial and Random Access to Data	137
14.6	Interfacing Processors to Peripherals	138
14.7	Automatic Checking During Data Transfer	139
14.8	Analogue Interfacing	140
14.9	Conclusion	140

15 Processor Case Studies 143
15.1	Research Machines Nimbus PC-386 Microcomputer	143
15.2	Digital Equipment VAX Mid-range Computer	149
15.3	ICL 2900 Series Computers	153
15.4	Cray-2 Supercomputer	154
15.5	Conclusion	159

Computer Software

16 Assembly Languages 161
16.1	The Nature and Objectives of Assembly Languages	161
16.2	The Development of Assembly Languages	162
16.3	Features of Assembly Languages	162
16.4	AMC Assembly Language	166
16.5	Example Program 16.1	167
16.6	Example Program 16.2	168
16.7	Example Program 16.3	169
16.8	Example Program 16.4	171
16.9	Example Program 16.5	172
16.10	Uses of Assembly Languages	174
16.11	Conclusion	175

17 Assemblers 178
17.1	Nature and Objectives of an Assembler	178
17.2	Tasks Performed by an Assembler	178
17.3	The Structure of an Assembler Program	180
17.4	The AMC Assembler	180
17.5	Languages of Assemblers	181
17.6	Conclusion	181

18 High Level Languages 183
18.1	What is a High Level Language?	183
18.2	The Development of High Level Languages	183
18.3	Types of High Level Languages	184
18.4	Objectives of High Level Languages	184
18.5	Features of High Level Languages	185
18.6	An Assessment of High Level Languages	189
18.7	Conclusion	189

19 High Level Language Case Studies 192
19.1	Fortran	192
19.2	Algol 60	195
19.3	Cobol	199
19.4	Basic	202
19.5	Pascal	205
19.6	C	209
19.7	Lisp	212
19.8	Prolog	214
19.9	Conclusion	216

20 Compilers and Interpreters 219
20.1 The Objectives of Language Translation 219
20.2 Principles of Compilation and Interpretation 220
20.3 Extended BNF 220
20.4 Editing 222
20.5 The Steps of Compilation 222
20.6 Linkage 226
20.7 Library Modules 226
20.8 Loading 226
20.9 Run-Time Diagnostics 227
20.10 Interpreters 228
20.11 Case Study: Prospero Pascal Compiler 228
20.12 Conclusion 230

21 Software Packages 234
21.1 Characteristics of Software Packages 234
21.2 Word Processing 234
21.3 Spreadsheets 236
21.4 Databases 237
21.5 Drawing and CAD Packages 238
21.6 Desktop Publishing Packages 240
21.7 Benefits of Software Packages 241
21.8 Conclusion 242

22 Operating Systems 244
22.1 Types of Computer Operation 244
22.2 The Nature of an Operating System 245
22.3 The Development of Operating Systems 245
22.4 Objectives of Operating Systems 246
22.5 The Functions of an Operating System 246
22.6 Desirable Features 247
22.7 The Structure of a Typical Operating System 247
22.8 Bootstrap Loaders 252
22.9 An Assessment of Operating Systems 253
22.10 Conclusion 253

23 Operating Systems Case Studies 256
23.1 MS-DOS 256
23.2 Unix 259
23.3 VME/B 261
23.4 Conclusion 264

24 Fourth Generation Languages 265
24.1 Limitations of High Level Languages 265
24.2 The Objectives of Fourth Generation Languages 265
24.3 Fourth Generation Languages: General Structure 266

24.4 Data Dictionary 267
24.5 Screen Design Facilities 267
24.6 Report Generator 268
24.7 Application Generator 268
24.8 Case Study: Powerhouse Software Development System 268
24.9 Conclusion 272

25 Software Engineering 273
25.1 The Objectives of Software Engineering 273
25.2 Program Structure 273
25.3 Program Design 274
25.4 Proving the Correctness of Programs 275
25.5 Computer-aided Software Engineering 276
25.6 Conclusion 276

Computer Applications

26 Information System Design 278
26.1 The Need for Information Systems 278
26.2 Types of Information System 278
26.3 Feasibility Study 280
26.4 System Analysis 281
26.5 System Design 281
26.6 System Development 287
26.7 System Testing 290
26.8 System Implementation 290
26.9 System Documentation 290
26.10 System Maintenance 291
26.11 System Troubleshooting 291
26.12 Conclusion 292

27 File Structure 294
27.1 Files, Records, Fields and Keys 294
27.2 File Structures 294
27.3 Blocking Strategy 296
27.4 Conclusion 297

28 File Processing 299
28.1 Data Capture 299
28.2 Validation 299
28.3 Sorting in Main Store 300
28.4 Merging 301
28.5 Sorting Large Files 301
28.6 Searching 302
28.7 Updating 304
28.8 Report Generation 304
28.9 Data Security 305
28.10 Conclusion 305

29 User Interfacing 308
29.1 Principles of User Interfacing 308
29.2 Command-driven Interfaces 308
29.3 Menu-driven Interfaces 309

29.4	Windows Environments	310
29.5	Intelligent User Interfaces	310
29.6	Conclusion	311

30 Database Systems 312
30.1	What is a Database System?	312
30.2	Advantages of Databases	313
30.3	Database Concepts	313
30.4	Database System Elements	315
30.5	Structuring the Data Model	316
30.6	An Assessment of Databases	318
30.7	Conclusion	318

31 Data Communications Systems 320
31.1	Concepts of Data Transmission	320
31.2	Communications Networks	324
31.3	Local Area Network Architectures	326
31.4	Message and Packet Switching	328
31.5	Case Study: Vaxmail	329
31.6	Conclusion	330

32 Control Systems 333
32.1	The Need for Automatic Control	333
32.2	Principles of Automatic Control	334
32.3	Analogue and Digital Control Systems	334
32.4	Electronic Control Systems	335
32.5	Conclusion	336

33 Expert and Knowledge-Based Systems 337
33.1	Objectives of Expert Systems	337
33.2	Techniques of Expert System Design	337
33.3	Intelligent Knowledge-Based Systems	338
33.4	Applications of Expert Systems	338
33.5	Case Study 1: Mycin	339
33.6	Case Study 2: Prospector	339
33.7	Conclusion	339

34 Applications Case Studies 340
34.1	Rolls Royce Advanced Integrated Manufacturing System	340
34.2	Sony Music Manufacturing System	346
34.3	Meteorological Office Atmospheric Model	352
34.4	Solo 1400 Asic Design System	359
34.5	London Underground Ticketing System	365

Computing in Context

35 The Computing Industry 371
35.1	The World Computing Situation	371
35.2	The Computing Industry by Activities	374
35.3	Working in the Computing Industry	377
35.4	Users and User Groups	380
35.5	Professional Associations	380
35.6	Conclusion	381

36 Computing in Perspective 383
36.1	Economic Reasons for Computerisation	383
36.2	Effects on Organisations and Individuals	384
36.3	Employment and Unemployment	384
36.4	Privacy of Personal Data	385
36.5	Security of Data	385
36.6	Consequences of System Failures	386
36.7	Computer Crime	386
36.8	Computers and Political Control	387
36.9	Political Consequences of Computerisation	387
36.10	Computers in a World of Change	387
36.11	Conclusion	389

37 Revision Exercises 392

38 Glossary of Terms 417

39 Teachers' Notes 429

40 Answers to Exercises 432

Index 464

1 Introduction

A study of computing at Advanced Level is no mean undertaking. At the start, it is essential to set out the objectives to be borne in mind, the skills which will be acquired along the way, and the ground which will be covered. This chapter covers these three areas. It states the objectives of a study of computing at this level, lists the skills which are taught, and concludes with an overview of the field of study – computing.

No previous knowledge of computing is assumed in this text. For those who do have previous knowledge of the subject, this chapter provides a concise review of what should already be known. It also paves the way for the following chapter, which discusses the fundamental concepts of computing in some detail.

1.1 Objectives of the Book

■ The overall objective of this text is to provide a grounding in all the major aspects of computing, which is both sufficiently broad and sufficiently thorough for the courses for which it is intended. Thus the book covers a wide range of material, and each aspect is treated in a fair amount of detail.

In more detail, the objectives of the book are as follows:

1 To introduce and develop the fundamental ideas which form the basis of computing and the design of computers.
2 To introduce the essential features of the design of computers, and of associated devices which make up a computer system.
3 To introduce the types of instructions which govern the way in which computers work, and discuss the functions performed by sets of these instructions at various levels.
4 To introduce the techniques used to apply computers to a wide range of tasks, and the associated skills of problem solving with the aid of computers.
5 To provide an introduction to the computing industry.
6 To place computing in its broader perspective, discussing the implications of the widespread use of computers.

These objectives indicate a mixture of theory and practice, of abstract ideas and specific implementations of these ideas. The overall structure of the book is based on these objectives, in the above order.

1.2 Skills Taught

■ The knowledge and associated skills acquired during a computing course are listed below, not in any particular order of importance. Some are related specifically to computing, others are more general. For many examination syllabuses, the sixth and seventh in the list are the most significant.

1 The ability to perceive structures in collections of information, and manipulate these information structures.
2 An appreciation of the concept of a system, and an ability to use this concept in practical situations.
3 A familiarity with the theory of logic which underlies much of the theory of computing.
4 An appreciation of the principles of computer design.

5 An appreciation of the tasks performed by the layers of software which transform the hardware of a computer into a useful device.

6 A thorough grounding in the principles of information processing in relation to computer applications.

7 The ability to apply a knowledge of computer systems to the solution of a range of problems, at an appropriate level.

8 Clear, concise use of language, particularly in communicating technical information.

It is unrealistic to expect that all the skills listed in this section will be completely mastered during this course; nevertheless they do represent directions in which efforts should be directed. There are many benefits in posssessing some or all of these skills. The last skill mentioned, the clear, concise use of language, cannot be overemphasised. A poor performance here can obscure capabilities in all the other areas.

These skills can only be developed through practice. Working through the exercises at the end of each chapter of the book is a vital first step. The project work which is an essential part of most computing courses at this level is where many of the ideas in this text are put into practice. It is important to regard project work as a natural implementation of the theory presented in this text, and not as a separate activity.

1.3
An Overview of Computing

Most activities in industrialised countries rely heavily on computer systems.

■ The word 'computing' is used frequently in this book. It is an old word which has acquired a new meaning. Computing is the theory, design, manufacture and application of computers and associated electronic systems for communications and control. In particular, it relates to the integration of computers, communications and control systems to provide services to users. Many activities in the industrialised world are heavily dependent on integrated electronic systems of this nature, and their use is increasing all the time.

Other terms, such as 'informatics' and 'information technology' (IT) are used in a similar context, but the word 'computing' is adequate for the purposes of this book.

Computing, as it is now understood, is a young, optimistic and sometimes aggressive activity. Like nuclear energy, radar and jet propulsion, it had its origins in the Second World War. Although the beginnings of computing were less spectacular than those of the other technologies, the computing industry has grown to become one of the world's largest single industries. Its growth has not always been steady, and a number of computer companies have prospered for a while, and

A computerised production line

then gone out of business. However, in spite of these short-term setbacks, and uncertain economic conditions at various times, computing continues to grow and prosper. The quality of the information systems in a company, and the extent of computerisation in an economy are key indicators of economic strength.

Computing is an activity which provides employment for millions of people, directly and indirectly. It affects hundreds of millions of others – everyone in the western world, and an increasing number in the east and the third world. Much of the prosperity of industrial countries can be attributed to the improvements in efficiency and productivity brought about by the widespread use of information technology. Although its effects are generally beneficial, this is not always the case.

1.4 What is a Computer?

■ This section introduces (or revises) some essential points about the nature of a computer.

In simple terms, a computer is a digital electronic information processing machine:

Digital means that computers work by storing information in digital form, in codes which represent letters or the digits of numbers. Sounds and pictures are also represented in digital form.

Electronic indicates that a computer is built up from solid-state electronic components, known as integrated circuits (ICs) or, more commonly, as chips.

Information processing is a general term which describes the range of work which computers can do. Almost everything we do, from writing a letter to landing spacecraft on the moon, involves the processing of information in some way. Many activities in commerce and industry are directly concerned with information processing. For example, a bank transaction is almost entirely an information processing activity, as is booking an air flight or a theatre ticket. Controlling a steel plant, nuclear reactor or a rocket in flight involves processing large amounts of information quickly. The main applications of computing are in activities such as these.

A **machine** is a device which performs useful work. Describing a computer as such puts computers in the same category as windmills, printing presses, locomotives and sewing machines. Machines can work well or badly, and no machine is infallible.

The commonest type of computer in use, a desktop computer.

1.5 Capabilities and Limitations of Computers

■ Computers can carry out seven types of operation, all involving information. These are input, output, storage, retrieval, sending, receiving and processing of information.

Input is the action of getting information into a computer. There are many methods of input, the commonest of which is via a keyboard like a typewriter keyboard.

Output is the action of getting information out of a computer. Two common methods of output are to display information on a screen or to print it.

Storage is making a permanent copy of information which the computer can use again later. The most popular means of storage are magnetic tapes and magnetic disks.

Retrieval is the action of reading the information back from a magnetic disk or tape.

Sending is transferring information to another computer or electronic system, via a data communications network. The network may be local, connecting computers in the same building, or long-distance, via telephone lines and satellite links.

Receiving is accepting information sent by another computer or electronic system.

Processing includes sorting, selecting, combining and re-arranging information, as well as performing calculations. Computers are also able to draw conclusions from information.

In addition to the above seven types of operation, some computers and many dedicated electronic systems are used for **control** purposes. They regulate the operation of other systems.

Information processing includes tasks which require some measure of intelligence when carried out by a person. However, the extent to which computers may be regarded as intelligent is limited. For example, computers cannot take initiatives, respond to unforeseen circumstances or make moral judgements. Artificial intelligence, discussed in a later chapter, is an area of rapid development.

1.6 Conclusion

■ This chapter has outlined the objectives of the book, given an indication of some of the skills which may be acquired during its study, and taken a general look at the field of computing, and at the nature, capabilities and limitations of computers.

The next chapter takes the ideas introduced here, and re-states them in a more precise way. At the end of the book is a discussion of the broader implications of computing.

2 Concepts of Computing

This chapter builds on the ideas about computing introduced in the previous chapter. It introduces a small number of key concepts of computing. Each concept is discussed, and a working definition of the concept is given which is adequate for the purposes of this book.

2.1 Information and Data

■ **Information** is a general term covering facts and figures, which may or may not be related. We gather information by looking, reading, listening, touching, tasting and smelling. The word is used in this book in its generally accepted sense. Information may be vital or trivial, true or false.

Data, on the other hand, has a much more precise meaning. Data is information in a form which is acceptable for input to, and processing by, a computer system. In other words, data is a representation of information.

Data may be in the form of individual items, but is much more commonly handled in large, structured collections. Items of data are significant in themselves, and in relation to the structure in which they occur. For example, a telephone number – an individual item of data – is not of much use unless it is associated with a name. The same applies to an address. The most useful grouping of such data is a name, together with the associated address and telephone number.

An important point to realise is that data, on its own, has no meaning. Only when some interpretation is placed on the data does it acquire meaning. In other words:

data + interpretation = meaningful information.

Furthermore, computers cannot place interpretations on data. Only people are capable of interpreting data. This must be borne in mind when considering the extent to which computers may be regarded as intelligent.

2.2 System

■ The idea of a **system** is very important in the world of computing. A computer is often referred to as a computer system (or just a system). Essentially, a system is a collection of parts working together towards some common goal. For example, a well trained sports team is a system, a poorly trained team is not.

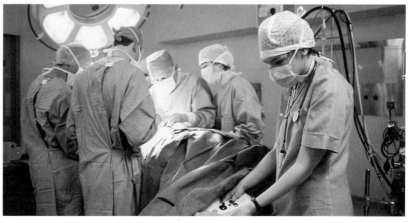

A surgical team in action. They are working together to perform an operation, using the necessary equipment. The team and their equipment are functioning as a system.

Just as goals have sub-goals, so do systems have **subsystems**. A subsystem is a part of a system which accomplishes a part of the goals of the system. For example, a motor car is a system, and its braking system is a subsystem. The braking system accomplishes one aspect of the goals of the car.

A system has a boundary which separates it from its environment. For example, a ship is a system, with its hull forming the boundary with part of its environment, the sea. Both physical matter and information can cross a system boundary. For example, water can pass through a hole in a ship's hull and the ship's echo sounder passes information about the depth of the water through the hull.

The way in which information passes across its boundary defines the interfaces of the system. An interface is a point of contact between one system and another. A system can be described in terms of its interfaces, and a specification of the tasks it performs. For example, a telephone is a system which accepts incoming sounds at the mouthpiece, and transforms them into electrical signals sent out on its cable, and accepts incoming electrical signals on its cable, and transforms them into sounds at the earpiece. There is an international standard which describes in detail the electrical interface of a telephone.

A computer is a system, containing a number of subsystems, with defined interfaces between the subsystems, and between the computer system and its environment. Computers in use are always part of larger systems: business systems, research systems, administrative systems, etc. In each case, the work done by the computer contributes towards the achievement of the goals of the larger system. For example, a cash terminal assists a bank in fulfilling its goal of providing financial services to its customers.

2.3 Computer and Program

■ In Section 1.4, a computer is described as a digital electronic information processing machine, capable of seven types of operation: input, output, storage, retrieval, sending, receiving and processing. In this section, a fuller definition is discussed.

Making use of the concept of data, a concise definition of a computer is as follows:

> A computer is a machine which, under the control of a stored program, automatically accepts and processes data, and supplies the results of that processing.

Although a slightly broader definition of a computer will be considered in a moment, several points in this definition deserve closer study.

A computer is controlled by a stored program. A program is a set of instructions which control the operation of a computer. The set of instructions which a computer is using at a particular time is stored inside the computer. The computer works through the instructions automatically. The ability to store a complete set of instructions, and then work through them, is one of the distinguishing features of a computer. It also applies to other programmable devices such as automatic washing machines and video recorders.

Furthermore, instructions and data are stored together, and no distinction is made between them. Under some circumstances, instructions are manipulated like data, for example when a program is being copied from a storage device into a computer memory.

A computer is a data processing machine. The phrase 'data processing' encompasses a wide range of activities. Processing includes sorting and selecting data, creating and maintaining data structures, performing calculations and making decisions based on the data. These operations can be put to use in a great number of applications.

Computers are sometimes referred to as intelligent machines. The word 'intelligent' in this context must be treated with caution. What it means is that computers can be instructed to manipulate data in a way which people regard as intelligent. Recent developments in computing are leading to increased intelligence built into computers, but it comes nowhere near the general level of intelligence of a person.

In Section 2.1 it was pointed out that data is a representation of information, without any inherent meaning. The data is represented in a computer as sets of symbols. Data processing is manipulating this data in a number of ways: a computer is essentially a symbol manipulation machine. It follows that processing does not have any inherent meaning – a computer does not 'understand' what it is doing. A computer can make decisions based on the values of items of data, and these decisions can be interpreted as reasoned conclusions. However, this decision-making capability can only be applied to specific situations, where one choice from a specified set is possible, and all the data needed to make the choice is available. Examples include certain types of medical diagnosis and prospecting for oil.

Many of the limitations of computers are shown up in the way in which they deal with text – data which represents statements in a natural language such as English. A computer can manipulate text as directed by a typist (word processing) and translate individual words and phrases from one language to another. However, at present a computer cannot interpret extended passages in a natural language, nor can it translate such passages from one language to another.

The above definition of a computer, as a single processing device controlled by a single program, although adequate for many purposes, is somewhat limited. An extended definition, more in line with contemporary computer design, is now developed.

Most computers contain more than one processing element, and require several programs for their operation. Computers draw on large stores of structured data and often communicate with other computing and associated systems as they work. They can control a wide range of input and output devices. The processing, input and output devices, programs, sets of data and communications links, are the resources of the computer. Accordingly, the working definition of a computer used in this book is as follows:

A computer is a collection of resources, including digital electronic processing and storage devices, input and output devices, communications links, stored programs and sets of data, which, under the control of the stored programs, automatically inputs, outputs, stores, retrieves and processes the data, and may also transmit data to and receive it from other computers. A computer is capable of drawing reasoned conclusions from the processing it carries out.

Although it is somewhat long-winded, this definition accurately describes what a computer system is, what it does, and the extent to which it may be regarded as intelligent.

2.4
Hardware and Software

A processor chip – the type of hardware device at the heart of all computer systems.

■ In theory, the distinction between the terms 'hardware' and 'software' is quite clear:

> hardware is the physical components, solid-state and otherwise, which make up a computer;

and

> software is the sets of instructions which control the operation of a computer.

In practice, the distinction becomes rather blurred. For example, in some computers multiplication is done directly by hardware, while in others it is done by repeated addition, controlled by software. As long as the hardware of a computer can do a small number of essential operations, more sophisticated operations can be done either by special hardware elements, or by software, or by any combination of these.

```
>L.
    10 REM CLAREMONT FAN COURT SCHOOL, ES
HER, JWP, 12/2/91
    20 REM Program to fill the screen
with "starbursts"
    30 MODE 2
    32 REPEAT
    33    GCOL0,RND(15)
    35    x=RND(1280):y=RND(1024)
    40    VDU29,x;y;:REM This moves the or
igin to the point (x,y)
    55    radius=RND(450)
    56    MOVE radius,0
    60    FOR angle = 0 TO 360 STEP 4
    65       PROCdraw_polygon
    80    NEXT angle
    90 UNTIL FALSE
   100 DEFPROCdraw_polygon
   106 radius=RND(450)
```

A computer screen showing a listing of a typical program.

Furthermore, computers have some software permanently stored in **read-only memory (ROM)**. This is known as **firmware**, being somewhere between hardware and software.

2.5
Algorithm

■ In order for a task to be carried out on a computer, a method for performing the task must be described precisely, in terms of the steps required. An **algorithm** is a description of the steps of a task, using a particular method. Writing an algorithm is the first step taken in preparing a task to be done by a computer.

For example, a common algorithm for calculating the square root of a (positive) number x, to a degree of accuracy a, is as follows. Successive estimates of the square root r are made, until the required accuracy is reached. A working variable rp holds the previous estimate of the square root.

Let r = x / 2	Start with half the number.
Repeat	Repeat next two steps:
Let rp = r	Copy to previous estimate.
Let r = (rp + x / rp) / 2	Calculate new estimate.
Until | r - rp | < a	Stop when accurate enough.

For it to be of any use to a computer, an algorithm must express a task as a finite number of steps. No matter how fast a computer works, there comes a point at which it must be told to stop, even if it means giving up. In the above example, the last step achieves this provided that a is a positive number.

A number of different notations for writing algorithms have been developed, including a series of programming languages called Algol. One of the commonest notations is also the simplest: it is to use a sequence of statements in clear, concise English, and simple algebra where necessary. This method is adopted in the above example, and in the rest of this book. Below is another example of a simple algorithm in this notation, for adding up a set of numbers:

Set total to zero.
While there are more numbers, repeat:
    Add next number to total.

Note that the third line above is indented to show that it is controlled by the line above it.

2.6 Module and Interface

■ Computers are probably the most complex artefacts ever produced. The concepts of **module** and **interface** are essential in reducing this complexity. They make it possible to design and program computers, and to understand how they work.

A module is a self-contained, interchangeable unit. It performs a specific function, and has specific connections with its environment.

A **module** is normally a subsystem of an operational system. For example, in many hi-fi systems, the amplifier, turntable, cassette deck and speakers are separate modules. In a computer system, the integrated circuits are separate modules, as are the disk drives, display screen, power supply, keyboard, etc.

In relation to a module, an **interface** may be defined as follows:

An interface is a point of contact between one module and another, or between a module and its environment. The interface defines the way information (or energy or any physical substance) passes across the boundary of the module.

There are numerous benefits in the concepts of module and interface. For example, if the task performed by a module and its interfaces are known, it is not always necessary to understand how the module performs the task. It makes no difference if a module is replaced by another one which works in a different way, but performs the same task using the same interfaces.

The interior of a typical desktop computer, showing its modular construction. The electronic components are integrated circuit modules, mounted on a printed circuit board. The disk drive and power supply are separate modules.

Modules and interfaces are used in the design and construction of the hardware and software of computers. In both cases, the task to be performed is split up into a number of sub-tasks. A module is specified for each sub-task, together with its interfaces to other modules. The task can be understood in terms of these sub-tasks and interfaces, without knowing the details of how each sub-task is performed. This approach makes the designing of hardware and software of computers, and the understanding of them, much easier.

An increasing number of standard interfaces are coming into use in the computing industry. These are particularly important in data communications, where any two devices conforming to the same interface standard can communicate. Standard interfaces also make it possible for equipment from a number of manufacturers to be used in the same computer system, and for the same item of software to run on a range of hardware.

One of the most important interfaces of a computer system is its point of contact with its human users. This is known as the **user interface**, **human interface**, or (unfortunately) **man-machine interface (MMI)**. The user interface consists of the information displayed or printed by the computer for the attention of the user, and the responses to this information entered by the user into the computer system. Most user interfaces are interactive, taking the form of a dialogue between the computer and the person using it.

In the past, user interfaces have been designed around the capabilities of the computer, without much regard for the needs and way of thinking of the user. The current trend is to reverse this situation, and make the computer conform to a much greater extent to the requirements of the users.

2.7 Design and Implementation

■ In computing, as in most activities, there is a certain gap between theory and practice. In theory, ideas are efficient, clean and neat, and programs always work. In practice, things are seldom so simple. Nevertheless, it is important to formulate ideas in theory before being concerned about how they can be put into practice.

For these reasons, a distinction is made between the **design** of a computer, communications system, program or a programming language, and its **implementation**. The design is theoretical, free of the awkward constraints so often found in practice. The implementation of a design is the way it is put into practice under a particular set of circumstances. Most designs have several implementations. For example, many computer languages are implemented on a number of different types of computers. In general, no two implementations are exactly alike.

Several key chapters of this book make use of a model computer, the AMC. This computer has been designed to illustrate concepts of computer design, free of the restrictions imposed by implementations.

2.8 General-Purpose and Dedicated Computers

■ Historically, computers evolved as calculating machines. Once the general principles of computer design had been established, it became evident that they could do far more than just calculate. The phrase 'information processing' was chosen to describe the overall capability of a computer. A **general-purpose** computer conforms to this description. It can do a wide range of information processing tasks, from scientific 'number crunching' to commercial file processing. The data it handles can represent numbers, words, pictures or sounds.

A **dedicated** computer is designed for a specific task, or narrow range of tasks. A common example is a computer or electronic device dedicated to controlling a machine. The introduction of cheap, small, microprocessor-based computers has led to a resurgence of dedicated systems.

In practice, dedicated and general-purpose computers must be regarded as two extremes. Most computers are somewhere between the two extremes, able to carry out a variety of tasks within a particular range. However, the emphasis in computing is strongly on general-purpose systems.

2.9 The Theory of Computing

A hand-held personal organiser. These special-purpose computers are designed to store and process personal diaries, names and addresses, shopping lists, price lists and similar information.

■ The fundamental principles behind the design and construction of digital electronic computers have been developed over a period of about a century. Although a large number of people have contributed in various ways to the development and understanding of these principles, the work of four people is of particular significance. These people are **Charles Babbage**, **George Boole**, **Alan Turing** and **John von Neumann**.

Charles Babbage (1791–1871) lived in the era of steam: from locomotives to factory machines, steam was the source of power. Accordingly, his ideas were conceived in relation to mechanical computers, but many of them apply to electronic devices. Babbage identified the stages of a computing task as input, processing and output, and designed the units of his machines accordingly. He originated the idea of a program as a set of instructions to control the operation of a computing machine.

George Boole (1815–1864) is the founder of the theory of mathematical logic. The general theory of logic dates back at least as far as classical Greece, but Boole devised an algebra for representing logical quantities, and investigated the operations which can be performed on these quantities. Boolean logic is the theoretical basis both for the design of the circuits in digital computers, and for many techniques in programming.

Alan Turing (1912–1954) formulated the general concept of a programmable computing machine. He expressed his ideas in terms of an abstract computer, called a Turing Machine. Although a Turing Machine can only carry out one simple operation at a time, he identified a very wide class of problems which it could solve in a finite number of steps. Turing's work has been particularly valuable in understanding the capabilities and limitations of computers, in the design of programming languages, and in the study of artificial intelligence.

John von Neumann (1903–1957) assisted in the design and development of several early electronic computers at the end of the Second World War. In 1946 he published a paper outlining the general design principles of a digital electronic computer. He envisaged a machine controlled by a set of instructions, with a small number of central processing elements. The instructions are processed one at a time in a repeated cycle of operations. The two main points in the paper relate to the concept of a stored program:

1 All data and instructions are represented in a binary code, and are stored together in the computer memory.
2 The computer makes no distinction between data and instructions.

Although the principles set out in this paper have been enhanced in modern computer designs (in particular parallel processing replacing a single sequence of instructions), the von Neumann principles remain to this day the theoretical basis of the design of digital electronic computers.

2.10 Integrated Circuit Technology

■ The concepts of computing discussed in the previous sections would be of academic interest only if there were not a way of making them economically available to anyone who has a need for information processing. The fundamental technology of computing is the means of producing a solid-state integrated circuit, a device only a few millimetres square, formed from a thin slice of silicon crystal, on which are implanted a large number of data storage and processing elements. The circuits in these devices can carry out the operations of Boolean logic directly, at high speeds and with absolute accuracy.

In spite of its great processing or data storage power, an integrated circuit uses little electricity, has an almost indefinite working life, and costs very little to fabricate in large numbers. Computers and other electronic systems based on integrated circuits have enormous capabilities in relation to their costs. Furthermore, the price/performance ratio is falling all the time: the computing capability which a decade ago would have required millions of pounds and an air-conditioned room is now available on a desktop for a few thousand pounds.

2.11 Conclusion

An enlarged portion of a very large-scale integrated circuit, built up as a series of layers on a slice of silicon crystal. Silicon chip technology is the key to the widespread availability of cheap, powerful computers and other electronic devices.

■ This chapter has set out the key ideas on which the rest of the book is based. The main points may be summarised as follows:

- Data is information in a form which is acceptable for input to, and processing by, a computer system:

  data + interpretation = meaningful information.

- A system is a collection of parts working together towards some common objectives. A computer is a system, part of a larger system in any particular application.
- A program is a set of instructions which control the operation of a computer.
- A computer is a collection of resources, including digital electronic processing devices, stored programs, communications links and sets of data, which, under the control of the stored programs, automatically inputs, outputs, stores, retrieves and processes the data, and may also transmit data to and receive it from other computers. A computer is capable of drawing reasoned conclusions from the processing it carries out.
- Hardware is the physical components, solid-state and otherwise, which make up a computer.
- Software is the programs which direct the operation of a computer.
- An algorithm is a description of the steps of a task, using a particular method.
- A module is an interchangeable unit which performs a specific function, and has specific connections with its environment.
- An interface is the point of contact between one module and another, or between a module and its environment.
- The implementation of a design is the way it is put into practice under a particular set of circumstances.

- A general-purpose computer is capable of a wide range of applications.
- A dedicated computer is designed for a specific task, or narrow range of tasks.
- Silicon-based integrated circuits are the fundamental technology of computing.

Exercise 2

1 The discussion of each key concept in this chapter includes a working definition of the concept. Identify the key concepts and their working definitions.

2 List some examples of systems, and some things which are not systems. In each case, justify your choice.

3 State, with reasons, which of the following devices satisfy the definition of a computer introduced in this chapter, and which devices do not: slide rule; automatic washing machine; programmable pocket calculator; television game; motor car electronic ignition system, set of traffic lights.

4 Make a list of devices which are programmable. In each case state what distinguishes the device from a computer, as defined in this chapter.

5 Make a collection of statements from the press or the media about computers, which contradict the definition of a computer contained in this chapter. Discuss your findings.

6 A hi-fi set is quoted in the chapter as an example of modular construction. For each module of a typical hi-fi set state:
   a) its function;
   b) its interface(s) with other modules;
   c) its external interface(s), i.e. those to its environment.

7 Write down at least three examples of modular systems, other than computers and hi-fi sets. For each example, work through parts a) to c) of Question 6.

8 Discuss the significance of the modular construction of systems.

9 Briefly state and discuss the similarities and differences between the user interface of a desktop computer system and that of a motor car.

10 Find out more about the work of Babbage, Turing, Boole and von Neumann. Write a report on the contributions of one or more of them to the theory of computing, expanding the ideas presented in the text.

◆ 11 Other people who have made contributions to the theory of computing include:

   Noam Chomsky (a classification of languages, applicable to programming languages)
   Marshall McLuhan (originator of the phrase 'information processing')
   Claude Shannon (the relationship between electrical circuits and Boolean algebra)
   Ada Byron (the first computer programmer)
   William Shockley, who headed the team at Bell Laboratories which invented the transistor, the basic element of an integrated circuit.

   a) Find out about, and write reports on, the work of one or more of these people.
   b) Find out about other people who have made significant contributions to computing, and write brief reports on their work.

3 Data

This chapter covers ways in which data is represented in computer systems, both in the internal storage of a computer, and on external media accessed by a computer. Data storage is discussed in general terms: the techniques introduced here are implemented in a variety of ways on different computers.

A certain amount of computer arithmetic is considered in this chapter. This is because the method of coding the numbers determines the way in which some arithmetic operations are performed. However, most of the discussion of computer arithmetic is in Chapter 5.

3.1 Binary Coding of Data

■ All data used by computers is stored in a coded form. Different computers use different codes, and different codes are used in various parts of the same computer. But all these codes have one thing in common – they are based on two characters, the digits 0 and 1 only.

The reason for the use of only two digits is that all the devices used in computer systems, and all the data storage media they access, have only two states. For example, switches are on or off, transistors are conducting or non-conducting, magnetic tape is magnetised in one or the other direction, a signal is a pulse or no pulse. This has several advantages, notably simplicity, and wide tolerances. As long as it is clear whether a signal is in a 0 or a 1 state, a high level of precision does not matter. For this reason, the electronic components of a computer are more crudely (and cheaply) constructed than those in, for example, a hi-fi set.

Most of the numeric codes used in computers are based on the binary (base two) number system, which also uses only the digits 0 and 1. A binary digit is called a **bit**.

3.2 Place Value

■ Much of what is to follow in this chapter depends on the concept of **place value**. A reminder of this concept is in order at this point.

In all modern number systems, the value of any digit depends on its position in the number. The place values for decimal integers are (from the right) units, tens, hundreds, etc. For binary integers they are units, twos, fours, eights, etc. Similarly, 'decimal' fractions have place values (from the left) tenths, hundredths, etc., and binary fractions halves, quarters, eighths, etc. The following examples illustrate these points.

Decimal Integers:

Place values:	1000	100	10	1	
Example:	5	7	3	2	$= 5 \times 1000 + 7 \times 100 + 3 \times 10 + 2$

Binary Integers:

Place values:	8	4	2	1	
Example:	1	0	1	1	$= 1 \times 8 + 0 \times 4 + 1 \times 2 + 1$

Decimal Fractions:

Place values:	$\frac{1}{10}$	$\frac{1}{100}$	$\frac{1}{1000}$	$\frac{1}{10000}$	
Example:	4	7	2	8	$= \frac{4}{10} + \frac{7}{100} + \frac{2}{1000} + \frac{8}{10000}$

Binary fractions:

Place values: $\quad \frac{1}{2} \quad \frac{1}{4} \quad \frac{1}{8} \quad \frac{1}{16}$

Example: $\qquad 1 \quad 1 \quad 0 \quad 1 \qquad = \quad \frac{1}{2} \ + \ \frac{1}{4} \ + \ \frac{0}{8} \ + \ \frac{1}{16}$

The digit with the highest place value in a number is called the **most significant digit**, or, in binary, the **most significant bit (MSB)**. The digit with the lowest place value is the **least significant digit** or **bit (LSB)**. If the digits of a number are grouped, then the phrase **high order** describes the group with higher place values than others.

3.3 Character Code

■ Input, output, backing store and data communications media and devices transfer, store and manipulate data in a character code. Characters include letters, digits and punctuation marks. These are called **alphabetic**, **numeric** (together known as **alphanumeric**) and **special** characters respectively. In addition there are **control characters** such as the Delete character. These have no printed or displayed representation, but cause various actions to be carried out when they are encountered. The set of characters which can be coded is called the character set of the particular computer or programming language.

A character code is one in which each character is coded separately as a set of binary digits. Six, seven or eight bits per character are most

Character	Bit pattern	Decimal equivalent	Hexadecimal equivalent	Character	Bit pattern	Decimal equivalent	Hexadecimal equivalent
space	0100000	32	20	P	1010000	80	50
!	0100001	33	21	Q	1010001	81	51
"	0100010	34	22	R	1010010	82	52
#	0100011	35	23	S	1010011	83	53
$	0100100	36	24	T	1010100	84	54
%	0100101	37	25	U	1010101	85	55
&	0100110	38	26	V	1010110	86	56
'	0100111	39	27	W	1010111	87	57
(	0101000	40	28	X	1011000	88	58
)	0101001	41	29	Y	1011001	89	59
*	0101010	42	2A	Z	1011010	90	5A
+	0101011	43	2B	[	1011011	91	5B
,	0101100	44	2C	\	1011100	92	5C
–	0101101	45	2D	]	1011101	93	5D
.	0101110	46	2E	↑	1011110	94	5E
/	0101111	47	2F	←	1011111	95	5F
0	0110000	48	30		1100000	96	60
1	0110001	49	31	a	1100001	97	61
2	0110010	50	32	b	1100010	98	62
3	0110011	51	33	c	1100011	99	63
4	0110100	52	34	d	1100100	100	64
5	0110101	53	35	e	1100101	101	65
6	0110110	54	36	f	1100110	102	66
7	0110111	55	37	g	1100111	103	67
8	0111000	56	38	h	1101000	104	68
9	0111001	57	39	i	1101001	105	69
:	0111010	58	3A	j	1101010	106	6A
;	0111011	59	3B	k	1101011	107	6B
<	0111100	60	3C	l	1101100	108	6C
=	0111101	61	3D	m	1101101	109	6D
>	0111110	62	3E	n	1101110	110	6E
?	0111111	63	3F	o	1101111	111	6F
@	1000000	64	40	p	1110000	112	70
A	1000001	65	41	q	1110001	113	71
B	1000010	66	42	r	1110010	114	72
C	1000011	67	43	s	1110011	115	73
D	1000100	68	44	t	1110100	116	74
E	1000101	69	45	u	1110101	117	75
F	1000110	70	46	v	1110110	118	76
G	1000111	71	47	w	1110111	119	77
H	1001000	72	48	x	1111000	120	78
I	1001001	73	49	y	1111001	121	79
J	1001010	74	4A	z	1111010	122	7A
K	1001011	75	4B	{	1111011	123	7B
L	1001100	76	4C			1111100	124	7C
M	1001101	77	4D	}	1111101	125	7D
N	1001110	78	4E	~	1111110	126	7E
O	1001111	79	4F				

Figure 3.1
ASCII code

commonly used. Figure 3.1 shows a common character code, the seven bit **American Standard Code for Information Interchange (ASCII)** code. Not shown in Figure 3.1 is the set of control characters which forms part of the ASCII code.

Alphabetic data remains in character code during processing by a computer, but numeric data is converted to one of the numeric codes described below. All conversion from one code to another is carried out by hardware, firmware or software within the computer system. The user need not be concerned with it.

3.4 Binary Coded Decimal

■ **Binary Coded Decimal (BCD)** is a simple and increasingly popular way of representing numbers within a computer. In this system, each decimal digit is coded separately in binary. For example:

    379 = 0011 0111 1001

Four bits are the minimum needed to code one decimal digit since 9 = 1001. BCD numbers using four bits per decimal digit are known as **packed decimal** numbers. In some implementations more than four bits are used per decimal digit, with the remaining bit positions filled with zeros.

3.5 Sign-and-Magnitude Code

■ This section, and the two which follow it, introduce the three commonest ways of dealing with negative numbers. The first method involves representing the sign of a number, and its magnitude (or modulus), separately. This is called **sign-and-magnitude** (or **sign-and-modulus) code**.

If one bit is used for the sign, the convention is 0 for positive and 1 for negative. For example:

    +13 = 0 1 1 0 1

    −13 = 1 1 1 0 1

The most significant bit is the sign bit.

3.6 Twos Complement Numbers

■ **Twos complement coding** is the commonest way of representing integers during processing on a computer. In this code, the normal binary place values are used, except that the most significant bit represents a negative quantity. For example, using six bits:

−32	16	8	4	2	1				
0	1	1	1	1	1	=			31
0	0	0	0	0	1	=			1
0	0	0	0	0	0	=			0
1	1	1	1	1	1	=	−32 + 31	=	−1
1	0	0	0	0	0	=			−32

This example shows the range of numbers which can be stored: −32 to 31.

One reason for using twos complement form is that it is easy to change from a positive to the corresponding negative number (and vice versa). Consequently, subtraction can be performed by negating the second number and then adding it to the first number. For example, 7 − 5 is the same as 7 + (−5).

The method of changing from a positive to the corresponding negative number is as follows: Change all the 0s to 1s and all the 1s to 0s, and then add 1. For example:

	−32	16	8	4	2	1		
19 =	0	1	0	0	1	1		
Interchange bits	1	0	1	1	0	0		
Add 1 +						1		
	1	0	1	1	0	1	=	−19

This method will also change a negative number to the corresponding positive number. For example:

	−32	16	8	4	2	1		
−23 =	1	0	1	0	0	1		
Interchange bits	0	1	0	1	1	0		
Add 1 +						1		
	0	1	0	1	1	1	=	23

Two examples of subtraction using this technique follow.

Example 1

29 − 7 = 29 + (−7)

	−32	16	8	4	2	1	
Code 7	0	0	0	1	1	1	
Interchange bits	1	1	1	0	0	0	
Add 1, gives −7	1	1	1	0	0	1	
Code 29	0	1	1	1	0	1	+
Add −7 and 29	0	1	0	1	1	0	= 22

Note that there is a 1 carried from the most significant bit. Most computers have a carry bit which is set to 1 if this occurs. The importance of this is discussed in Section 5.2.

Example 2

5 − 18 = 5 + (−18)

	−32	16	8	4	2	1	
Code 18	0	1	0	0	1	0	
Interchange bits	1	0	1	1	0	1	
Add 1, gives −18	1	0	1	1	1	0	
Code 5	0	0	0	1	0	1	+
Add −18 and 5	1	1	0	0	1	1	= −13

Problems arise when the result of a calculation is outside the range of numbers which can be represented. For example:

14 + 19

	−32	16	8	4	2	1		
14 =	0	0	1	1	1	0		
19 =	0	1	0	0	1	1	+	
	1	0	0	0	0	1	=	−31

The result, −31, is not correct. This problem is examined in Section 5.2.

3.7 Ones Complement Numbers

■ Similar to twos complements, but less popular, is the method of storing integers known as **ones complements**. In this system, the most significant place value is one less (in magnitude) than the corresponding twos complement place value. For example, using six bits:

−31	16	8	4	2	1			
0	1	1	1	1	1	=		31
0	0	0	0	0	1	=		1
0	0	0	0	0	0	=		0
1	1	1	1	1	1	=	−31 + 31 =	0
1	1	1	1	1	0	=	−31 + 30 =	−1
1	0	0	0	0	0	=		−31

Notice the range of numbers (31 to –31) and the two different codes for 0.

The advantage of using ones complements is that the negative of a number is produced simply by reversing the bits. For example:

	–31	16	8	4	2	1	
20 =	0	1	0	1	0	0	
Interchange bits	1	0	1	0	1	1	= –31 + 11 = –20

This technique is used in subtraction. However, any carry produced by the most significant bit of the result must be added at the least significant end to produce a correct answer. The examples of the previous section are repeated using ones complement coding.

Example 1

29 – 7 = 29 + (–7)

	–31	16	8	4	2	1	
Code 7	0	0	0	1	1	1	
Reverse bits, gives –7	1	1	1	0	0	0	
Code 29	0	1	1	1	0	1	+
Add –7 and 29	0	1	0	1	0	1	
Add carry						1	+
	0	1	0	1	1	0	= 22

This technique is called **wrap-around carry**.

Example 2

5 – 18 = 5 + (–18)

	–31	16	8	4	2	1	
Code 18	0	1	0	0	1	0	
Reverse bits, gives –18	1	0	1	1	0	1	
Code 5	0	0	0	1	0	1	+
Add –18 and 5	1	1	0	0	1	0	= –13

In this example, no wrap-around carry is generated.

3.8 Fractions

■ Fractions may be coded in ways very similar to those introduced above for coding integers. For example, using sign-and-magnitude coding:

	sign	$\frac{1}{2}$	$\frac{1}{4}$	$\frac{1}{8}$	$\frac{1}{16}$	$\frac{1}{32}$
$\frac{-13}{32}$ =	1	0	1	1	0	1

Twos complement coding may also be used. For example:

	–1	$\frac{1}{2}$	$\frac{1}{4}$	$\frac{1}{8}$	$\frac{1}{16}$	$\frac{1}{32}$
$\frac{-13}{32} = -1 + \frac{19}{32}$ =	1	1	0	0	1	1

These methods of coding fractions, and the methods of coding integers introduced above, are called **fixed point** codes. In these codes, the binary point is at a fixed position, though it is not coded explicitly.

The problem with fixed point codes is that the range of values that can be represented is limited. For example, some computers allocate 16 bits to store integers. Using twos complement notation, this gives a range of – 32768 to 32767, which is not sufficient for many applications.

■ The technique of floating point numbers is used to extend the range of numbers that can be represented by a given number of bits. Floating point numbers are similar to the scientific method of representing base ten numbers, called standard form. A standard form number is the product of two parts. The first is a number between 1 and 10, and the second is a power of ten. For example:

$$5.75 \times 10^4 = 57\ 500$$
$$6.7 \times 10^{-5} = 0.000\ 067$$

Note that the size of the number is determined by the power of ten, and the number of significant figures, or precision of the number, is determined by the number of decimal places in the first part.

Floating point numbers apply the same principles in base two. A number is expressed as the product of two parts. The first part is a fraction between $\frac{1}{2}$ and 1 (the **mantissa**), and the second is a power of two (the **exponent**). The following examples use four bits for each, in sign-and-magnitude coding:

	mantissa				exponent		
sign	$\frac{1}{2}$	$\frac{1}{4}$	$\frac{1}{8}$	sign	4	2	1
0	1	0	0	0	0	0	1
0	1	0	1	0	1	0	0
0	1	1	0	1	0	1	0
1	1	1	1	0	1	1	0

$$= \frac{1}{2} \times 2^1 = 1$$
$$= \frac{5}{8} \times 2^4 = 10$$
$$= \frac{3}{4} \times 2^{-2} = \frac{3}{16}$$
$$= -\frac{7}{8} \times 2^6 = 56$$

The bit in the $\frac{1}{2}$ column is a 1, unless the whole number is zero. This is to ensure that the fraction part lies between $\frac{1}{2}$ and 1, and is called **normalisation**. Normalisation ensures that the maximum number of bit positions are available to store the fraction part of the number. It provides maximum precision of a number within the available number of bits.

Ways of implementing floating point numbers differ considerably between different types of computer. The mantissa may be coded in sign-and-magnitude or twos complement form. The exponent is sometimes coded in one of these forms, but the **biased exponent** method of coding is also used. With this method, a fixed value is subtracted from the stored representation of the exponent in order to determine its actual value.

For example, if eight bits are allocated to the exponent, the stored values can be between 0 and 255. The fixed value 128 (the bias) is subtracted from the stored value, giving an actual range of exponents of – 128 to 127. In some computers, the exponent does not represent a power of two, but some larger base, such as sixteen.

The number of bits allocated to each part of a floating point number also differs between computers. The general principle is that between two and three times as many bits are allocated to the mantissa as to the exponent. Below is an example using sixteen bits for a floating point number, with eleven bits for the mantissa and five bits for the exponent. Sign-and-magnitude coding is used for both parts of the number.

	mantissa											exponent			
sign	$\frac{1}{2}$	$\frac{1}{4}$	$\frac{1}{8}$	$\frac{1}{16}$	$\frac{1}{32}$	$\frac{1}{64}$	$\frac{1}{128}$	$\frac{1}{256}$	$\frac{1}{512}$	$\frac{1}{1024}$		sign	8	4	2	1
0	1	0	1	1	0	0	0	0	0	0		0	1	1	0	0

$$= \frac{11}{16} \times 2^{12} = \frac{11}{16} \times 4096 = 2816$$

The same number with a biased exponent (offset 16) is:

					mantissa							exponent			
sign	$\frac{1}{2}$	$\frac{1}{4}$	$\frac{1}{8}$	$\frac{1}{16}$	$\frac{1}{32}$	$\frac{1}{64}$	$\frac{1}{128}$	$\frac{1}{156}$	$\frac{1}{512}$	$\frac{1}{1024}$	16	8	4	2	1
0	1	0	1	1	0	0	0	0	0	0	1	1	1	0	0

The stored exponent is 11100 = 28, which gives 12 when the bias of 16 is subtracted.

Arithmetic using floating point numbers, and errors which can arise in this arithmetic are discussed in Chapter 5.

The method of representing floating point numbers in the IBM 370 range of computers illustrates many of the techniques described above. Either one or two 32-bit words are used. In both cases, the most significant bit is the sign bit. The next seven bits are for the exponent, and the remaining 24 or 56 bits are used for the mantissa, which is stored as a binary fraction. The exponent is biased by 64, and represents a power, not of 2, but of 16. For example, in a 32-bit data item:

	sign	exponent							mantissa						
Bit position	31	30	29	28	27	26	25	24	23	22	21	20	19	...	0
	0	1	0	0	0	0	1	0	1	1	1	0	0	...	0

$$= \frac{7}{8} \times 16^{66-64} \quad = \frac{7}{8} \times 256 \quad = 224$$

	sign	exponent							mantissa						
Bit position	31	30	29	28	27	26	25	24	23	22	21	20	19	...	0
	1	0	1	1	1	1	1	0	1	0	1	0	0	...	0

$$= \frac{-5}{8} \times 16^{62-64} \quad = \frac{-5}{8} \times \frac{1}{256} \quad = \frac{-5}{2048}$$

3.10 Bits, Bytes and Words

■ For most purposes, a bit (a 0 or a 1) is too small a unit of data to be manipulated separately. Hence bits are generally handled in groups. **Bytes** and **words** are the two commonest groupings.

A byte is a set of bits containing the code for one character. A byte is now generally accepted as comprising eight bits. The data on most input, output and backing store media is grouped in bytes. Early microcomputers – the 8-bit micros – did all their processing in units of bytes.

A **word** is a larger grouping of bits, from 16 to 512 bits depending on the size of the computer. A word is a set of bits which can be manipulated by a particular computer in one operation. The wordlength is the number of bits in one word. The registers in processors, which store one data item during processing, contain one word.

However, in many modern computers, the number of bits which are manipulated in one operation can vary. The phrase variable wordlength describes this situation. Whether a word is of fixed or variable length, it almost always contains an integral number of bytes: 16, 24, 32 or 64 bits.

3.11 Octal and Hexadecimal Numbers

■ Binary numbers and codes suffer from the disadvantage of being very long for the amount of information they represent. Decimal numbers are much more concise, but are difficult to convert to binary. As a compromise, **octal** (base eight) and **hexadecimal** (base sixteen) numbers are often used to represent binary quantities. These numbers have the advantages of conciseness and ease of conversion to binary.

Octal

To convert from base eight to base two, convert each octal digit to its binary equivalent, using three bits. For example:

$725_8 = 111\ 010\ 101_2$

Converting from binary to octal is done by grouping the bits in threes from the least significant end, and converting each group to an octal digit. For example:

$11\ 110\ 000_2 = 360_8$

Hexadecimal

Conversion between binary and hexadecimal numbers is similar to octal-to-binary conversion, except that groups of four bits are used. The hexadecimal digits A to F are used for the decimal quantities 10 to 15. For example:

$3A7_{16} = 0011\ 1010\ 0111_2$

and

$1\ 1111\ 0010_2 = 1F2_{16}$

It must be remembered that octal and hexadecimal digits are a shorthand way of representing binary codes, which themselves may represent non-numeric data. For example, the ASCII code for the symbol ? is 0 1 1 1 1 1 1. This may be represented by the octal digits 077, or the hexadecimal digits 3F.

Octal and hexadecimal numbers are used for writing certain types of computer programs, for representing data stored in a computer during processing, and for recovering from errors. They are very seldom used for input and output of data. Hexadecimal numbers have the advantage that two hexadecimal digits represent eight bits, or one byte. For this reason they are more commonly used than octal numbers.

3.12 Self-Checking Codes: Parity

■ Much attention is devoted, in the design of computer systems, to the detection and correction of errors. One valuable technique in achieving this objective is the concept of a **self-checking code**. A self-checking code is one which contains enough information within the coded form of a data item, to determine whether that data item has been coded (or transmitted) correctly.

The simplest and commonest self-checking code requires the inclusion of a **parity** bit in the code of a data item. The parity is set to a 0 or a 1 so that the total number of 1s in the data item is even, for even parity, or odd, for odd parity . For example, using even parity and the most significant bit as the parity bit:

0 1 1 0 1 0 1

is correct, with four 1s, but:

1 0 0 1 1 0 0

is incorrect, with three 1s.

Parity checks are used to determine whether the parity of a data item is correct. These are most commonly carried out after a data item has been transmitted to or from an input, output or backing store device or on a data communications network, as this is where errors are most likely.

Odd parity is slightly more useful than even parity, as it will detect the failure of a transmission line, which will result in all the bits of a data item being zero. Other self-checking codes are discussed in Section 14.7.

3.13 Data Encryption

■ In many computer applications, it is essential that the data stored on disk or transmitted on a communications network is completely secure. One technique which provides a high level of security is **data encryption** – 'scrambling' the bits representing the data items so that they do not follow any standard data code, and require decoding in a secret way before they can be interpreted. In all cases where data is encrypted in this fashion, the encryption and decryption is done automatically by hardware or software within the secure computer system.

A variety of encryption techniques are used. Some are based on an algorithm which uses random numbers. Others are based on remainders when the data values are divided by a very large prime number. The key to codes of this nature is an even larger integer (more than 100 decimal digits) which is the product of two large prime numbers, one of which is used for the division. Even if the key integer is known to an outsider, the process of factorising it is very difficult, and takes a long time on even the largest computers. By the time the codebreaker has decoded the information, it is generally out of date.

The making and breaking of secret codes for data is one of the oldest applications of digital electronic computers. It remains a topic of intense interest and extreme secrecy to this day.

3.14 Analogue Data

■ Digital computers store and process data in one of the digital codes described in the previous sections of this chapter. However, in many applications, a digital computer has inputs and/or outputs in analogue form. These are in the form of electrical voltages which are proportional to some physical quantity. For example, a computer which has voice input receives an analogue signal which varies according to the sound waves reaching it. If it produces synthesised speech output, the final form of the output signal is an analogue voltage which follows the pattern of the speech.

The conversion from analogue to digital form is done by an interfacing device known as an **analogue-to-digital converter** (**ADC**). These devices sample the analogue signal at fixed intervals, and convert the values they obtain to digital form, using one of the numeric codes described above, or the Gray code below. The sampling frequency measures the rate at which samples are taken. Some form of scaling is carried out so that the results are in appropriate units. No matter how many bits are allocated to the digital representation of the signal, there is always a loss of precision when changing from analogue to digital form.

When converting in the other direction, an ADC converts a stream of digital values to their analogue equivalents, and produces a smoothed analogue waveform from them. The reconstructed analogue waveform is again an approximation to the original, the closeness being determined by the precision of the digital numbers, and the conversion frequency. See Figure 3.2.

A common problem in analogue-to-digital converters is the error which arises if the analogue signal is sampled just as its value is changing from one digital value to another. In many cases the digital bit positions are determined by separate circuits, which do not all switch at exactly the

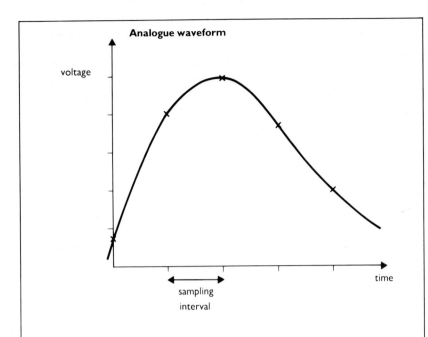

Analogue waveform

voltage

sampling
interval

time

Digital samples

Time	Voltage
0.0	1.3
0.2	8.0
0.4	9.8
0.6	7.4
0.8	4.0

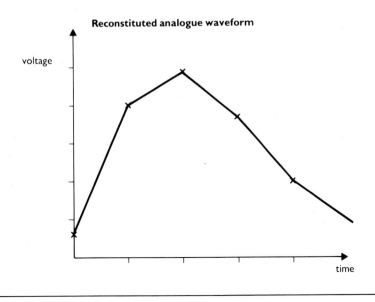

Reconstituted analogue waveform

voltage

time

Figure 3.2
Analogue to digital conversion

same time. For example, if a signal were changing from (digital) 0 1 1 1 to 1 0 0 0, and the most significant bit changed from 0 to 1 before the others changed from 1 to 0, it could be read as 1 1 1 1 if it were sampled during the transition. One way of minimising the errors which can arise in this situation is to use a **Gray** code for the digital representation, where there is never more than one change in a bit value between two successive numbers. The four bit Gray code is shown below:

Decimal	Gray Code
0	0 0 0 0
1	0 0 0 1
2	0 0 1 1
3	0 0 1 0
4	0 1 1 0
5	0 1 1 1
6	0 1 0 1
7	0 1 0 0
8	1 1 0 0
9	1 1 0 1
10	1 1 1 1
11	1 1 1 0
12	1 0 1 0
13	1 0 1 1
14	1 0 0 1
15	1 0 0 0

3.15 Conclusion

■ The main points of this chapter are as follows:

- All codes used for data storage are based on the binary digits 0 and 1 only.
- A major reason for the use of binary codes in computers is that all the devices used in the construction of computers have two states only.
- Character code is one in which each character is coded separately as a set of binary digits.
- The set of characters which can be coded by a particular computer or programming language is the character set of that computer or language.
- Binary coded decimal is a numeric code in which each decimal digit is coded separately. Packed decimal is a variant of this code, with four bits per decimal digit.
- Sign-and-magnitude code involves coding the sign and the magnitude of a number separately.
- Twos complement is a binary code, using the usual place values, except that the most significant bit represents a negative quantity.
- Ones complement is a binary code, similar to twos complement, except that the most significant place value is one less in magnitude.
- Fixed point codes are numeric codes in which the (assumed) binary point is in a fixed position in the number.
- Floating point codes are numeric codes in which a number is expressed as a product of a fraction between $\frac{1}{2}$ and 1 (the mantissa) and an integral power of two (the exponent).
- A byte is a set of bits containing the code for one character. A byte is eight bits.
- A word is a set of bits which can be manipulated by a particular computer in one operation.

- Octal (base eight) and hexadecimal (base sixteen) numbers are often used as 'shorthand' representations of binary numbers.
- A common self-checking code includes a parity bit which adjusts the total number of 1s in the data item to an even (for even parity) or odd (for odd parity) number.
- Analogue input and output data is converted to digital form for processing by analogue-to-digital converters.

Exercise 3

1 Briefly define the following terms: binary; bit; place value; most significant digit; character code; alphanumeric character; special character; control character; character set; ASCII; binary coded decimal; packed decimal; sign-and-magnitude code; twos complements; ones complements; carry bit; wrap-around carry; fixed point number; floating point number; standard form; mantissa; exponent; normalisation; biased exponent; byte; word; wordlength; variable wordlength; octal; hexadecimal; self-checking code; parity bit; even parity; parity check; data encryption; encryption key; analogue data; analogue-to-digital converter; sampling frequency; Gray code.

2 Why are all data codes used by computers based on two digits only? List the advantages of this system.

3 Name a number system still in use which does not use the concept of place value. Discuss the problems of converting between this number system and a computer code.

4 What is the distinguishing feature of character code?

5 a) Write an informal algorithm for the process of adding two BCD digits, and producing the sum in the form of a BCD digit together with a carry bit.

◆ b) Using the algorithm from Question 5(a), write an informal algorithm for the process of adding two complete BCD numbers. State any additional assumptions you make, such as the lengths of the numbers.

6 Write the decimal numbers 1, –1, 3 and –3 in twos complement form, using (a) four bits, (b) six bits, (c) eight bits. In the light of your answers, state how a twos complement number can be extended to a larger number of bits without altering its value.

7 Repeat Question 6 using ones complement numbers.

8 In twos complement notation, what is the range of integers which can be represented by (a) four bits, (b) six bits, (c) eight bits, (d) sixteen bits, (e) n bits? What are the corresponding ranges using ones complements?

9 Change the following (decimal) fractions into six bit, twos complement notation: $\frac{3}{8}, \frac{5}{16}, \frac{-17}{32}, \frac{1}{5}$.
Hint: in the last case, change the numerator and denominator to binary, and divide the denominator into the numerator. The result is a recurring fraction.

10 The following numbers are in floating point form:

mantissa											exponent				
sign	$\frac{1}{2}$	$\frac{1}{4}$	$\frac{1}{8}$	$\frac{1}{16}$	$\frac{1}{32}$	$\frac{1}{64}$	$\frac{1}{128}$	$\frac{1}{256}$	$\frac{1}{512}$	$\frac{1}{1024}$	sign	8	4	2	1
0	1	0	1	0	0	0	0	0	0	0	0	0	1	0	0
0	1	1	1	1	0	0	0	0	0	0	0	1	1	1	0
1	1	0	0	0	0	0	0	0	0	0	0	0	0	0	1
0	1	1	1	0	0	0	0	0	0	0	1	0	1	0	0
1	1	0	1	0	0	0	0	0	0	0	1	0	1	1	1
1	1	1	1	1	0	0	0	0	0	0	0	1	0	0	0

a) Convert the numbers to base ten.
b) Express the decimal numbers 80, –3072, $\frac{5}{512}, -\frac{1}{2}$, 1.5 in this form.
c) Bearing in mind that floating point numbers must be normalised, what is the range of positive numbers which can be expressed in this form ?

d) Convert the decimal numbers from part b) into the biased exponent floating point form used in the second example in Section 3.9.

◆ e) Convert the decimal numbers from part b) into the IBM 370 floating point format illustrated at the end of Section 3.9.

11 If the floating point numbers in Question 10 are stored with twos complements mantissas, the most significant bit represents the value -1.

a) Convert the decimal numbers obtained in part a) of Question 10 back to floating point form, using twos complement mantissas.

b) Examine the results from part a) and derive a rule for the normalisation of mantissas of floating point numbers stored in twos complements form.

12 A computer has a 64 bit wordlength.

a) How many bytes are contained in one word?

b) How many packed decimal digits can be stored in one word?

c) Suggest a way in which a word may be used to contain a floating point number. Justify your allocation of bits.

13 Convert the following decimal numbers (a) to binary, (b) to octal, (c) to hexadecimal: 45, 21, 32, 4097.

14 The main store of a particular computer has an extra parity bit for every byte stored. Furthermore, after every eight bytes, there is an additional parity byte, where each bit adjusts the parity of the corresponding 'column' in the eight bytes. Odd parity is used throughout. Below is the contents of a portion of the main store of this computer:

bytes								parity bits
1	0	0	1	0	0	1	0	0
0	0	0	0	0	0	0	0	1
1	1	1	1	1	1	1	1	1
1	0	1	1	0	1	0	1	0
1	1	0	1	1	0	1	1	0
0	1	1	0	1	1	0	1	0
0	0	0	0	0	0	0	0	1
1	0	1	1	1	1	0	1	1

parity byte   0   0   1   0   1   1   1   0   1

a) Check the parity of each byte.

b) Check the parity of each column against the parity byte.

c) Assuming that only one bit has been stored incorrectly, identify this bit.

15 a) A data item and its parity bit are copied from one part of a computer to another. A subsequent parity check fails. Is it certain that the data item is now incorrect? Explain your answer.

b) If, in the above case, the parity check does not fail, is it certain that the data item is now correct? Explain your answer.

c) In the light of your answers to parts a) and b), comment on the usefulness of parity checks.

16 a) List some examples of digital computer systems with analogue inputs and/or outputs.

b) One application of Gray code is in measuring the rotation of a shaft. A disk attached to the shaft has concentric segments coloured in dark and light zones in order to provide the Gray code of the shaft position. The shades are read by a set of photo-electric cells, one for each bit position. List other similar applications of Gray code.

4 Data Structures

The previous chapter showed how items of data may be represented on computer systems. This chapter shows how individual items of data may be associated in various ways to form data structures. These structures enable large and potentially unwieldy collections of data to be managed by relatively simple operations. Techniques of creating and manipulating data structures have led to advances in computer architecture, and in the design of computer software.

Six data structures are introduced in this chapter: **strings**, **arrays**, **stacks**, **queues**, **lists** and **trees**. They are the most important data structures used in the main stores of computers. In Chapter 26, the backing store data structures **files**, **records**, **fields** and **hash tables** are discussed.

4.1 The Concept of Structured Data

■ The structure of a set of data is defined by relationships between individual data items. These relationships can be formally expressed as a set of rules, or more simply, by specifying how to insert and delete items of data, while preserving the structure. Together with a description of an empty data structure, this is sufficient for a structure to be created and used.

Structured Information in Everyday Life

Most of the information we encounter in everyday life is structured in some way. The commonest example is the words of a language, which are linked together in phrases, sentences and other more complex structures. The rules for creating these structures are extremely complicated, yet we apply them by intuition.

Other examples of structured information include dictionaries, telephone directories and encyclopaedias. These are all large stores of information which would be useless if the information were not strictly arranged according to a few simple rules. The structure of a collection of information makes it easy to locate individual items of information, and to insert new items, or delete items. The same reasoning applies to structured information stored in computers.

4.2 Pointers

■ A **pointer** is a data item which indicates the location of another data item. It may be thought of as an arrow, as shown in Figure 4.1.

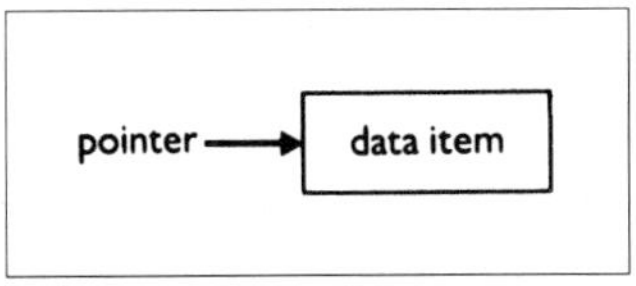

Figure 4.1
A pointer

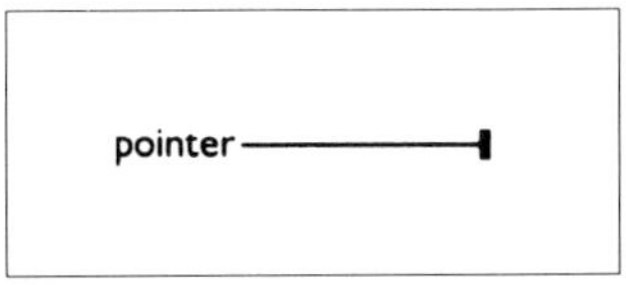

Figure 4.2
A null pointer

Pointers are used to build many data structures. They provide the links which join elements of the structure. Of particular significance are pointers to the front and back of a data structure. Occasionally it is required that a pointer does not point to anything; in this situation, the pointer is said to have a null value. See Figure 4.2.

4.3 Strings

■ A **string** is a sequence of characters regarded as a single data item. Strings may be of fixed or variable length. The length of a string may be indicated either by the number of characters in the string placed at the front of the string, or by a special character called an end-of-string marker at the end. The following example shows these two methods of representing the same variable length string:

        10CAPITAL194   CAPITAL194#

Operations on strings are of two types: operations which join two or more strings to produce a single string, and operations which divide a string to produce two or more sub-strings.

4.4 Arrays

■ An **array** is a set of data items of identical type, stored together. The number of elements in the array is fixed when the array is created. Each element is accessed by an **index**, which indicates the position of the element in the array.

For example, if the array BEATLES has elements as follows:

        BEATLES: JOHN
                   PAUL
                   GEORGE
                   RINGO

then the element with index value 3, BEATLES(3) is the name GEORGE. Sometimes it is more useful to use the index value 0 for the first array element. Under this arrangement, BEATLES(3) is the name RINGO. In some ways, the entire main store of a computer may be regarded as an array. The index of each memory cell is known as the **address** of the space. The address is a number which locates a cell within the main store.

Arrays can have more than one **dimension**. A two-dimensional array may be thought of as having rows and columns like a matrix. Two indices are required to locate an item in the array, corresponding to row and column indices in a matrix. For example, the state of a game of noughts and crosses may be represented by a two-dimensional array, GAME, with three rows and three columns:

        GAME: O   X   O
                X   X   O
                O   X

If the top left element is GAME(1,1), then the O in the third column of the second row is GAME(2,3) and the blank element is GAME(3,1).

When the word 'array' is used on its own, it is generally understood to mean a one-dimensional array. Arrays with more than two dimensions are occasionally used.

4.5 Static and Dynamic Data Structures

■ An array is a **static data structure**, which means that it stays the same size once it has been created. Data structures which change in size once they have been created are called **dynamic data structures**. A string can be a static or a dynamic data structure. The structures introduced in the remainder of this chapter are dynamic data structures. They generally require pointers for their implementation.

4.6 Stacks

■ You have probably seen the way in which plates are sometimes stored in restaurants. A pile of plates is in a cylindrical recess supported on a spring. As a new plate is put on top of the pile, it pushes the rest down into the recess. When a plate is taken from the pile, the next plate pops up. Such a structure is a **stack** in the computing sense of the word. A stack is a collection of data items which may only be accessed at one end, called the top of the stack.

Only two operations may be carried out on a stack. Adding a new item, called **pushing** or **stacking** the item, involves placing it on top of the stack. Removing an item is **popping** it from the stack.

If a number of items are pushed onto a stack, and then popped from it, the last item added will be the first one removed. For this reason a stack is called a **last-in-first-out (LIFO) stack**. Other names for a stack are **push-down stack** and **push-down list**.

When a stack is stored in a computer memory, the elements do not move up and down as the stack is pushed and popped. Instead, the position of the top of the stack changes. A pointer called a **stack pointer** indicates the position of the top of the stack (or, in some applications, the first free space above the top of the stack). Another pointer is used to indicate the base of the stack. This pointer, called the **stack base**, keeps the same value as long as the stack is in existence. Figure 4.3 shows a stack pointer and stack base in use. If the sequence of operations `pop, pop, push 5.9`, is carried out on this stack, the result is shown in Figure 4.4. Representing an empty stack is important. If the stack pointer indicates the first available space above the top of the stack, then this is shown in Figure 4.5. When the stack is empty, the stack pointer has the same value as the stack base.

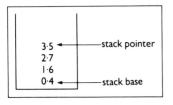

Figure 4.3
A stack

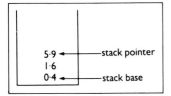

Figure 4.4

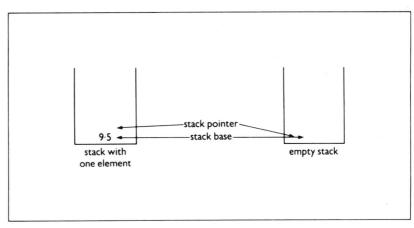

Figure 4.5
A stack with one element and an empty stack

The stack is one of the most important data structures in computing. Stacks are used in calculations, for translating from one computer language to another, and for transferring control from one part of a program to another. Most modern processors include a stack pointer as an architectural feature, and some regard their entire memory as a set of stacks.

As an example of the use of a stack, consider a program which needs to calculate square roots. A subprogram is written for this purpose, which is called from the rest of the program whenever it is needed. The subprogram requires the number whose square root is to be calculated, and returns the value of this square root. One way of transferring these numbers between the subprogram and the point in the program from which it is called is to use a stack. The number is pushed onto the stack before the subprogram is called. Within the subprogram, the number is popped from the stack for use in the calculation. The square root is then pushed onto the stack at the end of the subprogram. When control returns to the point from which the subprogram was called, the square root is popped from the stack.

4.7
Queues

■ In spite of the American origins of many ideas associated with computers, that great British institution, the **queue**, has found its way into the theory of computing. Everyone knows how a queue works: newcomers join at the rear, service is provided at the front, and no pushing-in is allowed. Exactly the same rules apply to queues of data stored in a computer memory: data items are added at the back and removed from the front. A queue is a **first-in-first-out (FIFO)** data structure.

There are several ways of implementing the storage of a queue in a computer memory. A particularly simple way involves storing the queue elements in adjacent memory locations, and providing pointers to the front and rear of the queue. See Figure 4.6. When an element is added to the queue, the rear pointer is adjusted to point to the new element. Similarly, when an element is removed from the queue, the front pointer is adjusted to point to the new front element.

The problem with this method of storage of a queue is that the queue moves down the store as the elements are added and removed. The usual solution is to allocate a fixed area of store for the queue, and then let the rear of the queue 'wrap around' to the start of the area. See Figure 4.7. An area of store used in this way is called a circular buffer.

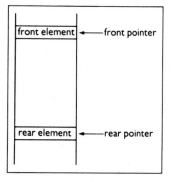

Figure 4.6
A queue

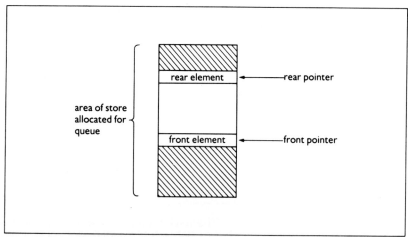

Figure 4.7
A queue wrapped around in a fixed area of store

Although queues are used less frequently than stacks, they do have a variety of applications. These include queuing data items in transit between a processor and a peripheral device, or at intermediate points in a data communications network. For example, most computer systems maintain a queue of data between the processor and the printer. When data is to be printed, the processor adds it to the back of the print queue, and then carries on with another processing task. The printer takes the data from the front of the queue and prints it at its own speed. In this way, the processor is not held up by the printer. Data is printed in the order in which it is sent by the processor.

4.8
Lists

■ A **list** is a set of data items stored in some order. Data items may be inserted or deleted at any point in the list. In this respect, a list is less restrictive than a stack or queue. The simplest way of implementing a list makes use of a pointer from each item to the one following it in the list. There is also a pointer to the start of the list, while the last item in the list has a null pointer. See Figure 4.8.

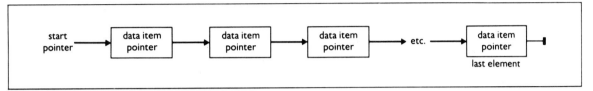

Figure 4.8
A list

The benefit of the use of pointers to create a list in this way is that list elements do not have to be in any particular order in the computer memory. When elements are added or deleted, all that happens is that the relevant pointers are adjusted. No movement of data itself takes place. This makes the operations of adding and deleting elements much faster than if a static data structure like an array were used to store the data.

A data structure of this type is also known as a **linked list**. A list element consists of a data item and its pointer. In many applications a list element contains a number of data items. Since elements can easily be added to the rear or removed from the front of the linked list, this structure may also be used to implement a queue. Inserting an element into a list is achieved by adjusting the pointers to include the new element. See Figure 4.9. Removing an element is achieved in a similar way, as shown in Figure 4.10.

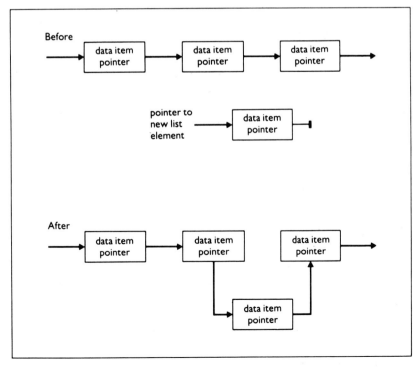

Figure 4.9
Inserting an element into a list

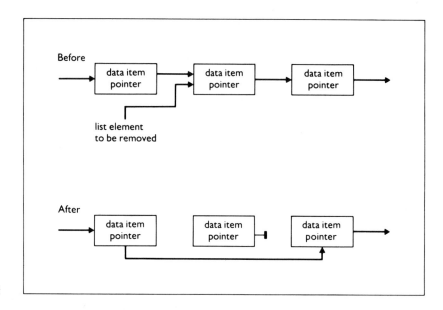

Figure 4.10
Removing an element from a list

A variation on the idea of a list is the case where the pointer from the end of the list is linked to the front of the list. This creates a **circular list**, as shown in Figure 4.11.

Data items in a list are in order, in the sense that one data item is behind another in the list. Lists are, however, frequently used in cases where the data items are in numerical or alphabetical order. Such lists are called **ordered lists**. Lists are very useful for storing ordered sets of data, if insertions and deletions of data items are frequent.

An alternative form of a list is a structure which contains an identified data item as the **head**, and the remaining items forming the **tail** of the list. The usual notation is as follows:

(A | B)   is the list with element A at the head and list B as the tail.

(A | (B | (C D)))   is the list with element A at the head, and a tail comprising a list with element B at the head, and the list containing elements C and D as the tail.

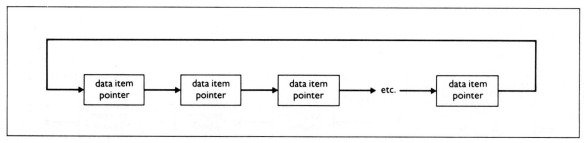

Figure 4.11
A circular list

Data items may themselves be lists. Lists of this nature are widely used in artificial intelligence research, and form the basis of the programming language **Lisp** (Section 19.7).

4.9
Trees

■ We are all familiar with the phrases 'family tree' and 'getting to the top of the tree'. In this sense, a **tree** is a structure implying a hierarchy, with each element of the tree being linked to elements below it. For example, the family tree in Figure 4.12 shows the descendants of Queen Elizabeth II.

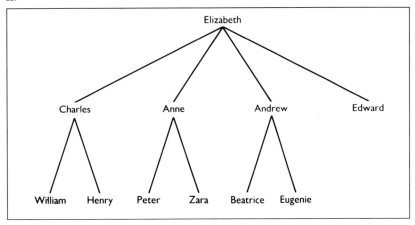

Figure 4.12
A family tree

Each data item in a tree is at a **node** of the tree. The node at the top of the tree is called the **root**. Each node may be connected to one or more subtrees, which also have a tree structure. A node at the bottom of the tree, which has no subtrees, is called a **terminal node**, or a **leaf**. See Figure 4.13.

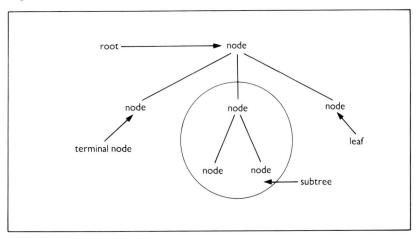

Figure 4.13
Tree concepts

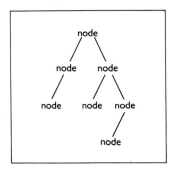

Figure 4.14
A binary tree

A special type of tree is commonly used in computing. This is a binary tree, in which each node may have at most two subtrees. These are called the left and right subtrees and are binary trees in their own right. Figure 4.14 shows a binary tree. Note how each node has zero, one or two subtrees.

The usual way of implementing a tree involves the use of pointers. For a binary tree, each node consists of a data item plus two pointers. One or both of the pointers may have null values if they have no subtrees to point to. Figure 4.15 shows how pointers may be used to construct the same tree as illustrated in Figure 4.14. Notice how terminal nodes have null values of both pointers.

A number of operations may be carried out on trees. Two binary trees may be joined to an additional node, which becomes the root of a larger binary tree, with the original trees as subtrees. A tree may be **traversed** in several ways. Traversing a tree is accessing its elements in a systematic way. Tree traversal is dealt with in the exercise at the end of this chapter.

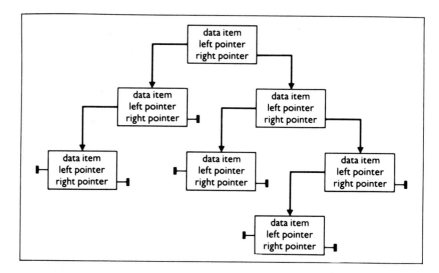

Figure 4.15
Pointers used to construct a binary tree

Trees have a number of applications in computing. The modules of many programs are linked together in a tree structure. Trees are also used to represent arithmetic expressions, and for sorting and searching. The file structures created by many operating systems form a tree structure. Some computers regard their entire memory as if it were partitioned into a tree structure.

The essential feature of a tree is that each node is connected to subtrees, which themselves have the structure of trees. In other words, wherever you are in a tree, the structure 'below' you is a tree. In this sense a tree is a **recursive** data structure, and can be manipulated by recursive programs (Section 18.5). This is the property of trees which makes them so useful from a computing point of view.

4.10 Data Types

■ A concept which links this chapter with the previous chapter is that of a **data type**. Data types include both individual data items and data structures. For many purposes it is covenient to treat entire data structures as single objects. Many program languages allow complete structures to be manipulated as if they were single data items. Data structures and individual items are often identified in the same way.

A number of program languages require that the type of each data item be declared before the data item is used in a program. A data item may be an integer, an array, or a list, to name just a few examples. The concept of data types is discussed further in the chapters on high level languages, Chapters 18 and 19.

4.11 Implementation of Data Structures

■ The data structures introduced in this chapter are described in general terms. In these terms they are sometimes known as abstract data types, with essential properties defined completely independently of computers. This is necessary to preserve the simplicity of these structures, and to investigate what further properties they possess.

A number of problems arise when representing any of these structures on a computer. In almost all cases the method of representation interferes with the properties of the structure. Some of the cleanness and simplicity of the abstract structure is lost. The commonest problem is that computers do not have an unlimited memory capacity. All the dynamic data structures introduced in this chapter have no theoretical limits on the size to which they can grow. In practice, a limit has to be placed on their size, and checks carried out whenever a new data item is added.

4.12 Conclusion

■ The significance of data structures cannot be stressed too much. The title of an important book on computer programming states the case very succinctly:

Algorithms + Data Structures = Programs.

Data structures are the fundamental building blocks of programs, and are also fundamental to the architecture of computers. One of the frontiers of computing science is research into new data structures and further properties of existing ones.

The main points of this chapter are as follows:

- A data structure is a set of data items which are related to each other in a particular way.
- The essential properties of a data structure can be described by specifying how data items are added and removed, and how an empty structure is created.
- A pointer, which is a data item indicating the location of another data item, is frequently used in the implementation of data structures.
- A string is a sequence of characters stored together and regarded as a single data item.
- An array is a fixed number of data items of identical type, stored together. Each element in an array may be accessed by one or more indices, the number of indices indicating the dimension of the array.
- Static data structures are ones which stay the same size once they have been created, whereas dynamic data structures can vary in size.
- A stack, or last-in-first-out (LIFO) structure, is a collection of data items which can only be accessed at one end, the top of the stack.
- A queue, or first-in-first-out (FIFO) structure, has items added at the rear and removed from the front.
- A list is a set of data where items may be inserted or deleted at any point.
- A tree is a data structure in which each element may be linked to one or more elements below it.
- The concept of data types includes individual data items, which may, for example, be literal or numeric, and data structures, which may be stacks, queues, lists or trees.
- In most cases when data structures are implemented, some restrictions on their properties have to be imposed. This has given rise to the concept of abstract data types, which retain their 'pure' features.

Exercise 4

1 Briefly define the following terms: data structure; pointer; null pointer; string; array; index; dimension; static and dynamic data structures; stack; top of stack; push; pop; LIFO; stack pointer; stack base; queue; FIFO; circular buffer; list; circular list; ordered list; tree; node; root;

subtree; leaf; binary tree; tree traversal; data type; declaration, and abstract data type.

2 Give three reasons for the use of data structures in computing.

3 a) Name some examples of structured data encountered in everyday life, in addition to those mentioned in the text.
   b) Describe a collection of data occurring in everyday life which could not be called structured. Give reasons for your choice of the particular collection.

4 Briefly state the requirements that a set of data must satisfy in order to be called structured.

♦ 5 Three different data structures have been mentioned in this chapter as models for a computer memory.
   a) Name the structures
   b) In the light of your knowledge of data structures, suggest why each of them might have been chosen.

6 Give three examples of the use of null pointers.

7 A text editing program allows strings of characters to be inserted into the middle of other strings. For example, the string THE CAT SAT ON MAT can be edited to become THE CAT SAT ON THE MAT.
   Give an informal algorithm, using separating and joining operations only, for this insertion operation.

8 An algorithm for setting all the elements of an array X to zero is as follows:
   Let index I = 1
   While I <= 10, repeat
     Let X(I) = 0
     Increase I by 1
   Write similar algorithms for each of the following processes:
   a) Adding each element of array X to the corresponding element of array Y, which also has ten elements, to produce array Z.
   b) Adding up all the elements of array X to produce a single total.
♦ c) Producing the 'product' of array X and array Y, defined as follows:
   $P = X(1).Y(1) + X(2).Y(2) +...+ X(10).Y(10)$
   (the dot means multiplication in this case).

9 The elements of the two-dimensional array A, with three rows and three columns, are to be copied into the one-dimensional array B, with nine elements, one row at a time. The first few elements are transferred as follows:
   A(1,1) into B(1)
   A(1,2) into B(2)
   A(1,3) into B(3), etc.
   a) Continue the above list, showing how all the elements of A are transferred.
♦ b) Derive a formula for the index of array B in terms of the indices of array A.
♦ c) Repeat the question with all the indices starting from 0 instead of 1. Comment on your results.

10 A stack is often used to do calculations on a computer in the manner introduced in the following examples:
   Example 1

   $6 + 7 \times 4$:   Stack 6 | 6 |

                        Stack 7 | 7 |
                                                                   | 6 |

                        Stack 4 | 4 |
                                                                   | 7 |
                                                                   | 6 |

                        Multiply 4 by 7, stack result | 28 |
                                                                   | 6 |

                        add 28 and 6, stack result | 34 |

Example 2

$6 \times 7 + 4$:

Stack 6	6
Stack 7	7 6
Multiply 6 and 7, stack result	42
Stack 4	4 42
Add 4 and 42, stack result	46

This procedure is based on the order in which the arithmetic operations must be performed. Taking this order into account, load the numbers onto the stack until an operation can be performed on the top two numbers. These two numbers are replaced by the result of the operation. The process continues until the final answer is left on the stack.

Using this method, show the steps of the following calculations. Make sure that you know the order in which the calculations must be performed before you start.

a) $21 - \frac{10}{5}$

b) $\frac{39}{13} - 2$

c) $6 \times 4 + 5 \times 3$

d) $6 \times (4 + 5) \times 3$

e) $7 + 9 + 15 - 2$

Another way of writing calculations, called **reverse Polish notation**, is introduced later in the book. It is intended for use when calculations are to be carried out using a stack.

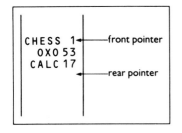

Figure 4.16

11 One method of representing a queue is to store the elements next to each other, with a pointer to the front of the queue, and a pointer to the space behind the rear of the queue. Figure 4.16 shows an example. The data items are names of programs waiting to be run on a computer.

a) Draw a diagram of the queue after the programs CHESS 1 and OXO53 have been run, and the program STRM5 has joined the queue.

b) If no further programs are added, draw diagrams of the queue when there is one program left to run, and when the queue is empty.

c) Mention a disadvantage of storing a queue in this way in a computer memory.

12 An alternative method of implementing a list is to have two pointers associated with each element. One pointer points to the list element in front, the other to the element behind.

a) Draw a diagram of a list implemented in this way.

b) Draw diagrams to show the process of inserting a new data item into a list, using pointers in both directions.

c) Labelling the relevant pointers, specify precisely what operations are performed to accommodate the new item.

13 Draw a diagram of a circular list using pointers in both directions.

14 A set of names is stored, in alphabetical order, in an array. The last few elements of the array contain free spaces. Write informal algorithms showing the principal steps of inserting and deleting elements of this array, while preserving its alphabetical ordering and keeping the free spaces at the back. (Write the algorithms as brief English sentences. Do not specify index values in detail.)

From your results, comment on the suitability of arrays for storing ordered data.

15 Trees can be used to describe the structure of arithmetic or algebraic expressions, as shown in the following examples:

Example 1

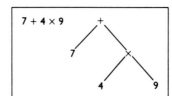

Figure 4.17

Example 2

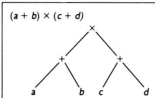

Figure 4.18

The parts of the calculations which are to be performed first form the lowest branches of the tree.

Represent the following expressions in a similar manner to the above examples:

a) $8 - \frac{5}{7}$

b) $(x - y) - (p \times q)$

c) $((x + y) \times 2) / (a - 7)$

d) $a + b + c$

e) $(s + t) \times (u - v) / (p + q)$

16 Two arrays are used to represent a tree, in the following manner. One array stores the data items in the tree. The other array contains blocks of pointers , one for each node. The first pointer in a node is the index of the data item at that node. Subsequent pointers point to blocks for nodes branching from the node. The block ends with a zero.

For example, the tree showing the component subjects of computing science is shown in Figure 4.19. The arrays corresponding to this tree are shown below.

pointers array		data array	
index	item	index	item
1	2	1	applications
2	7	2	computing
3	9	3	data
4	11	4	hardware
5	13	5	software
6	0		
7	3		
8	0		
9	4		
10	0		
11	5		
12	0		
13	1		
14	0		

Arrows have been drawn to show the effects of the first few pointers.

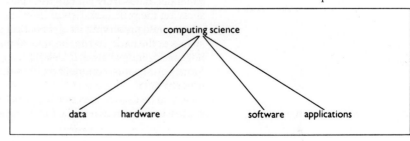

Figure 4.19

Construct similar arrays to represent the following trees:
a) Figure 4.20   b) Figure 4.21

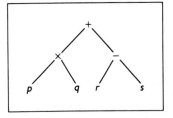

Figure 4.21

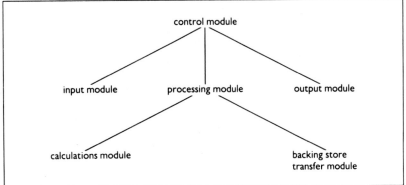

Figure 4.20

17 An array can be used to store the elements in a binary tree in a fairly simple manner. The correspondence of array indices and nodes in the tree is shown in Figure 4.22
a) Store the tree in part (b) of Question 16 in this manner.
b) The array: $\begin{bmatrix} a \\ b \end{bmatrix}$ stores the binary tree: a
   b

Represent the binary tree in Figure 4.23 in an array in this way.
c) Compare this method of representing trees by arrays with one introduced in Question 16. Comment on the suitability of this method of storing binary trees.

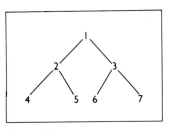

Figure 4.22

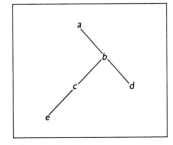

Figure 4.23

◆ 18 Traversing a tree is accessing its elements in a systematic way. The commonest order is 'from left to right', i.e. left subtree, node, right subtree. This way can be described by the following algorithm:
traverse tree:
    if tree not null
        then traverse left subtree
            output node
            traverse right subtree
This algorithm is recursive, in the sense that it 'calls' itself. Applied to the tree in Figure 4.15, it produces the elements in the order $7 + 4 \times 9$.
a) Apply this algorithm to the trees in Figures 4.22 and 4.23, and list the elements in the order in which they are output.
b) Change the algorithm so that it traverses both subtrees before the node is output.
c) Write down the output produced by applying the revised algorithm to the trees in Figures 4.17, 4.22 and 4.23.

5 Computer Arithmetic

This chapter concerns one aspect of the processing carried out by computers: **computer arithmetic**. Arithmetic is only one of the ways in which a computer can process data – the days of computers being used for 'number crunching' only have long passed. On the other hand, computers do a certain amount of simple arithmetic during the running of all programs, whether they are for numerical applications or not.

This chapter introduces the elementary theory of computer arithmetic. Pencil and paper calculations are done here in a manner similar to the way in which they are done on computers. Some of the electronic circuits which carry out the various arithmetic operations are introduced in Chapter 8.

This chapter builds on foundations laid in Chapter 3 concerning data representation. Ways of representing numbers and some elementary operations of computer arithmetic are introduced in that chapter.

5.1 Characteristics of Computer Arithmetic

■ The arithmetic carried out by computers differs from our customary way of doing arithmetic in a number of ways. Although arithmetic operations are implemented differently on different computers, they all have a few common characteristics. These are a binary representation of numbers, a finite range of numbers, a finite precision of numbers, and certain operations done in terms of other operations. Each of these characteristics is now discussed.

Binary Representation of Numbers

Various binary representations of numbers are discussed in Chapter 3. The most important point to remember at this stage is that numbers can be represented in several ways, such as in binary coded decimal form, as integers or fractions, or as floating point numbers. Furthermore, integers and fractions can be in sign-and-magnitude form, or as twos complement or ones complement numbers. The way in which arithmetic operations are carried out depends on the way numbers are represented.

This chapter is confined to a discussion of twos complement integers and floating point numbers, as these are the commonest ways of representing numbers on computers. In many programming languages the programmer can choose which of these two forms is to be used for each numeric data item.

Finite Range of Numbers

Whichever way numbers are represented on a computer, there is always an upper and a lower limit on their size. These limits depend on the number representation used, and on the number of bits allocated to their number. The term **overflow** is used if an operation results in a number which is outside these limits (the term **underflow** is used in relation to the lower limit).

For example, if a computer uses eight bits for the storage of positive integers, the largest number which can be stored is 1 1 1 1 1 1 1 1 (binary) = 255 (decimal). An attempt to store a larger number as eight bits results in an overflow.

Most computer systems have different types of number, to reduce the probability of overflow errors (while not wasting space through unnecessarily long numbers). For example, in many computer systems ordinary integers are represented in sixteen bits, while long integers occupy 32 bits. Programmers choose the most suitable type for each number they require.

Finite Precision of Numbers

When a base ten number is written as a decimal fraction, the number of decimal places reflects the **precision** of the number. Most fractions cannot be represented exactly in a finite number of decimal places. The precision of a decimal fraction is a measure of how closely it comes to representing the number exactly. For example, in base ten, the fraction $\frac{1}{3}$ cannot be represented exactly as a decimal. However, a representation using four decimal places, 0.3333, is more precise than one using only two, 0.33.

In computers, fractions and floating point numbers are stored in a finite number of binary places. As in the case of decimal fractions, this limits the precision of these numbers. This means that a calculation using floating point numbers seldom gives exactly the right answer. In most computer systems, single precision and double precision floating point numbers are available. The double precision numbers occupy more bits, making them more precise.

Operations Done in Terms of Other Operations

Most computers do not have separate processing circuits for all arithmetic operations. One of the reasons for using complementary numbers is that subtraction can be done by complementation and addition. On many computers multiplication is done by a process of shifting and addition. Division is done by shifting and subtraction. An algorithm for doing multiplication in this way is given in Section 5.2.

The roles of hardware and software in computer arithmetic are important. Operations such as integer addition are done directly by hardware. Operations done in terms of other operations are controlled by software. Each type of computer has its own mixture of hardware and software implementation of arithmetic operations. In general, the larger the computer, the more operations are done directly by hardware.

5.2 Integer Arithmetic

■ In this section, integers are assumed to be represented in twos complement form. This form is introduced in Chapter 3, where it is explained how subtraction can be carried out by complementation and addition. Three further aspects of integer arithmetic are now discussed: overflow, multiplication and division.

Overflow

Overflow occurs when the result of a calculation is outside the range of numbers which can be represented. There is no way of preventing overflow; all that a computer can do is detect it when it occurs.

In twos complement arithmetic, overflow is related to the numbers carried into and out of the most significant place value during addition. Four examples are introduced below to illustrate this point, after which some general conclusions are drawn. Six bit twos complement numbers are used throughout.

Note carefully the numbers carried into and out of the most significant bit of the calculations below, and whether or not the result is correct.

	−32	16	8	4	2	1	
Example 1: 14 + 9							
14 =	0	0	1	1	1	0	
9 =	0	0	1	0	0	1	+
	0	1	0	1	1	1	= 23
	0	0					
	carry out		carry in				

Carry in = 0, carry out = 0, answer correct.

	−32	16	8	4	2	1	
Example 2: 25 + 18							
25 =	0	1	1	0	0	1	
18 =	0	1	0	0	1	0	+
	1	0	1	0	1	1	= −21
	0	1					
	carry out		carry in				

Carry in = 1, carry out = 0, answer incorrect.

Example 3: 17 − 13 = 17 + (−13)

17 =	0	1	0	0	0	1	
−13 =	1	1	0	0	1	1	+
	0	0	0	1	0	0	= 4
	1	1					
	carry out		carry in				

Carry in = 1, carry out = 1, answer correct.

Example 4: −8 − 31 = −8 + (−31)

−8 =	1	1	1	0	0	0	
−31 =	1	0	0	0	0	1	+
	0	1	1	0	0	1	= 25
	1	0					
	carry out		carry in				

Carry in = 0, carry out = 1, answer incorrect.

From the four results it can be seen that the answer is correct when the number carried in to the most significant place is the same as the number carried out. This is true in general. In other words, overflow occurs when, at the most significant bit, carry in is not equal to carry out. Most computers have a special overflow bit which is set to 1 when overflow is detected in this manner. The above examples use six bit arithmetic, but the situation is the same, in twos complement arithmetic, however many bits are used.

Integer Multiplication

If multiplication is not performed directly by computer hardware, the commonest technique is to use a process of shifting and addition. It is very similar to the method of doing binary multiplication by hand.

You will recall that there are rules for determining the sign of a product from the signs of the numbers which are multiplied. These rules are generally applied separately from the actual multiplication process. Accordingly, this section considers the multiplication of positive integers only.

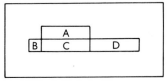

Figure 5.1

An algorithm is presented below for the multiplication of two positive binary integers, by a process of shifting and addition. It is not the only one used by computers, but is representative of them. The algorithm requires a working area, which might be imagined as shown in Figure 5.1. There are three storage spaces for binary integers, labelled A, C and D. The storage space labelled B is for the carry bit resulting from an addition.

The algorithm is as follows:

Initially, B and C contain zeros, while A and D contain the two numbers to be multiplied.

Repeat, for each bit of the numbers:

If the least significant bit of D is 1, then add A to C, placing the sum in C and the carry in B.

Shift the bits in B, C and D together one place to the right. Thus B passes into C, a bit passes from C to D and the least significant bit of D is lost.

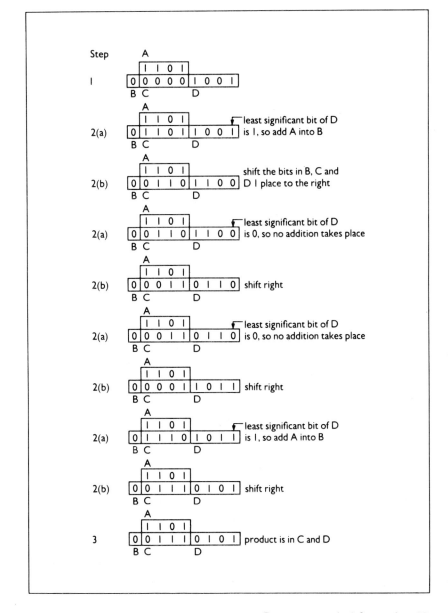

Figure 5.2
1101 x 1001

When this process is complete, the product of the two numbers is in C and D.

An example of this process is shown in Figure 5.2. For simplicity, four bit integers 1 1 0 1 and 1 0 0 1 are used. Thus the shifting and addition is repeated four times. Afterwards the product of the two numbers, 0 1 1 1 0 1 0 1, is in C and D. The result can be checked by converting the numbers and the product to decimal.

You will notice that the product is twice as long as the original numbers. Overflow can occur if this number must be stored in the space for a single integer. Four bit numbers are used in the above example for simplicity. The steps of the algorithm are the same if longer numbers are used.

Integer Division

Integer division is done by a process of shifting and subtraction, very similar to the process of integer multiplication. The result is obtained as a quotient and a remainder. In most computers the result of the division is taken to be the quotient, without any rounding up being done. In other words, the result of dividing 20 by 7, using integer arithmetic is 2.

5.3 Floating Point Arithmetic

■ Methods of representing floating point numbers are discussed in Chapter 3. You will recall that a floating point number consists of a fraction part, or mantissa, multiplied by a power of two, or exponent. For simplicity, all floating point numbers used in this chapter are of the following form:

		mantissa					exponent	
sign	$\frac{1}{2}$	$\frac{1}{4}$	$\frac{1}{8}$	$\frac{1}{16}$	sign	2	1
For example 0	1	1	0	1	0	1	0

$$= \frac{13}{16} \times 2^2 = \frac{13}{16} \times 4 = 3 \quad \frac{1}{4}$$

This form is far shorter than any actual floating point representation, but serves to illustrate the principles involved.

Three aspects of floating point arithmetic are now discussed: **overflow**, **addition** and **multiplication**. Loss of precision is investigated in the context of addition and multiplication.

Overflow in Floating Point Arithmetic

As in the case of integers, there is an upper and a lower limit to the size of floating point numbers which can be represented by a particular number of bits. These limits are determined by the number of bits allocated to the exponent. For the above allocation of bits, the limits to the exponent are −3 and 3. This gives an approximate range of the size of the numbers of 2^{-3} to 2^3, i.e. $\frac{1}{8}$ to 8. In practice , this range is of course much wider.

If a number exceeds the upper limits of the range, **overflow** is said to occur. If a number exceeds the lower limit, some computers will set the number to zero. The term **underflow** is used when this occurs.

Floating Point Addition

An algorithm for the addition of two floating point numbers is as follows:
    If the exponents of the two numbers are not equal
        then For the number with the smaller exponent, repeat:

Shift the mantissa one place to the right
Increase the exponent by 1
Until the exponent equals that of the other number.
Add the mantissas of the two numbers.
If the addition results in a carry from the most significant place
then Shift this carry bit into the mantissa and the
rest of the mantissa one place to the right
Increase the exponent by 1.

This is quite a complicated procedure just for the addition of two numbers. The example below shows how it works.

		mantissa				exponent	
sign	$\frac{1}{2}$	$\frac{1}{4}$	$\frac{1}{8}$	$\frac{1}{16}$	sign	2	1

	sign	$\frac{1}{2}$	$\frac{1}{4}$	$\frac{1}{8}$	$\frac{1}{16}$	sign	2	1	
	0	1	1	0	1	0	1	0	$(= 3\frac{1}{4})$
+	0	1	0	0	1	0	0	1	$(= 1\frac{1}{8})$

The second number has the smaller exponent, so the mantissa is shifted one place to the right and the exponent is increased by 1. One bit of the mantissa is lost. The result is as follows:

0	0	1	0	0	0	1	0

As the exponents are now equal, the mantissas can be added:

	0	1	1	0	1
+	0	0	1	0	0
	0	0	0	0	1

carry: 1

The carry bit is shifted into the mantissa, and the exponent is increased by 1. Again one bit of the mantissa is lost. The result is as follows:

		mantissa				exponent	
sign	$\frac{1}{2}$	$\frac{1}{4}$	$\frac{1}{8}$	$\frac{1}{16}$	sign	2	1

sign	$\frac{1}{2}$	$\frac{1}{4}$	$\frac{1}{8}$	$\frac{1}{16}$	sign	2	1
0	1	0	0	0	0	1	1

$$= \frac{1}{2} \times 2^3 = \frac{1}{2} \times 8 = 4$$

Adding the decimal values of the original numbers gives the result as $4\frac{3}{8}$. An error has been introduced, due to the limited number of bits allocated to the mantissa. This type of error is called a truncation error. A remedy for this kind of error is to allocate more bits to the mantissa. This increases the precision of the numbers. Although it reduces this kind of error, it will never eliminate it. The error can be reduced by rounding, discussed in the exercise at the end of this chapter.

Subtraction of floating point numbers is carried out by a very similar process, and can result in the same kind of errors.

Floating Point Multiplication

An algorithm for the multiplication of two floating point numbers is as follows:

Multiply the mantissas of the numbers, and add their exponents.
Shift the bits of the product to the left until there is a 1 in the most significant place. Reduce the exponent by 1 for each place shifted.
Truncate the product to the number of bits allocated to the mantissa of a floating point number.

The following example, using the same floating point numbers as before, shows how this algorithm works.

	mantissa				exponent			
sign	$\frac{1}{2}$	$\frac{1}{4}$	$\frac{1}{8}$	$\frac{1}{16}$	sign	2	1	
0	1	1	0	1	0	1	0	$(= 3\frac{1}{4})$
× 0	1	0	0	1	0	0	1	$(= 1\frac{1}{8})$

Multiplying the mantissa and adding the exponents gives the following results:

product of mantissas   :   0   1   1   1   0   1   0   1
sum of exponents   :   1   1

The product is shifted one place to the left, and the exponent is reduced by 1. This gives:

product of mantissas   :   1   1   1   0   1   0   1
sum of exponents   :   1   0

Truncating the product into the mantissa gives the following floating point result:

	mantissa				exponent		
sign	$\frac{1}{2}$	$\frac{1}{4}$	$\frac{1}{8}$	$\frac{1}{16}$	sign	2	1
0	1	1	1	0	0	1	0

$$= \frac{7}{8} \times 2^2 = \frac{7}{8} \times 4 = 3\frac{1}{2}$$

Multiplying the decimal values of the original numbers gives the result $3\frac{21}{32}$. Once again a truncation error has been introduced. As before, this error can be reduced, but not eliminated, by increasing the number of bits allocated to the mantissa or by rounding. Floating point division suffers similar limitations.

5.4 Conclusion

■ This chapter has introduced some of the techniques of computer arithmetic, and demonstrated, by means of a few simple examples, some of the errors which can arise. Although the number representations used in this chapter are much shorter than those used by any actual computer, the principles and the problems are the same.

The main points raised in this chapter are as follows:

• The characteristics of computer arithmetic are a binary representation of numbers, generally in more than one code, a finite range and a finite precision of numbers, and some arithmetic operations done in terms of other operations.

• In integer arithmetic, overflow is related to the numbers carried into and out of the most significant place value during addition.

• Integer multiplication can be carried out by a process of shifting and addition. Integer division results in a quotient and a remainder.

• In floating point arithmetic, the range of numbers which can be represented depends on the number of bits allocated to the exponent. Overflow or underflow occurs if this range is exceeded.

• Truncation errors occur in floating point arithmetic when the mantissa of the result is cut off to fit the number of bits allocated to it. Truncation errors are reduced by normalisation (shifting the mantissa so that there is always a 1 in the most significant place), and rounding the result (see Question 9 below). If rounding is carried out, the error is known as a rounding error.

Exercise 5

1 Briefly define the following terms: overflow; precision; normalisation; overflow bit; truncation error, rounding error.

2 For a number of different computers, find out what arithmetic operations are carried out by hardware and what operations are supervised by software.

3 Verify the rule established in the chapter relating carry to overflow, by carrying out the following calculations, using four bit, twos complement numbers: 2+5; 6+3; 4–5; –2–7.

4 Do the four calculations in the examples from the section on carry and overflow, using ones complement representation. From your results, state under what conditions overflow occurs in this representation.

5 Use the algorithm for integer multiplication to multiply 1 1 0 1 by 1 1 1 0.

◆ 6 Design an algorithm for integer division by a process of shifting and subtraction. A similar layout of working areas can be used to that for integer multiplication. Test your algorithm with some suitable numbers

7

		mantissa				exponent		
	sign	$\frac{1}{2}$	$\frac{1}{4}$	$\frac{1}{8}$	$\frac{1}{16}$	sign	2	1
Let A =	0	1	1	0	0	0	1	0
Let B =	0	1	1	0	1	0	0	1
Let C =	0	1	0	1	0	0	0	0
Let D =	0	1	1	1	1	0	1	1

Perform the following calculations on these numbers, using floating point arithmetic: A+B; B+C; A×B; A×C; A×D; B×D; C×D; A+D. In each case, comment on any errors which arise.

8 A particular computer allocates 24 bits to a floating point number. Six of these bits are for the exponent, the first of which is a sign bit. What is the approximate range of numbers which can be represented in this way?

9 Errors can be reduced in computer arithmetic by the technique of rounding. Rounding is carried out when bits of a number, generally the mantissa of a floating point number, are discarded. The retained bits are rounded by adding 1 to the least significant retained bit if the most significant discarded bit is 1.

For example, if the eight bit mantissa 1 1 0 1 1 0 1 1 is rounded to four bits, the result is 1 1 1 0.

a) Round each of the following numbers, discarding the rightmost bits:

0	1	1	0	1	1	0	1	to four bits
0	1	1	1	1	0	1	1	to four bits
1	0	0	1	1	0	0	1	to six bits

b) Round the results of the floating point addition and multiplication examples in this chapter, and repeat Question 7, rounding the results. Convert the numbers obtained to decimal, and comment on your results.

◆ 10 Write an algorithm to convert an eight-bit integer, stored in sign-and-magnitude form, into a floating point number using the format of Question 7. Test your algorithm by converting the following integers:

0	1	1	0	0	0	0	0
0	1	0	1	1	1	0	1
1	0	0	0	1	0	1	0
1	1	0	1	0	1	0	1

Boolean Logic

This chapter introduces the theory behind the way in which computers manipulate data. This theory has been given the name **Boolean logic** after the English mathematician George Boole (1810–1864). In 1847, Boole published the first thorough investigation of the principles of mathematical logic.

This chapter builds on ideas introduced in earlier chapters, particularly Chapter 3, on data representation and storage. Concepts introduced in this chapter form the basis of the material in Chapter 8, on logic circuits, and the part of the book devoted to computer architecture, Chapters 9 to 15. The set of logic symbols used in this chapter is becoming the most widely accepted in the computing industry. If another set is preferred, Figure 6.7 compares the common sets of logic symbols.

6.1 Two-state Representation of Data

■ Boolean logic comprises a set of operations which manipulate logical, or Boolean variables. A **Boolean variable** is a quantity which can have either of two values, or states only. Depending on the context, these states may be called true and false, set and clear, high and low, or 0 and 1.

As discussed in Chapter 3, all data inside a computer is represented in terms of two states only. In other words, all data is made up of Boolean variables. Furthermore, all processing of this data by the computer is carried out in terms of Boolean operations. The elementary operations of Boolean logic are introduced in this chapter. Chapter 8 shows how these operations are combined in various functional circuits of a computer.

6.2 The Elementary Logic Operations

■ Boolean operations transform one or more Boolean variables, producing a further Boolean variable. The value of the resulting (output) variable depends on the values of the original (input) variables.

Each logic operation is characterised by a **truth table**. This table shows values of the output variable for all combinations of input variables. Two symbols associated with each logic operation are also introduced. The first symbol is the **logic circuit** symbol. This symbol indicates the logic operation in a logic circuit, which is rather like an electrical circuit. The circuit elements which perform these operations are referred to as gates. The other symbol is the **Boolean algebra** symbol for the operation. Boolean algebra is a way of representing logic operations, similar to the way ordinary algebra represents arithmetic operations.

Later in the chapter, combinations of logic operations are introduced. Like individual operations, these combinations can be described by truth tables, logic circuits or expressions in Boolean algebra.

The six commonest operations of Boolean logic are discussed below:

NOT

The **NOT** operation has one input variable and one output variable. The value of the output variable is the opposite of that of the input variable. See Figure 6.1.

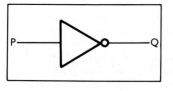

Figure 6.1
A NOT gate

Truth table

Input	Output
P	Q = NOT P
0	1
1	0

Boolean expression: $Q = \overline{P}$

AND

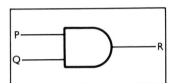

Figure 6.2
An AND gate

The **AND** operation has two or more input variables and one output variable. The output variable is 1 if all input variables are 1, otherwise it is 0. See Figure 6.2.

Truth table (for two inputs)

Input		Output
P	Q	R = P AND Q
0	0	0
0	1	0
1	0	0
1	1	1

Boolean expression: $R = P.Q$

The truth table for an AND operation may be extended to three or more input variables using the rule for the AND operation quoted above.

OR

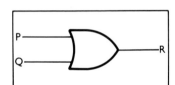

Figure 6.3
An OR gate

The **OR** operation has two or more input variables and one output variable. The output variable is 1 if any of the input variables are 1, otherwise it is 0. See Figure 6.3.

Truth table (for two inputs)

Input		Output
P	Q	R = P OR Q
0	0	0
0	1	1
1	0	1
1	1	1

Boolean expression: $R = P + Q$

It turns out that combinations of the NOT gate and either the AND or the OR gate are sufficient to carry out any logical operation on any number of inputs. However, three other logic gates are in common use, as introduced below.

Exclusive OR

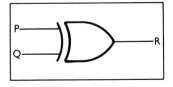

Figure 6.4
An Exclusive OR gate

The **exclusive OR** or non-equivalence operation has two input variables and one output variable. Considered as an exclusive OR, the rule for its operation is as follows: the output variable is 1 if either, but not both, inputs are 1. (An alternative rule is that the output is 1 if the inputs are different.) See Figure 6.4.

Truth table

Input		Output
P	Q	R = P EOR Q
0	0	0
0	1	0
1	0	1
1	1	0

Boolean expression: $R = P \oplus Q$

NAND

The **NAND** operation may be considered as an AND operation followed by a NOT operation. It has two or more input variables and one output variable. The output variable is 0 if all the input variables are 1, otherwise it is 1. See Figure 6.5.

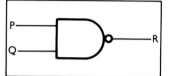

Figure 6.5 A NAND gate

Truth table (for two inputs)

Input		Output
P	Q	R = P NAND Q
0	0	1
0	1	1
1	0	1
1	1	0

Boolean expression: $R = \overline{P.Q}$

NOR

The **NOR** operation may be considered as an OR operation followed by a NOT operation. It has two or more input variables and one output variable. The output variable is 0 if any of the input variables are 1, otherwise it is 1. See Figure 6.6.

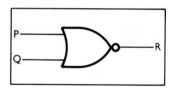

Figure 6.6 A NOR gate

Truth table (for two inputs)

Input		Output
P	Q	R = P NOR Q
0	0	1
0	1	0
1	0	0
1	1	0

Boolean expression: $R = \overline{P + Q}$

6.3 Logic Operation Symbols

■ There are several sets of symbols for logic operations in current use. Figure 6.7 shows the relationship between them.

Operation	Boolean algebra symbols		Logic circuit symbols	
NOT	$\bar{P}$	$\sim P$		NOT
AND	$P.Q$	$P \wedge Q$		AND
OR	$P + Q$	$P \vee Q$		OR
Exclusive OR	$P \oplus Q$	$P \neq Q$		EOR
NAND	$\overline{P.Q}$	$\sim (P \wedge Q)$		NAND
NOR	$\overline{P + Q}$	$\sim (P \vee Q)$		NOR

Figure 6.7
Different sets of logic symbols

6.4 Combinations of Logic Operations

■ The logic operations introduced in the previous section are seldom used on their own. Combinations of these operations may be imagined as connecting the output of one gate to the input of another gate. Some of the logic circuits of even the simplest computers are extremely complex. Such complexity is deliberately avoided here. The objective of this section is to show how logic elements can be combined, and how the truth table for a combination can be determined from the truth tables of the individual gates. Boolean expressions for the combinations of operations are also given.

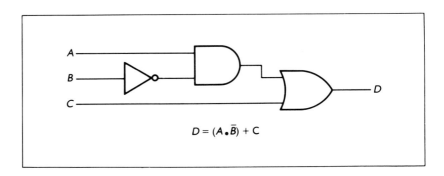

$$D = (A.\bar{B}) + C$$

Figure 6.8
Logic circuit Example 1

Example 1

The logic circuit shown in Figure 6.8 combines an AND, an OR and a NOT gate. The Boolean expression for this combination is:

$$D = (A.\bar{B}) + C$$

There are two ways of obtaining the truth table for a circuit such as this. One is to follow all possible combinations of inputs through the circuit, and obtain the value of the output for each input. The other is to build up the truth table through a series of intermediate columns. There is a column for each part of the Boolean expression. The columns are combined according to the rules for Boolean operations, until a column for the whole expression is obtained. This process is shown in the following table.

Input					Output
A	B	C	$\bar{B}$	$A.\bar{B}$	$D = (A.\bar{B}) + C$
0	0	0	1	0	0
0	0	1	1	0	1
0	1	0	0	0	0
0	1	1	0	0	1
1	0	0	1	1	1
1	0	1	1	1	1
1	1	0	0	0	0
1	1	1	0	0	1

Example 2

The logic circuit shown in Figure 6.9 combines a NAND and a NOR gate. The Boolean expression for this combination is:

$$S = \overline{(P + Q).R}$$

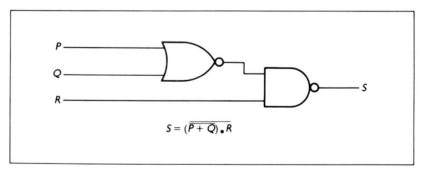

$$S = (\overline{P + Q}).R$$

Figure 6.9
Logic circuit Example 2

As before, the truth table for the circuit is obtained by using intermediate columns for parts of the Boolean expression.

Input				Output
P	Q	R	$\overline{P + Q}$	$S = \overline{(P + Q).R}$
0	0	0	1	1
0	0	1	1	0
0	1	0	0	1
0	1	1	0	1
1	0	0	0	1
1	0	1	0	1
1	1	0	0	1
1	1	1	0	1

Example 3

The logic circuit shown in Figure 6.10 combines two 3-input AND gates, two NOT gates and an exclusive OR gate. The Boolean expression for this combination is:

$$D = (\overline{A}.B.C) \oplus (A.\overline{B}.C).$$

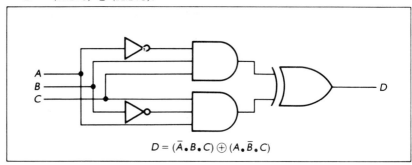

$$D = (\overline{A}.B.C) \oplus (A.\overline{B}.C)$$

Figure 6.10
Logic circuit Example 3

The truth table for the circuit is obtained by the same method as before.

		Input					Output
A	B	C	$\overline{A}$	$\overline{B}$	$\overline{A}.B.C$	$A.\overline{B}.C$	$D = (\overline{A}.B.C) \oplus (A.\overline{B}.C)$
0	0	0	1	1	0	0	0
0	0	1	1	1	0	0	0
0	1	0	1	0	0	0	0
0	1	1	1	0	1	0	1
1	0	0	0	1	0	0	0
1	0	1	0	1	0	1	1
1	1	0	0	0	0	0	0
1	1	1	0	0	0	0	0

These examples show how the truth table for a logic circuit can be obtained from the expression for the circuit. In practice, in designing the logic circuits of a computer, one starts with a required truth table, and derives the Boolean expression and logic circuit to produce this table.

6.5
Conclusion

■ This chapter has introduced the elementary operations which form the basis of all processing done by computers. Ways of combining these operations have been demonstrated.

The concepts which have been introduced here form the basis of the next few chapters of this book. These chapters cover some of the more important logic circuits used in computers, and how the structure of a computer is built up from these circuits.

The most important points of this chapter are as follows:
• The theoretical basis for the operation of computers is Boolean logic. It consists of a number of operations which can be applied to Boolean or logical variables, having two states only.
• Boolean operations can be represented by symbols in Boolean algebra, truth tables, or logic circuits, in which they appear as gates.
• All logic operations can be expressed as a combination of the elementary operations AND, OR and NOT. However, three other operations, NAND, NOR and non-equivalence, are in common use.

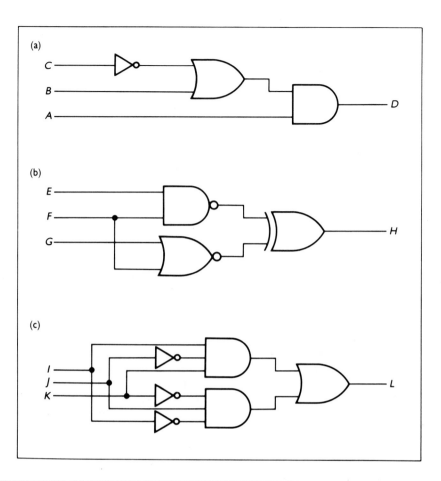

Figure 6.11
Logic circuit exercises

1 Briefly define the following terms: Boolean logic; Boolean variable; truth table; logic circuit; Boolean algebra; Boolean operation; gate; sum of products.

2 Draw the truth tables for three-input AND, OR, NAND and NOR gates.

3 Summarise the connection between two-state representation of data and Boolean logic.

4 a) Write Boolean expressions for each of the logic circuits in Figure 6.11.
b) Obtain the truth table for each of these logic circuits.

5 Draw logic circuits for each of the following Boolean expressions:

$$V = \overline{K.\overline{L}}$$

$$W = \overline{K.L}$$

$$X = P.Q + \overline{P}.R$$

$$Y = A.\overline{(B + C)}$$

$$Z = \overline{(D + E).(\overline{D} + F)}$$

◆ 6 Express the exclusive OR operation in terms of AND, OR and NOT operations.

7 a) Draw logic circuits for each of the following Boolean expressions:

$$K = \overline{\overline{A} + \overline{B}}$$

$$L = (C + \overline{D}).(C + \overline{E})$$

$$M = (\overline{P.(Q.\overline{R})}) + (P.(Q.R))$$

◆ 8 Write a Boolean expression and draw a logic circuit for the following truth table:

Input			Output
A	B	C	D
0	0	0	0
0	0	1	0
0	1	0	0
0	1	1	1
1	0	0	1
1	0	1	0
1	1	0	0
1	1	1	0

9 Express the AND operation in terms of the OR and NOT operations.

◆ 10 a) Draw a diagram to show how a two-input NAND gate can be used as a NOT gate.

b) Hence show how the AND and OR operations can be expressed in terms of the NAND operation only.

c) What conclusion can you draw from these results?

◆ 11 The specification for a multiplexer with data inputs A and B, control input C and output X is:

If $C = 0$ then $X = A$
else $X = B$

Draw a logic circuit, write a Boolean expression and draw up a truth table for a multiplexer as specified above.

Artificial Intelligence

Ever since computers were first thought of, there has been research, discussion and speculation about the extent to which they may be regarded as intelligent. In spite of all these investigations, there has been progress in only limited areas in resolving the problem of machine intelligence. The progress which has been made does, however, mean that the computer systems which are planned for the 1990s are being designed to incorporate a higher level of intelligence than those introduced in the past.

Underlying the question of artificial intelligence is a serious difficulty. Our knowledge of human intelligence is not clear enough to provide a firm basis for ideas of artificial intelligence. For this reason, there is no definition of the term 'artificial intelligence' as a straightforward concept which can be implemented.

7.1 Notions of Intelligence

■ It is quite possible to set out an approximate scale of intelligence: most people are more intelligent than most chimpanzees, a word processor is a more intelligent machine than a typewriter, and so on. Nevertheless there is no scientific definition of intelligence. Intelligence is related to the ability to recognise patterns, draw reasoned conclusions, analyse complex systems into simple elements and resolve contradictions, yet it is more than all of these. It contains an indefinable 'spark' which enables new insights to be gained, new theories to be formulated and new knowledge to be established.

Intelligence can also be examined from the point of view of language. Information can easily be represented as words, numbers or some other symbols. Knowledge is generally expressed in a language or as mathematical formulae. Intelligence is at the upper limit of language. Instances of patterns or deductive reasoning can be written down, and certain general principles can be stated. However, the creative 'spark' of intelligence is almost impossible to express in language.

7.2 Machine Intelligence

■ The only widely accepted definition of artificial intelligence is based on a test devised by Alan Turing in 1950:

> Suppose there are two identical terminals in a room, one connected to a computer, and the other operated remotely by a person. If someone using the two terminals is unable to decide which is connected to the computer, and which is operated by the person, then the computer can be credited with intelligence.

The definition of artificial intelligence which follows from this test is:

> Artificial intelligence is the science of making machines do things that would require intelligence if done by people.

No computer system has come anywhere near to passing the Turing test in general terms. Nevertheless, progress has been made in a number of specific fields. It would take a very good chess player in the 1990s to be able to tell whether he or she were playing against a computer or a human opponent. Most car drivers are unaware which parts of their cars have been assembled by robots, and which by manual workers. Computers are used routinely in some countries to assist with certain types of medical diagnosis.

■ Conventional data processing is based on information; artificial intelligence is based on knowledge. A central problem for artificial intelligence is an adequate representation of knowledge on a computer. On the one hand, the representation must be 'rich' enough to be of practical use. On the other hand, it must be simple enough for processing by a computer.

The Three Levels of Knowledge Representation

The method of knowledge representation which has been most sucessful is to use three levels. At the lowest level are **associations** between objects. For example 'smoking is a cause of lung cancer', generally written as follows:

```
cause-of (smoking, lung-cancer).
```

Associations of this form are known as **propositions** in knowledge-based systems. The relations themselves (such as 'cause-of') are known as **predicates**.

At the second level of representation of knowledge are sets of **rules** which connect propositions. For example:

```
If cause-of (x, y) and practices (z, x) then risk-
of (z, y)
```

which means that if x is a cause of disease y, and person z practices x, then z is at risk of y.

Rules of this nature may be manipulated by a set of general **rules of inference**, such as:

```
If A is true and B is true then (A and B) is true.
```

The problem, in any particular situation, is to know in what sequence to apply the rules of inference to the given set of rules. This gives rise to the third level of representation of knowledge on a computer: a **strategy** to control the application of the rules of inference to the particular rules in any situation. Development of effective control strategies has been one of the most difficult problems facing researchers in artificial intelligence.

There have been two approaches to this problem. One has been to look for general methods, which apply to large numbers of situations. This has led, amongst other things, to the development of the Prolog programming language (Section 19.8). The other has been to develop strategies which are applicable in certain areas. This approach has been behind the development of expert and knowledge-based systems (Chapter 33).

Semantic Networks

A technique of knowledge representation which is widely used is **semantic networks**. As shown in Figure 7.1, a semantic network shows a set of relationships between objects. It is a flexible method of representation, allowing new objects and new relationships to be added to a knowledge base. Accordingly, semantic networks are often used in computer systems which have some form of learning capacity.

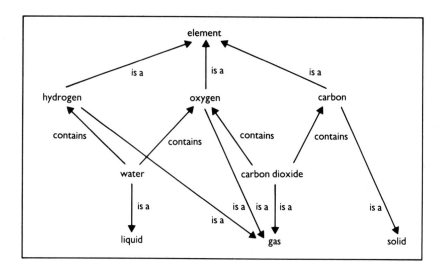

Figure 7.1
A semantic network

Frames

More formal than semantic networks is the idea of a **frame** to represent a related set of information. A frame, shown in Figure 7.2, contains a set of related data items, together with certain properties of the items. For example, a frame may contain the range of possible values of a data item. In some cases a frame may include the formula for the calculation of the value of a data item. A frame may also contain pointers to other frames.

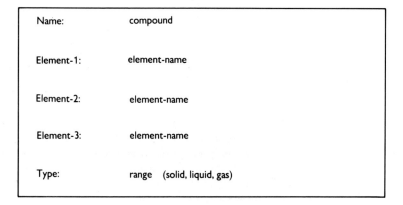

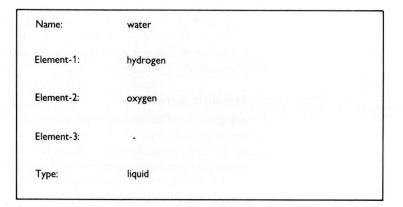

Figure 7.2
An empty frame and a frame for a particular compound

Production Rules

A popular method of expressing the rules which specify how new knowledge is derived from existing knowledge is the use of **production rules**. These are sequences of rules of the form:

```
if <condition> then <action>
```

which are applied according to some strategy. For example, a set of rules to control a robot fitting car door handles could be as follows:

```
If <car in position> and <got handle> then
                              <fit handle>.
If not <got handle> then <pick up handle>.
If not <handle fits> then <report and stop>.
If not <found handle> then <report and stop>.
```

The rules are repeatedly checked, and if the condition for any one is true, then the corresponding action takes place.

7.4 Game Playing Programs

■ Much of the progress in artificial intelligence has come through work on game playing programs. Games such as chess have the advantage of being simple enough to represent on a computer, while requiring a high level of intelligence on the part of the player. A number of successful strategies for playing games have been worked out. They are all based on searching a large number of possible moves and counter-moves, and selecting the best one to make.

In some games, such as noughts and crosses, it is possible to search right through to the end of the game for each possible next move. In other games, notably chess, this is not possible, as the number of moves is too large even for the most powerful computer. The best chess programs achieve the right balance between the breadth of the search (the number of possible moves investigated), the depth of the search (the number of consequent moves investigated for each possibility) and the way of assessing the favourability of the moves. Chess programs have now reached grandmaster level.

Many of the methods used for game playing programs are being transferred to other fields of artificial intelligence.

7.5 Reasoning Programs

■ Reasoning programs have been used to solve the kind of pattern recognition problems found in intelligence tests, and to solve problems in formal logic. An example of programs of this sort is the use of a computer to assist in the proof of the Four Colour Theorem. It has been known for centuries that no more than four colours are needed to colour in any map, so that no two adjacent zones have the same colours. See Figure 7.3. This theorem was finally proved with the aid of a computer program in 1976.

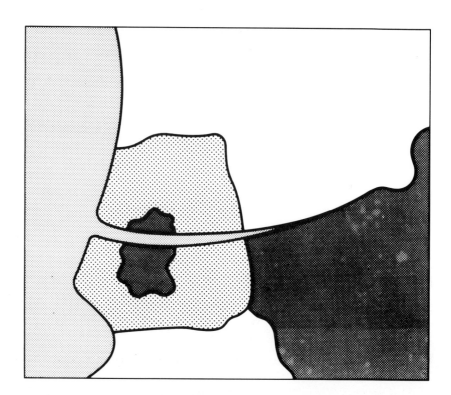

Figure 7.3
The Four Colour Theorem

7.6 Natural Language Recognition

■ One of the conclusions reached in Chapter 1 is that computers cannot interpret continuous passages in a natural language. Nevertheless, computers can cope with individual words and phrases, and longer passages of natural language in specific topics. A major topic of artificial intelligence research has been the recognition of natural language by computer. There are two aspects of this work: **syntax** and **semantics**.

Natural languages are composed of structures such as sentences, which are constructed according to rules of syntax. For example, the sentence:

```
The boy stood on the burning deck
```

can be analysed (or **parsed**) as:

```
<subject> <verb> <object>
```

where <subject> ('the boy') can be further parsed as

```
<article> <noun>    etc.
```

The problem with syntax analysis is that the rules for sentence construction are very complex, there are many exceptions, and the rules are gradually modified as languages evolve.

In order to understand a passage in a natural language, the semantics or meaning of the piece must be studied. This depends on the context and what has been said before, as well as the meanings of individual words. Semantics is very difficult. In some cases an alternative interpretation of a single word can alter the meaning of a whole passage.

Computer programs have been devised which will cope with the syntax and semantics of complete sentences, but only within limited contexts. Even for these restricted situations, the programs are very complex. However, if current research into natural language recognition is successful, systems with a much more powerful natural language capability will be available during the 1990s.

7.7 Image Recognition

■ Although computers can construct complex graphics displays, far less progress has been made with the problem of interpreting visual information, supplied, for example, by a video camera. Image processing is an important computer application in its own right, and also as an interface for a number of other applications, notably robots.

The commonest approach to this problem has been to construct sets of general rules for the interpretation of visual patterns, and apply these to various situations. Most systems start by identifying the boundaries of the objects (a much more difficult task than it first appears), and then deducing their shape and other properties. Programs have been developed which will decide correctly, in most cases, whether the silhouette of a person is that of a man or a woman, and identify blocks of various shapes. Software for fingerprint matching by image processing is now quite advanced. Research is being directed towards a visual capability for robots which will enable them to 'see' where to position themselves, and to distinguish between the objects they are manipulating.

7.8 Expert Systems

■ The most successful aspect of artificial intelligence has been expert systems. An expert system is a computer program which matches the level of human expertise in a particular field. Expert systems are a product of the line of research which has concentrated on transferring specific aspects of human intelligence to computers. Expert systems are discussed further in Chapter 33.

7.9 Conclusion

■ In spite of many difficulties, progress has been made in certain aspects of artificial intelligence. In particular, it has proved possible to transfer a measure of intelligence from person to computer in specific fields. One of the biggest challenges to be overcome, before major breakthroughs are possible, is the automation of human common sense.

The main points of this chapter are as follows:

- One of the most serious problems of artificial intelligence is the lack of a precise understanding of human intelligence.
- Intelligence can be placed in a scale: information, knowledge, intelligence and wisdom.
- Language and mathematics can cope with information and knowledge, but only to some extent with intelligence.
- A widely accepted test for artificial intelligence is the Turing test:

  Suppose there are two identical terminals in a room, one connected to a computer, and the other operated remotely by a person. If someone using the two terminals is unable to decide which is connected to the computer, and which is operated by the person, then the computer can be credited with intelligence.

- A definition of artificial intelligence is as follows:

  Artificial intelligence is the science of making machines do things that would require intelligence if done by people.

- The commonest way of representing knowledge on a computer is in terms of three levels:

  associations between objects (propositions)

  rules which relate propositions and higher level rules known as rules of inference

  strategies for applying rules.

- Advances in artificial intelligence have been made in game playing programs, reasoning programs, natural language recognition, image recognition and expert systems.

Exercise 7

1 Briefly define each of the following terms: artificial intelligence; proposition; predicate; rule of inference; syntax; semantics; parse; expert system.

2 a) Place the following tasks in ascending order of the intelligence (in your view) required to perform them:
   Calculating a weekly wage.
   Formulating the economic policy for a country.
   Reading road signs.
   Selecting the right size nut for a particular bolt.
   Choosing a meal from a menu.
   Deciding which car to buy for a particular purpose.
   Interpreting the instructions from an air traffic controller.
   b) Compare your ordering with those of others, and discuss the reasons for the differences.
   c) Which of the above tasks can be carried out entirely by computers at present?
   d) Which of the above tasks can be carried out with the assistance of computers at present?
   e) In your view, how will the answers to parts c) and d) change over the next ten years?

3 Given the following propositions:

   likes (John, Fred)
   likes (Susan, John)
   likes (John, Helen)
   likes (Helen, Jean)

   and the rule:

   if likes (x, y) and likes (y, z) then likes (x, z)

   what new propositions can be generated by applying the rule to the given propositions?

4 a) Comment on the different meanings of the word 'saw' in the following sentence:

   When he saw the red light, he saw that he had to stop.

   b) Collect as many other sentence or pairs of sentences as you can in which the same word is used with different meanings.
   c) Comment on the significance of your findings for natural language recognition by computer.

5 The instructions given by the person in charge of a ship are an example of the use of a small subset of natural language in a practical situation. All the statements have precisely defined meanings. List other such situations, and in each case state whether a computer could be usefully employed to generate or interpret some or all of the statements.

6 List some potential applications of robots with some form of visual perception.

8 Logic Circuits

This is the first chapter in the part of the book concerned with computer hardware. It examines some of the essential processing circuits inside a computer. The electronic components of these circuits are briefly considered, but the emphasis is on their logical structure and properties. The circuit designs presented here are independent of any actual computer, but form the basis of the types of circuits commonly used.

This chapter relates closely to a number of other chapters. It is an application of the theory of Boolean logic introduced in Chapter 6. The logic gates introduced in that chapter are used extensively here. This chapter also relates to earlier chapters on data representation and computer arithmetic. Many of the circuits introduced here show how ideas from these chapters are put into practice. Finally, this chapter paves the way for the rest of this part of the book, which is a study of various aspects of computer hardware.

8.1 Hardware Implementation of Logic Operations

■ A Boolean variable is one which can take on the values 0 and 1 only, and Boolean operations manipulate variables of this nature. It turns out that solid-state electronic components can be made to behave like Boolean operations. The 'variables' which they manipulate are voltages. In many, but not all, cases, a high voltage represents the value 1, and a low, or zero, voltage represents the value 0. The devices which carry out these operations are solid-state **integrated circuits (ICs)**, commonly known as **chips**.

Transistors

You will recall from Chapter 6 that a logic operation can be regarded as a gate. The most general gate combines one or more inputs to produce a single output. Its behaviour is described by a truth table.

A **transistor** is an electronic component with three connections. The connections can be at a high or a low voltage, corresponding to logic 1 or 0. A simple combination of transistors can be arranged to correspond to the operation of a logic gate. This is the basis of the way in which electronic logic circuits are constructed. Figure 8.1 shows a logic gate and a transistor.

Integrated Circuits

For about ten years, from 1955 to 1965, the logic circuits of computers were made from individual transistors for logic gates, as described above. Then it was realised that circuits could be constructed containing a number of transistors and other components as a single, solid-state unit. These integrated circuits perform the function of a large number of logic gates. The principle on which they work is, however, the same as that for an individual transistor.

The design of integrated circuits has evolved through several stages. The first integrated circuits were equivalent to approximately ten transistors. Then came **medium scale integration (MSI)**, with hundreds of components on one chip. Today we are moving from the era of **large scale integration (LSI)**, with thousands or tens of thousands of components on one chip, and entering the phase of **very large scale integration (VLSI)**, with hundreds of thousands or millions of individual

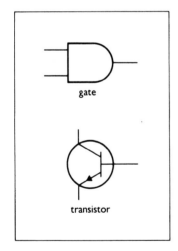

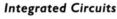
gate

transistor

Figure 8.1
A gate and a transistor

elements on a chip. Single chips can contain large portions of computer memories, or all the processing circuits of a computer. The latter type of chip is called a **microprocessor**. A recent type of chip, the **transputer**, combines processor, memory and input/output channels on a single very fast chip.

There are several reasons for the rapid acceptance of very large scale integrated circuits. These chips are small, consume very little electrical energy (and therefore do not produce much heat), and are very reliable. However, the overriding consideration is cost. As the capabilities of individual chips have increased, their costs have continued to decrease. The cost per unit of storage or performance has decreased dramatically, and continues to do so.

Gate Delay

One property of integrated circuits must be mentioned at this point. This is that, after the input voltages have been altered, there is a delay before the output voltage stabilises at its new value. This property is called **gate delay**. It is one of the factors which limits the speed of the computer, and it affects the design of logic circuits.

8.2
Control
Switches

■ Data, addresses and control signals are sent from place to place inside a computer by means of data **channels**, also known as data **buses**. Data channels are parallel connections, with one path for each bit of the data item. **Control switches** regulate the flow of data in a channel. A control switch is opened to allow a data item to pass, or closed to block the passage of the data.

A control switch uses a set of AND gates, one for each bit of the data item, arranged in parallel. Figure 8.2 shows a four bit control switch. Each AND gate has one input from the data channel, and one from the common control input.

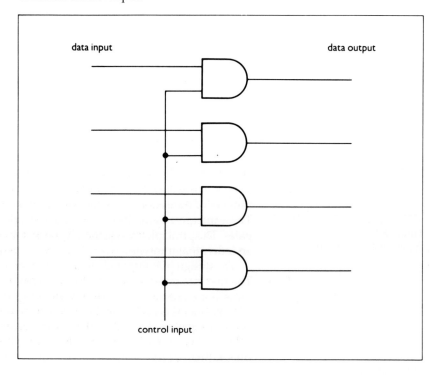

Figure 8.2
A four bit control switch
64 Logic Circuits

A control switch works in the following manner. If the control input is 0, then all outputs are 0, no matter what the data inputs are. The switch is open, and no data passes. However, if the control input is 1, then each output has the same value as the corresponding data input. This can be checked from the operation table of an AND gate. The switch is closed, and data passes along the channel.

Computers contain a number of control switches of this type. They regulate the flow of data between the functional circuits, and into and out of the storage elements. They often form part of multiplexers, where two or more data buses are merged into one.

8.3 Masks

■ More general-purpose than a control switch, but still using parallel AND gates, is a **mask** circuit. It can be imagined as a set of control switches, with a separate switch for each bit of the data. Figure 8.3 shows a four bit mask circuit.

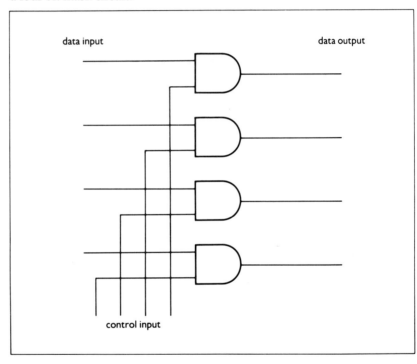

data input   data output

control input

Figure 8.3
A four bit mask circuit

The purpose of a mask is to select certain bits of a data item, and 'mask out' the remaining bits. If a particular bit of the data item is required, then the corresponding control input is set to 1. If the bit is to be masked out, then the corresponding control input is set to 0. The operation table of an AND gate can be used to verify this. The control input is sometimes referred to as a mask. For example, if the most significant three bits of an eight bit data item are required, then a mask of 11100000 is used.

8.4 Decoders

■ A **decoder** is a circuit which selects one of a number of outputs according to the code of an input data item. Working in base ten for a moment, the principle is as follows: if there are 20 outputs, then an input number between 1 and 20 will cause the corresponding output to be selected. For example, the number 13 will cause the thirteenth output to be selected.

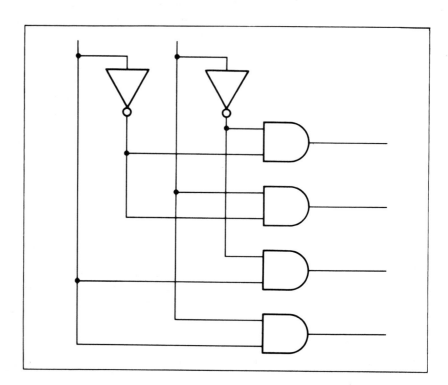

Figure 8.4
A two-to-four decoder

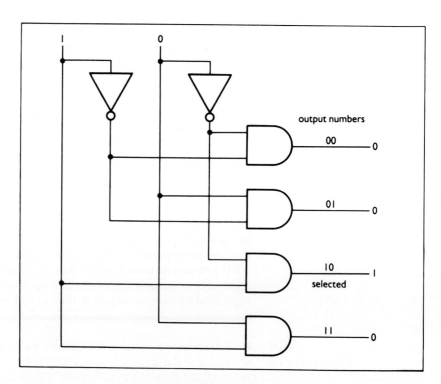

output numbers

00   0

01   0

10   I
selected

11   0

Figure 8.5
A two-to-four decoder in
operation

The decoder shown in Figure 8.4 has two inputs and four outputs. The outputs may be numbered (in binary) 0 0, 0 1, 1 0 and 1 1. The circuit works in such a way that any binary number input will cause the output with the corresponding number to be selected. Figure 8.5 shows the input 1 0 causing the output numbered 1 0 to be selected.

The decoders used in most computers contain more inputs and far more outputs than those illustrated here. They are used to locate memory cells (where they are known as **address decoders**), and in carrying out program instructions (**instruction decoders**).

8.5 Addition Units

■ All computers do addition by hardware: the logic circuits forming the addition units of a computer are discussed in this section.

The rules for adding two binary digits are given in the following table:

Inputs		Sum	Carry
0	0	0	0
0	1	1	0
1	0	1	0
1	1	0	1

You will notice that the sum column can be produced by an exclusive OR gate, and the carry column by an AND gate. A logic circuit containing these gates is shown in Figure 8.6. It is called a **half adder** (because it cannot incorporate a carry from a previous column).

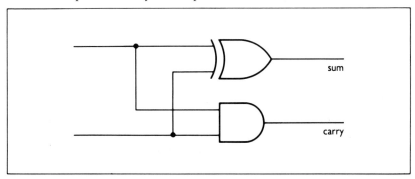

Figure 8.6
A half adder

If two complete binary numbers are added, the carry from the previous column must also be taken into account. A **full adder** is a circuit which adds two bits, together with a previous carry, to produce a sum and a carry. A full adder may be constructed from two half adders, as shown in Figure 8.7, or it may be implemented directly. This latter method is discussed in the exercise at the end of the chapter.

There are two approaches to adding complete binary numbers. One is to have a full adder to each pair of bits. All the additions take place at the same time. A circuit of this type is called a **parallel adder**, shown in Figure 8.8. The other (less common) method is to add one pair of bits at a

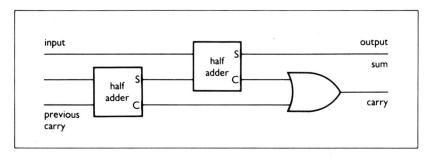

Figure 8.7
A full adder made from two half adders

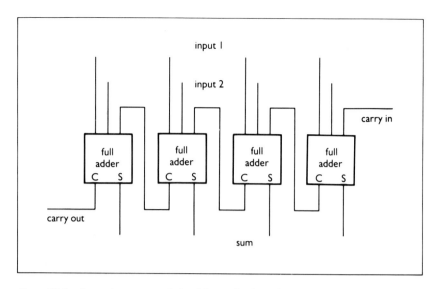

Figure 8.8
A four bit parallel adder

time. This gives rise to a **serial adder**, which is discussed in the exercise at the end of the chapter.

Returning to the parallel adder for a moment, Figure 8.8 shows that a parallel adder has a carry out and a carry in. The carry out is the same as the carry bit discussed in Chapters 3 and 5. The carry in is very useful, as it enables a number to be increased by 1. One application of this which has already been discussed is the process of obtaining the twos complement of a number, by negating the bits and then adding 1. Figure 8.9 shows a combined addition/subtraction unit based on this principle.

As mentioned in Section 8.1, there is a delay associated with data passing through each logic gate in a circuit. Although the circuits in Figure 8.8 operate in parallel, a carry might have to be passed across all the full adders in the circuit. This involves a considerable delay, and addition is not quite 'in parallel'. To minimise this delay, some parallel adders include **carry prediction circuits**, which determine the value of each carry directly from the inputs.

8.6
Flip-Flops

■ The logic circuits introduced up to now are all concerned with the processing of data. Attention is now focused on an important class of circuits used to store data. Storage circuits differ from processing circuits in one important respect. The output of a processing circuit is completely determined by the state of its inputs at the time (the name **combinational logic** is used to describe this property). However, the output of a storage circuit is determined by its inputs and also its previous output state. This is because storage circuits always contain connections which 'feed back' from output to input. Circuits whose output depends on past states are called **serial logic** circuits.

Several types of storage circuits are used in computers. Two of the commonest ones are discussed here; a further type is introduced in the exercise at the end of the chapter.

RS Flip-Flop

The simplest storage circuit is called an **RS flip-flop** or **bistable**. One way of constructing it is to use two NOR gates, connected as shown in Figure 8.10. Notice how the outputs are 'fed back' into the inputs.

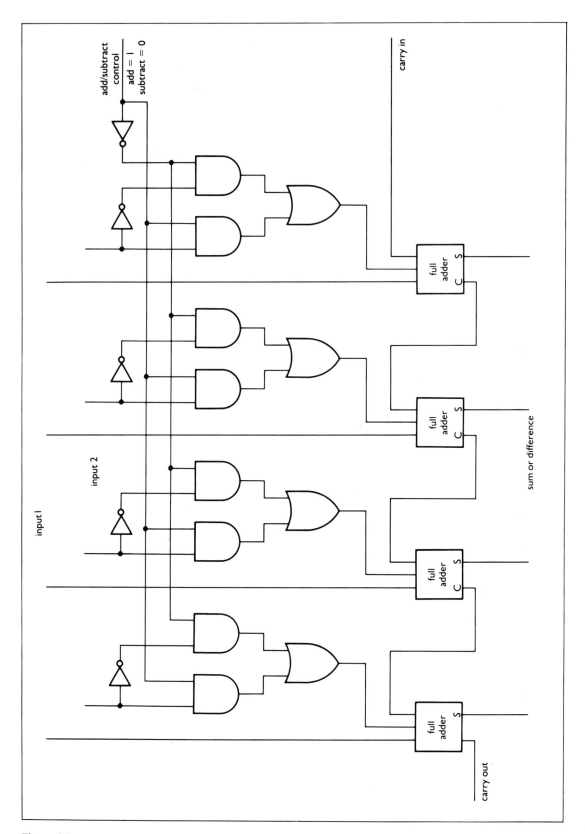

Figure 8.9
A four bit combined addition/subtraction unit

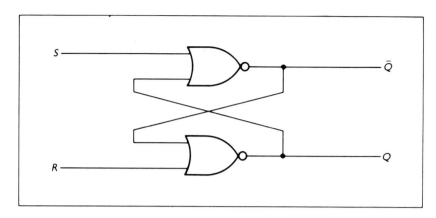

Figure 8.10
An RS flip-flop made from two
NOR gates

This circuit has acquired its name because it can be made to 'flip' from one stable output to the other by a signal at the inputs. One input is called the **set** input, the other is called the **reset** input. The two outputs are always in opposite states, hence their labels Q and Q'.

The operation table for an RS flip-flop is given below. It shows the current output Q in terms of the inputs R and S, and the previous value of Q.

R	S	previous Q	current Q
0	0	0	0
0	1	0	1
0	0	1	1
1	0	1	0
0	0	0	0
1	0	0	0
0	1	1	1
1	1	0	0 or 1
1	1	1	0 or 1

The rows of the table have been written in an unusual order, to illustrate the way the circuit is used. The rows are considered one at a time.

The first row shows that if both inputs are zero, the output does not change. The second row shows that a one at the S input changes the output from zero to one. The flip-flop is set. The third row shows that if S now returns to zero, the output stays at one.

The first three rows indicate that a pulse at input S, i.e. a change from zero to one and back to zero, causes the output to flip from zero to one and stay there. In other words, the pulse at S is 'remembered'.

Rows 3, 4 and 5 of the table illustrate the reverse process. Row 3 shows the circuit in the set state. If input R becomes one, as shown in the fourth row, then the output changes from one to zero. The fifth row, which is a copy of the first row, shows that input R can return to zero without affecting the output state. These rows show that a pulse from R causes the output to flip from one to zero and stay there. The flip-flop is reset.

The next two rows show that a pulse at R will not affect the output if it is already zero, and a pulse at S will not change the output if it is already one.

The last two rows show the problem associated with this circuit. If both inputs become one at the same time, then the output is not known. It can be either zero or one.

From this description of the way in which an RS flip-flop works, you will realise that it can be used to store one bit of data. A pulse at S causes a one to be stored, and a pulse at R causes a zero to be stored.

JK Flip-Flop

There are a number of problems associated with RS flip-flops, in particular the undefined state when both inputs are one. Accordingly, a more sophisticated circuit, known as a **master-slave** or **JK flip-flop** is commonly used to store data. See Figure 8.11. You will notice that it contains two RS flip-flops and a **clock input**. The clock input is used to control the timing of the storage of data.

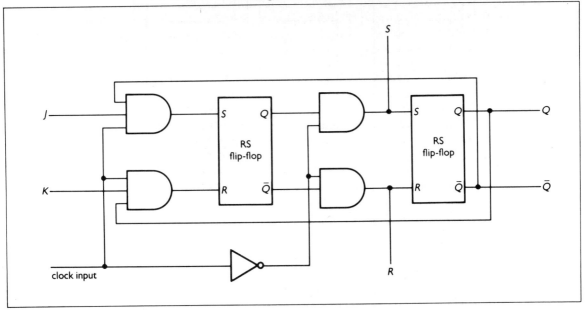

Figure 8.11
A JK flip-flop

The operation table for a JK flip-flop is shown below. It is written in the same order as the table for an RS flip-flop. The only difference between the two is in the last two lines. For simplicity, the clock signal and the set (S) and reset (R) inputs are omitted.

K	J	previous Q	current Q
0	0	0	0
0	1	0	1
0	0	1	1
1	0	1	0
0	0	0	0
1	0	0	0
0	1	1	1
1	1	0	1
1	1	1	1

RS and JK flip-flops are not the only circuits used to store data on computers. However, all data storage circuits have the property that a pulse at one input causes the output to change from one state to the other and stay there. All computers incorporate large numbers of data storage elements.

8.7 Registers

■ Several data storage circuits may be combined to form a **register**, which stores a complete data item. Figure 8.12 shows one arrangement of a register. Notice how all the bits can be cleared from one input, and how the storage of input data is timed by a clock input.

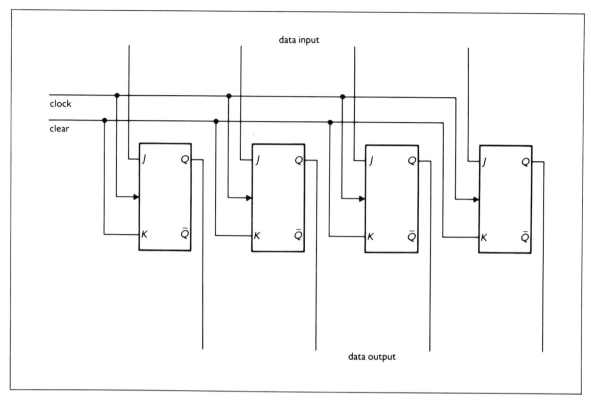

Figure 8.12
A four bit register made from
JK flip-flops

Computers contain a number of registers to store, among other things,
data items which are currently being processed, and instructions which
are currently being carried out.

Shift Registers

A type of register which deserves special mention is a **shift register**. Such
a register enables bits of a data item to be shifted from one position to the
next. Figure 8.13 shows how a number of JK flip-flops can be combined to
form a shift register. Every time the clock line is pulsed, each bit of the
data item moves one place to the right.

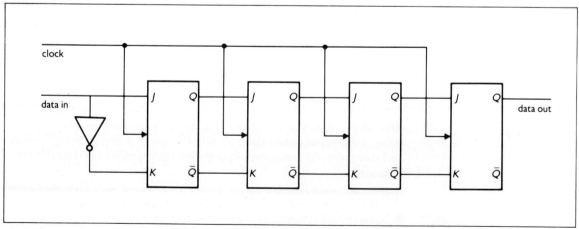

Figure 8.13
A four bit shift register made
from JK flip-flops

Shift registers have a number of uses. These include multiplication,
division and serial addition, and accepting input from serial input

devices. One significant application, known as a **USART**, is discussed in the exercise at the end of this chapter.

8.8 Uncommitted Logic Arrays

■ A useful type of chip is made up of a regular pattern of identical elements, such as NAND gates. (It can be proved that any logic operation can be carried out by a combination of NAND gates only, and similarly for NOR gates.) This arrangement of gates on a chip is known as an **uncommitted logic array (ULA)** or **gate array**. The connections between the gates are specified by the purchaser of the chip, and form a separate layer from those forming the processing elements. The chip is fabricated in two stages: first the array of processing elements, then the interconnections.

ULA chips are one way of enabling small runs of special-purpose chips (known as **application-specific integrated circuits** or **Asics**) to be produced quickly and cheaply. Asics may also be made using conventional integrated circuit technology. They are used for particular processing and control operations, or such tasks as encoding and decoding signals for data communication. In many computers, the circuits for all the 'odd jobs' required are collected together and placed on an Asic. This reduces the size and price of the computer, and helps to improve reliability.

8.9 Conclusion

■ The most important points made in this chapter are as follows:
- The electronic components used to implement logic operations are integrated circuits or chips.
- Solid-state circuits have now reached the stage of very large scale integration, including complete processors on a single chip, called microprocessors.
- Control switches regulate the flow of data on data channels.
- A mask is a logic circuit which selects certain bits in a data item.
- A decoder selects one of a number of outputs according to the code of an input data item.
- Addition is generally carried out by means of a parallel adder, containing a number of full adders which add pairs of bits.
- The basic storage element in a computer is a flip-flop, which has two stable output states. A signal at either of its inputs can cause it to flip from one state to another.
- A register is a storage element for a complete item of data.
- A shift register enables bits of a data item to be shifted from one position to the next.

Exercise 8

1 Briefly define the following terms: integrated circuit; microprocessor; gate delay; data channel; control switch; mask; decoder; full adder; parallel adder; bistable; register; shift register; uncommitted logic array; Asic; transputer.
2 The first, third and fifth bits (counting from the left) of an eight bit data item are to be examined. The remaining bits are not required.
   a) What arrangement of mask bits will enable this to be done?
   b) What is the result of masking the data item 11011010 in this way?
3 The decoder shown in Figure 8.4 has two inputs and four outputs.
   a) How many outputs does a three-input decoder have?
   b) How many outputs does an n-input decoder have?

c) Design a three-input decoder similar to the one in Figure 8.4. Number the outputs from 000 to 111. Show how the input bit pattern 101 will cause the 101th output to be selected.

◆ 4 a) Draw up the operation table for a full adder. Label the inputs A, B and C (for carry in), and the outputs S (sum) and T (carry out).

b) Use this table to verify that the logic expressions for S and T are as follows:

$$S = A.B.C + A.\bar{B}.\bar{C} + \bar{A}.B.\bar{C} + \bar{A}.\bar{B}.C$$
$$T = A.B + B.C + A.C$$

c) Use the above expressions to design a logic circuit for S and one for T. The circuit for S requires three NOT gates, four three-input AND gates and one four-input OR gate. The circuit for T uses three two-input AND gates and one three-input OR gate

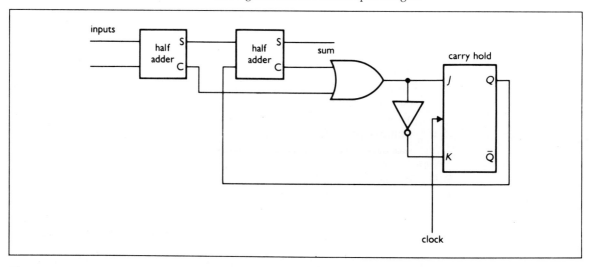

Figure 8.14
Part of a serial addition unit

◆ 5 Figure 8.14 shows the processing part of a serial addition unit. If two bits are supplied at the inputs, and the clock line at the carry hold flip-flop is pulsed, it will add the input bits and the previous carry, producing a sum bit and storing the carry bit in the carry hold. It is now ready to repeat the process for the next pair of bits.

a) Connect three four-bit shift registers to this circuit, to supply the input numbers and store the sum. Draw a diagram showing the complete serial addition unit.

b) Draw two extra connections onto your diagram, showing how a carry in and a carry out can be included.

◆ 6 At the beginning of this book, the concept of a module is introduced (Section 2.6). Although it has not been explicitly mentioned, this concept has been used a number of times in this chapter. Explain, with examples, how the concept of a module is used in the context of logic circuits.

7 Combine two four-bit control switches with additional dates to form a multiplexer which combines two four-bit buses into a single four-bit bus, with a selection input to determine which set of input data pases to the output.

8 A commonly used data storage element is the D type flip-flop. It has the following properties:

i) Inputs are a single data line and a clock line.

ii) A NOT gate and an RS flip-flop are used.

iii) The flip-flop takes the value at its input when a clock pulse appears, and remains in the same state until the next clock pulse appears.

iv) Outputs are the same as those for an RS flip-flop.
From this information, draw a circuit diagram of a D type flip-flop.

◆ 9 A circuit frequently used for serial input and output is a Universal Synchronous/Asynchronous Receiver/Transmitter, or USART. It is a register which can be loaded with either serial or parallel data, and which will output either serial or parallel data.

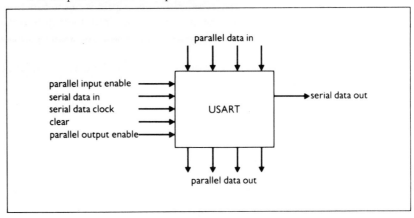

Figure 8.15
A USART

A 'black box' view of a four bit USART is shown in Figure 8.15. Notice that there are control signals for parallel data in and parallel data out, a clear signal and a clock signal for serial data in and out.

Using JK flip-flops, AND gates and a NOT gate, construct the internal circuits of this black box.

Hints: Use the S inputs of the flip-flop for parallel data in, and the R inputs for the clear signals. Also see Figures 8.12 and 8.13.

10 A multiplexer is a logic circuit with a number of data inputs, a number of control inputs and a single data output. Its purpose is to select a single data input which is copied to the data output.

Using the design of a four bit decoder (Figure 8.4) draw a logic circuit diagram of a four bit multiplexer. It has four data inputs, two control inputs and a data output. The binary number formed by the control inputs determines which data input is copied to the output. For example if the control inputs form the binary number 01 then the data item on the input labelled 01 is copied to the output.

9 Computer Structure

This chapter gives an overall view of the hardware of a computer system. The units making up typical computer configurations of various sizes are discussed. Brief descriptions of the functions of these units are given, and some problems arising from their different characteristics are mentioned.

9.1 The Functional Units of a Computer

■ Computers vary enormously in size, processing power and cost. Nevertheless, all computers consist of one or more functional devices, each carrying out one or more of the tasks shown in Figure 9.1. Each device (or module) performs a precisely specified task, and connects to other modules via defined interfaces. The input, output and backing store devices are together known as peripheral devices. These are discussed in detail in Chapter 14.

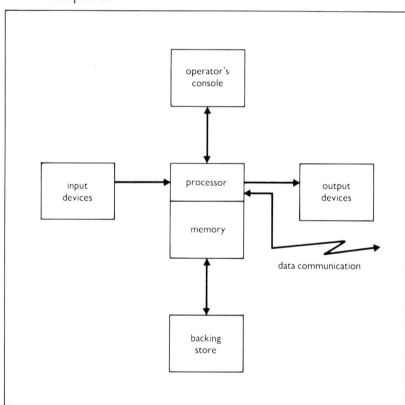

Figure 9.1
The general structure of a computer

Modules of the same type of computer may be exchanged, and new modules added, without modification to their internal workings. The phrase **plug-compatible** describes units which may be connected in this manner. To an increasing extent, modules from different manufacturers are plug-compatible.

9.2
The Seven
Classes of
Computer
System

■ Very broadly speaking, there are seven classes of computer system, according to their capability and price. In practice, there are no precise divisions between these classes, but most systems fall into one of them. Classified by order of magnitude of price, they are as follows:

Class	Price (order of magnitude)
pocket calculator	£10
laptop microcomputer	£100
desktop microcomputer	£1 000
workstation	£10 000
mid-range system	£100 000
mainframe	£1 000 000
supercomputer	£10 000 000

Pocket calculators are the smallest and cheapest computing devices based on silicon technology. They have a keypad for input and a single-line display for output. Some contain a certain amount of memory, and a few are programmable. A few have data links to larger systems.

Laptop microcomputers are based on single-chip microprocessors, with simple keyboards for input, and flat text-only displays for output. They are generally battery powered, with mains rechargers. Their main uses are simple word processing, electronic diaries, or data entry for other systems.

Desktop microcomputers are numerically the largest class of computers. Based on a single-chip microprocessor, a desktop microcomputer can be used stand-alone, or as a network station. Designed for a single user, they can usually have only one process in operation at any time. They have keyboard and mouse input, display screen output and quite substantial memory and backing store capacities. They are capable of a wide range of tasks, from word processing to graphics applications, spreadsheets, databases and desktop publishing. There is a substantial overlap in computing power (and price) between the top-end laptop systems and desktop microcomputers.

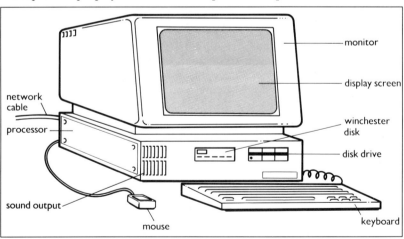

Figure 9.2
A microcomputer

Workstations are the fastest-growing class of computer systems. They are based on powerful microprocessors, and have large memory and backing store capacities, usually including Winchester disks. They are able to run a number of processes at the same time. They are most commonly connected into local area networks, sharing such resources as large-capacity Winchester disks, high-speed printers, plotters and external communications links. Workstations are used for such applications as computer-aided design, analysis of experimental results and tasks involving high-resolution graphics.

Mid-range systems (formerly known as minicomputers) comprise several functional devices mounted in a rack in a single central unit. Their processors are formed from a number of chips, and they have correspondingly large memories and backing store facilities. Some have multiple processors operating in parallel. Mid-range systems can support more than one application running concurrently from a number of different users. They can be linked into both local and wide-area networks which may include terminals, desktop microcomputers, workstations or other mid-range systems. They are to be found in laboratories, factories and offices for applications which require shared access to large stores of data, and/or substantial processing power.

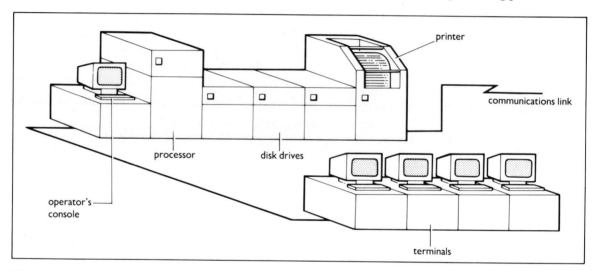

Figure 9.3
A mid-range computer

Mainframes are large computer systems, comprising a number of free-standing units. They generally have multiple central processors, and additional dedicated processors which control the flow of data to and from peripherals and data communications channels. Mainframes are generally housed in specially designed, air-conditioned rooms. Connections between the units are by wires running beneath the floor of the room. Mainframes are very powerful, and support large numbers of applications from many different users running concurrently. They are almost always the centre of a large network, forming the central computing resource of large organisations such as banks, airlines, government departments and universities.

Large mainframes are known as **supercomputers**. They consist of multiple processors running in parallel, with access to very large memories. They are based on integrated circuits using advanced silicon technologies. Separate mainframe processors are generally required to handle the throughput of data to and from peripherals and high-speed data communications links. Specialised cooling systems are required to carry off the large quantities of heat generated. Most supercomputers are used to run small numbers of specialised, complex processes which require large quantities of data and very fast calculations. Applications include weather forecasting, aerodynamic and hydrodynamic modelling and very high resolution graphics.

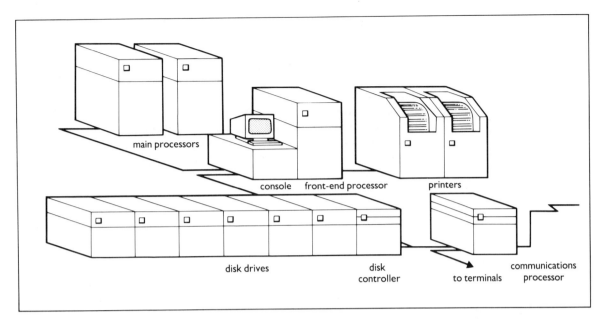

Figure 9.4
A supercomputer

9.3
A Typical Microcomputer

■ Figure 9.2 shows the structure of a typical microcomputer. It consists of a single unit housing the microprocessor, memory, Winchester disk and floppy disk drive. Memory and floppy disk capacities are around one megabyte, with 20 or 40 megabytes of hard disk storage.

The keyboard and display screen are separate units. The screen is typically a colour monitor capable of both text and fairly high resolution graphics. The most common type of printer is a dot matrix printer capable of text and graphics, but laser printers are becoming increasingly popular with microcomputers. A connection for a local area network is common.

9.4
A Typical Mid-range Computer

■ Figure 9.3 shows the units of a typical mid-range computer, and the flows of data between them.

Processing of data takes place in the **central processing unit**, or **CPU**, containing one or more processors and a large memory. Linked to the processor, generally via a network, are a number of peripheral devices. Network links may be local or long-distance.

A typical mid-range computer system.

Terminals are general-purpose peripheral devices. They consist of a keyboard for input, and a display screen for output. Special-purpose terminals such as cash terminals in shops incorporate input or output devices such as bar code readers. Microcomputers or workstations may also be used as terminals. Terminals are linked to the CPU by local or long distance networks.

Backing store is storage of large quantities of data for rapid access by the CPU. Magnetic disks and magnetic tapes are the most common storage media. Optical disks are beginning to be used for (read-only) backing store.

The operator's console allows the system manager to interact with the system. In many systems, any terminal may be used as the system console.

9.5 A Typical Supercomputer

■ With processing power (and cost) tens of thousands of times that of a microcomputer, the supercomputer is the most powerful computing device available. As can be seen from Figure 9.4, supercomputers are characterised by multiple processing units, and a number of different types of peripheral devices.

A typical supercomputer.

At the centre of the supercomputer system is a **front-end processor**. This controls the flow of data between the central processors and the various peripheral devices in the system. A separate **communications processor** is often required to control the flow of data to and from the terminals and data communications links. There may be hundreds of terminals. A backing store control unit controls the passage of data to and from the various backing store units.

The front-end processor, communications processor and backing store control unit are powerful processors in their own right. They have facilities for storing a certain amount of data, routeing data to the required channel, and transforming data from one code to another.

An essential unit in all large computer systems, although it has no data links to other units, is an **uninterrupted power supply (UPS)** unit. This device smooths the flow of electricity to the computer. It 'irons out' any fluctuations in voltage, and has batteries to ensure that there is no break in the electricity supply to the computer should there be a power failure. The batteries are sufficient to keep the computer going until standby generators can be started, or the system shut down in a controlled way.

9.6
Conclusion

■ This chapter has introduced the overall structure of computers of various sizes, and provided a classification for the types of computer at present in use. Various units making up the computers have been introduced, and their relationships to the rest of the system indicated. In the next six chapters, aspects of the devices introduced in this chapter are discussed in more detail.

Although the units of a computer are all part of the same system, it must be noted that they have very different operating characteristics, particularly with regard to speed, data formats and storage capabilities. In general, processors are many times faster than peripheral devices. This causes problems in the co-ordination of the devices which make up a computer system in an efficient way.

The main points of this chapter are as follows:

- Computers consist of input, output, processing and backing store devices, and may include communications links.
- Computer systems can be roughly categorised as calculators, laptop systems, desktop microcomputers, workstations, mid-range systems, mainframes and supercomputers.
- The units of a computer are modular in design; most may be unplugged and replaced by more powerful versions in order to increase the capacity of the computer system as a whole.

Exercise 9

1 Briefly define the following terms: plug-compatible; peripheral; front-end processor; front panel; microcomputer; workstation; mainframe; supercomputer.

2 Discuss the concept of a module in relation to the structure of a computer system.

3 Identify one distinguishing difference between:
   a) Microcomputers and workstations
   b) Workstations and mid-range systems
   c) Mid-range systems and mainframes
   d) Mainframes and supercomputers.

4 Describe the overall structure of one or more computers known to you, and classify them in one of the categories given in this chapter. In each case, make a sketch of the units of the system and their inter-connection, in details similar to the diagrams in this chapter.

5 It is becoming increasingly common for manufacturers to produce peripheral devices which are plug-compatible with processors made by other manufacturers. Discuss the advantages and disadvantages of this practice from the point of view of the users of the systems.

6 One of the major areas of competition on the computing market is between networks of workstations and mid-range systems with terminals. Make a list of applications which, in your view, are better suited to one or the other of these. Give reasons, based on the capabilities of the two configurations, for your choice of system for each application.

10 Processor Architecture

This chapter is concerned with the architecture of the processor of a computer. The objectives of a processor are discussed, together with various aspects of the structure of a typical processor. To simplify this discussion, a model computer, specially designed for this course, is used.

It must be mentioned at this point that the term 'processor' is not very precise. In some contexts it means the whole central processing unit of a computer, including the memory. In other cases, it means the processing circuits only. In other cases, it means one chip within a processing unit - a microprocessor.

10.1 Objectives of a Processor

■ The primary objective of a processor is to carry out the steps of a data processing task. In order to become familiar with the level at which a processor operates, this objective needs some clarification.

In Chapter 3 the point is made that data is a representation of information, in a binary code. You will also recall that data and instructions (also in a binary code) are stored together in a computer memory, and no distinction is made between them. Accordingly, a step of a data processing task involves the manipulation of one or more items of data, in a binary code, in response to an instruction, also in a binary code. The manipulation is carried out by logic circuits on individual bits of the data items. This, then, is the level at which a processor operates.

In addition to accomplishing its primary objective, a processor must work as quickly as possible, using a minimum of electricity, and avoiding errors and breakdowns. These objectives sound rather difficult to achieve, but in practice they are attained to a remarkable extent. Forty years of intensive research and development have led to processors which are fast, powerful, reliable, efficient and cheap. Nevertheless, the basic design principles of processors, formulated just after the Second World War, have, until recently, remained the same. It is these design principles which are the subject matter of this chapter.

10.2 The Structure of a Processor

■ As explained in the previous chapter, computers are manufactured in a range of sizes. Although the design principles are similar in most cases, these priciples are implemented in a variety of ways. It is therefore impossible to choose one computer as a representative, and discuss various features of the structure of its processor. To overcome this

problem, a model computer has been designed, specifically for this course. It is used in this chapter to introduce the important features of a processor. It is also used in subsequent chapters, to help explain how a processor operates, and to introduce the program languages used to control a computer.

The following sections introduce the overall structure of a processor, using the model computer as an example.

10.3 A Model Computer - the AMC

■ The **A-level model computer**, or **AMC**, has been designed to assist in the teaching of a number of topics in this book, the first being processor architecture. The design of the AMC reflects a compromise between the requirements of Computing Science syllabuses and the features of a number of actual computers. Design principles are implemented in as straightforward a manner as possible. Because of its simple construction and small set of instructions, the AMC is an example of a **reduced instruction set computer (Risc)** architecture. Risc chips are a recent development which is becoming very popular.

In common with most processors, the AMC may be thought of as a number of functional units, connected by one or more **buses**, as well as control links. Figure 10.1 shows the overall block structure of the AMC. Control links are omitted for simplicity.

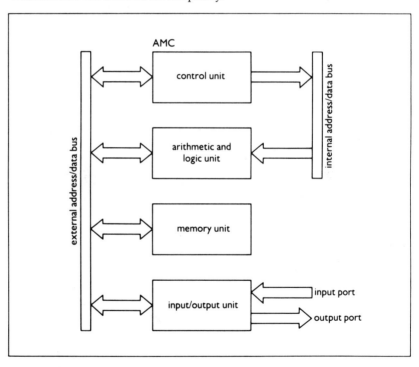

Figure 10.1
AMC block structure

A bus is a pathway along which data, address and control signals pass within a processor. The two buses in the AMC are both 16 bits wide, and are used for both data and addresses. The input and output ports are, however, 8 bits wide, as most input/output devices work in units of 8 bits.

The AMC is a **16 bit processor**. This means that all operations are performed on 16 bit quantities and internal transfers of data are in units of 16 bits. In the context of the AMC, a 16 bit quantity is called a word, and an 8 bit quantity a byte. The four functional units in Figure 10.1 each contain a number of registers (introduced in Section 8.7) and other logic circuits. Most of the registers are 16 bits wide, and most AMC logic circuits process 16 bit quantities in parallel.

10.4
The AMC
Memory Unit

■ The AMC memory unit consists of the **memory address register, address decoder, main store** and **memory data register**. See Figure 10.2. The function of the memory unit is to store and retrieve data and instructions. The interface between the memory unit and the rest of the AMC is the external address/data bus.

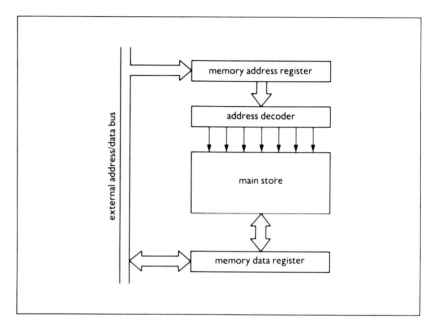

Figure 10.2
AMC memory unit

The main store of the AMC is an **immediate access store**. The store is partitioned into a number of locations or cells, each of which is identified by a number called an address. Each location stores one byte. Given its address, any cell may be accessed immediately.

Like most AMC registers, the **memory address register** holds 16 bits. This means that there can be 2^{16} (=65536) distinct addresses – the **address space** of the AMC. A unit of memory size commonly used is the K unit, where $1K = 2^{10} = 1024$. The AMC address space is 65536/1024 = 64K locations.

The 16 bit **memory data register** holds data during transfer to or from main store. Data may be stored or retrieved in units of bytes or words. A word occupies two consecutive store locations. The lower byte address is always used to locate a word.

The concept of addressing is fundamental to the way a computer works. Several techniques of addressing are used in the AMC. These are discussed in Chapter 12.

Reading from Store

When a data item is accessed, or **read from** main store, the following sequence of actions takes place:

1 The address of the data item is placed in the memory address register.

2 The address decoder accesses the store location addressed.
3 If a word is being read, the byte addressed by the memory address register is placed in the most significant half of the memory data register, and the byte at the next address is placed in the least significant half.
4 If a byte is being read, it occupies the least significant half of the memory data register, and the most significant half of the register is filled with copies of the most significant bit of the byte. This process is called sign extension.

Writing to Store

When a data item is placed in, or **written to** main store, the following sequence of actions takes place:

1 The address of the store location to be used is placed in the memory address register.
2 The data item is placed in the memory data register.
3 If a word is being written to store, the most significant byte of the memory data register is placed in the store cell addressed by the memory address register, and the least significant byte in the next store location.
4 If a byte is being written to store, it is taken from the least significant half of the memory data register.

A Memory Cycle

The sequence of actions for reading from or writing to store are very much the same. One such sequence is called a **memory cycle**. The complexity of an operation often depends on how many memory cycles it involves, and the time taken for a memory cycle is an important factor in determining the overall speed of a processor.

10.5 Construction of Immediate Access Store

■ The AMC address space is 64K, which is smaller than that even of a small microcomputer. The address space of most computers is measured in megabytes (a megabyte is one million bytes) or millions of words, if each cell holds a word rather than a byte. A typical desktop microcomputer has between one and four megabytes, a workstation from four to sixteen megabytes. Mid-range computers and mainframes tend to have memories partitioned in words of 16 or 32 bits. Capacities range from 4 to 64 million words. A supercomputer like the Cray-2 has up to 256 million words (each of 64 bits) in its main memory. In many computer systems the address space is larger than the actual number of cells available. This enables more memory to be added without altering the memory access mechanism.

Some of the largest chips in a computer system are used for main store. There are two types: **random access memory (RAM)** and **read-only memory (ROM)**. ROM holds permanent instructions and data which may be read but cannot be altered, while RAM holds temporary data and instructions which may be altered at any time. Each type of computer has its own mixture of the two types. These areas are further divided into spaces for various purposes. A memory map shows the various partitions. Some are fixed, such as those occupied by programs, while others, notably stacks for data, grow and shrink as a program run proceeds.

The silicon layout of a RAM chip, showing the regular arrangement of cells.

Two types of RAM chips are used: **static** RAM and **dynamic** RAM. Static RAM has the property that data is retained for as long as power is supplied to the memory circuits. In the case of dynamic (or **volatile**) RAM, data gradually 'leaks away', and must be **refreshed** periodically. Memory refresh is accomplished by reading an item from the store and writing it back into the same location. Locations are refreshed in rotation all the time that the computer is running. Memory refresh does not interfere with the operation of the processor.

Some ROM chips have their bit patterns permanently written into them when they are constructed. Others are initially blank, and can be 'blown' with a specific bit pattern using appropriate equipment. These are **programmable read-only memories** or **PROMs**. Certain PROM chips can have their bit patterns changed, again using special equipment for the purpose. These are known as **EPROMs** (for erasable programmable read-only memory). In all cases, however, ROM chips installed in a computer memory can only be read. Any attempt by the computer to write data to a cell in ROM has no effect. Instructions and data in ROM remain after the computer has been switched off.

The capacities of ROM and (particularly) RAM chips are increasing all the time. Most memory chips are only one bit 'wide'– each address locates a single-bit cell, thus requiring eight identical chips to implement a memory holding a byte at each cell. At present one megabit memory chips are the most common, with four megabit capacities becoming increasingly popular.

10.6 The AMC Arithmetic and Logic Unit

■ The AMC **arithmetic and logic unit**, or **ALU**, consists of an **accumulator**, a set of **logic circuits**, a **result register** and four **condition codes**. These form the part of the processor concerned with the actual manipulation of data. See Figure 10.3.

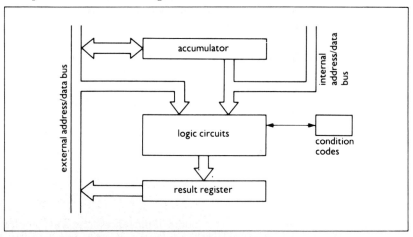

Figure 10.3
AMC arithmetic and logic unit

The **accumulator** is the principal 'working area' of the computer. It contains the data item being processed at any time. The **logic circuits** carry out various operations on one or two data items. The logic circuits have two inputs and one output, as well as a connection to the condition codes register. They consist of a set of NOT gates, an addition unit, sets of AND, OR and non-equivalence gates, and a shift register. The **result register** is a temporary store for the output from the logic circuits. All processing is in units of 16 bits. See Figure 10.4.

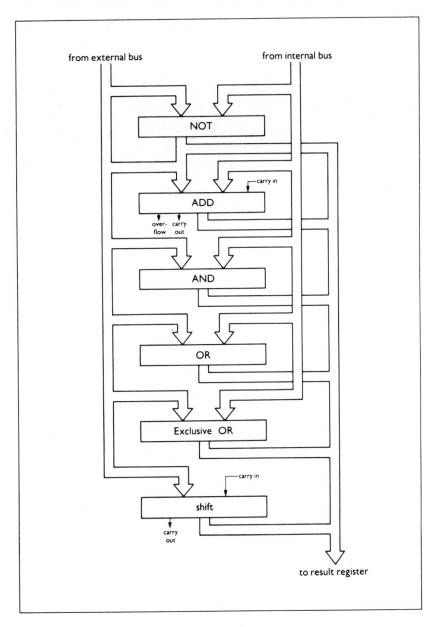

from external bus   from internal bus

NOT

ADD

carry in

over-   carry
flow   out

AND

OR

Exclusive OR

shift

carry in

carry
out

to result register

Figure 10.4
AMC logic circuits

This seemingly limited set of logic circuits is quite sufficient to perform all the data processing operations carried out by the computer. The reason for this is that operations are expressed as a large number of small steps, each step involving one or two of the logic circuits of the ALU. Ways in which this can be done for various arithmetic operations are discussed in Section 5.1.

The **condition codes** are four bits which provide information about the most recent operation carried out by the ALU. These codes are also known as **program status bits** or **flags**. The AMC has four condition codes, as follows:

Zero (Z) is set to 1 if the output from the current operation is zero.

Negative (N) is set to 1 if the output from the current operation is negative, i.e. the most significant bit is 1.

Carry (C) is set to 1 if there is a carry out of the most significant bit during shifting or addition.

Overflow (V) is set to 1 if an addition results in an overflow. The method of determining whether overflow has occurred is discussed in Section 5.2.

Values of condition codes are used in the control of programs, and in carrying out certain operations. This is discussed in more detail in Chapter 12.

10.7 The AMC Input/Output Unit

■ Communication between the AMC processor and peripheral devices is via an **input** and an **output register**, and a **peripheral device selection register**. Unlike the storage, processing and control registers, these registers are only eight bits wide. They are connected to the least significant eight bits of the external address/data bus. See Figure 10.5.

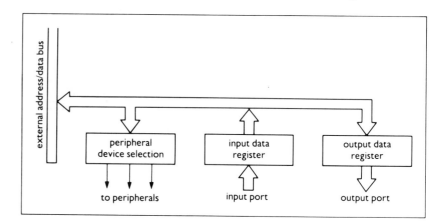

Figure 10.5
AMC input/output unit

All input and output to and from the AMC is assumed to be in character form. This is the case for the majority of peripheral devices. For this reason, input and output registers contain one byte, or one character. When a character is input to the AMC, the sequence of events is as follows:

1 The identification of the input device is placed in the peripheral device selection register.
2 The input device thus selected is requested to send a character to the input register.
3 When the input register has been loaded, a signal is sent to the AMC control unit.
4 The character is then copied from the input register into the AMC.

When a character is output by the AMC, the sequence of events is as follows:

1 The character to be output is placed in the output register.
2 The identification of the output device is placed in the peripheral device selection register.
3 The output device thus selected is requested to copy the character from the output register.
4 When the character has been copied, a signal is sent to the AMC control unit.

It can be seen that there are several steps involved in the input or output of a single character. Furthermore, each step requires one program instruction. Although this is a cumbersome process, it is representative of the way some actual computers work.

10.8
The AMC
Control Unit

■ The **control unit** of the AMC comprises the **program counter**, **instruction register** and **decoder**, **stack pointer** and **index register**. The control unit also contains a clock pulse generator which controls the timing of the whole processor. See Figure 10.6.

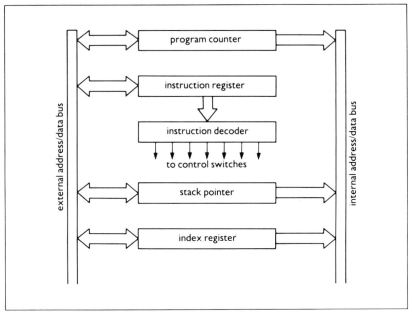

Figure 10.6
AMC control unit

The task of the control unit is to direct the step-by-step working of the processor as it carries out each instruction of a program. More specifically, the functions of the control unit are:

1 To control the sequence on which instructions are executed.
2 To control access to the main store of the processor.
3 To regulate the timing of all operations carried out within the proceesor.
4 To send control signals to, and receive control signals from, peripheral devices.

The **program counter** contains the address of the current program instruction. After the instruction has been fetched from the main store, the contents of the program counter is increased, ready for the next instruction. AMC instructions occupy 2, 3 or 4 bytes, thus the amount of the increase varies from one instruction to another. If an instruction transfers control to another part of the program, the address to which control is transferred is loaded into the program counter.

The **instruction register** stores a copy of the current program instruction. This register is connected to an **instruction decoder**, which in turn connects with control switches at various points throughout the processor. In this way, control switches are opened or closed according to the instruction in the instruction register.

In common with most modern processors, the AMC organises part of its main store as a stack. The stack serves a number of purposes, most of

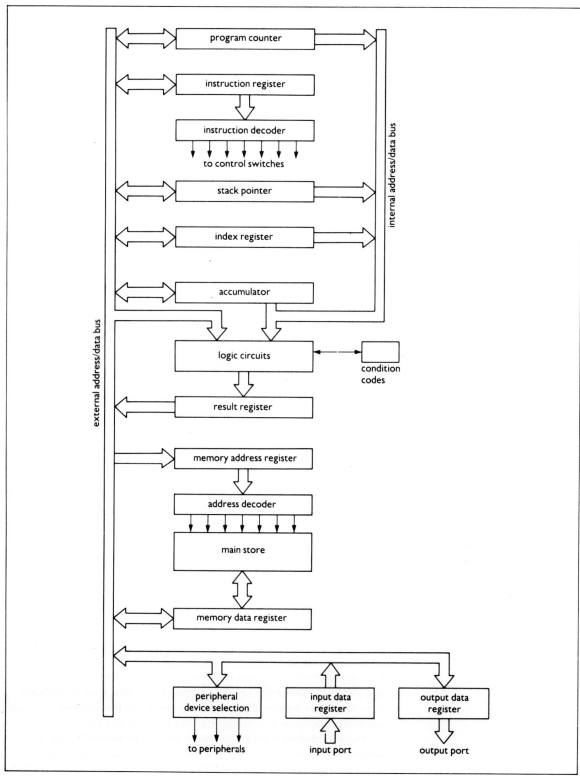

Figure 10.7
AMC register layout

which are introduced in Chapter 12.

The **stack pointer** stores the current address of the top of the stack.

The **index register** is used to implement a particular type, or **mode**, of addressing. Address modes are explained in Chapter 12.

Not shown in the diagrams is the **clock pulse generator**. This produces regular clock signals, and control signals in a number of control lines at fixed intervals. These control signals switch on, or **enable** various components of the AMC. In this way, timing and co-ordination of the whole processor is achieved.

To complete the description of the AMC at register level, Figure 10.7 shows the register layout of the whole AMC processor.

10.9 The AMC and Real Processors

■ The AMC is a model computer: it implements a number of concepts of processor architecture in as simple and direct a way as possible. Among the differences between the AMC and real processors are the following:

1 In many processors, the program counter, index register, stack pointer and accumulator are not specific **dedicated** registers, but can be any one of a set of **general-purpose** registers. In other words, any register in the set can be used as an accumulator, index register, etc.

2 Some processors have restrictions on the storage of words in memory. In many cases words may only be stored at even addresses.

3 In many processors, particularly microprocessors, input and output is done via memory locations, rather than input and output registers.

4 Most computers have far larger main stores than the AMC. Further registers are used in connection with the partitioning of these memories.

5 Some processors have special-purpose hardware for certain operations such as floating-point multiplication.

6 The trend in processor design is towards increased parallelism, both within each processor, and between procesors, by the incorporation of several processing elements, operating in parallel, in a CPU.

More about the architecture of the processors of real computers is to be found in Chapter 15, which contains a number of case studies of processor architectures.

10.10 Conclusion

■ This chapter has introduced the architecture of a simple processor, described at the level of registers, decoders and other logic circuits. The objective is to give a feel for the structure of a computer at this level.

Several general points can now be made about the structure of a processor:

• A central processing unit consists of a control unit, an arithmetic and logic unit and a main store. Units are connected by one or more data buses and control lines.

• The structure of a processor, at register level, is quite simple, and the range of operations which can be carried out directly by the hardware of a processor is limited.

• In order to be carried out by a computer, a data processing task must be expressed as a large number of simple steps, each step being an operation within the capabilities of the hardware of the processor.

• All the circuits of the processor are devoted to carrying out one program instruction at a time.

• The most important concept introduced in this chapter is the idea of an **address**. Addresses are used to locate instructions and data.

Chapter 12 describes how the registers and other functional circuits of a processor are put to work. It again uses the AMC as an example.

Exercise 10

1 Briefly define the following terms: main store; ALU; bus; control unit; immediate access store; address; address space; memory map; cell; RAM; ROM; PROM; EPROM; volatile memory; memory cycle; accumulator; condition codes; program counter; enable; dedicated register; sign extension; program status bits; risc architecture.

2 a) In your own words, explain the concept of an address.
  b) State why addresses are so important to the functioning of a processor.

3 In a particular type of computer, addresses are 24 bits.
  a) Calculate the address space of the computer.
  b) The precise value of the M unit is 2²⁰ = 1048576. Express the answer to part (a) in M units.
  c) Express the M unit in terms of the K unit (1K = 2¹⁰ = 1024).
  d) Calculate, in M units, the address space of a computer with a 32-bit address register.
  e) What is the advantage in having an address space larger than the actual physical memory of a computer?

4 Discuss the concept of a module in relation to the architecture of a processor.

5 Briefly distinguish between static and dynamic memory.

6 a) Draw a logic circuit to show how the zero (Z) condition code is determined from the output of the AMC logic circuits. The output carries 16 bits.
  b) Design a logic circuit to perform the process of sign extension mentioned in Section 10.4. It requires a control link which enables the circuit when it is required.
  c) Design a logic circuit for the overflow condition code, using the carry in and the carry out from the most significant bit of the parallel adder.

7 The chips which make up the processing and storage components of a computer can be made using several different silicon technologies. Popular types include complementary metal oxide semiconductor (CMOS), transistor-transistor logic (TTL), bipolar logic and emitter coupled logic (ECL). Find out about these chip fabrication processes, and write short notes on each of them and their relative advantages and disadvantages.

8 What problem can occur when part of the address space of a computer is used for a stack?

11 Processor Fabrication

This chapter covers the steps involved in the design and construction of silicon chips and computers. It shows how the theory introduced in the previous three chapters is put into practice. It describes the work done at a number of chip fabrication plants and computer manufacturing factories throught the world.

11.1 Transistors and Integrated Circuits

■ An integrated circuit (chip) is a solid-state device containing a number of individual elements, the most important of which are **transistors**. A transistor can be used to amplify a signal or to act as a switch. It has three external connections, as shown in Figure 11.1. A small signal at one connection causes a large change in the flow of current between the other two: the current can be stopped entirely, or allowed to flow unhindered. This is due to the electrical properties of the **semiconductor** material (silicon or gallium arsenide) from which transistors are made. A semiconductor is a substance which conducts electricity better than an insulator such as porcelain, but not as well as a conductor such as copper.

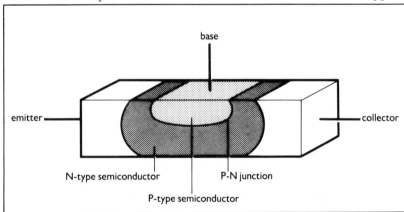

Figure 11.1
A transistor

The silicon crystals from which integrated circuits are made are extremely pure. To this pure crystal are added small, precisely controlled quantities of impurities, a process known as **doping**. Two kinds of semiconductor are created: dopants such as arsenic or phosphorus give rise to **n-type** semiconductor, with an excess of electrons. A dopant such as boron makes **p-type** semiconductor, with a shortage of electrons (it is said to have **holes**). It is the electrical properties of the junction between the two types of semiconductor (known as a **p-n junction**) which gives a transistor its switching and amplification powers.

The size of a p-n junction has little effect on its operation – it can be microscopically small and still work perfectly well. For this reason individual transistors are a very inefficient way of making use of the capabilities of a p-n junction. It is preferable to combine large numbers of them, together with other electrical elements such as resistors and capacitors, into integrated circuits.

There are a number of methods of chip fabrication, which give rise to chips with different electrical properties. These include:

● **Transistor-transistor logic (TTL)**, which is relatively fast, but uses more power than the others.

An individual transistor. These are no longer found in computers, but are still used for power amplification and similar purposes.

- **Complementary metal oxide silicon (CMOS)**, which uses less power than TTL, but is somewhat slower.
- **Emitter-coupled logic (ECL)**, the fastest chip technology, but the one with the highest power consumption. Special systems are needed to cool densely packed ECL chips.

A close-up view of a small portion of a silicon chip, showing the individual p-n junctions.

At present, the majority of computer chips are made by TTL or CMOS techniques. ECL chips are used in very fast computers such as the Cray-2.

11.2 Integrated Circuit Design

■ There are three overall stages of chip design: **logic design**, **simulation** and **silicon layout**.

Logic Design

The logic design of an integrated circuit is derived from the functional requirements of the chip: it may be a processing chip, a memory chip, a control or communications chip, a graphics support chip, etc. The logic design is entered into a **computer-aided design (CAD)** system, as a set of logic circuits (also known as schematics) as described in Chapter 6. A modular design approach is adopted, with the circuit being built up as a hierarchy of parts. The simplest parts, at the bottom of the hierarchy, are designed directly from gates and flip-flops. The CAD system includes libraries of parts which can be included into designs. The lowest-level parts are then used to build up the more complex parts. The final logic design is checked very carefully before it is approved.

Simulation

The operation of the chip is then simulated to check that it functions according to the way it was specified. A set of inputs is supplied to the simulation, and the behaviour of the logic circuits in response to these inputs is observed. Simulation results are displayed as waveforms, as if the actual chip were connected to an oscilloscope. The logic circuits are revised and the simulation repeated until the results are satisfactory.

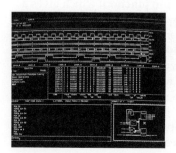

The waveform produced for a chip simulation.

Silicon Layout

The logic design is then transformed into an equivalent silicon layout, comprising gates and other electrical components for the logic elements. This design is separated into a layout for each layer of the chip, in terms of the areas of n-type and p-type semiconductor, and the layers of metal

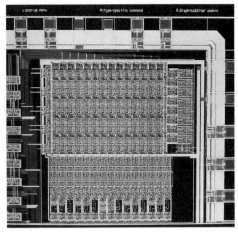

Left Silicon artwork being produced on a CAD system. *Right* The logic circuit for a chip being entered on a computer-aided design system.

interconnections. P-n junctions are formed when required between two adjacent layers in the silicon. Including insulation and other layers, most silicon technologies require about twenty layers.

The translation from a logic circuit to a physical arrangement of gates is becoming increasingly automated. Some CAD systems can perform the entire operation automatically, others give varying degrees of assistance to the designer. The CAD system adjusts the layout of gates in order to minimise the lengths of the connections between the gates, as this is one of the determining factors of the speed of operation of the chip. The complete silicon layout is checked against the original schematic. Large diagrams (about 500 times the actual size of the chip) are produced, one for each layer of the chip. These diagrams – the **artwork** – are then reduced photographically to make the **masks** used in the fabrication of the chips. Other fabrication plants use the silicon layout from the CAD system to control an electron beam, which etches the silicon layers directly.

11.3 Integrated Circuit Fabrication

■ The raw material of a chip is a crystal of pure silicon or gallium arsenide. These are grown under precisely controlled conditions to cylindrical shapes approximately one metre in length and between 100 and 150 millimetres in diameter. The level of impurities in the crystal is so low as to be negligible. The crystals are cut into circular slices or **wafers**, 1 millimetre thick and polished on one surface so that they are perfectly flat. On each wafer are formed about one hundred chips.

Chips have around twenty layers, each containing a pattern of areas of either p-type or n-type semiconductor, insulator, metal conductor, etc. As shown in Figure 11.2, n- or p-type layers are built up in four stages: **oxidation, masking, etching and doping**:

1 Oxidation is the formation of an insulating layer of silicon dioxide. The silicon dioxide also forms a barrier for the later diffusion stages. Oxidation is done by heating the wafer in a furnace containing a controlled amount of oxygen.

2 Masking involves coating the wafer with **photoresist** – a substance which is hardened on exposure to light. The mask with the layout of the particular layer is placed on top of the wafer. The wafer is then exposed to ultra-violet light. The areas not covered by the mask are hardened.

A silicon chip fabrication plant in operation.

3 The mask is removed and the unexposed photoresist is dissolved away. The pattern it has created is etched with acid into the silicon dioxide layer of the chip, exposing the silicon below.

4 The exposed silicon areas are doped by a **diffusion** process to produce n-type or p-type semiconductor. The heated wafer is placed in an atmosphere containing a vapour of the dopant at precisely the required temperature and concentration. This process generally oxidises the chip as well, performing the first step of the formation of the next layer. An alternative method of **ion implantation**, using an electron gun, is used to dope larger chips.

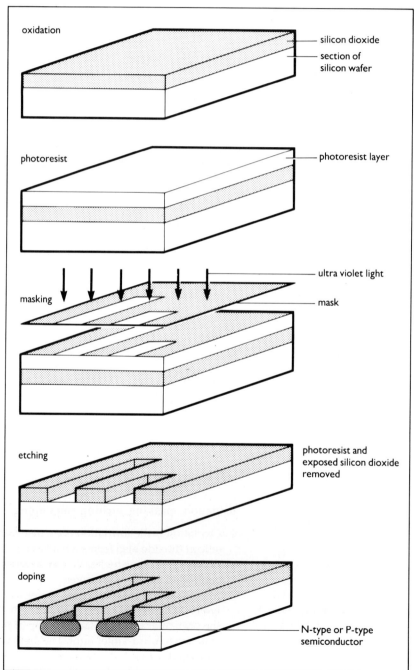

Figure 11.2
The stages of forming a layer on a chip

After all the layers have been formed, windows are etched at appropriate positions through the oxide to provide electrical contact points for each element on the chip. A further mask is used for this process. The wafer is then **metallised**, by evaporating a layer of a conductor (usually aluminium) onto it. The metal is masked and etched to produce the required network of connections within the chip. A second metal layer is often added, with an insulating layer of silicon dioxide in between. The conducting paths are about a micron (one millionth of a metre) wide.

The chips on the wafer are then tested by touching the connecting pads on the edge of each one with fine probes, and carrying out a complete, computer-controlled check on all the required chip functions. The same inputs which were used for the final simulations are used on the chips. Any chips not passing these tests completely are marked with an ink spot and later discarded. The percentage of acceptable chips is known as the **yield** of the wafer. Yields can vary from close to 100% to 0% if something has gone wrong.

After testing, the wafer is scribed with lines on the boundaries of the chips, using a diamond cutter. It is then broken into individual chips. The ones which have passed the initial tests are given a visual inspection before being mounted onto their carriers. Fine wires, generally made of gold, are bonded onto the connector pads on the chip edges and run outwards to the external chip connections. The tops of the carriers are then sealed on, and the packaged chips are again tested. Most chips are cased in plastic, but ceramic is used for applications requiring more rugged chips.

The fabrication steps are carried out under very precisely controlled conditions. The air in the fabrication rooms is constantly filtered. All workers wear protective clothing including gloves and face masks. The temperature required for each step is finely adjusted, as are the quantities of the various chemicals involved. The masks are aligned with extreme care, typically to an accuracy of a quarter of a micron, as only a very slight error will ruin the whole wafer.

The chips are now ready for despatch and use. Because of the high standards of construction and testing, the chances are that they will work perfectly for years. Figure 11.3 shows the overall stages of chip design and fabrication.

11.4 Computer Manufacture

■ The process of designing and manufacturing a complete computer system is long, complex and very expensive. It involves the work of teams of highly skilled computer architects, engineers and systems software writers. In the case of mainframe computers, it can take several years. It is very seldom a continuous sequence of steps from the original concept to the final product. In most cases, problems are encountered at various stages which require designs to be modified and earlier stages repeated. The techniques of computer design used by most companies take account of these requirements for modification.

11.5 Computer Design

■ Computer design starts with an overall concept of what the complete computer will do. It may be a general-purpose personal computer, a special-purpose computer such as a word processor, a minicomputer or a large mainframe for scientific use. Whatever type of computer it is, it will be intended for a certain market and a certain price range. In most cases it

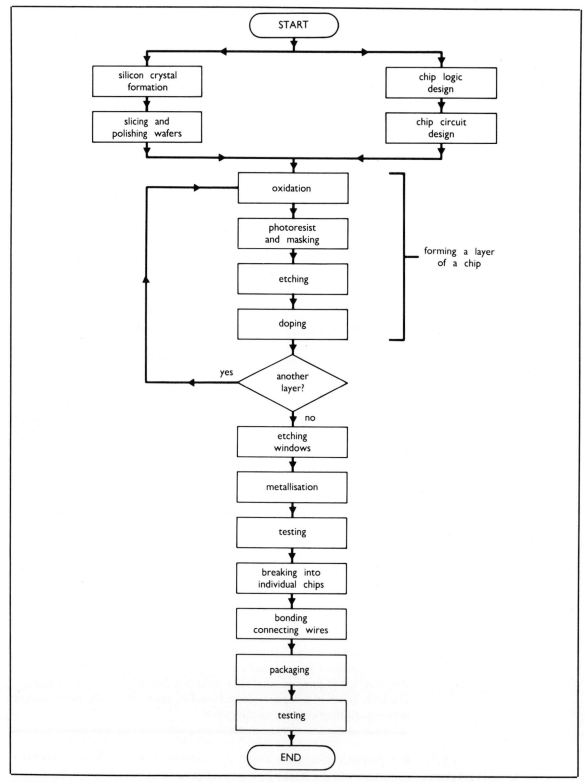

Figure 11.3
Chip fabrication

will compete with existing computers from other manufacturers. A certain amount of market research is undertaken to find out more about the requirements of the prospective users, and the extent to which these are

are being satisfied by existing products. This latter process is referred to as searching for a gap in the market.

The overall configuration and performance characteristics of the new computer are clarified, and stated in some detail in a **functional specification**. This document describes the features of the computer, its levels of performance, processing power, memory capacity, external interfaces and projected price. It generally requires a number of revisions before the marketing staff, salesmen, engineers and managers of the computer manufacturer are satisfied with it. It is generally revised further as design and manufacture progress.

Once the functional specification has been established, teams of engineers set to work on the various components of the computer – the processing unit, the input, output and backing store devices and the data communication equipment. A start is also made on the computer software, often using an existing computer to simulate the new machine. In most cases, complete sub-systems such as display screens, keyboards and disk drives are bought in from outside suppliers. The design work is precisely scheduled, with target dates set for completion of various stages, and for checking the compatibility of different units. The management of the design process requires some skill, to ensure that the schedule is adhered to in spite of the inevitable revisions.

11.6 Printed Circuit Board Design

■ Computer processors are constructed internally from one or more **printed circuit boards** (**PCBs**). A PCB is a rectangular fibreglass board, with metal tracks providing connections between the chips, which are soldered into holes in the board, or pressed into chip carrier sockets which are soldered to the board. Standard PCBs have two layers of **tracks**, one on each side of the board; multilayer boards have up to eight layers of tracks. The external connections of a PCB are generally **edge connectors** which plug into sockets on other boards, or on the racks in which PCBs are mounted. Edge connectors are sometimes made of gold. The normal layout inside a computer is a **baseboard**, sometimes called a **motherboard**, with boards for various functions plugged into it at right angles. (Small microcomputers generally have a single PCB with areas for processor, memory, disk control, etc.)

There are similarities between the design of printed circuit boards and chip design. Each starts with a specification of the required operation of the unit, which is then translated into a physical arrangement. In both cases, computer aided design systems are used. In the case of printed circuit boards, the chips required to perform the various operations are selected, and their interconnections specified. For certain operations custom-designed chips (Asics) are required, sometimes based on uncommitted logic arrays (ULAs). The layout of the board is then determined, with the tracks linking the chips via the shortest possible routes and with the minimum number of crossovers.

When the design is complete, a **prototype** printed circuit board is constructed, filled with chips and tested. After any errors have been identified and corrected, the boards are ready for bulk production.

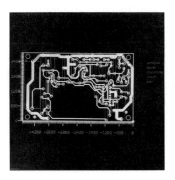

A printed circuit board.

11.7 Computer Assembly

■ The final stage of the design of a computer system is the construction and assembly of a complete working **prototype**. The newly developed systems software is loaded into the hardware, and the entire system, both

A computer assembly plant

hardware and software, is tested very thoroughly. When all the required modifications have been made to the first prototype, a small production run is generally made. These units are sent to potential users for **beta tests**, during which they are made to run operational software, and their performance is carefully monitored. When the reports from the beta tests have been analysed and faults rectified, the new computer is ready for volume production. Mainframe and mid - range computer systems are produced to order; workstations and microcomputers are generally produced in lerge volumes and sold from stock.

Printed circuit boards are constructed in the required quantities, and chips, display screens, disk drives and all the other components are purchased. All vital components such as processor chips are **second sourced** – two independent suppliers are nominated, and components from both suppliers are evaluated in prototypes. This is to ensure that a shortage or delivery delay of a vital component will not hold up production of the whole computer.

The first stage of assembly is to insert the chips and other components into the printed circuit boards. Machines or robots are sometimes used for this operation, although it is still most frequently done by hand. Printed circuit boards are labelled with the identity of each component to be inserted. PCBs with all their components are sent to a flow soldering machine, which solders all the chips onto the PCB in one operation. It passes the board over a bath of molten solder which adheres to all the points where connections are to be made. The PCBs are then inserted into their racks or baseboards, which are in turn mounted in the casings of the various units. All the external connections are wired up, and the units are now ready for testing.

11.8 Testing, Commissioning and Maintenance

An engineer testing a printed circuit board, before it is inserted into its case

■ The various units of the computer are connected together and the computer is switched on. It is then thoroughly tested, both by hand and by means of special software designed for the purpose. Manual checks include tests with an oscilloscope at various points inside the computer to ensure that the waveform at the point is of the required shape and size. Software tests include soak tests which try out every function of the new computer repeatedly, generally over a period of several days. For example, the computer memory is filled with a known bit pattern, which is then read back and compared with the original. In a similar way, disks are written to and then read from. All faults are automatically logged, and appropriate remedial action taken. When all tests have been passed, the computer is approved for delivery.

On delivery to the user, the computer is **commissioned**. In the case of mainframes and mid-range systems, this is done by field engineers from the suppliers; microcomputer purchasers generally have to commission the computers themselves. Commissioning involves unpacking the various units and connecting them together, by cables under the computer room floor in the case of a mainframe. The computer is started, often using special commissioning software, and tested thoroughly. When suppliers and users are satisfied that the new computer is working properly, it is handed over to the user, ready for productive operation.

All computers require some form of maintenance. This is either carried out by the manufacturer under a maintenance agreement signed with the user, or by an independent maintenance company. Routine checks are carried out periodically, and maintenance engineers are called out if a fault occurs. Most computer systems have enough duplication of units to

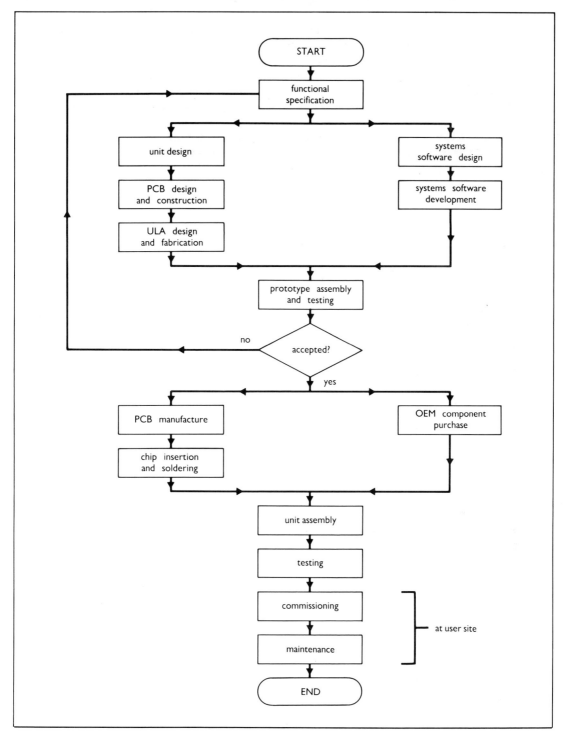

START

functional
specification

unit design

PCB design
and construction

ULA design
and fabrication

systems
software design

systems software
development

prototype assembly
and testing

accepted?

no

yes

PCB manufacture

chip insertion
and soldering

OEM component
purchase

unit assembly

testing

commissioning

maintenance

at user site

END

Figure 11.4
Computer manufacture

ensure that the majority of failures do not halt the entire system. From time to time the computer is upgraded with new peripherals, a larger memory or more powerful processing facilities.

The useful life of most computers seems to be between five and ten years. Most spend very little time out of service due to faults, and the majority of large computers operate round the clock, seven days a week. When the time comes to replace them they are unplugged and sold as scrap, in almost every case in perfect working order. The most common reason for their replacement is that they are obsolete, and their place is being taken by another computer which is smaller, faster, more powerful, and cheaper.

The overall process of computer design and construction is shown in Figure 11.4.

11.9 Conclusion

■ The main points of this chapter are as follows:

- Chips are semiconductor devices made from silicon which has been treated by the addition of precisely controlled quantities of impurities. They have around twenty layers of active elements.
- Chips are made from wafers of pure silicon or gallium arsenide crystal. Each active layer is built up in four steps: oxidation, masking, etching and doping. One or two metallisation layers complete the chip, which is then tested and cased.
- Computer design starts from a functional specification. Work on the printed circuit boards in each unit, as well as the systems software, then proceeds in parallel. At the end of the design stage, a working prototype is constructed.
- Further prototypes are then constructed and sent for beta testing. When final modifications have been made as a result of the tests, volume production commences.
- A computer is assembled by inserting the chips into the PCBs, soldering the connections, mounting the boards in their racks and the racks in the casings, and wiring up all the external connections.
- Computers are commissioned on delivery to the user, and require periodic maintenance. The useful life of a computer is generally between five and ten years.

Exercise 11

1 Briefly define the following terms: transistor; semiconductor; p-type and n-type semiconductor; p-n junction; ECL; TTL; CMOS; CAD system; artwork; wafer; oxidation; masking; etching; photoresist; doping; diffusion; ion implantation; metallisation; yield; functional specification; track; flow soldering machine; second source; soak test; beta test; commissioning; upgrade.

2 a) What steps are taken to ensure the high standard of cleanliness in chip fabrication plants?
   b) Why is this level of cleanliness necessary?

3 Comment on the significance of the concept of a module in relation to the design of chips and printed circuit boards.

4 Discuss the uses of computer-aided design systems in chip and printed circuit board manufacture.

5 At what stages are robots used in the manufacture of computers? List any other stages of chip and computer manufacture where you think robots may be used in the future.

6 Discuss the significance of Asic chips in the design and construction of computers.

7 Discuss the importance of beta testing of new computers.

8 Discuss the similarities and differences between chip fabrication and:
   a) steelmaking
   b) motor car production
   c) producing medicines.

9 a) How long do most computer systems remain in service?
   b) What are the main reasons for the replacement of most computer systems?

12 Processor Operation

This chapter describes the way in which the processor of a computer operates. The instructions which control the step-by-step working of a processor are introduced, and the sequence of actions needed to carry out one instruction is explained. The AMC model computer is used as an example throughout the chapter. Some features of actual computers, which are not found in the AMC, are outlined at the end of the chapter.

This chapter relates closely to Chapter 10, which describes the structure of a processor. It is essential to an understanding of several subsequent chapters, notably the following chapter, on advanced processor features, and Chapter 16, on assembly languages.

12.1 Machine Language

■ The instructions which control the step-by-step working of a processor are in a language called machine language. Machine language instructions are closely related to the architecture of a computer. There is one machine instruction for each operation performed directly by the hardware of the computer. Consequently, each type of processor has its own machine language.

The length and composition of machine language instructions vary considerably from one processor to another, but all have certain features in common. These include the following:

1 Machine instructions are in a binary code.
2 Machine instructions relate directly to registers and functional units of the processor.
3 Every machine instruction includes an **operation code**. This specifies the type of operation to be carried out.
4 Some machine instructions refer to the main store of the computer. Ways of doing this are discussed in the next section.
5 All the instructions in the machine language of a processor make up the instruction set of that processor.

12.2 Addressing

■ Some machine instructions refer to the main store of the computer. This is accomplished by specifying, in some manner, the **address** of the particular memory location. Addressing can be done in a number of ways, some of which are quite complex. Only the essential (and most common) features of addressing are dealt with here.

The Number of Addresses

The number of addresses in a single machine instruction can vary. Computers can be classified according to the maximum number of addresses they permit in a machine instruction. One- and two-address computers are the most common, but three- and four-address computers have been constructed as well as zero-address computers, where the entire main store is regarded as a stack.

Examples of machine instructions with various numbers of addresses are given below. They are not taken from the instruction sets of any actual processor, and are written in English, rather than in machine code.

One-address instruction

ADD J   Add the number in memory location J to the number in the accumulator, and store the sum in the accumulator.

Two-address instruction

ADD J,K Add the numbers in memory locations J and K, and store the sum in location J.

Three-address instruction

ADD J,K,L Add the numbers in memory locations J and K, and store the sum in location L.

Zero-address instruction

ADD   Pop the two top numbers from the stack, add them together, and push the sum onto the stack.

The instruction set of a particular computer can contain more than one of the above types of instructions. A common combination in microcomputers is zero-address and one-address instructions.

Addressing Modes

Each address in a machine instruction may refer to a memory location in one of several different ways. These methods of addressing are called **addressing modes**. Part of the machine instruction is a specification of the addressing mode used. Addressing modes vary between different types of computers. The following modes are, however, common to most types.

Absolute or direct address

This is the simplest addressing mode. The number in the address part of the machine instruction is the number of the memory location holding the data item.

Indexed address

The number in the address part of the machine instruction is added to the contents of a register, called the **index register**, in order to obtain the address of the memory location. This mode is particularly useful when a set of data items is stored in consecutive memory locations. The machine instruction contains the address of the first element in the set, and the index register contains the number (or **offset**) of the particular element in the set.

Indirect address

The address in the machine instruction does not locate a data item, but the address of the data item. The latter address is used to locate the data item. In theory, this principle can be extended to several layers of indirect addresses, although this is not very common. Indirect addressing is particularly useful if data is structured into linked lists or trees. The address of the data item, which is located by the machine instruction, is a **pointer** to the data item.

Relative address

The address in the machine instruction indicates the offset of the data item from the machine instruction, i.e. the address of the data item relative to the machine instruction. In order to locate the data item, the value of the program counter is added to the relative address (the program counter stores the address of the current instruction). Relative addresses are used if a block of instructions and data must be moved from one place to another in the computer memory, without alteration to the addresses being needed. Such a block is called **relocatable code**. Addresses within it are valid wherever it is in memory.

Immediate operand

An immediate operand is a data item located in the address part of a machine instruction. In this case, the memory is not accessed at all. Immediate operands are a useful way of including constants in a program.

The above are the most common addressing modes, implemented on most types of computers. The phrases **address modification** or **address transformation** are used to describe indexed, indirect and relative addressing. Other, more complex addressing modes may be formed by combining two or more of the above modes. An example is indexed indirect addressing. Such addressing modes are, however, beyond the scope of this course.

The reason for having these various addressing modes is that they enhance the power of a computer, and make it easier to program at machine language level. They also make it easier to program the data structures described in Chapter 4. On the other hand, complex addressing modes mean that several memory cycles and passes through the addition unit are needed before the data item required by a machine instruction is obtained. This slows down the computer.

12.3 AMC Machine Language

■ The AMC is a one-address computer. In other words, instructions which refer to the main store contain at most one address. Addressing modes available are immediate operand, absolute, indirect and indexed.

AMC machine instructions occupy one word (16 bits), followed, in some cases, by a word containing an address, or a word or a byte containing a data item. Hexadecimal notation is used to describe the instructions, being far more compact than binary. You will recall from Chapter 3 that one hexadecimal digit represents four bits. Thus four hexadecimal digits will describe an AMC instruction.

The AMC instruction set is divided into **groups**. All the instructions within a group perform similar operations. The first hexadecimal digit of the instruction identifies the group. The second hexadecimal digit of an AMC instruction identifies the operation within the group. Taken together, the first two hexadecimal digits of the machine instruction form the operation code. The interpretation of the remaining two hexadecimal digits in an instruction depend on its group.

Three of the AMC registers are under program control. They are the **accumulator**, **index register** and **stack pointer**. These registers are numbered 1, 2 and 3, respectively, in machine instructions. In most cases the third hexadecimal digit of the machine instruction identifies the register used. The fourth digit indicates the addressing mode.

Figure 12.1 shows the layout of the different groups of AMC instructions. The table in Figure 12.2 contains the complete AMC instruction set. The instructions in a group perform similar operations, and have the same layout. Figure 12.2 also specifies the effect of each instruction on the condition codes. This is explained in more detail later.

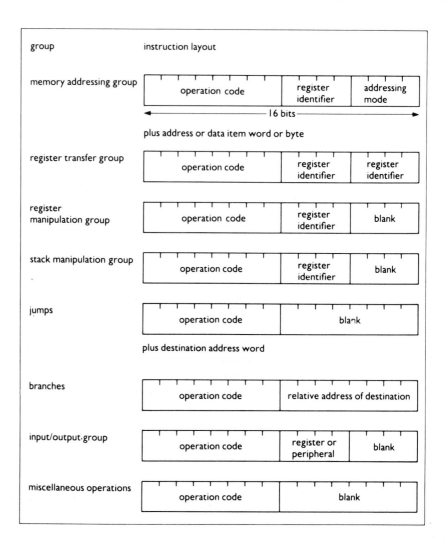

Figure 12.1
Bit layout of AMC machine
instructions

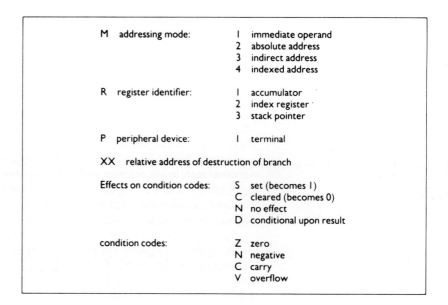

Figure 12.2
AMC instruction set

machine instruction (hexadecimal)	interpretation	Z	N	C	V
memory addressing group					
11RM	load data word to register	D	D	N	N
21RM	load data byte to register	D	D	N	N
12RM	store register word in memory	D	D	N	N
22RM	store register byte in memory	D	D	N	N
13RM	add data word to register	D	D	D	D
23RM	add data byte to register	D	D	D	D
14RM	add data word and carry bit to register	D	D	D	D
24RM	add data byte and carry bit to register	D	D	D	D
15RM	subtract data word from register	D	D	D	D
25RM	subtract data byte from register	D	D	D	D
16RM	subtract (data word plus carry bit) from register	D	D	D	D
26RM	subtract (data byte plus carry bit) from register	D	D	D	D
17RM	AND data word with register	D	D	C	C
27RM	AND data byte with register	D	D	C	C
18RM	OR data word with register	D	D	C	C
28RM	OR data byte with register	D	D	C	C
19RM	NEQ (exclusive OR) data word with register	D	D	C	C
29RM	NEQ (exclusive OR) data byte with register	D	D	C	C
1ARM	compare register with data word	D	D	D	D
2ARM	compare register with data byte	D	D	D	D
register transfer group					
31R₁R₂	move word from register 1 to register 2	D	D	N	N
register manipulation group					
01RO	clear register	S	C	C	C
02RO	increment register (increase by 1)	D	D	D	D
03RO	decrement register (decrease by 1)	D	D	D	D
04RO	rotate register right, 1 bit, via carry bit	D	D	D	D
05RO	rotate register left 1 bit, via carry bit	D	D	D	D
06RO	arithmetic shift right, 1 bit	D	D	C	C
07RO	arithmetic shift left, 1 bit	D	D	C	C
08RO	complement register	D	D	D	D
09RO	negate register (NOT operation)	D	D	C	C
stack manipulation group					
41RO	push register word onto stack	D	D	N	N
42RO	pop top of stack word to register	D	D	N	N
jumps					
5100	unconditional jump to specified address	N	N	N	N
5200	jump to subprogram, stack return address	N	N	N	N
branches					
61XX	unconditional branch	N	N	N	N
62XX	branch if zero (Z = 1)	N	N	N	N
63XX	branch if non-zero (Z = 0)	N	N	N	N
64XX	branch if greater than or equal to zero (Z = 1 or N = 0)	N	N	N	N
65XX	branch if greater than zero (Z = 0 and N = 0)	N	N	N	N
66XX	branch if less than or equal to zero (Z = 1 or N = 1)	N	N	N	N
67XX	branch if less than zero (N = 1)	N	N	N	N
68XX	branch if carry clear (C = 0)	N	N	N	N
69XX	branch if carry set (C = 1)	N	N	N	N
6AXX	branch if overflow clear (V = 0)	N	N	N	N
6BXX	branch if overflow set (V = 1)	N	N	N	N
6CXX	branch if input not complete	N	N	N	N
6DXX	branch if output not complete	N	N	N	N
input/output group					
71PO	signal peripheral device to load input register	N	N	N	N
72RO	copy byte from input register to register R	D	D	N	N
73PO	signal peripheral device to unload output register	N	N	N	N
74RO	copy byte from register R to output register	D	D	N	N
miscellaneous operations					
3100	set carry bit	N	N	S	N
8200	clear carry bit	N	N	C	N
8300	return from subprogram (unstack return address)	N	N	N	N
8400	no-operation	N	N	N	N
8500	halt	N	N	N	N

Figure 12.2
AMC instruction set
(continued)

Memory Addressing Group

All the instructions which refer to the AMC memory are in this group.
Each operation can be applied to a word or a byte of data. An instruction
in this group consists of an operation code, register identifier, and
addressing mode, followed by an address word, or a data word or byte.

For example:

1312 423B	operation code	13:	add word
	register identifier	1:	accumulator
	addressing mode	2:	absolute address
	address 423B		

This means: add the word (i.e. 16 bit number) at (absolute) address 423B to the accumulator.

2234 17B5	operation code	22:	store byte
	register identifier	3:	stack pointer
	addressing mode	4:	indexed
	address 17B5		

This means: store the (least significant) byte from the stack pointer at memory address 17B5 plus contents of index register.

2111 BB	operation code	21:	load byte
	register identifier	1:	accumulator
	addressing mode	1:	immediate operand
	data item BB		

Because the addressing mode indicates an immediate operand, the instruction is followed by a data item, rather than an address. The instruction means: load the byte BB into the accumulator.

All the instructions in this group affect the Z (zero) and N (negative) condition codes. For example, if an addition results in a negative number, then Z becomes 0 and N becomes 1. Addition, subtraction and comparison operations affect the C (carry) and V (overflow) codes as well. The three logic operations clear these codes, while load and store operations leave them unchanged.

Register Transfer Group

The single instruction in this group copies the contents of one register into another register. For example:

3123	operation code	31:	move
	register identifiers	2:	index register
		3:	stack pointer

This means: copy the contents of the index register into the stack pointer. This instruction affects the zero and negative condition codes, but does not alter the carry and overflow codes.

Register Manipulation Group

This group of instructions operates on the contents of one of the registers. The clear, increment, decrement and negate instructions are obvious enough, but a word or two of explanation is needed about the others.

The complement instruction forms the twos complement of the contents of the register. As explained in Chapter 3, this is done by negating the bits and then adding 1.

The rotate operations include the carry bit, and are best explained by means of a diagram. See Figure 12.3.

The arithmetic shift operations preserve the most significant bit of the word (the sign bit) and shift the rest. The arithmetic shift left has the effect of multiplying by 2, and the arithmetic shift right has the effect of

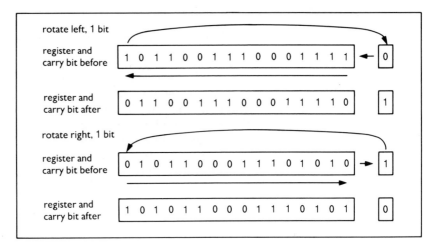

Figure 12.3
Rotate instructions

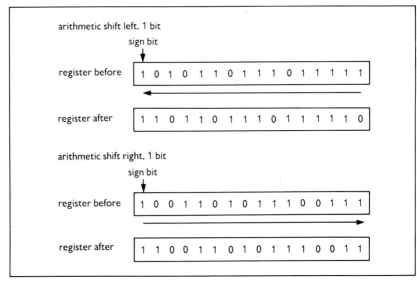

Figure 12.4
Arithmetic shift instructions

dividing by 2. In the latter case the sign bit is copied into the next position. See Figure 12.4.

An example of a machine instruction in this group is:

0320	operation code	03: decrement
	register identifier	2: index register

This means: decrease contents of index register by 1.

All the instructions in this group affect all the condition codes.

Branches

The branching instructions transfer control to another part of the program, using relative addressing. The first instruction in the set is an unconditional branch, the remaining 13 transfer control depending on the value of one or more condition codes. These enable a branch to be made depending on the outcome of some previous operation.

For example, suppose that a branch has to be made if two numbers are equal. One number is loaded into the accumulator, and compared with the other. The compare operation in the memory addressing group is used. It subtracts the numbers, sets the condition codes depending on the result, but does not retain the result. If the numbers are equal, the difference is zero, and the Z code is set to 1. The branch if zero instruction is then used.

The address of the destination of the branch is contained in the second byte of the instruction word. This byte is interpreted as a twos complement integer, and can thus have a value in the range –128 to 127. This limits the range of the branches, which are sometimes called 'short' branches. This address is relative to the current value of the program counter. By the time the branch instruction is executed, the program counter has been reset to contain the address of the next instruction. Thus the destination of the branch is the address of the next instruction plus the relative address contained in the branching instruction. For example:

678A	operation code	67: branch if less than zero
	relative address	8A: 138 in base ten

If this instruction is at address 0049 (=73 in base ten), then the program counter contains 004B (=75 in base ten), the address of the next instruction. The destination address of the branch is 138 + 75 = 213 in base ten, or 00D5 in hexadecimal. Accordingly, if condition code N = 1 (i.e. less than zero), control will be transferred to the instruction at address 00D5. If N = 0, control passes to the next instruction, at address 004B.

The reason for having this rather awkward addressing mode in branching instructions is to save memory space. Instructions of this type occupy only one word, whereas a jump to an absolute address occupies two words. Although these instructions depend on values of various condition codes, they do not alter these codes in any way.

Input/Output Group

The input/output instructions control the transfer of data between the AMC processor and peripheral devices. Two branching instructions are also concerned with input/output.

Communication between the AMC processor and peripheral devices is via input and output registers, each with a capacity of one byte. All input and output is done one character at a time.

An example of the sequence of instructions to input a character is given below:

7110	operation code	71: input request
	peripheral device	1: terminal

This instruction requests the terminal to load a character into the input register.

6CFE	operation code	6C: branch if input not complete
	relative address	FE= –2 in base ten

This instruction branches back to itself until the character has been loaded.

7210	operation code	72: copy character from input register
	register identifier	1: accumulator

This instruction copies the character from the input register to the accumulator.

This example shows the number of instructions needed for the input of a single character. The second instruction causes the processor to wait until the input has taken place. Although it is very inefficient, it is one way of synchronising a processor with a slower peripheral device.

The instructions in this group which relate to peripheral devices have no effect on condition codes. The instructions which move data to or from input/output registers affect the zero and negative condition codes.

12.4 Example Program 12.1

■ The objective of this program is to input a sequence of characters and store them in consecutive memory locations. The end of the input is marked by a special character, with hexadecimal code FF. The address of the memory location to contain the first character is known when the program is written.

The program uses the technique of indirect addressing. The address of the first character is loaded into a convenient memory location. A character is input, and compared with the end-of-input marker. If the character is not the marker, it is stored at the address specified in the memory location, using indirect addressing. This address is then increased by 1, and the next character is input. When the end-of-input marker is found, the program ends. For convenience, the program is written starting at address 0000.

Program

Address	Instruction		Comments
0000	001F		Address of first character, later of current character.
0002	7110		Signal terminal to load character into input register.
0004	6CFE		Branch back to this instruction if input not complete.
0006	7210		Copy character from input register to accumulator.
0008	2A11	FF	Compare character with end-of-input marker.
000B	6210		Branch if equal, to address 001D.
000D	2213	0000	Store character at address in location 0000.
0011	1112	0000	Load address of current character to accumulator.
0015	0210		Increase contents of accumulator by 1.
0017	1212	0000	Store address of next character in location 0000.
001B	61E5		Branch to address 0002, to input next character.
001D	8500		Halt.
001F			First character.

Points to Notice

- Location 0000 initially contains the address of the first character, namely 001F. After each character has been input, the contents of this location is increased by 1. In this way, characters are stored in consecutive memory locations.
- The first program instruction is at address 0002; the previous word is used for data. Program instructions occupy 2, 3 or 4 store locations. The length of an instruction determines the address of the next instruction.
- The relative address in the first branching instruction is FE (= –2 in base ten). This instruction has the effect of branching back to itself

repeatedly, until a character has been input. In this way, the processor 'waits' for the terminal.

- Three different addressing modes are used in this program. They are immediate operand (at address 000B), indirect address (at address 000D) and absolute address (at addresses 0011 and 0017).
- The characters are stored immediately after the program. If a different memory area is required for them, all that needs to be changed is the address in location 0000.
- The portion of program from address 0002 to address 001B is repeated, once for each input character. A portion of a program which is repeated is called a loop.
- The relative addresses in branching instructions are the differences between their destination addresses and the addresses of the instructions which follow them.

12.5 Stack Manipulation and Subprogram Calls

■ Since the AMC stack is an essential part of its subprogram calling mechanism, the two aspects are dealt with together.

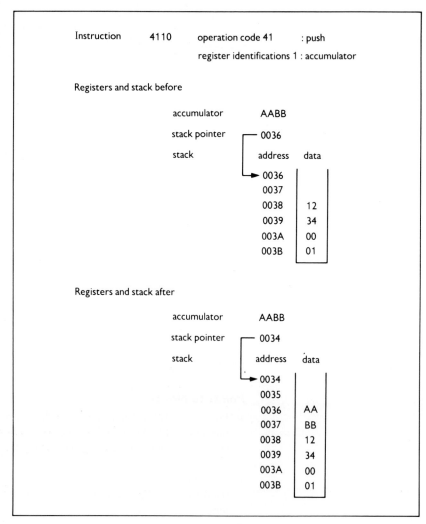

Figure 12.5
The push instruction

Stack Manipulation Group

The two instructions in this group implement the **push** and **pop** operations introduced in Chapter 4.

Any part of the AMC memory may be used for the stack. Before the stack is built, the stack pointer is loaded with the address of the stack base. As the stack is used, it points to the next available space above the stack top. The stack grows 'upwards' in the memory, from high addresses to low addresses. Stack elements are words, occupying two memory locations.

The **push** operation involves the following steps:

1   The data item is copied from the register specified in the push instruction, into the two memory locations addressed by the stack pointer.
2   The contents of the stack pointer is reduced by 2, so that it again contains the address of the memory location into which the next stack element is to be pushed.

See Figure 12.5.

The **pop** operation is as follows:

1   The contents of the stack pointer is increased by 2. It now addresses the top element of the stack.
2   The word addressed by the stack pointer is copied into the register specified in the pop instruction.

See Figure 12.6.

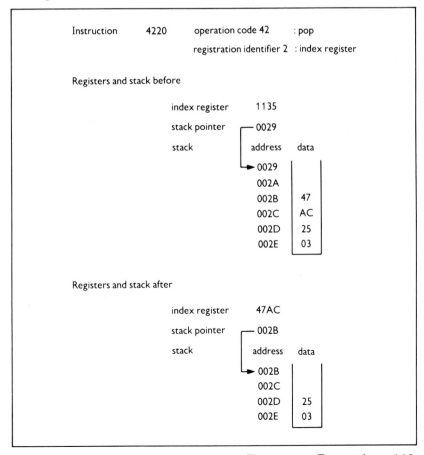

Figure 12.6
The pop instruction

Jumps and Subprogram Calls

The two instructions in this group transfer control to another part of the program. Unlike the branching instructions, these instructions are followed by the (absolute) address of the destination of the jump, in a separate word. For example:

```
5100 341A      operation code     51:  jump
               destination address  341A
```

This instruction transfers control to the instruction at address 341A. Because a complete word is used for the destination address, any location in the AMC memory can be reached.

The second instruction in this group introduces the idea of a **subprogram**. A subprogram is a set of instructions, carrying out a specific task, which is called from any other part of the program. When the subprogram is complete, control returns to the point in the program from which the subprogram was called. See Figure 12.7.

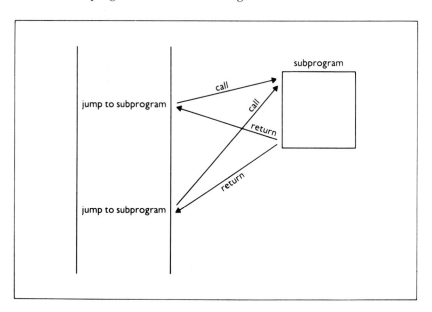

Figure 12.7
Calls to and returns from a subprogram

From a machine language point of view, the problem with subprograms is how to remember the address to which control returns after the subprogram is complete. In the AMC, and in many other modern computers, this problem is solved by means of the system stack.

When a jump to subprogram instruction is executed, the program counter contains the address of the next instruction (it has already been reset). This is the required return address. It is loaded onto the stack, and the stack pointer is updated. Control then passes to the subprogram, by loading the destination address of the jump to subprogram instruction into the program counter.

The last instruction in the subprogram is a **return** instruction. Although it is in the miscellaneous instructions group, it is discussed here. This instruction causes the return address to be popped from the stack to the program counter. Control thus returns to the instruction following the jump to subprogram instruction. Although the stack may be used by the subprogram, it is important that the return address is at the top of the stack when the subprogram ends.

Dealing with return addresses in this way means that subprograms may contain calls to other subprograms, or even calls to themselves, a technique known as recursion. The use of the stack ensures that control returns in the reverse order to that of the subprogram calls.

Miscellaneous Instructions

The remaining few AMC machine instructions are grouped together in the miscellaneous instructions group. Only the operation code part of the instruction word is used.

Apart from the return from subprogram instruction, which is discussed in the previous section, the only instruction which deserves special mention is the **no-operation** instruction. This causes the AMC processor to 'idle'. It may be used to slow down a program, to synchronise the processor with a peripheral device, or to reserve space in a program so that other instructions can be inserted later.

12.6
Example
Program 12.2

■ This program illustrates the use of a subprogram, and shows how information can be passed to and from a subprogram by means of the stack.

The purpose of the subprogram is to decide which of two given numbers is larger. The numbers are passed to the subprogram on the stack, and the larger number is returned on the stack.

You will recall that the return address is placed on the stack when the subprogram is called. This address must be stored in the memory during the running of the subprogram, as the numbers are beneath it on the stack. Just before the subprogram ends, the return address is again placed on the stack.

Program

Address	Instruction		Comments
0000			Temporary storage for return address.
0002			Temporary storage for one number.

Start of subprogram

Address	Instruction		Comments
0004	4210		Pop return address to accumulator.
0006	1212	0000	Store return address in location 0000.
000A	4210		Pop first number to accumulator.
000C	1212	0002	Store first number in location 0002.
0010	4210		Pop second number to accumulator.
0012	1A12	0002	Compare second number (in accumulator) with first number (in location 0002).
0016	6404		Branch to address 001C if greater than or equal to zero (i.e. second number is larger, or numbers are equal).
0018	1112	0002	Load first number to accumulator.
001C	4110		Stack larger number.
001E	1112	0000	Load return address to accumulator.
0022	4110		Stack return address.
0024	8300		Return from subprogram.

End of subprogram, start of main program

Address	Instruction		Comments
0026	1131	007F	Initialise stack pointer (to 007F).
002A	1111	4135	Load second number (4135) to accumulator.

002E	4110		Stack second number.
0030	1111	62A4	Load first number (62A4) to accumulator.
0034	4110		Stack first number.
0036	5200	0004	Jump to subprogram.
003A	4210		Pop larger number to accumulator on return.
003C	8500		Halt.

Points to Notice

- The return address is stored in location 0000 for the duration of the subprogram.
- In the main program, the numbers are stacked in reverse order. The last number pushed onto the stack is the first number popped from the stack in the subprogram.

12.7 The Instruction Cycle

■ The sequence of actions required to carry out one machine instruction is called the **instruction cycle**. The instruction cycle of a computer depends on its register architecture and the nature of its machine instructions. Consequently, the actions carried out for a machine instruction vary from computer to computer. Nevertheless, the overall pattern is much the same in all cases. The general pattern of the instruction cycle is discussed below, with the AMC used as an example.

Fetch

The first action is to fetch the machine instruction from the memory. The program counter contains the address of the instruction. The address is used to locate the instruction. If the instruction occupies more than one memory location, several memory cycles are needed to fetch it. The instruction is loaded into the instruction register.

Reset

As soon as the current instruction has been fetched, the contents of the program counter is updated so that it contains the address of the next program instruction. The amount by which it must be increased depends on the length of the current instruction.

Locate Operand

If the instruction contains an address, or an immediate operand, the data item, or operand, referred to by the instruction must be located. Details of the way this is done depend on the addressing mode of the instruction. Apart from the immediate operand mode, all modes require at least one access to the memory. The number of memory locations occupied by the operand also influences the number of memory cycles required.

Execute

The operation required by the machine instruction is carried out. In most cases, one or more registers are involved, as well as the operand from memory. The arithmetic and logic unit carries out the process involved. In some cases a data item is stored in memory. Condition codes are set or cleared according to the result of the operation.

Timing

An instruction cycle involves at least one memory cycle, to locate the instruction itself. If a long data item is used, located by means of a

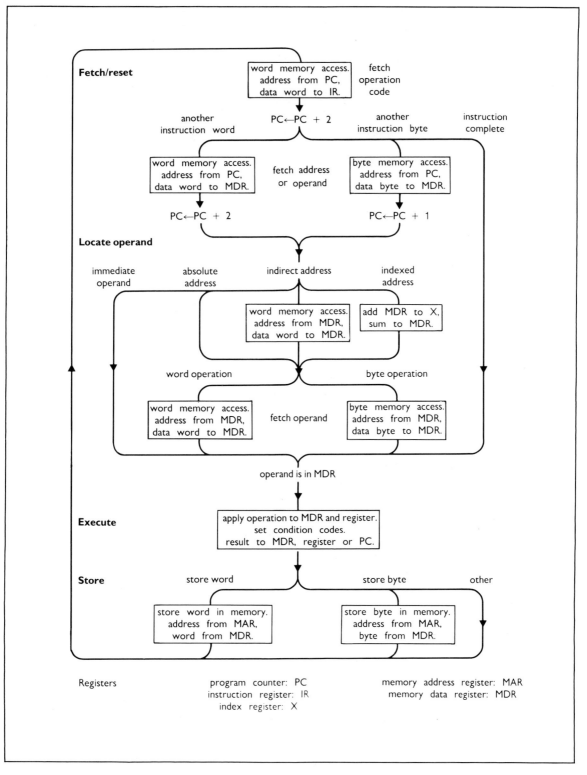

Figure 12.8
The AMC instruction cycle

modified address, several more memory cycles are involved. The speed of a memory cycle, and the number of memory cycles per instruction cycle, are important factors in determining the duration of an instruction cycle. This duration is typically from 10 microseconds (μs) to 10 nanoseconds (ns), over the range of computers currently in operation (1μs = 1 millionth of a second, 1ns = 1 thousand millionth of a second).

The steps of an instruction cycle are controlled by the timing circuits of the computer, and either by outputs from the instruction decoder or by microcode (Section 12.9). The timing circuits provide a signal at fixed intervals of one **clock cycle**. A clock cycle is the smallest unit of time for one step of the instruction cycle, and is generally the duration of one memory cycle, or a half or quarter of the length of a memory cycle.

The AMC Instruction Cycle

Figure 12.8 shows the AMC instruction cycle. It must be studied in conjunction with the AMC register layout, Figure 10.7. The flow of instructions, addresses and data items between the main store and various registers can be followed. Note that:

1 The fetch and reset phases are combined. The program counter (PC) is updated more than once if the instruction comprises more than one word.
2 The locate operand phase results in the operand being placed in the memory data register (MDR), no matter what addressing mode is in the instruction.
3 Accordingly, execution of the operation only involves the memory data register, and one of the program-controlled registers (accumulator, index register or stack pointer).
4 The last part of the cycle is only carried out if a store word or a store byte instruction is being executed.

12.8 Interrupts

■ At the beginning of this book, the point was made that modern computers are seldom controlled by one program. Rather, they are controlled by a hierarchy of programs. At the top of the hierarchy is a program called an **operating system**, which forms the subject of Chapter 21.

There are two methods of transferring control from one of these programs to another. One is when one program calls another, as a program calls a subprogram. For example, an application program calls an operating system routine to transfer data to or from disk. The other is a mechanism whereby the running of a particular program can be **interrupted**. An interrupt is an external event or signal which causes the running of a program to be suspended. This interrupt signal is generally placed on one or more **interrupt lines**, which are part of the bus connecting the processor to peripheral devices.

When an interrupt occurs, the current contents of all the registers are saved and control passes to an interrupt service routine, which is part of the operating system. See Section 21.7. The **interrupt service routine** determines the source of the interrupt, generally by examining a number of flags, and transfers control to a routine to handle the particular type of interrupt which has occurred. At a later stage, running of the interrupted program is resumed, from the point at which it was interrupted. This is achieved by restoring the values of all the registers which were saved when the interrupt occurred.

Common causes of interrupts include the input or output of data, the detection of an error in a program, or the fact that a program has exceeded the time allocated to it. The instruction sets of most computers include instructions which disable interrupts, effectively switching them off, and enable interrupts, switching them on. On most computers, interrupts have levels of priority, so that high-priority interrupts can supercede the handling of lower priority interrupts. Interrupts are not implemented in the AMC for simplicity.

12.9 Microcode

■ In the AMC, and a number of actual computers, the step-by-step control of each instruction cycle is carried out directly by the instruction decoder and the timing circuits of the control unit. Such computers are said to have **hard-wired control**.

In contrast to this method of control, many other computers have another level of instructions, beneath that of machine language. These are **micro-instructions** or **microcode**. Micro-instructions are stored in a special read-only memory known as the **control memory**, and control the detailed steps of each machine instruction. Each machine instruction accesses a set of micro-instructions, which control the opening and closing of control switches as the machine instruction is carried out.

There are several advantages of microcode. One is that the instruction set of a computer does not have to be 'frozen'. Changes at microcode level enable different instruction sets to be used. In this way one type of computer can be made to **emulate** another type of computer, by adopting its machine code. Another advantage is cost. Control circuits of microcoded computers are generally simpler, and therefore cheaper, than those of hard-wired computers. Most microprocessors use microcode control.

The major disadvantage of the use of microcode is speed. Microcoded computers are generally slower than hard-wired computers with similar instruction sets. This is because access to control memory takes longer than the gate delay in hard-wired instruction execution.

12.10 Conclusion

■ The main points of this chapter are as follows:
- The program language which controls the step-by-step working of the processor of a computer is called machine language.
- Machine language instructions refer directly to the hardware of the computer.
- All machine instructions include an operation code, which specifies the type of operation to be carried out.
- Some machine instructions refer to the main store of the computer. Data is located by specifying the address of the required store location.
- A number of different addressing techniques are in common use. Some require address transformation before the data item, or operand, is located. Common addressing modes are absolute address, indexed address, indirect address and immediate operand.
- The AMC is a one-address computer. AMC machine instructions occupy one word, sometimes followed by a word containing an address, or a word or byte containing an operand.
- AMC machine instructions are divided into groups. The instructions in each group have the same bit layout, and perform similar operations. The operation codes of instructions in the same group have the same initial hexadecimal digit.

- The sequence of actions required to carry out one machine instruction is called an instruction cycle. Instruction cycles include fetch, reset, locate operand, and execute phases.
- All computers have a mechanism to enable the running of a program to be interrupted by some external signal.
- Two ways of controlling the steps of an instruction cycle are hard-wired control, and micro-instructions.

Taken together, this chapter and Chapter 10 describe what might be called a traditional computer architecture. A distinguishing feature of this type of architecture is that only one processing step takes place at a time. This limits the speed and processing power of the computer. The next chapter introduces some advanced processor features. Most of these are ways of permitting various operations inside a processor to take place in parallel.

Exercise 12

1 Briefly define the following terms: machine language; operation code; instruction set; addressing mode; offset; pointer; address modification; subprogram; recursion; instruction cycle; clock cycle; interrupt; micro-instruction; hard-wired control; emulate; loop.

2 Describe one use for each type of addressing mode mentioned in this chapter.

3 Consider the following three locations of AMC main store:

Address	Contents	
2A61	1113	49B6
3521	AB02	
49B6	3521	

State clearly the result of carrying out the instruction in location 2A61.

4 For each of the following decimal numbers: 16, 56, -128
   a) Express the number as a 16 bit twos complement integer.
   b) Apply the operation arithmetic shift left to the 16 bit integer, and convert the result to a decimal number.
   c) Apply the operation arithmetic shift right to the 16 bit integer, and convert the result to a decimal number.
   Comment on your findings.

5 Calculate the destination addresses (in hexadecimal) of these AMC branching instructions:

Address	Instruction
0024	6120
0120	61E4

6 Show the contents of the AMC stack after the following sequence of instructions:

Address	Instruction		Comments
0100	1131	0200	Initialise stack pointer (to 0200).
0104	1111	AABB	Load AABB to accumulator.
0108	4110		Push contents of accumulator to stack.
010A	1111	CCDD	Load CCDD to accumulator.
010E	4110		Push contents of accumulator to stack.

Also write down the value of the stack pointer after the instructions.

7 If the byte 80 (hexadecimal) is copied into a sixteen bit AMC register, the contents of the register is FF80 (hexadecimal). Explain why this is so (convert both of above quantities, regarded as twos complement integers, via binary to decimal to assist your explanation).

8 The program shown below, written in AMC machine language, is

designed to add up the corresponding numbers in two arrays, and store the results in a third array. In other words, the first number in the third array is the sum of the first number in the first array, and the first number in the second array.

In the program, each number occupies one word, i.e. two storage locations, and each array contains four numbers. The length of each array is thus eight bytes.

The index register serves a dual purpose. It is used to locate array elements via the indexed addressing mode, and also to count the number of additions which have been made. Processing starts at the back of the arrays, working towards the front. Because the numbers occupy two storage locations, the index is decreased by two for each addition.

The part of the program which adds together two array elements is repeated four times. Such a portion of a program is called a loop.

Program

	Address	Instruction		Comments
	0000	08		Length of arrays, 8 bytes or 4 words.
	0001			Array 1, assumed
to	0008			already loaded.
	0009			Array 2, assumed
to	0010			already loaded.
	0011			Array 3.
to	0018			

Start of program

	0019	2122	0000	

Start of loop to add each pair of numbers

	001D	0320		
	001F	0320		
	0021	670E		
	0023	1114	0001	
	0027	1314	0009	
	002B	1214	0011	
	002F	61EC		

End of loop

	0031	8500		

a) Copy down the program, and write an appropriate comment next to each instruction. The comment must state clearly, in a few words, precisely what the instruction does.

b) What is the value of the index register at the end of the program?

c) Will the program instructions need to be altered if arrays of a different length are to be added? If so, what changes must be made?

d) Replace one instruction in the program, so that array elements are subtracted rather than added.

You will see in Chapter 15 that some computers have a single machine instruction to add corresponding elements of two arrays.

9 Write a program in AMC machine language to output a set of characters, stored in consecutive memory locations. The character with hexadecimal code 7E is used to mark the end of the set. The memory area used to store the characters can be immediately after the output program. Next to each machine instruction write a comment which explains clearly what the instruction does.

13 Advanced Processor Features

The principles of the design of digital electronic computers were first set out in 1946 by John von Neumann. These principles lead to a computer architecture like that described in the previous four chapters. A great many computers have been built in accordance with these principles, and it is likely that many more will be built in the future.

The advantages of the 'traditional' Von Neumann design are its simplicity and versatility. A Von Neumann processor operates on a fixed cycle of fetching an instruction from store, and then executing it, before fetching another instruction. The major disadvantage is that only one action is performed, inside a processor, at any one moment. Many of the advances from Von Neumann architecture are centred around attempts to introduce a measure of **parallelism** into the design of computers. Parallelism means that several actions can be performed simultaneously within a computer. It is essential in coping with the demands for data throughput placed on modern computers, and for such applications as voice recognition and image processing, both of which require the simultaneous processing, at a number of levels, of very large amounts of data.

This chapter examines a number of advanced processor features which have been incorporated into contemporary computers. Each is an attempt to enhance the processing power of a computer in some way. Some are only suitable for special-purpose computing, particularly scientific computing. Others are suitable for computers of all types. The features are discussed in broad outline only, as the details of some of them are extrememly complicated. Developments in computer architecture which are part of the fifth generation initiative are discussed in Section 34.3.

13.1 Duplicate Processing Circuits

■ The most obvious way to achieve a measure of parallelism is to duplicate some of the processing circuits in a processor. A common example is a simple addition unit which resets the value of the program counter while an instruction is being executed. In a few computers, the entire mechanism which deals with the address part of an instruction is separate from the circuits which execute the instruction.

13.2 Distributed Array Processing

■ In scientific and similar computing applications, the situation is frequently encountered where large arrays of data items must be processed. The operations carried out on each element of an array are identical. In such cases, a significant amount of time can be saved by carrying out the operations on all the elements of an array simultaneously. This can be done by a computer with a large number of identical arithmetic and logic units arranged in parallel, and circuits which can supply the required data to each ALU at the same time, and similarly deal with the outputs from all the ALUs. This kind of processing is called **distributed array processing**. A variation on distributed array processing, known as **vector processing**, is discussed in Section 15.4.

The problem with distributed array processing is to ensure that the processing power of the computer is used effectively. Sophisticated programming techniques are required if this to be achieved.

13.3 Advanced Memory Architecture

■ One of the slowest aspects of the operation of a computer is the transfer of data between processing units and peripheral devices. In a conventional computer, all the steps of such transfers are controlled directly by the program. Peripheral devices are much slower in operation than processors. This often involves 'idling' a processor while a peripheral device completes the transfer of a data item.

Several techniques have evolved to deal with this problem. The most common is **autonomous peripheral operation**, with the peripheral having direct access to the main store of the processor. This technique is also known as **direct memory access** or **DMA**. It requires hardware known as **DMA controllers**.

Data is input or output under DMA, not as individual characters, but in blocks of characters. The DMA controller is supplied with the start address of the data in main store, and the number of characters to be transferred. The controller then proceeds independently of the processor, until the transfer of the data is complete. Memory cycles are 'stolen' from the processor whenever they are required by the DMA controller. Because the processor works much faster than the peripheral which governs the speed of the DMA controller, this does not slow the processor down very much.

A further development, which eliminates the need for cycle stealing, is the **multi-port** memory. A large common main store has a number of high-speed read/write channels which operate in parallel. These enable several data items to be stored or accessed simultaneously. The only restriction is that only one channel must write to a particular memory address at one time. See Section 15.4 for an example.

The memory of most computers is not regarded as a single unit, but as a series of areas, each allocated to one process. In order to ensure that a process does not exceed its allocated area, there is a **base register** which holds the address of the start of the area, and a **limit register** which holds the address of the end of the area. All addresses used by the process are checked to ensure that they lie within these two bounds.

A smaller subdivision of memory is into **pages**, of fixed length, and which are transferred to and from backing store in one unit, generally by DMA. This enables the main memory and the backing store of the computer to be regarded as a single entity known as a **virtual memory**. See Section 15.2 for an example. The concept of virtual memory is important in the study of operating systems: see Section 21.7.

13.4 Pipelining

■ The feature which has contributed the most towards improving the performance of a processor is a technique known as **pipelining**. Pipelining is widely used, even among fairly small computers.

Pipelining can be used whenever an operation can be expressed as a sequence of steps. A functional unit is constructed for each step. These are connected by storage areas, or **buffers**, which hold the items as they pass through the pipeline. See Figure 13.1. A requirement of a pipeline is that each step takes the same length of time. During this time interval, called a

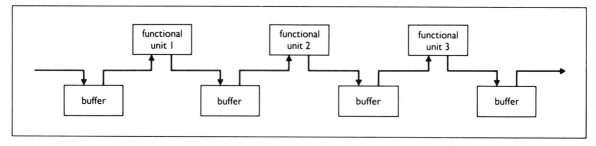

Figure 13.1
A pipeline

beat, each item in the pipeline moves from a buffer, through a functional unit, into the next buffer. At any one time, a number of items are at different stages of processing, each only one beat behind the previous item.

Another requirement of a pipeline is that each step in the process is independent of all other steps. This means that separate functional circuits can be constructed for each step, and items are not held up at any step because information from some other step is not available. This requirement of independence of steps is not always met in practice, and causes problems in the design and operation of pipelines.

The concept of pipelining is implemented in two ways in computers. These are **instruction pipelines** and **arithmetic pipelines**. In an instruction pipeline, each functional unit carries out one step in the instruction cycle of the computer. Items moving through the pipeline are instructions. Each instruction is only one beat behind the previous instruction. Problems arise when the results from one instruction are needed by the next instruction, and when a branching instruction is encountered. Details of the way in which these problems are dealt with are beyond the scope of this course.

An arithmetic pipeline is especially useful when dealing with floating point numbers, and for multiplication of all types of numbers. In this case items in the pipeline are numbers, and each functional unit carries out one step of the calculation.

13.5 Cache Stores

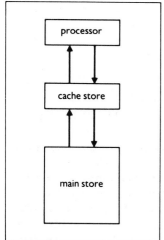

Figure 13.2
A cache store

■ One of the slowest activities taking place within a processor is access to memory. As a memory access can occur a number of times during one instruction cycle, the speed of memory access is a major factor in determining the speed of the processor.

One way of improving the speed of memory access is to use a **cache store**, also known as a **slave store**. This is a small store, with a very fast access time, situated between the main store and the rest of the processor. See Figure 13.2. The arrangement of cache store, main store and backing store is known as a **three level memory**.

The use of the cache store is based on the assumption that, for most of the time, processing requires data and instructions close to each other in main store. Areas of main store surrounding the current machine instruction and data item are loaded into the cache store. This is generally done independently of the operation of the processor, at the maximum speed of the main store. Data and instructions required by the processor are then accessed from the cache store. From time to time the processor is slowed down when an item it requires is not in the cache store. A cache store is frequently used in conjunction with an instruction pipeline.

13.6 Content-Addressable Memory

■ The fundamental principle of the operation of a computer memory is that an address is used to locate a data item. However, for certain operations it is very useful to have a portion of store which works the other way round – a data item is used to locate an address. A portion of store which works in this way is called a **content-addressable memory**, or **associative store**.

The most common application for a content-addressable memory is looking up an item of data in a table. What is required is the position of the item in the table. The table is loaded into content-addressable memory, and the data item is compared, simultaneously, with all the entries. The address of the location at which a match is found is returned. This process is illustrated in Figure 13.3.

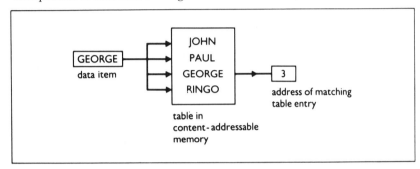

Figure 13.3
A content-addressable memory

13.7 Risc Processors

■ Up to about 1985, advances in processor architecture all involved increasing complexity – a larger instruction set, more complex instructions, more sophisticated addressing modes, etc. The problem with this increasing complexity is that it slows the processor down. Detailed studies of processors in operation disclosed that for most applications thay spend the majority of their time carrying out a few instructions, and the rest are used very seldom.

This realisation led to a reversal of the trend towards greater complexity in some new processor architectures. Instead, **reduced instruction set computers** (**Risc**) were devised. These are single-chip microprocessors, with small, simple instruction sets, concentrating on the operations which are carried out most frequently in practice. Because of their simple construction, Risc processors operate very quickly. In many typical processing applications, they are able to out-perform the traditional complex instruction set computers (Cisc) by a large margin.

Risc processors are particularly popular in high-performance workstations. They are ideal for applications which involve graphics (which requires a small set of screen control instructions to be carried out repeatedly). Recently Cisc processors have also advanced in processing speed, and it remains to be seen which will dominate the workstation market during the remainder of the decade.

13.8 Parallel Computer Architectures

■ The main line of development in parallel computer architectures is the inclusion of multiple processors in one computer. The distinguishing features of the various approaches are the number of processors, and the degree of independence with which they operate.

The approach used with increasing success in supercomputers is a small number of powerful processors, operating with a large measure of

An Inmos transputer chip.

independence. Each has independent access to a multi-port memory, and to a commmon input/output channel. The computer is able to run a number of applications autonomously, or partition a single application into a number of independent modules, for parallel processing. Special compilers (Chapter 20) are used to prepare programs to run on these architecures.

A more radical approach is a much larger number of less powerful but faster processors, closely coupled together. The processing chip which is at the centre of many such architectures is the **Inmos transputer**, a Risc processor with on-board memory and four high-speed communications channels. A large number of these are arranged in a rectangular array, each closely coupled to its four nearest neighbours. Programs are broken down by special compilers into small modules, each of which resides on one transputer. These modules are processed in parallel, with data flowing to adjacent transputers as required. For certain classes of application, notably image processing and certain mathematical computations, these massively parallel architectures are far more powerful than single-processor computers, or ones with a small number of loosely coupled processors.

13.9 Conclusion

■ This chapter has shown some of the ways in which computer architecture is evolving away from the traditional 'one step at a time' concept. Some of the ideas presented, such as pipelining and cache stores, are fairly well established, while others, such as massively parallel architectures, are relatively recent. In all cases, the motivation for these new developments is the same: faster, more powerful and more versatile computer systems at a lower cost.

Exercise 13

1 Briefly define each of the following terms: parallelism; distributed array processing; direct memory access; DMA controller; multi-port memory; base and limit registers; page; virtual memory; pipelining; cache store; three level memory; content-addressable memory; Risc and Cisc; massively parallel architecture.

2 The overall steps of the AMC instruction cycle are fetch, locate operand, execute and store. Briefly describe how an instruction pipeline could be used to implement these steps, and some of the problems which would be encountered.

3 A particular computer has an instruction cache with a capacity of 256 instructions. Explain the benefits of this facility when executing program loops of less than 256 instructions.

4 A multiplication pipeline has a beat time of 10 microseconds, and contains 32 stages.
   a) How long does it take for one complete multiplication operation?
   b) How long does it take for 32 multiplication operations?
   c) How long does it take for n multiplication operations?

5 To what extent, if at all, do the advanced CPU features in this chapter alter the concept of a computer, discussed in Chapter 1?

6 Example Program 12.1 can be generalised to input data from any peripheral device, to AMC main store. Assume that it is used to read data from a disk drive, and the speed of the disk drive is such that the instruction at address **0004** must be executed 10 times per data item.
   a) Count the number of memory cycles per data item transferred.
   b) Use this figure to estimate the number of memory cycles needed to transfer 1K of data from the disk drive.

c) If a DMA controller requires 32 memory cycles to set up, and thereafter steals one memory cycle per data item transferred, calculate the number of memory cycles needed for 1K of data.

d) Comment on your results from parts (b) and (c).

7 What investigations led to the development of Risc processors? What differentiates them from conventional (Cisc) architectures?

8 At which level of computer system are Risc processors becoming most popular? Suggest some reasons for their popularity in this market.

9 Distinguish between the two main approaches to parallel computer architectures. Give the strengths and weaknesses of each approach. Suggest some applications for which each might be best suited.

14 Peripheral Devices

Peripheral devices carry out six of the seven types of operation which characterise a computer: input, output, storage, retrieval, transmission and reception. As their name implies, they are on the 'outside' of the computer system, and provide its external interfaces. This chapter describes the commonest of the large number of input, output and storage devices which are now in use, and how they are connected to, and controlled by, a processor. (Data communication is described in Chapter 31.) The devices are described in outline only, and precise figures of speeds of operation and storage capabilities are not given. This is because the technology of peripheral devices is constantly changing, and improved performance figures are being attained all the time.

At the start of this chapter it is important to clarify the terms **medium** and **device** in the context of peripherals, and recall the terms **module** and **interface**. A medium is a material used for the storage of data. An example of a medium is magnetic tape. A device is a machine which transfers data, generally to or from a storage medium. The majority of peripheral devices may be regarded as modules. What they do is important, whereas how they do it is less significant. A peripheral may be unplugged and replaced by one which carries out the same task in a different way, without affecting the computer system as a whole in any way at all. The interface between a processor and its peripherals, and the external interfaces of the peripherals, are important aspects of computer system design.

In the early days of computing, the processor was the largest and most expensive item of equipment in a computing installation. In many cases, the present-day situation is almost the opposite. The processor is often the smallest and cheapest item, and may sometimes be regarded merely as a control device for the peripherals.

14.1 Terminals

■ A **terminal** is the simplest and most common way of gaining access to a computer system. A terminal may be an integral part of the computer system, as in the case of microcomputers or workstations. Alternatively it may be a stand-alone device, connected by a local or long-distance network to the central processor. A terminal is used for both input and output.

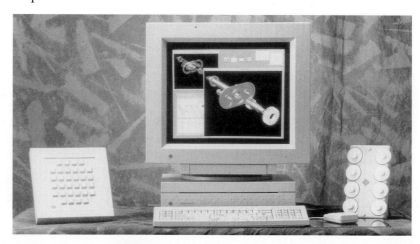

Desktop computers and workstations have keyboards and monitors as integral parts of the system.

The most popular form of terminal consists of a keyboard, resembling that on a typewriter, and a display screen, also known as a **monitor**, similar to a television screen. A terminal of this type is called a **visual display unit**, or **VDU**. Input is typed at the keyboard, and output appears, in character form, on the display screen. Some computer systems allow their terminals to display **windows** which show the output from several programs simultaneously.

An enhanced version of a VDU is a **graphics terminal.** In addition to characters, a graphics terminal allows shapes and patterns to be displayed on the screen. Diagrams, maps, animated cartoons and graphs may be generated by these patterns. The patterns are formed by closely-spaced rows of dots or **pixels** on the screen. Many graphics terminals work in colour, and most permit **high resolution graphics**, with a much finer level of detail (the closer the spacing of the pixels, the higher the resolution).

In a number of computing systems, terminals are used for **direct data entry**. Data input at the terminal is stored on magnetic disks until ready for processing. See Section 27.1 for details on data capture using terminals. Terminals are also used to enter and edit programs. In most modern computers the **operator's console** is in the form of a terminal. A **software front panel** enables the contents of registers and key memory cells to be displayed when necessary. In most microcomputers, the integral terminal has the role of input/output device and operator's console.

14.2 Input Devices

■ **Input devices** transfer data from an external medium to a computer processor. They interpret the data, in the representation used by the input medium, and send it to the processor, often having changed the data to a code used by the processor.

In the early days of computing, the commonest input media were punched cards and paper tape. They have now been superseded by data entry devices attached directly to a computer or terminal, the commonest of which are the **keyboard, mouse, digitising pad, light pen, touch-sensitive screen** and **scanner**. There are also a number of methods of reading data directly from its source. These include **optical character recognition, magnetic ink character recognition** and the use of **magnetic strips** and **bar codes**.

Keyboard

A **keyboard** is by far the commonest input device to a computer system. Keyboards are fitted to desktop computers and workstations, as well as to terminals and operator's consoles. Keyboards are used to enter both operating instructions and data.

Computer keyboards are based on the traditional layout of a typewriter keyboard. This is known as the 'qwerty' layout, after the keys in the top left row. There are additional keys for control purposes, and most computer keyboards have a numeric keypad on the right. The qwerty layout dates back to the era of mechanical typewriters, where it was designed to slow down the typist, to prevent the keys from being jammed. The letters do not follow any logical arrangement. Most people take quite a long time to become familiar with a keyboard, and there is a certain resistance in industry, particularly on the part of senior managers, against learning to use one. 'Keyboard illiteracy' is often given as one of the reasons for the slow acceptance of desktop computers in companies.

In spite of these problems, the traditional qwerty layout remains the standard, and keyboards look likely to be the main method of data entry into computer systems for the foreseeable future.

Mouse

A **mouse** is a hand-held device which is moved by the user over a flat surface. It can be connected to a terminal or to a stand-alone computer system. As the mouse moves, a pointer moves in a corresponding way on the display screen. Pressing a button on the mouse selects the data item or control option at the pointer. The three main uses of a mouse are to select options from menus displayed on screen, to select portions of text or images on the screen for processing in some way, and to draw diagrams. A mouse greatly simplifies the operation of a computer, reducing or eliminating the need for a keyboard. The advent of mouse control has overcome some of the problems of keyboard illiteracy mentioned above.

Digitising Pad

A digitising pad in use.

A **digitising pad** is a device which allows the user to 'trace' from a large pad onto the screen. It consists of a hand-held device, similar to a mouse, which is moved over the surface of the pad. The position of the device on the pad is reflected precisely by the position of a cursor on the screen. The pad often has a transparent portion, with cross-hairs indicating the precise position of the reference point. Digitising pads are special-purpose devices, most commonly used in conjunction with drawing or computer-aided design software, and high-resolution graphics screens. Maps, plans or diagrams can be placed on the pad, and be traced accurately onto the screen.

Although a digitiser is similar in some respects to a mouse, it is far more precise. A mouse cannot easily be used to 'trace' from a drawing or map to the screen.

Light Pen

A **light pen** is a hand-held device, shaped like a pen, which allows the user to 'draw' directly on the screen. Like a digitiser, it is a special-purpose device, suited to graphics and computer-aided design applications. The precision of the drawn point on the screen is limited by the resolution of the screen itself. The advantage of a light pen over a digitiser is that it draws directly onto the screen. Its disadvantages are that it cannot be used to trace from a document to the screen, and holding a pen against a vertical screen for any length of time is tiring. Light pens are less common than digitisers.

Touch-sensitive Screen

Computer screens can be fitted with a touch sensitive device which detects the position of an object near the surface of the screen. A touch-sensitive screen is much less precise than a light pen. It is a special-purpose device, restricted to certain types of application. Its main function is to allow users to select control options directly from menus displayed on the screen. It is also useful in computer systems designed for use by disabled people.

Scanner

A **scanner** is an input device which resembles a video camera, and is used for entering complete images into a computer system. It is normally positioned on a stand, above the image to be entered. The image must be suitably illuminated. A scanner is a special-purpose device, used in conjunction with graphics software and high-resolution display screens. The resolution of the image varies, from that of a conventional video camera, to considerably higher. (Some computer systems can accept input from a conventional video camera used as a scanner.) Most scanners can capture images in colour. Because of the amount of storage space needed for a scanned image, it is not generally practicable to scan moving images.

The software which controls a scanner normally displays the scanned image on the computer screen. The colours are not necessarily correct - full colour input may be transformed to black and white for display, or the colours may be transformed by some internal algorithm to modify or enhance the image. However, the colours as input by the scanner are generally accurate.

Optical Character Recognition

Optical character recognition (OCR) is based on a data input device which can recognise printed or typed characters by a light scanning process. Many commercial documents such as gas, electricity and telephone bills, have a row of figures across the bottom which are read by an OCR scanner. New European Community passports have a page of OCR text, holding all the details of the passport holder. A special typeface is used for the characters, to enable them to be read more easily. Some OCR equipment can read ordinary typeface, and some, such as that used by the UK Post Office for sorting letters, can even read neat handwriting.

A simpler variation of this system is **mark sensing**. Mark sense equipment can recognise whether certain areas of a document have been shaded in pencil. Mark sense documents include football pool coupons, forms used to record gas and electricity meter readings, and multiple choice question papers. OCR and mark sensing have the advantage of being able to read directly from source documents, but are slow and error-prone by comparison with other methods.

Magnetic Ink Character Recognition

Magnetic ink character recognition (MICR) is the process of reading characters which are printed in magnetic ink. It is used almost exclusively within the banking system for the automatic clearing of cheques, and is fairly fast and relatively error-free. Cheques have a row of figures printed along the bottom in magnetic ink. These are read by the automatic equipment which sorts the cheques and inputs the data from them.

Bar Codes

Bar codes are becoming the standard way of displaying machine-readable information on merchandise, particularly in supermarkets. A bar code consists of a number of vertical stripes, in black (or dark) ink or paint on a white (or light) background. Characters are coded by combinations of thick and thin stripes, and check characters are always included. The commonest type of bar code used outside the USA is the **European Article Number (EAN)** code. Every item is allocated a unique, twelve-digit number, together with a parity digit. The digits are printed below the bars to allow for visual checks if necessary. The bar codes incorporate a number of checks to detect errors in reading, and to allow them to be read in either direction.

A **bar code reader** interprets the pattern of stripes and produces the equivalent character code. Bar code readers are either hand-held, similar to pens, or larger devices incorporating a window against which the bar code is held. Laser beams are used in the latter type. Bar code readers are generally incorporated into terminals, such as the most recent type of cash terminal used at supermarkets. Experience to date indicates that bar code input is fairly fast and acceptably reliable.

Magnetic Strips

Magnetic strips are used on such things as credit cards, train tickets, building society passbooks and some product labels. They hold identifying data such as account numbers or product codes, prices, etc. These strips are read, either by hand-held readers resembling pens, or by detectors in slots into which the credit card, passbook or label is inserted. The advantage of this form of data entry is that the data is almost impossible to alter, once it has been written to the strip. This provides a security check against data printed on the credit card or passbook.

Voice Recognition

Voice recognition has been the subject of intensive research for many years. Although success has been limited, this is a promising growth area for certain applications in the future.

Current voice recognition systems can respond to a fairly small number of words or phrases from a person whose voice has been 'learned'. Recognition rates are fairly high, but not yet adequate for a wide variety of applications. Speed of input is, of course, limited by the rate at which a person can speak coherently. Continuous speech from a 'stranger' cannot at present be interpreted.

14.3 Output Devices

■ **Output devices** transfer data from a processor to an external medium or visual display. As in the case of input devices, the data code used by the output device is often different from the internal code used by the processor. Changing to the output code is generally done by the processor.

The commonest type of output device is the display screen or monitor, described in the section on terminals (Section 14.1). Other popular types of output device are described below.

Printers

Printers are one of the commonest forms of output device, with a wide variety currently available. They produce a permanent copy (**hard copy**) of the output.

Line Printer

The largest and fastest printers are **line printers** which print all the characters in an entire line in one operation. Lines generally contain one hundred and twenty characters, and speeds vary from three hundred to twelve hundred lines per minute. At the top of the range are **high-speed text laser beam printers**, which achieve up to twenty thousand lines per minute.

Character Printers

More suited than line printers to desktop computers and word processors are **character printers**, which print one character at a time. Character printers are slower but cheaper than line printers, with print speeds of between twenty and one hundred lines per minute. Some models speed up the operation by printing alternate lines in alternate directions. The commonest character printers are **dot matrix printers, daisy wheel printers** and **ink jet printers**.

Enlarged characters produced by dot matrix, daisy wheel and ink jet printers, highlighting their differences in quality.

Dot Matrix and Daisy Wheel Printers

Dot matrix printers form characters by combinations of dots, produced by an array of needles in the print head. They are simple, low-cost devices, which can also be used for hard copy of low-resolution graphics. **Daisy wheel printers** have a print wheel with one or two characters on each 'petal'. The wheel is rotated in order to select the characters to be printed. Daisy wheel printers produce characters of typewriter quality.

In the past, dot matrix printers did not produce characters of acceptable quality for commercial correspondence. However, an increase in the number of needles in the print heads of newer dot matrix printers has improved the quality of output to the point where it is now acceptable as letter quality. There is often a 'draft' option, which produces lower-quality output quickly, and a 'letter' option which produces letter-quality output more slowly. With dot matrix printers far cheaper than daisy wheel printers, the former are now far more popular than the latter.

A problem with both dot matrix and daisy wheel printers is the noise they produce. Sound-absorbant covers are available to reduce this noise.

Ink Jet Printers

Ink jet printers spray a fine stream of ink onto the paper, using a dot matrix pattern. Some models can print in more than one colour. They are special-purpose devices, used mainly for the output of text and graphics where colour is required. Their main benefit is that they are much quieter than dot matrix or daisy wheel printers.

Laser Printers

Printers for combinations of text and graphics are becoming increasingly popular. Dot matrix and ink jet printers can be used for this purpose, but their resolution is somewhat limited. **Image laser printers** (of different construction from the high-speed text laser printers mentioned above) are the most popular output devices for printing high-quality images which combine text and graphics. Output is in terms of a matrix of dots, but resolution is so high (generally 300 dots per inch both vertically and horizontally) that the dots are hardly visible. At present only monochrome output can be produced. Their main application is desktop publishing (Section 21.6).

Computer Output on Microfilm

Computer output on microfilm (COM) is an output technique gaining wide acceptance in certain applications. For example, COM is now used by banks for their daily records of account balances. It avoids the bulk and expense of the large quantities of paper produced by printers. It is also used for archives and public records such as census information.

A 'page' of output is displayed on a screen and photographed by a special camera. The film image of one page measures less than a quarter of an inch square. The film is either on a long roll, or in postcard-sized microfiches, which contain the images of approximately one hundred pages. A microfilm reader is used to project the enlarged image of a page onto a screen.

Digital Plotters

Digital plotter in operation.

Computer-aided design (CAD) applications in areas such as chip and PCB design, engineering and architecture use **digital plotters** for output. These devices produce plans, engineering drawings, chip layouts and maps. A digital plotter has a pen whose motion across the surface of the paper is controlled by a computer. In some models (**flat bed plotters**), the pen moves both vertically and horizontally. In others, the pen moves horizontally while the paper moves vertically. The former can generally handle much larger sheets of paper than the latter. Some models work in a range of colours. Digital plotters are slow output devices, and require special software to control them. In some applications they have been replaced by image laser printers.

Speech Synthesis

Speech synthesis output is the counterpart of voice recognition input. Like voice recognition, speech synthesis is currently the subject of intensive research. A few speech synthesis output devices have been implemented, for example the British Telecom speaking clock and reading machines for the blind, but the full potential of this technique is far from being realised.

Speech synthesis works by storing a digitally coded form of a number of key sounds. Words are constructed by combining these codes, and then decoding the digital patterns through a suitable set of circuits connected to a speaker. It is possible to incorporate inflexions, pauses and the natural rise and fall of a voice during a phrase or a sentence.

14.4 Backing Store

■ Permanent copies of data in machine readable form are kept on **backing store**. In many computer applications, a bank of stored data is the most important element in the system. Backing store technology is being developed all the time. Improvements in speed and storage capacity, and reductions in cost, are frequently announced. A variety of backing store media and devices are in use, the commonest of which are described in the following sections.

Magnetic Disks

Magnetic disks are the commonest way of storing data for access by computer. A magnetic disk is made of metal or plastic, coated with a layer of a magnetisable substance. Data is stored as small spots of magnetisation in one direction or the other.

Magnetic disks are made in a number of different sizes. At the top end of the range, with the highest storage capacity, are **exchangeable disk packs**, with a number of large disks mounted on a common shaft. These are generally used by mainframe systems. Next in the range are **single disk cartridges**, used mainly by mid-range computers. Microcomputers generally use diskettes (**floppy disks**), which are small, flexible disks made of plastic. A recent development is the **Winchester** disk. A Winchester disk is a high precision hard disk, with a high storage capacity. It is permanently mounted and sealed in its drive. Storage capacities range from a few **gigabytes** for a large disk pack to about one **megabyte** for a floppy disk (1 megabyte = 1 million bytes, 1000 megabytes = 1 gigabyte).

Magnetic disks generally store data on both surfaces. On each surface, data is arranged in concentric rings, or **tracks**. Corresponding tracks, directly above and below each other in a disk pack, form a **cylinder**. All the data in a cylinder can be reached without moving the read-write head of a magnetic disk drive. Each track is divided into units called blocks or **sectors**. A block is the unit of data transfer to or from a magnetic disk. The gaps between the sectors allow for movement of the read-write head. See Figure 14.1. To locate a block of data on a disk, it is necessary to know which surface it is on, which cylinder it is in, and the position of the block

A winchester disk, permanently mounted in its drive.

around the circumference of the disk. This information, generally expressed as a sequence of numbers, forms the **address** of the block. This disk address is very similar to the system of addressing in the main store of a computer.

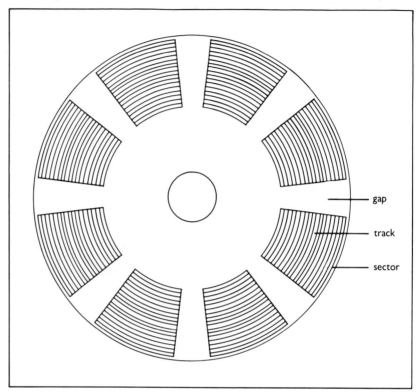

Figure 14.1
Data layout on a magnetic disk

Magnetic disks are made in a small number of standard sizes. The layout of data on each standard type of disk is generally the same. This makes it possible for an exchangeable magnetic disk to be used to transfer software or data from one computer system to another. For example, software for desktop computers is often distributed on magnetic disk.

A **magnetic disk drive** writes blocks of data to a magnetic disk, or reads blocks of data from the disk. The disk rotates at a high speed, and a **read-write head** moves very close to the surface of the disk to detect magnetised areas, or create them. Speeds of data transfer vary from a few thousand characters per second for floppy disk drives to more than a million characters per second for large disk drives.

There is, however, a delay in locating the data before transfer can commence. This delay has two components: the **seek time** while the read-write head moves to the required track, and the **latency** while the disk rotates until the required sector reaches the head. Latency is eliminated by transferring data to or from consecutive sectors, and seek time is reduced by transferring data to or from adjacent tracks or cylinders. Many disk drives have controllers which optimise head movements by careful control of the arrangement of data in tracks and cylinders, and handling requests for transfers in such a way as to reduce head movement.

The biggest problem affecting the use of magnetic disks is dust. Large magnetic disks are made of metal, machined to a very high precision. The gap betwen the surface of the disk, which rotates at a high speed, and the read-write head is very small. If a speck of dust is caught in the gap, it can cause a **disk crash**, damaging both the disk and the read-write heads. Floppy disk drives have read-write heads which rub against the surface of the disk. Dust can cause the disk to be scratched. Winchester disks are sealed in dust-free environments in their drives.

Magnetic Tape

Magnetic tape is the cheapest medium for storing large quantities of data. The tape is made of plastic, coated with a magnetic substance, and resembles ordinary sound recording tape. Magnetic tapes vary in length from several hundred to a few thousand feet. The longest tapes can store one hundred million characters. Workstations often use tape **cartridges** which contain a sealed length of tape on two spools. A recent development is low-cost magnetic tape units called **streamers**, whose sole purpose is to provide backup copies of magnetic disks, particularly Winchester disks.

Data is arranged on magnetic tape as magnetised spots set out in tracks running along the length of the tape. Eight-track tape is the commonest. Each data item is represented as a frame which is a set of magnetised spots running across the tracks. The unit of transfer of data to and from a magnetic tape is a **block**. Like a disk sector, a block is a physical unit of data, of a fixed number of frames for any particular computer system. Between successive blocks on a tape is a blank area known as an **inter-block gap**. The reason for this arrangement is that data can only be read from or written to a tape when it is running at full speed. The inter-block gaps are for the tape to be started up, slowed down or reversed.

Magnetic tape units transfer data to and from magnetic tape. They include spools for the tape, a read-write head, and, in many cases, **vacuum columns** to allow the tape to be started and stopped rapidly without snapping. Many magnetic tape units can read from or write to a tape when it is running in either direction.

Optical Disks

The most recent development in backing store technology is **optical disks**, also known as **CD-ROM** (for **compact disk read-only memory**). These are made of plastic, coated with a transparent layer. The surface beneath the transparent layer has data encoded by very small indentations, which can be read by a laser beam in an optical disk reader. Storage capacities are in the **gigabyte** range (one gigabyte is a thousand megabytes). At present, optical disks are read-only media, but the development of read/write optical disks is well advanced, using a combination of optical and magnetic disk technology. If these prove successful, they could make magnetic disks obsolete.

A CD-ROM disk and its drive.

14.5 Serial and Random Access to Data

■ There is a significant difference between magnetic disks and magnetic tape, which determines which is more suitable for a particular application. Magnetic tape is a **serial** access medium, while magnetic disks and optical disks are **random** or **direct** access media.

On a magnetic disk, blocks of data can be accessed (more or less) equally quickly, regardless of their positions on the disk. (Data items in the same cylinder or consecutive tracks can be accessed more quickly than data items in different cylinders. Nevertheless it is true to say that any block of data on a disk can be accessed in an acceptably short time for most purposes.) Together with the fact that blocks of data can be located by address, this means that files of a far more complex structure can be stored on magnetic disks than on magnetic tape.

On magnetic tape, the time taken to access a block of data depends on its position on the tape. The quickest way to access all the data on the tape is in the order in which it was written to the tape. This has a number of implications as far as the structure of files which can be stored on magnetic tape is concerned. This issue is discussed further in Chapter 27.

14.6 Interfacing Processors to Peripherals

■ Linking peripherals to a processor can be a complicated task. Several characteristics of a peripheral must be taken into account by a system designer, particularly:

• the character code used by the peripheral,
• the rate of transfer of data,
• the number of characters transferred in one operation.

Changing from the character code of the peripheral to that used by the processor is done either by the peripheral or the processor. In some cases a considerable amount of data conversion is required. For example, a bar code is detected as a sequence of wide and narrow bars, and is decoded into a thirteen-digit number, stored as a character code. Conversion to and from analogue data requires special hardware and software to control it. See Section 14.8.

In most cases the peripheral device works much more slowly than the processor. The aim of peripheral control systems is to transfer data in such a way as to minimise the delay and disruption to the processor. Many peripherals and their control systems now incorporate microprocessors and memory of their own. Laser printers are a good example – they often have a more powerful processor and a larger memory than the desktop computer to which they are connected. Large computers have separate front-end processors to handle transfers to and from peripherals.

The three main approaches to peripheral control are **polling**, **interrupts** and **autonomous peripheral operation**. If polling is used, the processor repeatedly checks the status of the peripheral to see whether it has an item or a block of data to transfer, or has completed a previous transfer. Interrupt-driven control allows the peripheral to operate at its own speed, and interrupt the operation of the processor when it has an item or a block of data to transfer to or from memory. Peripherals which operate autonomously have direct access to memory (DMA) and, once instructed by the processor, carry out a transfer entirely independently of it. Most disk drives operate in this way.

Data **buffers** are used to store blocks of data at various stages of transfer to or from a peripheral. A portion of main store is generally set aside for peripheral buffers, and most peripherals contain buffers of their own. In many cases the data passes through a series of buffers during a transfer. The size of the buffer generally corresponds to the number of characters passed to or from the peripheral in one operation. For example, the buffer for a line printer generally contains the number of characters in one line. Disk buffers hold one block of data.

Rapid transfers are achieved by **double buffering**, where the peripheral transfers a block of data to or from the one main store buffer while the processor deals with the other. The peripheral and processor then swap buffers to deal with the next block. The concept of buffering is taken further in some cases with spool files which hold large quantities of data in transit to of from a slow peripheral such as a printer or communications link.

The synchronisation and step-by-step control of peripheral devices is carried out by single-bit registers known as **flags**. A flag may be **set** (value 1) or **cleared** (value 0). For example, two flags may be used in the control of a line printer. When the printer buffer has been filled by the processor, one flag is set, to signal the printer to start printing the contents of the buffer. When the printing is complete, the printer sets the other flag. The flags are cleared once the signal has been noted.

Most microcomputers handle input and output through a **parallel input-output (PIO)** chip which deals with all peripheral devices except for the monitor. The PIO operates by setting and clearing flags, as described above.

The monitor in most desktop computer systems and workstations is linked directly to a reserved area of main store. The characters on the screen are copies of the characters in this memory area, which is known as a **map** of the screen. If the screen is displaying graphics, the pixels on the screen correspond to the bit patterns in the screen memory area. In other words, when a character or pixel is to be displayed on the screen, the code or bit pattern for it is written into the memory location corresponding to the desired position on the screen. This **bit map** in memory is a simple but extremely powerful method of interfacing the display screen to the processor.

It must be noted that all the problems of peripheral interfacing discussed in this section arise when the elements of a computer system are being selected for a particular application. None of these problems concern a user once a system has been assembled. All data conversion between peripheral devices and processor takes place automatically, and the differences in speeds between the different devices are dealt with by the software running the system. All the user is required to do is operate the equipment.

14.7 Automatic Checking During Data Transfer

■ Transfer of data to and from backing store media is a relatively error-prone operation. Accordingly, on many computer systems a number of checks are carried out automatically during these transfers. In addition to **parity checks**, discussed in Chapter 3, these checks include **read-after-write checks**, the use of **block sums**, and self-correcting codes such as **Hamming codes**.

A read-after-write check is carried out on most disk systems. After a block has been written to the disk, it is read back again and compared with the original, which is still in the transfer buffer. If the two versions do not match exactly, the data is written again. If the error persists, it is reported.

When a set of data items, such as a block, is transferred, a block sum or check sum is formed from the numeric value of the code for each data item. After the set of data and its check sum have been read, the check sum is again calculated. If the new value does not match the transferred value of the sum, then an error has occurred during transfer. In some cases an error is recorded as soon as this occurs. In other cases, the set of data is re-transferred and checked again. If a number of transfers are all unsuccessful, then an error is reported.

Hamming codes are binary codes, used to represent data items, which have a number of extra bits for checking purposes. The check bits are assigned in such a way that it is possible to detect and correct an error in the transmission of a single bit, and detect errors in the transmission of more than one bit. This is known as single error correction, **double error detection** (or **SECDED**). See Exercise 31.

14.8 Analogue Interfacing

■ Many computing and control systems are linked to input devices which take measurements in analogue form. These measurements are generally in the form of voltages, over a continuous range, which are proportional to some physical quantity such as temperature or acidity. These measurements are taken continuously.

A laboratory experiment using an analogue probe, which is linked via an analogue-to-digital converter to a computer

In order to be input into a computer system, these analogue measurements need to be converted into a digital form. This is done by an **analogue-to-digital converter** (**ADC**), which may be an integral part of the computer system, or (more often) a separate unit. Some ADCs are part of self-standing data loggers which input a number of channels of analogue data, convert to digital form and store it in integral RAM. Data is then transferred to the computer in blocks.

An ADC samples the analogue voltage at regular intervals, and converts these sampled voltages to digital signals, according to some suitable scale. The sampling rate is variable, and is generally controlled by the computer which is receiving the digital signals.

The reverse process is performed by a **digital-to-analogue converter** (**DAC**). This accepts a sequence of digital signals, and converts them to an analogue voltage, again using some suitable conversion factor.

The combination of analogue input and output with digital processing is extremely useful in a range of scientific and industrial applications, particularly those involving the monitoring and control of processes.

14.9 Conclusion

■ The most important point in this chapter is that the transfer of data between a processor and a peripheral device is a complex process. In many computer applications, it is the most time consuming activity carried out by the system. The speed of input and output, or the speed of transfer to or from backing store, is very often the limiting factor in the performance of a computer system. In most systems, the details of the transfer of data to and from peripheral devices are taken care of by the **operating system**. Operating systems are discussed in Chapters 22 and 23.

The main points of this chapter are as follows:

- Terminals are general-purpose input/output devices.
- Graphics terminals can display pictures as well as text on the screen.
- Methods of input include keyboards, mice, digitising pads, light pens, scanners, optical character recognition, magnetic ink character recognition, bar codes, magnetic strips and voice recognition.
- Output techniques include printers, digital plotters, computer output on microfiche and speech synthesis.
- The commonest backing store media are magnetic or optical disks (random access) and magnetic tape (serial access). In both cases, data is stored and transferred in blocks. Data on a magnetic disk is arranged in tracks and cylinders.
- Peripherals are controlled by polling, interrupts or autonomous peripheral operation, and data is transferred to or from them via buffers and sometimes spool files.
- A number of checks are carried out during transfer of data to or from peripherals.
- Interfacing between digital computers and analogue peripherals is achieved by means of analogue-to-digital converters (ADCs) and digital-to-analogue converters (DACs).

Exercise 14

1 Briefly define the following terms: medium; device; terminal; block; track; sector; cylinder; microfiche; disk crash; CD-ROM; serial access; random access; polling; interrupt; buffer; spool; flag; ADC; DAC.

2 A line printer outputs 600 lines per minute, each line comprising 120 characters. What is the average rate of output in characters per second?

3 A twenty megabyte disk is to be dumped onto magnetic tape, i.e. the entire contents of the disk is to be copied onto a magnetic tape. The data is in blocks each containing 1K of characters.
   a) How many blocks are there on the disk? (Assume that 1 megabyte = 1000K of characters).
   b) A 1K buffer is used for the transfer. At a transfer rate of 500K characters per second, how long does it take to fill the buffer from the disk? (Give your answer in microseconds, where 1 second = 1000 microseconds).
   c) At a transfer rate of 20K characters per second to the magnetic tape, how long does it take to empty the buffer to the tape?
   d) If there is an additional 15µs overhead on the transfer of each block, how long does the whole copying operation take?
   e) How much time is saved if a double buffer is used, so that one is being filled at the same time as the other is being emptied?

4 The transfer of a data item from a processor to a peripheral device is controlled by three flags, labelled A,B and C. The data item is loaded into a buffer by the processor, and removed from the buffer by the peripheral.
   Algorithms for the functioning of the processor and of the peripheral are as follows:

   Processor
   Repeat
       If flag A = 1, then set it to zero and continue else wait.
       If flag B = 1, then set it to zero and continue else wait.
       Load data item into buffer.

Set flag B to 1.
Set flag C to 1.
Peripheral
Repeat
If flag C =1, then set it to zero and continue else wait.
If flag B =1, then set it to zero and continue else wait.
Copy data item from buffer.
Set flag B to 1.
Set flag A to 1.

Initially, flags A and B are 1, and flag C is zero.

a) Write down the steps involved in transferring one character from the processor to the peripheral. State the values of the flags at each step.

b) By studying the algorithms, and from your answer to part (a), you will realise that the purpose of flag B is to protect the buffer while it is being loaded or unloaded. Briefly state the purposes of flags A and C.

c) If the peripheral works much more slowly than the processor, at which point will most of the waiting occur?

◆ 5 Write a program, in AMC machine language, to accept ten characters as input, and store them in consecutive memory locations. The first eight characters are data, the last two together are the check sum of the numeric value of the previous eight characters.

Having input the data, re-calculate the check sum and compare it with the input value. Output 1 if the check is successful , and 0 if the check fails.

6 Find out more details about some of the peripheral devices mentioned in this chapter, particularly ones which are relatively recent, such as voice recognition and speech synthesis systems, and optical disks.

7 A method of checking data, in addition to those mentioned in the text, is the **cyclic redundancy check** (**CRC**). Find out how this checking method works, and how it is used.

8 a) Explain briefly, in your own words, how an analogue-to-digital converter works.

b) If an ADC can accept analogue voltages in the range 0V to 5V, and converts them to 8-bit numbers, what is the resolution of the ADC (the voltage represented by the least significant bit of a digital quantity)?

15 Processor Case Studies

This chapter examines the topic of computer hardware from a practical point of view, by presenting case studies of a selection of computer processors. In choosing the case study computers, an attempt has been made to give an idea of the range in size and complexity of processors, while selecting ones which are up-to-date, widely used and regarded as having a sound architecture. Accordingly, the following four computers have been chosen:

> Research Machines Nimbus PC-386 desktop microcomputer,
> Digital Equipment VAX mid-range computer,
> ICL 2900 Series mainframe computer,
> Cray-2 supercomputer.

In the sections which follow, each computer is described in general terms, and then its register layout and machine language are discussed. The intention is to present the overall design features of each processor, and to show how the principles of processor architecture are put into practice in each case.

15.1 Research Machines Nimbus PC-386 Microcomputer

■ The RM Nimbus PC-386 is a desktop microcomputer based on the Intel 80386 SX microprocessor chip. It is built around the microchannel architecture (MCA) bus, making it compatible with the industry-standard IBM PC/2 range of computers. It can be used as a stand-alone system or as a network station.

The Nimbus PC-386 has one megabyte of RAM (extendable to 16 megabytes), and can support one or two 3.5 inch disk drives and a Winchester disk. Its high-resolution colour screen is compatible with the industry-standard IBM display modes (including VGA). It has a serial and a parallel port for peripheral connections. A mathematics co-processor (the Intel 80387) can be fitted for additional computational power.

In software terms, the Nimbus PC-386 can support the operating systems MS-DOS (Section 23.1), OS/2 (the IBM successor to MS-DOS) or Unix (Section 23.2). It can run software developed for the IBM PC range of computers (or compatible systems) or for earlier systems in the RM Nimbus range.

Overall Configuration

The Nimbus PC 386 system block diagram (Figure 15.1) shows the main functional units and their interconnections. These functional units are implemented in a small number of VLSI chips, making for a highly compact main board layout.

The main internal connection between the processor and the peripheral controllers is the MCA bus. This is designed for communication between a number of processors and peripheral units, and has facilities for different devices connected to the bus to take control of it. The bus has an external connection, allowing MCA expansion cards to be connected. This gives the system flexibility for a wide range of enhancements.

A Research Machines Nimbus PC-386 microcomputer.

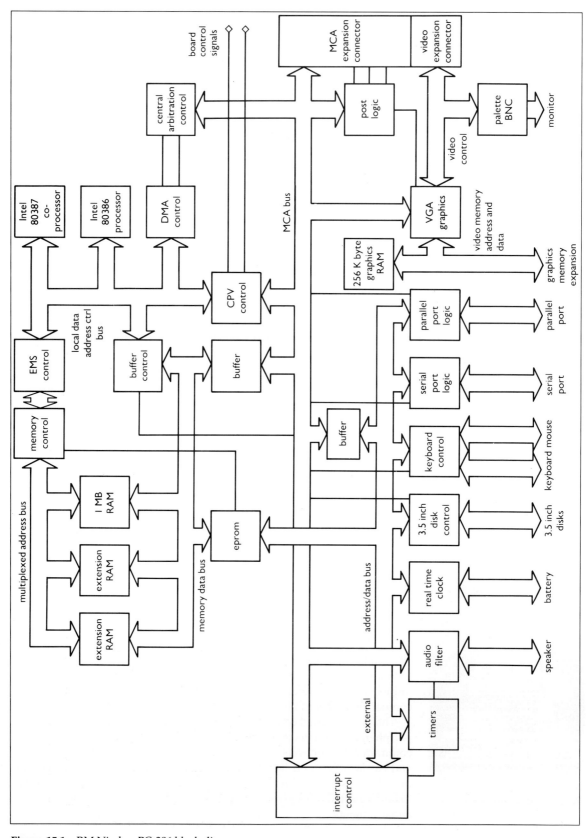

Figure 15.1 RM Nimbus PC-386 block diagram

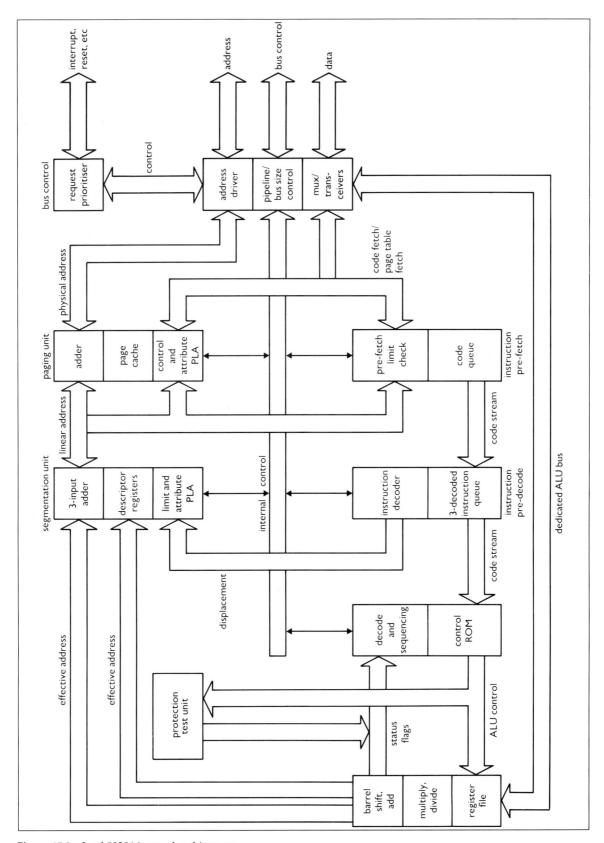

Figure 15.2 Intel 80386 internal architecture

Also shown in the system block diagram are the slots for add-on RAM boards, and the direct memory access (DMA) controller, which gives peripherals direct access to main memory (Section 13.3). The real-time clock is battery-powered, so that it continues to operate when the system is powered down. There is a separate 256K graphics memory, which speeds up the handling of screen graphics, and means that graphics do not use up main memory.

Intel 80386 SX Processor

The Intel 80386 SX microprocessor is a 32-bit processor with a 16-bit external data bus and a 24-bit external address bus. It is internally compatible with earlier Intel processors, notably the 8086, 80286 and 80386 DX. It makes use of advanced processor features such as internal pipelining to achieve an instruction throughput of up to 3 million instructions per second (mips).

The internal configuration of the 80386 is shown in Figure 15.2. Its processing unit consists of the instruction pre-fetch, instruction pre-decode, control and ALU modules. The memory management unit comprises a segmentation unit and a paging unit, which together support virtual addressing (Section 13.3). The bus interface connects the external address, data and control lines with the internal buses.

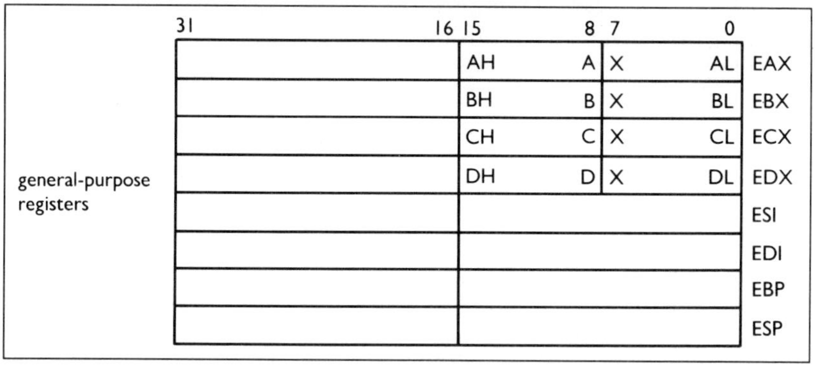

	31		16	15		8	7		0	
				AH	A	X		AL	EAX
				BH	B	X		BL	EBX
				CH	C	X		CL	ECX
general-purpose registers				DH	D	X		DL	EDX
									ESI
									EDI
									EBP
									ESP

Figure 15.3
Intel 80386 general-purpose registers

The register set includes eight 32-bit general purpose registers (Figure 15.3) which can be used as accumulators for arithmetic or logical data. Four of them can optionally be used as 16-bit registers, or split into pairs of 8-bit registers. Other registers in the set (not shown in Figure 15.3) include processor control flags, and segment registers used for the virtual memory.

Memory Organisation

The 80386 views memory as partitioned into bytes, 16-bit words or 32-bit double words. Addressing is per byte, with words and double words stored in consecutive bytes, with low-order bytes at the lowest address. Memory is also organised into 4K byte pages, and into **segments**, which are logical units of variable size, which can be swapped between memory and backing store in order to maintain the virtual memory.

There are three address spaces: the logical (or virtual) address, as seen by programs, the linear address space and the physical address space. The segmentation unit looks up the start address of the segment in which the logical address belongs, and translates the logical address into a 32-bit linear address, lying within the selected segment. If paging is not activated, this linear address is truncated to 24 bits to form the physical

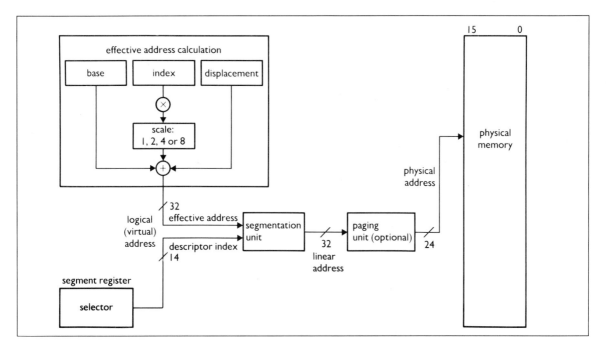

Figure 15.4
Intel 80386 address translation
mechanism

address. If paging is active, the address is looked up in the page table in order to produce the 24-bit physical address, which gives a real address space of 16 megabytes. Figure 15.4 shows the address translation mechanism.

The 80386 has two modes of memory access: **real mode** (designed for compatibility with earlier processors) and **protected mode**. In real mode, paging is disabled, and linear addresses (which are truncated to physical addresses) are limted to a one megabyte address range. In protected mode, paging may be active or inactive, and physical addresses may occupy the full 16 megabyte address space.

Data Types

The 80386 supports 18 data types, including all those commonly used by high-level languages. These are:
- an individual bit, a bit field of up to 32 bits, and a bit string which can (in theory) be up to 4 gigabits long.
- a signed or unsigned byte.
- a signed or unsigned integer (16 bits), long integer (32 bits) or quad word (64 bits).
- a pointer (16 or 32 bits) or long pointer which includes a segment selector (16 bits) and a pointer.
- an ASCII character occupying one byte, or a string of up to 4 gigabytes.
- a BCD digit which may be packed (two per byte) or unpacked (one per byte).
- a floating point number occupying 32, 64 or 80 bits. This data type is only available in conjunction with the 80387 mathematics co-processor.

Instruction Set

The 80386 instruction set has nine categories of operation, namely:

data transfer
arithmetic

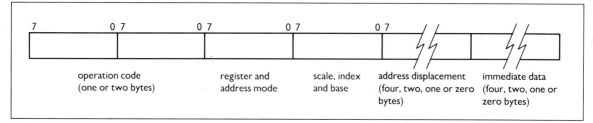

Figure 15.5
Intel 80386 machine instruction format

shift/rotate
string manipulation
bit manipulation
control transfer
high level language support
operating system support
processor control.

Instructions operate on zero, one, two or three operands, which may reside in a register, in memory or in the instruction itself. Instructions consist of a one-byte or two-byte operation code, followed optionally by a register and address mode specifier (two bytes), an address displacement (up to four bytes) or an immediate data item (up to four bytes). See Figure 15.5. Most zero-operand instructions occupy one byte only.

Addressing Modes

There are eight addressing modes, selected to allow for efficient execution of instructions compiled from popular high level languages. Two modes provide for operands in registers or in the instruction itself:

1 register operand mode specifies an operand in one of the general-purpose registers.
2 immediate operand mode specifies an operand contained within the instruction itself.

The remaining six addressing modes locate an operand by its segment base address and an effective address, which is a sum of any of the following:
- displacement, an 8, 16 or 32-bit offset within a segment,
- base, the contents of any general-purpose register, which may point to the start of a data area,
- index, the contents of any general-purpose register, used to access the elements in a string or array. The index is multiplied by a scale factor depending on the number of bytes in each array element.

The addressing modes are:

3 direct: use the displacement only.
4 register indirect: use the contents of the base register only.
5 based: add the contents of the base register to the displacement.
6 scaled index: multiply the index register contents by a scale factor, and add the result to the displacement.
7 based scaled index: multiply the index register contents by a scale factor, and add the result to the contents of the base register.
8 based scaled index mode with displacement: use the sum of the displacement, the contents of the base register and that of the index register multiplied by the scale factor.

Input/output

The 80386 processor has a 64K byte I/O address space for links to peripheral devices. This space may be regarded as 32K of 16-bit ports, or any combination of wider ports equivalent to 64K bytes. Data is output to a peripheral by writing it to its port, or read from a peripheral by reading it from its port. Peripherals mapped onto the main memory are also supported.

The I/O ports are accessed via the IN and OUT machine instructions, with the port address supplied. Port addresses are real addresses - there is no address transformation.

Assessment

The RM Nimbus PC-386 microcomputer is an industry-standard desktop microcomputer, using one of the most powerful single-chip microprocessors generally available, the Intel 80386 SX. The PC-386 is suited to a wide range of tasks, for commercial, scientific, engineering or educational applications. It supports the three most popular operating systems for computers in this range: MS-DOS, OS/2 and Unix, giving it access to a large number of software packages and tools for software development. Its networking capabilities give it further flexibility.

15.2 Digital Equipment VAX Mid-range Computer

A digital equipment VAX mid-range computer.

The VAX range of mid-range computers manufactured by Digital Equipment is a series of general-purpose computers, designed for commercial, industrial and research applications. The range was first introduced in 1980 as a successor to the popular PDP-11 series. Models in the range are upgraded at frequent intervals, but all are compatible at machine code level.

The name VAX - for **Virtual Memory eXtension** – emphasises the main architectural feature of the processor: the virtual memory, which gives each computer in the range a virtual address space of 4096 megabytes. The computers are designed to run in a multiprogramming environment, with any number of active processes loaded at any time.

Virtual Memory

The VAX computers have 32-bit virtual addresses, which mean that programs and data can be designed as if they were accessing a main store of 2^{32} bytes (4096 megabytes). This relieves designers of applications of the need to swap program and data segments between backing store and memory under program control. Although the physical memory of the computer is considerably less than its virtual address space, all memory transfers required to support the virtual memory are carried out by the memory management mechanism, under control of the operating system.

Both virtual and physical memory are regarded as sets of **pages**, where one page is 512 bytes. Each process running in the computer has a **page table** which relates virtual adresses to physical addresses. The virtual page number is used as an index to this table, which supplies the physical page address. The offset within the virtual page is the same as that within the physical page, and is appended to the physical page address to locate the memory location. The process of translating from a virtual to a physical address is illustrated in Figure 15.6.

The virtual memory also has a protection mechanism, based on four levels of privilege assigned to processes: kernel, executive, supervisor and user. The first two levels are reserved for the operating system, the third

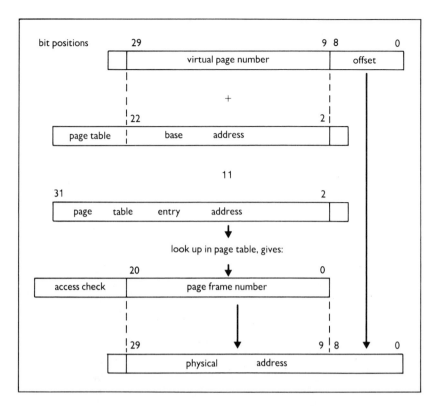

Figure 15.6
VAX virtual address
translation mechanism

is for certain users only, and the lowest level, user mode, is for applications. All memory accesses (to read or write data, or to execute code) are checked to ensure that they are permitted according to the level of privilege of the process requesting the memory access.

Data Representation

Seven types of data are represented directly on the VAX hardware: integer, floating point numeric, packed decimal, numeric string, character string, variable length bit field and queue. The lengths of the data items vary considerably: from 1 to 16 bytes for integers and packed decimal numbers, from 4 to 16 bytes for floating point numbers, and up to 64K bytes for character strings. Queues are equivalent to the linked list data types described in Section 4.8, with forward and backward pointers.

Register Structure

VAX computers have sixteen 32-bit registers, as illustrated in Figure 15.7. Some are used for special purposes, such as the Program Counter and Stack Pointer, others are for general use. The general-purpose registers may be regarded as accumulators, index registers, registers for indirect addressing, or any combination of these.

Instruction Set

The 256 machine instructions cover a wide range of numeric and string processing operations. The **operation code** occupies one or two bytes, and may be followed by one or more **operand specifiers**, each occupying between one and four bytes. The operation code implicitly specifies the type(s) of the operands, and each operand specifier includes the addressing mode to be used for that operand.

		Conventional Software Use
R15:PC	program counter	program counter
R14:SP	stack pointer	stack pointer
R13:FP	frame pointer	frame pointer
R12:AP	argument pointer	argument pointer
R11	general-purpose register	general purpose
R10	general-purpose register	general purpose
R9	general-purpose register	general purpose
R8	general-purpose register	general purpose
R7	general-purpose register	general purpose
R6	general-purpose register	general purpose
R5: AC	address counter	general purpose
R4: LC	length counter	general purpose
R3: AC	address counter	general purpose
R2: LC	length counter	general purpose
R1: AC/R	results/address counter	results of functions
R0: LC/R	results/length counter	results of functions

Figure 15.7
VAX register structure

Addressing Modes

There are sixteen addressing modes, which are **orthogonal** to the
operation code. In other words, any operand may have any addressing
mode (apart from a small number which are logically impossible, and
which are checked for by the hardware). Addressing modes include
direct, indirect and indexed addressing, addresses relative to the program
counter, and several which use a register for an index or indirect address
and then increase or decrease the contents of the register. The latter are
known as **autoincrement** and **autodecrement** addressing modes.

Some examples of VAX machine code instructions are as follows:

- Op Code   Operand 1   Operand 2

  00001000   0101 0001   0101 0010

Interpretation:

Operation Code: 00001000:			Move word
Operand 1:	Address Mode	0101:	Register
	Register Number:	0001	
Operand 2:	Address Mode	0101:	Register
	Register Number:	0010	

Move the word in Register 1 (the least significant 16 bits) to the least
significant 16 bits of Register 2.

- Op Code   Operand 1   Operand 2

  11010000   1000 0001   0101 0010

Interpretation:

Operation Code: 11010000:			Move long word
Operand 1:	Address Mode	1000:	Autoincrement

	Register Number:	0001	
Operand 2:	Address Mode	0101:	Register
	Register Number:	0010	

Move the long word (32 bits) whose address is in Register 1 to Register 2, and then increase the contents of Register 1 by 4 (the number of bytes in a long word). Register 1 now points to the next long word in memory.

Links to Peripheral Devices

Access to peripheral devices is provided by memory locations which contain control instructions to the peripheral and the data items being transferred. Device controllers transfer data to and from these locations by means of **interrupts**; programs can initiate transfers by means of **exception calls**. In both cases, control is transferred to a handling routine in the operating system, which runs at a higher priority than a user program. This routine supervises the data transfer, before returning control to the user program.

Assessment

The distinguishing features of the VAX range are the very large virtual address space, the flexible combination of special-purpose and general-

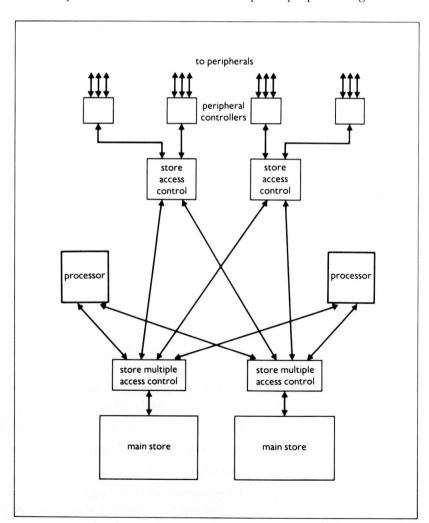

Figure 15.8
ICL 2900 series multiprocessor configuration

purpose registers, and the orthogonality of operation codes and addressing modes. Programs written for the PDP-11 computers can run on the VAX range, in most cases without any modifications.

In its time, the PDP-11 range was the most successful series of mid-range computers available; the VAX series has continued in this vein. VAX computers are very widely used, either running under the operating system supplied by Digital Equipment, or the Unix operating system (Section 22.2) which is becoming increasingly popular.

15.3
ICL 2900 Series
Computer

■ Designed and manufactured by International Computers Limited, the ICL 2900 series has the aim of creating a mainframe architecture which is the basis of a powerful, versatile hardware and software system. A particular objective is the efficient processing of machine code translated from a program in a high level language.

The design principles of the processor are implemented over a range of models in the 2900 series. The largest computers in the range are many times as powerful as the smallest. The largest models use hard-wired control, cache stores and pipelining, while smaller models make extensive use of microprogramming. Computers in the series can be configured in a number of ways. Large configurations have more than one processor. In all cases, peripheral devices and processors have independent access to main store, via **store multiple access controllers**. Figure 15.8 shows a large 2900 series configuration, including two processors.

Register Structure

Figure 15.9 shows the processor register structure and logical main store layout of the ICL 2900 series. The single accumulator can store 32, 64 or 128 bits, other registers are 32 bits wide. Broadly speaking, the ICL 2900 has a 32-bit wordlength.

The main store is partitioned in a fairly complex manner, because it is designed to be occupied by a number of programs (more properly called processes in this context) at the same time. Each process is allocated a separate portion of store, structured as a stack. Most addressing is relative to the base of the stack belonging to the particular process. Stacks are 32 bits wide.

Instruction Set

An ICL 2900 is basically a one-address computer, though a few two-address instructions are available to move data from one store location to another. Most addressing modes refer to various portions of the stack allocated to the particular process. Any data items not in this stack are accessed via a descriptor register. All addressing modes are available to all instructions. In this way, the address transformation hardware is kept separate from the instruction decoding hardware in the instruction pipeline.

Machine instructions are available for a wide range of fixed and floating point operations, including multiplication and division. Floating point numbers can occupy up to 128 bits. Packed decimal representation, using four bits per BCD digit, may also be used for the storing and processing of integers.

Memory Protection

Because the ICL 2900 main store is designed to be occupied by a number

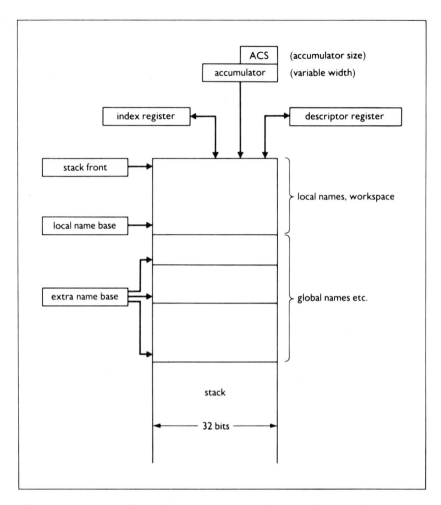

Figure 15.9
ICL 2900 register and main store structure

of processes at any time, it incorporates a sophisticated protection mechanism. This allows portions of processes to be shared, under strictly controlled conditions, while preventing errors in one process from corrupting the store area allocated to other processes, and making it almost impossible to 'break into' a process without authorisation.

The question of protection is discussed further in Chapters 22 and 23, on operating systems.

Assessment

The most significant features of the ICL 2900 processor architecture are its single accumulator, stack-oriented addressing and extensive use of cache stores and pipelining. The 2900 series architecture is an attempt to design a 'high level language' processor, suitable for multi-purpose configurations and interfacing to data communications networks. It reflects advanced concepts in computer design in these areas.

15.4 Cray-2 Supercomputer

■ The Cray-2 is a supercomputer designed for scientific and engineering applications. First marketed in 1985, Cray-2 computers are used for such diverse applications as weather forecasting, nuclear physics research, defence systems, structural analysis, economic modelling, electrical power distribution and very high resolution animated graphics.

A Cray-2 offers both **scalar processing** on individual numbers, and **vector processing** on arrays of numbers, wherever possible carrying out identical operations on each element of an array simultaneously. A number of the registers in a Cray-2 are vector registers - banks of registers, each containing a number. The vector register is regarded as a single unit in many operations. Most functional circuits are duplicated,

Figure 15.10
Cray-2 processor configuration

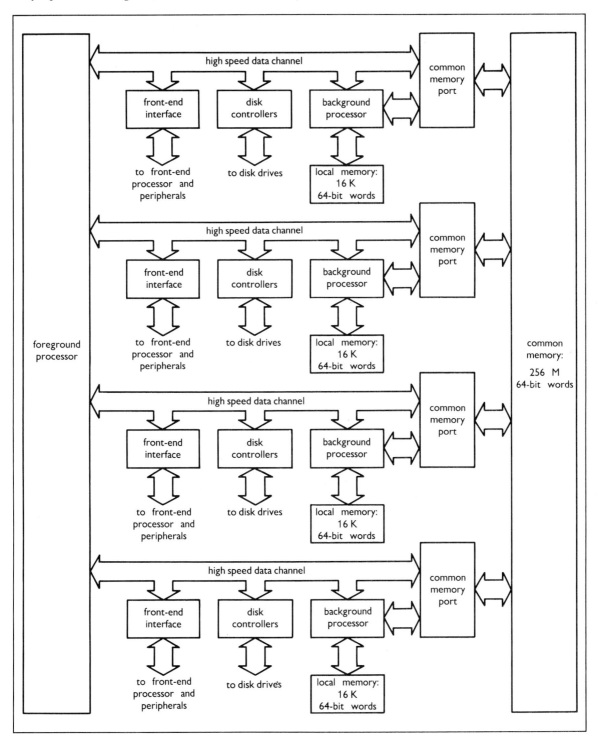

and many processing operations take place in parallel. A number of pipelines are provided, for multi-stage operations such as floating point multiplication. A very high transfer rate to and from memory is achieved, with a similar input/output transfer rate, to match the computational speeds.

Overall Configuration

A Cray-2 mainframe consists of a **foreground processor** and four identical **background processors** working in parallel. The foreground processor is in overall control, sharing work amongst the background processors, and providing the external interface to backing store and the front-end processors which control other peripherals. All processors have access to a common memory of 256 million 64-bit words. Four high-speed data channels connect the common memory to the processors, disk controllers and front-end interfaces. The total rate of transfer of data to and from the common memory is one billion 64-bit words per second.

Each background processor has a local memory containing 16K of 64-bit words. Local memory is used as a programmable cache store, and has faster access times and transfer rates than those of the main memory. Each background processor operates at a cycle time of 4.1 nanoseconds. Figure 15.10 shows the overall configuration of processors and memory.

A Cray-2 processor uses a quarter of a million VLSI chips, closely packed on some 750 three-dimensional carrier modules. All carrier modules are of a standard size. Because of the close packing of components, Cray processors are liquid cooled, using an inert liquid with a high thermal capacity. The computer continuously monitors the performance of all its components. A maintenance control console allows faults to be monitored and rectified.

Register Structure

Figure 15.11 shows the registers, functional units and memory links of a Cray-2 background processor. The processor is divided into an **instruction section**, an **address section**, a **scalar section** for individual data items, and a **vector section** for arrays of data items. Each section has its own registers and functional units, and uses the local memory as a cache store. All functional units operate independently of each other, and are all internally pipelined. This configuration provides several dimensions of parallelism.

The significant features of the Cray-2 architecture are its very large common memory, parallel processors and the vector processing circuits within each processor. Each of the eight vector registers holds an array of 64 data items, each 64 bits in length. Successive elements from a vector register enter a functional unit in successive clock periods. The vector and scalar registers share the floating point functional units, which do addition and multiplication, and calculation of reciprocals and square roots. The vector length register holds the number of elements (between 1 and 64) to be processed in a vector operation. The vector mask has 64 bits, each corresponding to one element of a vector register. In a vector test instruction, each bit is set according to the result of the test for the corresponding element. The bits also control the selection of vector elements for logical operations.

Each of the eight buffers in the instruction cache can contain 64 consecutive instructions. Instructions occupy 16 bits; addresses, which may be stored either in the instruction buffers or in the address registers,

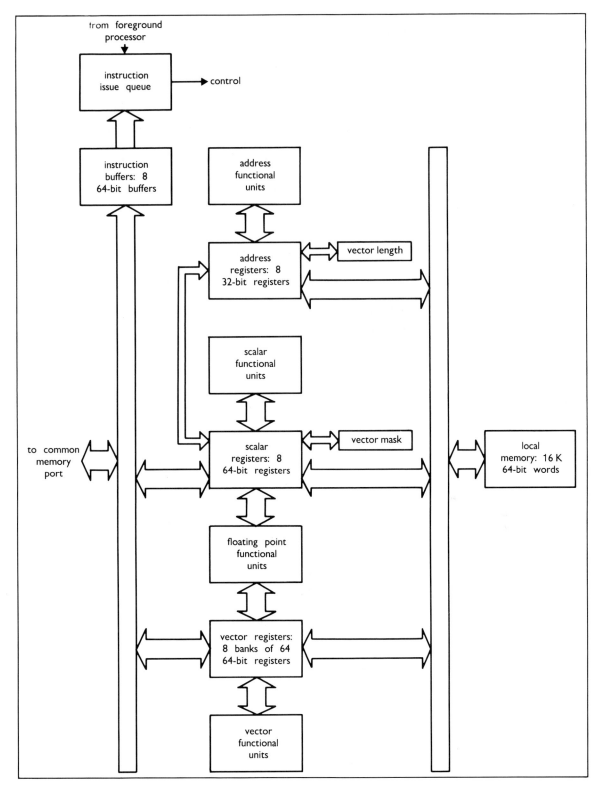

from foreground
processor

instruction
issue queue

→ control

instruction
buffers: 8
64-bit buffers

address
functional
units

address
registers: 8
32-bit registers

vector length

scalar
functional
units

scalar
registers: 8
64-bit registers

vector mask

to common
memory
port

floating point
functional
units

vector registers:
8 banks of 64
64-bit registers

vector
functional
units

local
memory: 16 K
64-bit words

Figure 15.11
Cray-2 background processor:
register configuration

comprise 32 bits. This means that program loops, provided that they are
reasonably short, can be executed without reference to main store.

The common memory consists of 128 banks, each of which has
independent access to each of the four memory ports. The ports in turn

are linked to the four high-speed data channels which connect the various elements of the system. In the common memory, each 64-bit word has an additional eight check bits. The check bits enable a single error to be corrected and a double error to be detected in the word (SECDED - see Section 14.7).

Instruction Set

The Cray-2 has 128 machine instructions in 11 groups, each instruction comprising a 16-bit operation code, some of which are followed by up to four 16-bit address or data specifications. Data items referred to by instructions may be addresses, scalars or vectors.

Instructions which transfer data to or from local memory are one-address instructions; those transferring to or from common memory may be one-address or two-address. Data may be transferred as single items (scalars) or arrays of items (vectors). It is possible to gather data from different parts of memory into one set of vector registers, and to scatter the data in a vector to different memory addresses. Instructions which process data refer to scalar or vector registers only. Arithmetic operations include addition, subtraction, multiplication and calculation of reciprocals, on integers and floating point numbers. Logical and shift operations are also provided.

Some examples of Cray-2 machine instructions are as follows:

Instruction (Octal)	Interpretation
014xjx <Address>	Branch to the address following the operation code if the contents of Scalar Register j is zero.
036xxk	Set the Vector Length Register (VL) to the value of the contents of Address Register k. All subsequent vector operations will use this value until VL is next altered.
070ijk	Read VL words from common memory, starting at the address in Address Register j, taking items at address intervals specified in Address Register k, and transferring the data items to Vector Register i.
072ijk	Gather from the VL memory locations at addresses with base in Address Register k, and offsets in Vector Register j, placing the data items in Vector Register i. (The address of the first data item is the sum of Address Register k and the first element in Vector Register j.)
155ijk	Multiply the VL corresponding floating-point numbers in Vector Registers j and k, placing the products in Vector Register i.

The Cray-2 may be programmed in its assembly language, or in Fortran (Section 19.1), Pascal (Section 19.5) or C (Section 19.6). The compilers for the high level languages are written to produce machine code which makes the best use of the vector architecture of the processors. Programmers may provide additional information to assist the compilers

(Chapter 20) in producing optimal machine code. Multitasking facilities are available so that programs can include modules which are executed in parallel on different background processors.

Links to Peripheral Devices

The four high-speed communication channels provide direct access by disk controllers to foreground and background processors and common memory. Other peripherals are linked to the system through the front-end interfaces, and may use separate front-end processors. All transfers of data between common memory and peripherals are carried out independently of the foreground and background processors.

Assessment

Distinguishing features of the Cray-2 are its multiple processors containing vector registers and processing circuits, the high degree of parallelism in its design, and its extensive use of pipelining. Its very large common memory, with four parallel access ports, means that most computation takes place using data already loaded into memory. Its flexibility of use - a program may use any or all of the background processors - broadens its potential range of applications. The Cray-2 is a specialised numerical processing computer. Static data structures like arrays can be handled directly at machine level, but there is little hardware provision for dynamic structures such as trees or linked lists.

The Cray-2 was the most powerful computer of its time. It was a milestone in scientific computing, and its architecture indicates clearly the prevalent trends in large computer systems design.

15.5 Conclusion

■ This survey of a few selected computer architectures has given some idea of the wide variety of ways in which the principles of computer design are put into practice. It shows the range in size and complexity, from a microcomputer to a supercomputer. It also brings to light a few differences of opinion on issues of computer design. For example should registers be dedicated to a specific task, or general-purpose?

However, there are a number of underlying similarities, common to these (and most other) contemporary processor architectures. These include the following:

- A centralised main store, from which both instructions and data can be drawn.
- An addressing mechanism, whereby instructions and data items are located in the main store.
- A place where instructions are decoded, to become sequences of pulses along control lines.
- Functional circuits which perform arithmetic and logical operations.

This chapter concludes the part of the book concerned with computer hardware. This part has described the structure and functioning of a computer at the very lowest level, namely registers, processing circuits and machine language. The next part of this book works outwards from this 'core' level, describing the various layers of software which surround the hardware of a computer, transforming it into a useful machine.

Exercise 15

1 Distinguish between general-purpose and dedicated registers. For each of the case study computers in this chapter, list the general-purpose and special-purpose registers.

2 State whether each case study computer is a one-address or a two-address computer.

3 Which features of the case study computers are also to be found in the AMC? In the light of your study of the AMC, state why you think each feature is included in its architecture.

4 Which of the case study computers use pipelining?

5 Consider the following Cray-2 machine instruction:

Instruction (octal)	Interpretation
161123	Add corresponding integers in Vector Register 2 and Vector Register 3, and store the sums in Vector Register 1.

In Exercise 10 there is a program , in AMC machine language, which performs an equivalent process on vectors in the AMC memory.

a) How many AMC instructions are equivalent to this Cray-2 instruction?

b) The Cray-2 instruction takes (number of array elements + 3) clock periods to execute. Assume that AMC instructions take 8 or 16 clock periods to execute, depending on whether they occupy one or two words.

If each array contains 64 elements, work out the number of clock periods required by each processor. Comment on your results, bearing in mind that a Cray-2 clock period is about one hundredth of the length of a feasible AMC clock period.

6 Which of the case study computers makes the most extensive use of a stack in its memory arrangement? Suggest which of the design objectives of the particular computer is the reason for this.

7 Discuss the extent of parallelism in the architecture of each of the case study computers. In each case, describe how parallel processing assists in achieving the design aims of the processor.

◆ 8 Find out the current prices of the four case study computers. Comment on their relative prices by comparison with their relative performancees.

◆ 9 By obtaining manufacturer's literature, carry out a case study of your own on a suitable computer. Write a report on the processor, in about as much detail as the ones in this chapter. Some suggested computers are:

Microcomputers: IBM PC/2, Apple Macintosh.
Workstations: Sun 3 and Sun 4 series.
Mid-range computers: Hewlett-Packard series, Prime series, Data General Eclipse.
Mainframes: IBM 3000 series, Unisys 6000 series.
Supercomputers: Cray Y/MP, CDC Cyber 205.

16 Assembly Languages

This is the first chapter in the part of the book devoted to computer software. An item of software, or a program, is a set of instructions to a computer, which transforms it from a general-purpose collection of hardware into a machine dedicated to a particular task. As you will see during this and the following chapters, the task of some programs is to set up a computer to be able to run other programs. Accordingly, software may be regarded as layers, surrounding the hardware of a computer, and bridging the gulf between the hardware and a user-oriented machine. Figure 16.1 illustrates this idea.

This chapter concerns a class of programming languages called **assembly languages**. It explains their nature and objectives, and outlines their development. Features of assembly languages are introduced, using the assembly language of the AMC as an example.

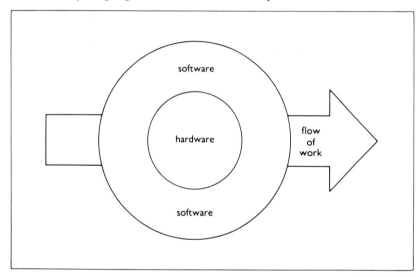

Figure 16.1
Hardware and software

16.1 The Nature and Objectives of Assembly Languages

■ In Chapter 12, a class of programming languages called machine languages was introduced. The step-by-step control of a computer is achieved through instructions in the particular machine language of the computer. Having studied this chapter, and having tried out some machine language programs, you will realise how slow and difficult it is to program a computer in its machine language.

Assembly languages have come into being to overcome these difficulties. Broadly speaking, the objective of an assembly language is to simplify the programming of a particular computer, while still enabling the programmer to control the hardware of the computer directly. An assembly language may be defined as a programming language whose data structures correspond to the physical structure of the registers and main store of its host computer, and whose instructions are closely related to the machine instructions of the computer.

From this it follows that each type of computer has its own assembly language, which is not too far removed from its machine language. Machine languages and assembly languages are together known as **low**

level languages. This is because they are both close to the architecture of the computer which supports them.

16.2 The Development of Assembly Languages

■ In their most primitive form, assembly languages are almost as old as digital electronic computers. The first computers, produced in the period 1945 to 1950, could initially only be programmed in machine language. Although programming in those days was confined to a small group of specialists, writing out programs in binary code and personally allocating each memory cell soon proved far too cumbersome and error-prone.

Assembly languages quickly began to evolve out of machine languages, with additional features being added as time went by. At first they were just a character representation of machine code. Then features such as symbolic addressing, automatic conversion of data, directives and macro-instructions (discussed in this chapter) were added, in different ways on different computers. The confusion caused by the piecemeal development of assembly languages was one of the incentives for the development of high level languages, starting in about 1955. Since then, the nature and objectives of assembly languages have become better understood. These languages have generally been simplified and their structure improved.

16.3 Features of Assembly Languages

■ Although assembly languages differ considerably from one type of computer to another, they generally have the following features in common: **mnemonic operation codes**, **symbolic addresses**, **automatic data conversion**, **directives** and **macros**.

Mnemonic Operation Codes

To preserve a close relationship to the architecture of its host computer, an assembly language includes a set of instructions which are in one-to-one correspondence with the machine language of the computer. In other words, for every machine language instruction, there is an assembly language instruction.

Whereas machine language instructions are written in binary, octal or hexadecimal notation, assembly language instructions use a group of letters for the operation code. This group of letters is known as a **mnemonic**. For example, the instruction to stop a program in AMC machine language and assembly language is as follows:

AMC machine language   AMC assembly language
8500   HLT

Symbolic Addresses

In machine language, the address of a data item or instruction is expressed as a number, in binary, octal or hexadecimal notation. This involves great inconvenience, particularly when indexed or relative addressing is used, or when the location of the program in the computer memory is not known. Assembly languages overcome this problem by the use of **symbolic addresses**. A symbolic address is a group of characters which represents the address of an instruction or data item.

For example:

AMC machine language	AMC assembly language	Interpretation
1312 00AB	ADD A NUM	Add the number at address 00AB, symbolic address NUM, to the accumulator.

Notice how the accumulator is also identified by a symbol, the letter A.

In order to associate the symbolic address with the data item or instruction to which it refers, the address is used to label the data item or instruction. The following program segment illustrates the idea of a label.

AMC machine language	AMC assembly language	Interpretation
	NM1 WRD	Location storing a number.
1A12 0002	CMP A NM1	Compare number in accumulator with number at address NM1.
6404	BGE DWN	Branch to instruction labelled DWN if greater than or equal to zero.
1112 0002	LOA NM1	Load number at NM1 to accumulator.
4110	DWN PSH A	Push number in accumulator onto stack.

Notice how the symbolic address NM1 labels the memory location storing the number, and the symbolic address DWN labels the instruction to which control is transferred by the BGE instruction.

The above program segment compares a number in the accumulator with one at address NM1, and pushes the larger of these numbers onto the stack.

Automatic Data Conversion

If the value of a data item is used in a machine language program, for example, as an immediate operand, then this value must be in the same notation as the rest of the machine language, namely binary, octal or hexadecimal code. In assembly languages, the value of a data item can generally be expressed as a decimal number, or as a set of characters. The characters are interpreted in a character code such as ASCII. For example:

AMC machine language	AMC assembly language	Interpretation
1121 0010	LOA X N +16	Load the number 16 to the index register.
1111 4243	LOA A N /BC/	Load the characters BC to the accumulator.

Notice how the letter N is used to denote an immediate operand.

Directives

In addition to instructions which correspond directly to the machine instruction set of the particular computer, assembly languages have certain instructions which operate at a slightly higher level. These are known as **directives**, or **pseudo-operations**, and have no direct counterpart in machine language. Directives greatly enhance the power of the assembly language, making the computer easier to program at this level.

Among the tasks performed by directives are marking the end of a program, which may be nowhere near a halt instruction, and reserving space for data items. AMC assembly language used the directives **BTE** and **WRD** to reserve space for a byte and a word of data. For example:

AMC assembly language	Interpretation
NM1 WRD +35	Reserve a word for a data item, loaded with the value 35, and with symbolic address NM1.

Macros

A macro, more properly called **macro-instruction**, is a single instruction which represents a group of instructions. A macro-instruction is defined at the start of a program by listing the set of instructions which it is to represent. Whenever the macro-instruction is subsequently used in the program, it represents the entire set of instructions previously defined.

For example, supposing a certain assembly language does not have an instruction which negates the number in the accumulator, but that the following two instructions would achieve this:

STO A TMP	Store number in accumulator in location TMP.
NEG A TMP	Negate the number in location T.MP into the accumulator.

A macro-instruction **NGA**, negate accumulator, could be defined in terms of these instructions as follows:

NGA MCD	Define a macro-instruction named NGA.
STO A TMP	
NEG A TMP	
EDM	End of macro definition.

The two directives **MCD** and **EDM** are used to start and end the macro definition. Whenever the instruction **NGA** is subsequently used in the

M addressing node:	N immediate operand (blank) absolute address	
	I indirect address	
	D indexed address	
R register identifier:	A accumulator	
	X index register	
	S stack pointer	
ADR	symbolic address	
OPD	operand	
P peripheral device	T terminal	
effects on condition codes:	S set (becomes 1)	
	C cleared (becomes 0)	
	N no effect	
	D conditional upon result	
condition codes:	Z zero	
	N negative	
	C carry	
	V overflow	

Figure 16.2
AMC assembly language

164 Assembly Languages

instruction			interpretation	Z	N	C	V
memory addressing group							
LOA R M		OPD	load data word to register	D	D	N	N
LOB R M		OPD	load data byte to register	D	D	N	N
STO R M		OPD	store register word in memory	D	D	N	N
STB R M		OPD	store register byte in memory	D	D	N	N
ADD R M		OPD	add data word to register	D	D	D	D
ADB R M		OPD	add data byte to register	D	D	D	D
ADC R M		OPD	add data word and carry bit to register	D	D	D	D
ACB R M		OPD	add data byte and carry bit to register	D	D	D	D
SUB R M		OPD	subtract data word from register	D	D	D	D
SRB R M		OPD	subtract data byte from register	D	D	D	D
SBC R M		OPD	subtract (data word plus carry bit) from register	D	D	D	D
SCB R M		OPD	subtract (data byte plus carry bit) from register	D	D	D	D
AND R M		OPD	AND data word with register	D	D	C	C
ANB R M		OPD	AND data byte with register	D	D	C	C
ORR R M		OPD	OR data word with register	D	D	C	C
ORB R M		OPD	OR data byte with register	D	D	C	C
NEQ R M		OPD	NEQ (exclusive OR) data word with register	D	D	C	C
NQB R M		OPD	NEQ (exclusive OR) data byte with register	D	D	C	C
CMP R M		OPD	compare register with data word	D	D	D	D
CPB R M		OPD	compare register with data byte	D	D	D	D
register transfer group							
MOV R_1 R_2			move from register 1 to register 2	D	D	N	N
register manipulation group							
CLR R			clear register	S	C	C	C
INC R			increment register (increase by 1)	D	D	D	D
DEC R			decrement register (decrease by 1)	D	D	D	D
ROR R			rotate register right, 1 bit, via carry bit	D	D	D	D
ROL R			rotate register left, 1 bit, via carry bit	D	D	D	D
ASR R			arithmetic shift right, one bit	D	D	D	D
ASL R			arithmetic shift left, one bit	D	D	D	D
COM R			complement register	D	D	D	D
NEG R			negate register (NOT operation)	D	D	C	C
stack manipulation group							
PSH R			push register word onto stack	D	D	D	N
POP R			pop top of stack word to register	D	D	N	N
jumps							
JMP		ADR	unconditional jump to specified address	N	N	N	N
JSR		ADR	jump to subprogram, stack return address	N	N	N	N
branches							
BRN		ADR	unconditional branch	N	N	N	N
BZE		ADR	branch if zero (Z = 1)	N	N	N	N
BNE		ADR	branch if non-zero (Z = 0)	N	N	N	N
BGE		ADR	branch if greater than or equal to zero (Z = 1 or N = 0)	N	N	N	N
BGT		ADR	branch if greater than zero (Z = 0 and N = 0)	N	N	N	N
BLE		ADR	branch if less than or equal to zero (Z = 1 or N = 1)	N	N	N	N
BLT		ADR	branch if less than zero (N = 1)	N	N	N	N
BCC		ADR	branch if carry clear (C = 0)	N	N	N	N
BCS		ADR	branch if carry set (C = 1)	N	N	N	N
BVC		ADR	branch if overflow clear (V = 0)	N	N	N	N
BVS		ADR	branch if overflow set (V = 1)	N	N	N	N
BIN		ADR	branch if input not complete	N	N	N	N
BON		ADR	branch if output not complete	N	N	N	N
input/output group							
IRQ P			signal peripheral device to load input register	N	N	N	N
INP R			copy byte from input register to register R	D	D	N	N
ORQ P			signal peripheral device to unload output register	N	N	N	N
OUP R			copy byte from register R to output register	D	D	N	N
miscellaneous operations							
STC			set carry bit	N	N	S	N
CLC			clear carry bit	N	N	C	N
RTS			return from subprogram (unstack return address)	N	N	N	N
NUL			no - operation	N	N	N	N
HLT			halt	N	N	N	N

Figure 16.2
AMC assembly language
(Continued)

program, it is replaced by the instructions in the above definition. Macros are an extremely powerful feature of most assembly languages, but are not implemented in AMC assembly language. Macros are also used in some operating system command languages. See Section 21.7.

■ AMC assembly language has been specifically designed for this course. It is simple, but fairly powerful, and illustrates the principal features of assembly languages.

Mnemonic Operation Codes

The operation code for an AMC assembly language instruction consists of three letters. A complete list of these codes is in Figure 16.2. If the operation refers to a register, a further letter is used to identify the register, as follows:

A	accumulator
X	index register
S	stack pointer

For example:

CLR A	Clear accumulator.
MOV X S	Copy from index register to stack pointer.

Symbolic Addresses

In AMC assembly language, a symbolic address consists of up to three characters. The first character must be a letter, the others can be letters or numbers. In addition, there is a letter for the addressing mode, as follows:

N	immediate operand
(blank)	absolute address
I	indirect address
D	indexed address

For example:

LOB A D CHR	Load the byte at address (CHR+Index) to the accumulator.
STO S I RES	Store the contents of the stack pointer at the address contained in the location with address RES.
ADD A NM1	Add the number at address NM1 to the accumulator.

Automatic Data Conversion

The value of a data item can be included in an AMC assembly language program in one of two ways, as follows:

1 An integer may be written as a signed decimal number.
2 A literal data item may be written as one or two characters, between the symbols / /, for example / I T /. (Remember that one character occupies a byte, and two characters occupy a word.)

Data items written in this way in a program are called **immediate operands**, or **constants**. Some examples of instructions using constants are as follows:

ADD X N +32	Add 32 to the contents of the index register.
LOB A N /J/	Load the character J to the accumulator.

Note that if a constant is used in a program instruction, the addressing mode must be immediate operand.

Directives

AMC assembly language has three directives, with mnemonics BTE, WRD, and END. They are used as follows:

BTE	reserves a byte of store for a data item.
WRD	reserves a word of store for a data item.

In each case, the value of the data item may be included as a constant, as described in the previous section.

END	marks the end of the program. It must be placed after all the other directives and instructions in the program.

Instruction Format

The spacing of an AMC assembly language instruction is important. There is a specific **field** for each part of the instruction. These fields are shown in Figure 16.3. If a field is not required in a particular instruction, it is left blank.

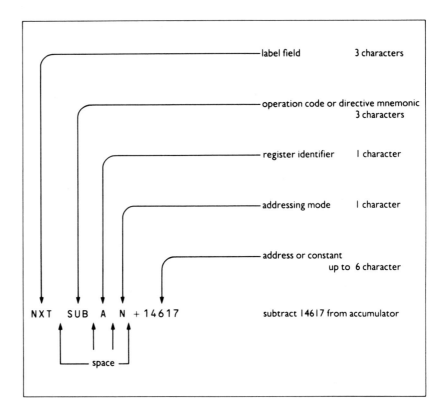

Figure 16.3
AMC assembly language
instruction format

16.5 Example Program 16.1

■ The objective of this program is to input a sequence of characters, and store them in consecutive location in the AMC memory. The end of the input is marked by the character *. Apart from the end-of-input marker, this program is identical to Example Program 12.1, in AMC machine language. It enables a comparison to be made between the two levels of language. For details of the method, see Chapter 12.

Program

PTR	WRD	CHR	Address of first character, later of current character.

Start of Loop

AGN	IRQ	T		Signal terminal to load character into input register.
HRE	BIN		HRE	Branch back to this instruction if input not complete.
	INP	A		Copy character from input register to accumulator.
	CPB	A N	/*/	Compare character with end-of-input marker.
	BZE		OUT	Branch if equal, to instruction labelled OUT.
	STB	A I	PTR	Store character at address in location PTR.
	LOA	A	PTR	Load address of current character to accumulator.
	INC	A		Increase contents of accumulator by 1.
	STO	A	PTR	Store address of next character in location PTR.
	BRN		AGN	Branch to instruction labelled AGN, to input next character.

End of Loop

OUT	HLT		Halt.

Start of Data Area

CHR	BTE		Space for first character.
	END		End of program.

Points to Notice

- It is most likely that this program is much easier to follow than its machine language equivalent.
- The address of the current character is in a location labelled PTR, short for pointer. This address may be said to point to the current character.
- Notice how the assembly language program is set out in columns.
- Apart from the directives, there is a one-to-one correspondence between instructions in assembly language and instructions in machine language.

16.6 Example Program 16.2

■ As discussed in Section 4.8, one method of constructing a list of data items is as follows:

Each element of the list consists of a data item and a pointer. The pointer holds the address of the next list element. The last element in the list has an end-of-list marker for its pointer value.

This example program assumes that a list, structured in this way, has been loaded into the AMC memory. Each list element consists of a byte storing the data item (one character), and a word storing the pointer to the next list element. The end-of-list marker is a zero pointer.

The objective of the example program is to output the data items in the list, given the address of the start of the list. The method is to output a data item, and then use the next word in store as an indirect address to locate the next data item.

Program

PTR	WRD	LE1	Address of first list item, later address of current list item.

Start of Program Loop

NXT	LOB	A I	PTR	Load current list item to accumulator, using location PTR as an indirect address.
HRE	BON		HRE	Branch to this instruction if output not complete.
	OUP	A		Copy current list item to output register.
	ORQ	T		Request terminal to output current list item.
	LOA	A	PTR	Load address of current list item to accumulator.
	INC	A		Increment accumulator, to become address of pointer part of current list item.
	STO	A	PTR	Store address of pointer part of list item.
	LOA	A I	PTR	Load pointer part of list item to accumulator.
	BZE		OUT	Branch to end of program if pointer is zero.
	STO	A	PTR	Store pointer part of list item, i.e. address of next list item.
	BRN		NXT	Branch to instruction labelled NXT to continue.

End of Program Loop

OUT	HLT			Halt.

Data Area

LE2	BTE	/B/	Second list element.
	WRD	LE3	Pointer to third element.
LE1	BTE	/A/	First list element.
	WRD	LE2	Pointer to second element.
LE3	BTE	/C/	Third list element.
	WRD	+0	End-of-list marker.
	END		End of program.

Points to Notice

- Notice carefully how indirect addressing is used to go from one list item to the next.
- The pointer part of each list element contains the address of the next list element.
- The portion of program from the instruction labelled NXT to the instruction BRN NXT is repeated once for each list element. This loop is ended when a zero pointer is found in a list element.

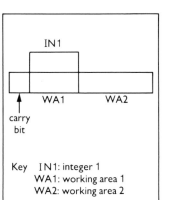

Figure 16.4
Working areas for multiplication algorithm

Key IN1: integer 1
     WA1: working area 1
     WA2: working area 2

16.7 Example Program 16.3

■ In Chapter 5, an algorithm is given for the multiplication of two unsigned integers, by a process of shifting and addition. This program puts the algorithm into practice.

The algorithm is given again below, using slightly different notation. The layout of the working areas used by the program is shown in Figure 16.4. Three words of store are used for these working areas in the program, but it is helpful to imagine them set out as in the diagram.

Algorithm

Initially, the carry bit and working area 1 contain zeros, while integer 1 and working area 2 contain the two numbers to be multiplied.
Repeat, for each bit of the numbers

Mask out all but the least significant bit of working area 2.

If the least significant bit is 1, then add integer 1 to working area 1, placing the sum in working area 1, and the carry in the carry bit.

Shift all the bits in the carry bit, working area 1 and working area 2 one place to the right.

When this process is complete, the product of the two numbers is in working area 1 and working area 2.

Program

IN1	WRD	+31465	Integer 1, with value declared.
WA1	WRD	+0	Working area 1: initially zero, finally most significant word of product.
WA2	WRD	+15437	Working area 2: initially integer 2, finally least significant word of product.

Start of Program

	LOA X N	+16	Initialise index register to 16. The index register is used to count the number of bits processed.
	LOA A	WA2	Load accumulator with working area 2.

Start of Loop

NXT	AND A N	+1	Mask all but least significant bit of accumulator.
	BZE	OVR	Branch if result is zero, to instruction labelled OVR.
	LOA A	WA1	Load accumulator with working area 1.
	ADD A	IN1	Add integer 1 to accumulator.
	BRN	DWN	Branch to instruction labelled DWN.
OVR	LOA A	WA1	Load accumulator with working area 1.
	CLC		Clear carry bit.
DWN	ROR A		Rotate accumulator right, 1 bit, via carry bit.
	STO A	WA1	Store new value of working area 1.
	LOA A	WA2	Load working area 2 to accumulator.
	ROR A		Rotate accumulator right, 1 bit, via carry bit.
	STO A	WA2	Store new value of working area 2.
	DEC X		Decrease index register by 1.
	BGT	NXT	Branch if index is still positive, to continue shifting and adding.

End of Loop

HLT		Halt.
END		End of program.

Points to Notice

- The carry bit is used to pass a bit from working area 1 to working area 2 during the rotation operation. In the first rotation operation, the least significant bit of working area 1 moves into the carry bit. In the second rotation, the same bit moves from the carry bit into the most significant bit position of working area 2.
- This program contains a loop from the instruction labelled NXT to the instruction BGT NXT. The index register is used to count the number of times the loop repeated.

■ This program scans a set of characters, and counts the number of occurrences of a given character. It is assumed that the set of characters is already loaded into the AMC memory, and is terminated by the character *.

The program is written as a subprogram, called from a main program. The address of the start of the set of characters is passed from the main program to the subprogram, together with the character whose occurrences are to be counted. On return from the subprogram, the number of occurrences of the character is passed back to the main program. Registers are used to pass the information to and from the subprogram.

Within the subprogram, indirect addressing is used to locate each character in the set. The algorithm for the subprogram is as follows:

Set the number of occurrences of the character to zero.

Repeat

Load a character from the set to the accumulator.

If the character is the required character, increase the number of occurrences by 1.

Until the end-of-set marker is reached.

Program

CHR	BTE			Character whose occurrences are to be counted.
LOC	WRD			Address of current character in set
CNT	WRD			Number of occurrences of character.

Start of Subprogram

SBP	STB	X	CHR	Store required character, passed to subprogram in index register.
	STO	A	LOC	Store address of first character in set, passed to subprogram in accumulator.
	CLR	A		Clear accumulator.
	STO	A	CNT	Set character count to zero.

Start of Loop to Inspect One Character

BGN	LOB	A I	LOC	Using indirect addressing, load current character to accumulator.
	CPB	A N	/*/	Compare with end-of-set marker.
	BZE		OUT	Branch to end of subprogram if equal.
	CPB	A	CHR	Compare with required character.
	BNE		DWN	Branch to instruction labelled DWN if not equal.
	LOA	A	CNT	Load character count to accumulator.
	INC	A		Increment character count.
	STO	A	CNT	Store new value of character count.
DWN	LOA	A	LOC	Load address of current character to accumulator.
	INC	A		Increment address of current character.
	STO	A	LOC	Store new address of current character.
	BRN		BGN	Branch back to repeat loop.

End of Loop

| OUT | LOA | A | CNT | Load character count to accumulator. |
| | RTS | | | Return to main program. |

End of Subprogram, Start of Main Program

```
      LOB   X N   /T/         Load character to be counted, T, to index
                              register.
      LOA   A N   SET         Load start address of character set to
                              accumulator.
      LOA   S N   +127        Initialise stack pointer to 127.
      JSR         SBP         Jump to subprogram.
      HLT                     Halt on return to main program.
```

End of Main Program, Start of Data Area

```
SET   BTE         /T/
      BTE         /H/
      BTE         /E/
      BTE         / /
      BTE         /C/
      BTE         /A/
      BTE         /T/
      BTE         /*/
      END                     End of Program.
```

Points to Notice

- The accumulator and index register are used to pass data to the subprogram. The accumulator is also used to pass data back from the subprogram.
- The branching instruction BNE DWN is designed to skip the next three instructions if the current character is NOT the one which is being counted. Branching in this manner, on a negative condition, is an efficient way of constructing a portion of a program such as this.
- The test for the end-of-set marker must be made before the test for the required character.

16.9 Example Program 16.5

■ This program takes a data structure in the form of a binary tree (Section 4.9), and scans the structure in a systematic way. The data item at each node is output, and the left subtree is scanned, followed by the right subtree. The process is known as **tree traversal**. It is a **depth-first scan**, since the left subtrees of all the nodes are scanned before any right subtrees are examined.

Each node of the tree is represented as a data item (one byte) followed by two pointers (one word each), holding the addresses of the left and right subtrees respectively. Null pointers have a value zero. The tree traversal program is written as a **recursive** subprogram – it repeatedly calls itself until the entire tree is scanned. The algorithm is as follows:

Traverse tree (tree pointer) is:
    Output data item at node
    If left subtree pointer is non-zero then
        Traverse tree (left subtree pointer)
    If right subtree pointer is non-zero then
        Traverse tree (right subtree pointer)

The subprogram requires as a parameter a pointer to the tree each time it is called. This parameter is passed to the subprogram in the accumulator. During the subprogram, it is stored on the stack, since it needs to be used again after recursive calls.

Program

Storage for Tree Pointer

TPR	WRD			Tree pointer

Tree Traversal Subprogram

TTR	STO	A	TPR	Store tree pointer in location TPR.
	PSH	A		Push copy of tree pointer to stack.
	LOB	A I	TPR	Load data item at tree node.
	OUP	A		Request terminal to output data item.

Left Subtree

	LOA	A	TPR	Load tree pointer to accumulator.
	INC	A		Increment tree pointer, now holds address of left subtree pointer.
	STO	A	TPR	Store address of left subtree pointer.
	LOA	A I	TPR	Load left subtree pointer to accumulator.
	BZE		RST	Branch if zero to deal with right subtree.
	JSR		TTR	Traverse left subtree.

Right Subtree

RST	POP	A		Pop original tree pointer to accumulator.
	ADD	A N	+3	Add 3 to tree pointer, now holds address of right subtree pointer.
	STO	A	TPR	Store address of right subtree pointer.
	LOA	A I	TPR	Load right subtree pointer to accumulator.
	BZE		OUT	Branch if zero to end of subprogram.
	JSR		TTR	Traverse right subtree.
OUT	RTS			Return from subprogram.

Main Program

	LOA	S N	+127	Initialise stack pointer to 127.
	LOA	A N	TRE	Load tree pointer to accumulator.
	JSR		TTR	Call tree traversal subprogram.
	HLT			Halt on return.

Data

TRE	BTE		/A/	Top tree node: data item.
	WRD		T1A	Left subtree pointer.
	WRD		T1B	Right subtree pointer.
T1A	BTE		/B/	Second level left node: data item.
	WRD		T2A	Left subtree pointer.
	WRD		T2B	Right subtree pointer.
T1B	BTE		/C/	Second level right node: data item.
	WRD		T2C	Left subtree pointer.
	WRD		T2D	Right subtree pointer.
T2A	BTE		/D/	Third level first node: data item.
	WRD		+0	Left subtree pointer.
	WRD		+0	Right subtree pointer.
T2B	BTE		/E/	Third level second node: data item.
	WRD		+0	Left subtree pointer.
	WRD		+0	Right subtree pointer.
T2C	BTE		/F/	Third level third node: data item.
	WRD		+0	Left subtree pointer.
	WRD		+0	Right subtree pointer.
T2D	BTE		/G/	Third level fourth node: data item.
	WRD		+0	Left subtree pointer.
	WRD		+0	Right subtree pointer.
	END			End of program.

Points to Notice

- Indirect addressing is used several times to locate data items from their pointers.
- Before the subprogram is called, the pointer to the tree or subtree to be traversed is loaded into the accumulator.
- The data for the program is shown in Figure 16.5. The order of traversal is also shown in the diagram.

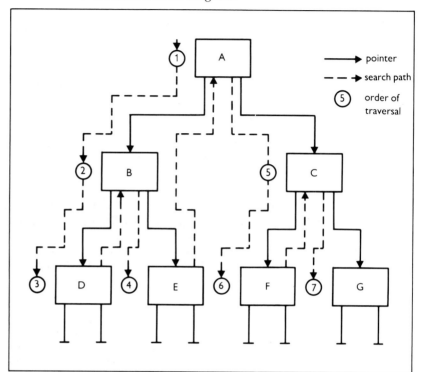

Figure 16.5
Tree traversal for Example
Program 16.5

<table>
<tr><td>16.10
Uses of
Assembly
Languages</td></tr>
</table>

16.10 Uses of Assembly Languages

■ With the development of high level languages (Chapter 18), there has been a gradual reduction in the relative importance of assembly languages. However, they still have a variety of uses, notably in the writing of **systems software**, and in the programming of special-purpose microprocessors.

Systems software is a name given to the layers of software which transform the raw hardware of a computer into a machine which can be programmed in a straightforward way. Systems programs include operating systems and language translation programs, both of which are discussed in later chapters. Most system software is written, at least in part, in a low level language, though high level languages are becoming increasingly popular in this area.

The advent of microprocessors has given low level languages a new lease of life. Some microcomputers based on small microprocessors cannot support anything but the most primitive subset of a high level language. Most software which uses high-speed, full-colour graphics is written in a low-level language. Most computer games fall into this category. Furthermore, a significant proportion of microprocessors are dedicated to the performance of a single task, such as controlling a camera. The only program which these microprocessors require is permanently stored on read-only memory. Such programs are almost always written in a low level language.

16.11 Conclusion

■ This chapter has introduced the concept of an assembly language, outlined the objectives and features of assembly languages, and then used AMC assembly language to demonstrate a number of techniques of low level language programming. The main points of the chapter are as follows:

- The objective of an assembly language is to simplify the programming of a particular computer, while still enabling the programmer to control the hardware of a computer directly.
- An assembly language is a programming language whose data structures correspond to the physical structure of the registers and main store of its host computer, and whose instructions are closely related to the machine instructions of the computer.
- Characteristic features of assembly languages include mnemonic operation codes, symbolic addresses, automatic data conversion, directives and macros.
- Assembly languages are used principally in the writing of systems software and in the programming of microprocessors.

Exercise 16

1 Briefly define the following terms: assembly language; mnemonic; symbolic address; label; directive; macro-instruction; low level language; immediate operand; pointer; recursive; tree traversal.

2 Write short sequences of instructions, in AMC assembly language, for each of the following operations:
   a) Set a store word, labelled DT1, to zero.
   b) Store the decimal value 16291 in a word labelled CS1.
   c) Increase the contents of a byte of store, labelled CTR, by 1.
   d) Test whether the contents of two store locations with addresses AB1 and AB2 are equal.
   e) Create a stack containing the code for the following ASCII characters:

   | AB |
   | CD |
   | EF |

3 Rewrite Example Program 12.2 in AMC assembly language.

4 Rewrite the program in Exercise 14, Question 6, in AMC assembly language.

5 A 'double length' integer may be stored in two consecutive words of AMC store, as follows:

The first word stores the high order part of the number, with the most significant bit representing a negative quantity. The place value of this bit is $-2^{31} = -2147483648$. The least significant bit in this word has the place value of $2^{16} = 65536$.

The second word stores the low order part of the number, with all bits representing positive quantities. Place values range from $2^{15} = 32768$ to $2^0 = 1$. See Figure 16.6.

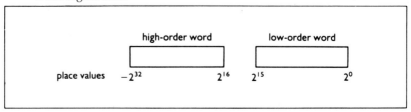

Figure 16.6
A double length integer

For example, if the high order part of the word contains the decimal value 10000 and the low order part contains the decimal value 8763, then the double length number represented is 216 x 10000 + 8763 = 655368763.

Addition of two double length integers is as follows: the low order words of the two numbers are added first, and the sum stored. The high order words are then added, together with the carry from the low order addition. The program shown below carries out this process:

Program

Data areas

HI1	WRD	+10000	High order word of integer 1.
LI1	WRD	+8763	Low order word of integer 1.
HI2	WRD	+20000	
LI2	WRD	+14261	
HSM	WRD		High order word of sum.
LSM	WRD		Low order word of sum.

Start of program

```
        LOA  A      LI1
        ADD  A      LI2
        STO  A      LSM
        LOA  A      HI1

        ___  _      ___
        STO  A      HSM
        HLT
        END
```

Make a copy of this program, and
   a) Fill in the missing instruction in the program.
   b) Write suitable comments next to each program line.
   c) Write a program to add three double length integers.
 ◆ d) Write a program to subtract two double length integers.
 6 Write a program in AMC assembly language to locate the end of a list of data, structured as in Example Program 16.2. The program is given the address of the first list element, and scans the list until the last element is located. The program halts with the address of the last list element in the accumulator.
 ◆ 7 Write a program in AMC assembly language which scans a tree, structured as in Example Program 16.5, in order to locate a given character. If the character is found at one of the nodes, a pointer to the node is returned, otherwise a zero value of the pointer is returned.
 8 Write a program in AMC assembly language to divide two unsigned integers by a process of shifting and subtraction.
 9 The simplest form of integer multiplication is by a process of repeated addition. For example, to multiply 4 by 9, add 4 nine times. This process was used on early computers. An algorithm for this method of multiplication is as follows:

To multiply positive integers IN1 and IN2, using working areas WA1 and WA2,
   Clear WA1, and load IN2 to WA2.
   While WA2 is greater than zero, repeat
       Add IN1 to WA1
       Reduce WA2 by 1.

Write a program in AMC assembly language to implement this algorithm. Either use data numbers which are small enough for the product to be accomodated in one word (WA1), or use a double length word for WA1, and add the carry arising from the addition into the high order word.

10 Integer division may be carried out by a process of repeated subtraction. For example, to divide 40 by 7, count the number of times 7 may be subtracted from 40.
   a) Write an algorithm for division by this method.
   b) Write a program in AMC assembly language to implement your algorithm.

11 Explain what is wrong with the following AMC instruction
   ```
   STO A N /AB/
   ```

12 The least significant bit of a 16 bit word is an even parity bit. This means that the parity of the word is correct if the total number of 1s is an even number.

   Write a program, in AMC assembly language, to check the parity of the word. Use repeated shifting, masking, and addition to obtain the total number of 1s in the word.

   Assume that, at the start of the program, the word to be checked is loaded into the accumulator. At the end of the program, the accumulator contains 0 if the parity is correct, and 1 if it is not correct.

13 Explain fully the reasons for the use of the stack in the subprogram in Example Program 16.5.

17 Assemblers

This chapter concerns the process of translating a program written in an assembly language to an equivalent program in machine language. The item of software which performs this task is called an **assembler**. The nature and objectives of an assembler are discussed, together with a brief examination of some of the techniques of assembly used in practice. As in previous chapters, AMC machine and assembly language are used as examples.

17.1 Nature and Objectives of an Assembler

■ The objectives of an assembler are to translate a program from the assembly language to the machine language of a particular computer, and to assist programmers in writing programs in assembly language. In addition to their translation function, assemblers perform other tasks, for example the detection and reporting of errors in programs which they are translating. Accordingly, an assembler may be defined as follows:

> An assembler is a program which translates from the assembly language to the machine language of a particular computer, and provides additional facilities to assist in the development of low level language programs for the computer

A more general objective of an assembler is to provide a programmer-oriented interface to the hardware of a particular computer. In other words, the assembler enables the programmer to 'see' the hardware of a computer in a simple, useful way. It must enable the hardware of the computer to be used in the most effective manner. In addition to these general objectives, an assembler must be acceptably short, and carry out its tasks quickly and efficiently. In practice, this objective must be balanced against the desire to include a large number of non-essential features in an assembler.

17.2 Tasks Performed by an Assembler

■ This section examines some of the tasks carried out by an assembler in the process of translating from assembly language to machine language. Most of these tasks are associated with the features of assembly languages described in the previous chapter. Although the details of the ways these tasks are performed vary from one assembler to another, their general nature is common to all assemblers. The tasks are: analysis of the structure of an assembly language program, decoding mnemonic operation codes, dealing with symbolic addresses, automatic data conversion, interpreting directives and macro expansion.

Analysis of the Structure of an Assembly Language Program

The first task of an assembler is to analyse the structure of an assembly language program, and determine the nature of each part of the program. Each assembly language has a set of rules which govern the structure of programs written in the language. These rules determine both the overall structure of a program, and the detailed structure of each program line. In most cases these rules are fairly simple. Programs generally consist of one instruction or directive per line. Lines either have fixed-length fields for specific purposes, or use punctuation marks to separate fields. AMC assembly language is an example of the first type.

The assembler uses these rules in the analysis of a program. The rules enable each group of characters to be interpreted as a mnemonic operation code, symbolic address, etc. Once the nature of a group of characters has been determined, more detailed work can be done, as outlined in the following sections.

If the structure of any portion of a program does not match the requirements of the rules, then an error is detected by the assembler. An error message is displayed.

Decoding Mnemonic Operation Codes

This is a straightforward procedure. As there is a one-to-one correspondence between assembly language mnemonics and machine instruction codes, a table is used to store each mnemonic together with its equivalent machine language operation code. Each mnemonic operation code in a program is looked up in this table, and the corresponding machine language operation code placed in the machine language program. If a mnemonic operation code is not in the table, then an error is recorded, and an error message is displayed.

Dealing with Symbolic Addresses

The objective here is to replace each symbolic address by a machine language address. The procedure is more complicated than decoding operation codes, and several stages are involved.

Every symbolic address used in a program must occur in one, and only one, position in the program as a label. As the assembler works through the program, the address of each instruction or directive is determined. If the instruction or directive has a label, then the address is associated with that label. Part of the task of an assembler is to build up a table of all the labels used in a program, together with the addresses at which they occur. If identical labels are encountered at different addresses, then an error is reported.

The table thus created is used to relate each symbolic address in a program to a machine address. If a symbolic address is not in the table, then an error is detected. In some assemblers, the process of creating the table is completed before symbolic addresses are looked up in it. In others, the two processes occur concurrently. This point is dealt with again in the section on the structure of assembler programs.

In some cases, the machine addresses allocated to symbolic addresses at this stage are the final ones which are used when the machine language is run. In other cases, they are relative addresses, generally relative to the start of the program. They are changed into absolute memory addresses at a later stage, when the machine language program is loaded into its position in memory for running.

Automatic Data Conversion

If an assembly language permits the representation of data values in various number bases and character codes, then conversion algorithms and tables are used to change these representations to machine code format. This is generally a straightforward process.

Interpreting Directives

As mentioned in the previous chapter, directives are assembly language instructions which do not have a counterpart in machine code. An assembler acts upon a directive as soon as it is recognised. The nature of the action depends upon the particular directive. For example, if, in AMC assembly language, the directive WRD is encountered, the assembler reserves a word of store.

Macro Expansion

You will recall from the previous chapter that a macro-instruction is a single instruction which is defined, within a program, to represent a set of instructions. When an assembler encounters the definition of a macro-instruction, it decodes the set of instructions which the macro-instruction represents, and records the mnemonic of the macro-instruction in a table. When the macro-instruction is encountered in the body of a program, the set of instructions is inserted at the corresponding position in the machine language program. In this way, the macro-instruction is **expanded** to the full set of instructions in the machine language program.

17.3 The Structure of an Assembler Program

■ Assembler programs consist of a number of modules, one for each task mentioned previously. The structure analysis module is in overall control. Once the nature of a set of characters in an assembly language program has been recognised, the appropriate module is called to carry out whatever detailed work is required.

There are, broadly speaking, two approaches to the analysis of the structure of an assembly language program. The traditional method involves scanning the assembly language program twice. Assemblers using this method are called **two-pass assemblers**. The more modern approach involves only one scan of the assembly language program. Assemblers of this type are called **single-pass** or **incremental assemblers**.

17.4 The AMC Assembler

■ The program which translates from AMC assembly language to AMC machine language is an example of a two-pass assembler. The tasks performed during each pass through an assembly language program are as follows.

First Pass

1 Break down the current assembly language program line into its constituent parts (label, operation code mnemonic, etc.)
2 If the label field is non-blank, store the label and its corresponding machine address in the symbolic address table.
3 Decode the operation mnemonic, register identifier and addressing mode, or directive.
4 Insert the operation code into the current machine language program instruction, and record the address of this instruction.
5 From the number of words used by the current machine language program instruction, calculate the address of the next machine language program instruction.

Second Pass

1 If the current assembly program line contains a symbolic address, look this address up in the symbolic address table. Insert the equivalent machine code address into the current machine code instruction.
2 If the current assembly program line contains the value of a data item as a decimal number or set of ASCII characters, obtain the hexadecimal

equivalent of this value and insert it into the current machine code instruction.

3 If the current assembly program line is a relative branching instruction, calculate the relative offset and insert it into the current machine code instruction.

If an error is detected during any of these steps, an error message is displayed. Assembly continues to the end of the current pass.

17.5 Language of Assemblers

■ Assemblers are programs which translate from the assembly language to the machine language of a particular computer. But in what language is the assembler program itself written? In the early days of computing, the answer was obvious: in the machine language of the particular computer. This is still the case for a some present-day assemblers, particularly those used by microcomputers.

However, a significant proportion of assemblers are written in the assembly language which they translate. Others are written in high level languages, which are introduced in the next chapter. Some assemblers are designed to run on a different computer from the one whose language they translate. Such assemblers are called **cross assemblers**.

17.6 Conclusion

■ The main points of the chapter are as follows:
- An assembler is a program which translates from the assembly language to the machine language of a particular computer, and provides additional facilities to assist in the development of low level language programs for the computer.
- Tasks performed by an assembler include:
  - analysis of the structure of an assembly language program
  - decoding mnemonic operation codes
  - dealing with symbolic addresses
  - automatic data conversion
  - interpreting directives
  - macro expansion.
- The overall control of an assembler is carried out by the structure analysis module. Other tasks are performed by modules called from this module.
- The two approaches to the analysis of an assembly language program are the two-pass method and the single-pass or incremental technique.

Exercise 17

1 Briefly define the following terms: assembler; symbolic address table; two-pass assembler; cross assembler.
2 Summarise, in about one hundred and fifty words, the tasks carried out by an assembler.
3 In addition to language translation, what other function does an assembler perform?
4 Why can a symbolic address be used as a label in only one position in a program?
5 If the machine and assembly languages of a computer were altered to include a new instruction, what changes would have to be made to the assembler program?
6 The machine code corresponding to the following AMC assembly language program is shown after the first pass of the AMC assembler. The table of symbolic addresses is also shown.

AMC assembly language			AMC machine language		Interpretation
	LOA X N +1		0000	1121 ___	Use index register as loop counter, initial value 1.
NXT	CMP X N +27		0004	1A21 ___	Compare index register with 27.
	BGT	OUT	0008	65___	Exit loop if greater than 27.
	LOA A N +100		000A	1111 ___	Load 100 in accumulator.
	STB A D W		000E	2214 ___	Store contents of accumulator in W + index.
	INC X		0012	0220	Increment index register.
	BRN	NXT	0014	61___	Continue loop.
OUT	HLT		0016	8500	Halt.
W	BTE		0018		Data item.

Table of symbolic addresses

NXT	0004
OUT	0016
W	0018

Make a copy of the program, and complete the machine language version by carrying out the steps of the second assembly pass. Remember that the relative address in a branching instruction is calculated from the address of the following instruction. For example, the relative address in the machine language version of BGT OUT is calculated from address 000A.

7 Select a program in AMC assembly language from Chapter 16, and convert it to AMC machine language. Start the machine language version at address 0000. Include a table of the symbolic addresses used in the program, together with their machine addresses.

18 High Level Languages

This chapter is concerned with a class of programming languages known as high level languages. It explains the nature of high level languages, outlines their development, discusses their objectives and features and assesses their significance.

18.1 What is a High Level Language?

■ A high level language is a **problem oriented** programming language, whereas a low level language is **machine oriented**. In other words, a high level language is a convenient and simple means of describing the information structures and sequences of actions required to perform a particular task.

A high level language is independent of the architecture of the computer which supports it. This has two major advantages. Firstly, the person writing the programs does not have to know anything about the computer on which the program will be run. Secondly, programs are **portable**, that is, the same program can (in theory) be run on different types of computer. However, this property of machine independence is not always achieved in practice.

In most cases, programs in high level languages are shorter than equivalent programs in low level languages. However, conciseness can be carried too far, to the point where programs become impossible to understand. More important features of a high level language are its ability to reflect clearly the algorithms and structure of programs written in it, and its readability.

18.2 The Development of High Level Languages

■ Work started on the development of high level languages in the mid-1950s, about ten years after the emergence of digital electronic computers. During those ten years it had become evident that the major shortcoming of computers was not their hardware performance but their software performance. Writing correct, useful machine and assembly language programs for the computers of the day was a difficult, time-consuming and expensive process.

During this period, advances in computer languages consisted of additional features to increase the capabilities of assembly languages. Although these features provided a few short cuts, they increased the complexity of the assembly languages. The languages lacked a clear, coherent overall structure.

There was resistance to the idea of high level languages on the grounds of inefficiency. High level languages require compilers to translate the programs into machine language before they can be run. It was feared that the machine language programs produced by compilers would be extremely inefficient (with large numbers of machine instructions wasting both memory space and processing time), compared with programs written directly in machine language. Considering the small size and low speed of computers in those days, this fear had some justification. Despite these objections, the period from 1954 to 1960 saw the development of three major high level languages, **Fortran**, **Algol 60** and **Cobol**. Some details about the development of these languages are provided in the next chapter.

In spite of the problems mentioned above, once high level languages became available, their use spread very rapidly. Many more languages were written, and compilers were produced to implement these languages on the various computers currently in use. It has been estimated that there were about 1700 programming languages by 1965, but two of the first three - Fortran and Cobol are still among the most popular.

Work on the development of high level languages still continues today. Existing languages are modified in the light of experience, and sometimes substantially revised. For example, a new version of Algol, Algol 68, was introduced in 1968. From time to time, new high level languages are produced, a prominent example being Ada, in 1979.

18.3 Types of High Level Languages

■ High level languages may be broadly classified as **general-purpose** or **special-purpose**. General-purpose languages are intended to be equally well suited to business, scientific, engineering or systems software tasks. The commonest general-purpose languages include **Ada** and **C**. Because of their broad capabilities, these languages can be large and relatively difficult to use.

The commonest categories of special-purpose languages are commercial, scientific and educational. In the commercial field, Cobol still reigns supreme, while Fortran is still the most widely used scientific language. In the computer education field, Basic is widely used in schools, as well as Logo and Prolog. Pascal is a popular language at universities and on some schools. Pascal is a powerful general-purpose languages in its own right.

Another way of classifying high level languages is as **procedural** and **declarative** languages. Procedural languages state how a task is to be performed, often breaking programs into **procedures**, each of which specifies how a particular operation is to be performed. Data structures are explicitly declared. All the early high level languages are procedural, with Algol (Section 19.2), Pascal (Section 19.5) and Ada as typical examples. Declarative programming languages describe the data structures and relationships between data relevant to a particular task, and specify what the objective of the task is. The process by which the task is to be carried out is not stated explicitly in the program. This process is determined by the language translation system. Prolog (Section 19.8) is an example of a declarative programming language.

18.4 Objectives of High Level Languages

■ Before going on to discuss the features of high level languages, it is essential to be clear about what high level languages are trying to achieve. The defining characteristics of a high level language are **problem-orientation** and **machine independence**. These are taken for granted in the following discussion.

The first objective of a high level language is to provide a convenient means of expressing the solution to a problem. There are two other common ways of doing this - mathematics, and natural languages, such as English. Most high level languages borrow, without much modification, concepts and symbols from mathematics. The problem with natural languages is that, in their full richness and complexity, they are impossible to use to instruct a computer. Nevertheless, high level languages use words from natural languages, and allow these words, and mathematical symbols, to be combined according to various rules. These rules create the structure of programs written in the language. The result, in a good high level language, is a clear structure, not too different from our customary ways of thinking and expressing ourselves.

This discussion leads to the second objective of high level languages – **simplicity**. Simplicity is achieved by a small set of basic operations, a few clear rules for combining these operations, and, above all, the avoidance of special cases.

The third objective of a high level language is **efficiency**. Programs in the language must be able to be translated into machine code fairly quickly, and the resulting machine code must run efficiently. This objective almost always conflicts with the first two. Most high level languages reflect a compromise between these objectives.

The final objective is **readability** of programs. Many languages allow for the inclusion of comments or additional 'noise' words, to make programs easier to read. However, a good high level language should enable programs to be written which are clear to read without additional comments. Regrettably, a few high level languages ignore this objective altogether.

18.5 Features of High Level Languages

■ The next few sections outline the features common to most high level languages. In this chapter, these features are discussed in general terms. The next chapter shows how these features are implemented in some popular high level languages.

Character Set and Reserved Words

The **character set** used by a language is the set of all characters which may be used in programs written in the language. Almost all languages use letters and decimal digits; differences arise in the use of special characters such as punctuation marks.

Most high level languages use **reserved words**. These are words which have a specific meaning in programs, and may not be used by the programmer for any other purpose. For example, in Pascal, reserved words include **read**, **if ... then ... else** and **write**. Some languages permit abbreviations of reserved words. The size and complexity of a language can be measured by the number of reserved words it uses. For example, Occam (Section 34.4) has 28 reserved words, while Ada uses more than 60.

Program Structure

Perhaps the most important feature of a high level language is the way in which programs in it are structured. The structure of a program is specified by a set of rules, called **rules of syntax**. Different languages have different ways of expressing these rules. In some, the rules are written in concise English. Others use **syntax diagrams**, while others (notably Algol) use a notation originally called **Backus-Naur form**, now known as **BNF**. See Section 20.3.

Much attention has been devoted, in the development and use of high level languages, to the way in which programs are split up into **blocks** or **modules**, each module doing a specific task. In some languages, notably Fortran, these blocks are called **subroutines**, in others such as Algol and Pascal, these blocks are called **procedures** or **functions**. Because of the careful structuring of programs into blocks which they permit, Algol, Pascal and similar languages are called **block-structured languages**.

Procedures, functions or subroutines are activated via **calls** from other parts of the program. For example, if a program contains a function to calculate the square root of a given number, this function is called every time a square root is required in the rest of the program. Most languages permit a procedure or function to call itself, a feature known as **recursion**. This is an extremely powerful feature for handling such data structures as lists, stacks and trees, and for such tasks as analysing the structure of arithmetic expressions. See Sections 16.9 and 19.5 for examples of the use of recursion.

Data

An important aspect of high level languages is the way in which they handle the data items and data structures used in a program. Broadly speaking, data items fall into two categories: **variables**, which can change their value during the running of a program, and **constants**, which keep the same value. In most program languages, variables are given names, or **identifiers**. In some languages, such as Fortran and Basic, constants are referred to by their values, while in others, such as Algol and Pascal, constants are also given identifiers.

Some program languages require that all variables be **declared** before they are used. Generally, variables are declared by listing them at the start of the procedure or subroutine in which they are to be used. An attempt to use a variable which has not been declared results in an error.

This gives rise to the idea of the **scope** of a variable. The scope of a variable is the part of a program in which it may be used. Variables which are declared for use in one procedure only are called **local** variables. Their scope is limited to that procedure. Variables which are declared for use in the whole program are called global variables. Their scope is the whole program. The intention of providing each variable with a scope is to enable a program to be broken up into 'watertight' blocks, or modules. Each block uses only the information it requires. This simplifies the task of designing, writing and testing programs, and limits the effects of errors.

Almost all high level languages include the notion of **data types**. In Basic language, the standard data types are **numeric** and **character strings**. These types can be incorporated into **arrays**, which are tables of items of the same type. In most high level languages, numbers can be **integers** or **real** numbers (generally stored in floating point form). PL/1 even permits the number of significant figures in a number to be declared. Another common standard data type is **Boolean**, with the range of values 'true' and 'false'. Data types can contain single elements, or be structures such as arrays, stacks, lists, trees, etc.

A **pointer** is a data type which contains the address of another data item. Pointers can be used to construct such data structures as lists and trees. For example, a list of people's names could be constructed as follows:

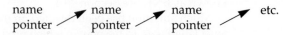

Pointer types are only available in certain high level languages, notably Algol and Pascal. The problem with pointers is that careless use of them can result in program errors which are very difficult to detect and correct.

Some languages permit the programmer to declare his or her own data types, built up from standard data types. **Records** can be constructed, containing data of different types. The following section of a Pascal program shows how this can be done.

```
type   name      = array [1...20] of char;
       day       = (mon,tues,wed,thur,fri,sat,sun);
pay record       = record
                      employee name: name;
                      payrate: real;
                      hours worked: integer;
                      pay: real;
                      payday: day
                   end;
```

In the above example, char is a standard data type. Variables of type char have values consisting of a single character. The data type name is an array of twenty characters. Variables of the data type day can have one of the values listed in the brackets.

The purpose of data types is to make programs more meaningful, and to provide additional checks for errors. For example, if an attempt is made to add an integer variable to a character variable, then an error will be caused.

Operations

The operations included in a high level language enable data items and data structures to be manipulated in various ways. Almost all program languages permit arithmetic operations. Many allow expressions of any degree of complexity to be evaluated in one statement. Most languages include the logical operations AND, OR and NOT, again combined to form expressions if necessary. Some program languages, notably Fortran and PL/1, have instructions to manipulate entire data structures such as matrices. In these languages, multiplying two matrices, for example, requires only one program instruction.

All program languages have rules of **precedence** which specify the order in which operations are carried out within the same expression. Arithmetic operations follow the usual rules: multiplication before addition, etc., but languages differ over the precedence of logic operations over arithmetic operations in the same expression.

The process whereby a variable takes on a value is called **assignment**. Different languages express assignment in different ways. For example, assigning the value of a variable Y to a variable X is expressed in Basic and Fortran as:

```
X = Y
```

Algol 60, Algol 68 and Pascal would express it as:

```
x:= y
```

while in Cobol it would be written as:

```
MOVE Y TO X
```

Input and Output

High level languages vary considerably in their treatment of input and output. The intention in all cases is to hide from the programmer the problems which surround input and output at machine level, although in many cases these problems are taken care of by the operating system.

Most high level languages provide a simple, logical method of transferring data to or from the computer. Some languages, notably Fortran and Cobol, pay considerable attention to the layout, or **format** of the data. Other languages deliberately 'play down' this aspect, to simplify matters for the programmer.

Control Structure

All program languages, both low level and high level, have ways of transferring control from one part of a program to another. In procedural high level languages, there are generally three aspects of the question: **sequencing**, **looping** and **branching**.

Sequencing is the flow of control from one instruction to the next. In most program languages this is achieved by writing instructions one after the other, separated by semi-colons, or on consecutive lines. Basic language is an exception, with instructions being executed in order of line number.

Looping is concerned with repeating instructions or groups of instructions. Most high level languages have instructions for performing loops a certain number of times, using one variable as a counter. Some languages allow loops to be repeated while some condition is true, or until a condition becomes true.

Branching concerns transferring control to one part of a program if a condition is true, and to another if the condition is false. The most general form of a branching instruction is as follows:

```
if <condition> then <instructions to be executed if condition is true>
                else <instructions to be executed if condition is false>
endif
```

A more sophisticated version of the conditional branching instruction is available in many languages. This is the multi-way branch instruction. In Pascal, the **multi-way branch** is implemented as the case statement. For example:

```
case   operator of
       add          : a:=a+b;
       subtract     : a:=a-b;
       multiply     : a:=a*b;
       end;
```

Depending on the value of the variable **operator**, one of the statements is executed.

There is some controversy about the use of the **unconditional branching** instruction, of the form:

```
go to <statement number>
```

in high level languages. Its use cuts across the structures created by the use of looping, branching and conditional transfers of control. It can also spoil the scoping of variables. **Go to** is regarded as a low level language feature, to be avoided in well-written high level language programs.

18.6
An Assessment of High Level Languages

■ A high level language is a programming language which is problem-oriented and machine independent, and has the objectives of a clear structure, simplicity, efficiency and readability. How well do high level languages match these criteria in practice?

Problem-orientation is generally well achieved, especially in special-purpose languages such as Cobol and in block-structured languages like Pascal. Machine independence does not score so highly. A 'standard' version of most popular high level languages has been published, but machine-dependent features persist in most implementations. Basic language is particularly bad, with different computer manufacturers offering different enhancements to the language on their own computers.

A clear structure of programs is achieved in many high level languages. Perhaps the best example of this is the fact that several large operating systems have been successfully written in high level languages. Simplicity is certainly possible in most high level languages, but it is limited by the complexity of the problem being programmed. Program readability is still very much a matter for the individual programmer.

The main success of high level languages has been their transformation of the art (or science...) of computer programming from the domain of a few highly skilled computer experts to a much wider group of people, including a large number of professional programmers, students and researchers in a wide range of fields, and a number of school pupils. With computers becoming cheaper, and programmers' time becoming more expensive, high level languages are becoming more and more cost-effective.

However, there is still a place for programming in low level languages. Systems software must still be written, at least in part, in a low level language. Some microcomputers are too small to support anything more than a simple subset of a high level language. If a microprocessor is to be dedicated to a specific task, such as control or monitoring of a system, all the software required is usually written in assembly language.

At present there is a move towards an even higher level of programming languages, known as **fourth generation languages** (**4GLs**), and an increasing use of software development tools. These are discussed in Chapter 24. The profession of programming is evolving into **software engineering** (Chapter 25). These developments are challenging the current dominance of high level languages for the development of applications software, and may eventually make them obsolete.

18.7
Conclusion

■ The main points of this chapter are as follows:
- High level languages are application-oriented, machine-independent programming languages.
- High level languages may be classified as special-purpose or general-purpose, or as procedural or declarative.
- Desirable features of high level languages are a clear structure, simplicity, efficiency and readability.
- Features of high level languages are their character set and reserved words, facilities for structuring programs and data, the processing operations they perform, input and output facilities and their control structures.
- The state of the art in programming is beginning to move beyond high level languages to the use of software development tools as programming evolves towards software engineering.

Exercise 18

1 Briefly define the following terms: high level language; portable; general-purpose language; procedural language; declarative language; character set; reserved word; syntax; block; subroutine; call; recursion; variable; constant; declaration; scope; local variable; global variable; data type; Boolean variable; pointer; rule of precedence; assignment; format.

2 What are the two distinguishing features of high level languages?

3 a) What factors were the driving force behind the development of high level languages?
  b) To what extent are the same forces making high level languages obsolete?

4 Summarise the objectives of high level languages.

5 What similarities and differences are there between natural languages (such as English) and high level programming languages?

6 Below is a complete program in Pascal language. It inputs a set of ten numbers and outputs them, together with their squares and reciprocals. Functions are used to calculate squares and reciprocals.

```
program question_6 (input,output);         (*line 1*)
var        x:real;                         (*line 2*)
   count    :integer;                      (*line 3*)
function square (y:real): real;            (*line 4*)
   var w    :real;                         (*line 5*)
begin w     := y*y;                        (*line 6*)
   square   :=w                            (*line 7*)
end;                                       (*line 8*)

function reciprocal (z:real):real;         (*line 9*)
   var v    :real;                         (*line10*)
begin if z=0.0   then v:=0.0               (*line11*)
                 else v:=1.0/z;            (*line12*)
            reciprocal :=v                 (*line13*)
end;                                       (*line14*)

begin for count :=1 to 10 do               (*line15*)
   begin readln(x);                        (*line16*)
     writeln(x,square(x),reciprocal(x))    (*line17*)
   end                                     (*line18*)
end.                                       (*line19*)
```

This program has three blocks, namely the two functions and the main program. The scope of a variable is the block within which it is declared. In Pascal, variables are declared by a **var** instruction, or in a function declaration. Thus the scope of variable w is the **function** square, from line 5 to line 8.

a) Write down the scope of the variables x, count and v.
b) Is it permissible to refer to variable x in line 7?
c) Is it permissible to refer to variable w in line 13?
d) Which variables are local variables, and which are global variables?
e) From which program line are the two functions called?

7 Consider the following segment of a Basic program, containing two assignment statements:

```
105 LET Y = X
110 LET X = Y
```

a) If X and Y initially have the values 3 and 4, what are their values after this segment of program?
b) Write a sequence of three assignment statements which will interchange the values of X and Y.

8 In Fortran, a **FORMAT** statement specifies the layout of input and output data. It contains a number of codes, for integers, spaces, real numbers, etc. For example, to input three integers, set out as follows:

```
314 2175 46629
```

the program segment below can be used:

```
     READ (1,100)I,J,K
100  FORMAT (I3,1X,I4,1X,I5)
```

where **I3** means a 3 digit integer and **1X** means a space.

a) Write a **READ** and **FORMAT** statement to input the following data:

```
41 23 16 4117 2234 1697
```

b) Write a set of data which would be read by:

```
     READ (1,120) K,L,M1,M2,N
120  FORMAT (I4,2X,I4,2X,I2,1X,I2,1X,I8)
```

c) Comment on the advantages and disadvantages of this type of input.

9 Consider this statement from a Pascal program:

```
if (x<0) or (x>9)  then y:=10
                   else y:=9-x;
```

Write down the value of y in each of the following cases:

a) x = 4
b) x = 10
c) x = –2
d) x = 0
e) x = 9

◆ f) Write a segment of a Basic language program to achieve the same effect as the Pascal statement above. Comment on similarities and differences between it and the Pascal language instruction.

10 Identify some shortcomings of many implementations of high level languages.

◆ 11 Examine the low level language introduced in Chapter 16. To what extent (if at all) does it satisfy the objectives of high level languages?

◆ 12 John Backus, leader of the team which developed Fortran, has the view that conventional programming languages are still far too closely tied to the general ideas of computer architecture, such as addresses, sequences of operations etc. In the light of your knowledge of computer architecture, and of high level languages, comment on this view.

19 High Level Language Case Studies

This chapter takes the general ideas from the previous chapter and relates them to eight significant high level languages: Fortran, Algol 60, Cobol, Basic, Pascal, C, Lisp and Prolog. Each language is discussed under the following headings: development, objectives, features and an assessment. Also included is a short example program in each language. The program is designed to illustrate the distinguishing features of the language.

The reasons for choosing the languages are as follows: Fortran, Algol 60 and Cobol are three of the oldest high level languages, Cobol and Fortran being two of the most popular programming languages currently in use. Algol 60 is the forerunner of a long line of high level languages, notably Algol 68, Pascal and Ada. Pascal, Basic and C are more recent languages, developed in the light of earlier experience. Lisp and Prolog are associated with artificial intelligence and the development of fifth generation computers.

As a group, these case studies cover a wide spectrum of high level languages, from special-purpose to general-purpose, from from scientific to commercial, and from procedural to declarative. The group represents a class of computer languages whose members number over a thousand.

19.1 Fortran

■ The name **Fortran** comes from the **For**mula **Tran**slation. Fortran, developed between 1954 and 1957, is a programming language designed for scientific and engineering applications.

Development

In December 1953, John Backus, an employee of IBM, proposed the idea of Fortran. At the time virtually all programming was in assembly language. Although some work had been done in the direction of high level languages, there was much scepticism about the efficiency of 'automatic programming' as it was then called.

Backus was motivated by an economic factor – the cost of programmers' time, as they laboriously wrote assembly language programs. His proposal was accepted, and in January 1954 a Fortran team was set up in New York, by IBM. The main objective of the team was to produce a language which could be translated into efficient machine code. The details of the language were made up as the team went along. In November 1954, the team produced a preliminary report. In early 1955, work started on the huge task of producing a Fortran compiler. The computer for which the compiler was written was the newly-released IBM 704. The compiler was reportedly 'always six months to completion', and was finally finished in April 1957.

From its first release, Fortran was very popular. From time to time, the language has been revised. The version in common use today is **ANSI 77 Fortran**, the version standardised by the American National Standards Institute. Fortran is available on most computers. Simple versions have been written for small computers, and very powerful versions, with a significant degree of parallel processing, have been written for large computers.

Objectives

Fortran is designed for use in mathematical, scientific and engineering applications. The prime objective of Fortran is to produce programs which can be translated into efficient machine code. Other objectives include ease of use, and close resemblance to ordinary mathematical notation.

As Fortran was originally sponsored by IBM, not much thought was initially given to the objective of machine independence. However, time has shown that Fortran is easy to implement on other computers. Most implementations conform to the ANSI 77 standard.

Character Set and Reserved Words

The character set used by Fortran includes capital letters, decimal digits and a few special characters. Fortran has a fairly large set of reserved words, including data type declarations (INTEGER, REAL, etc.) and instruction words (READ, WRITE, CALL, RETURN, etc.) All statements except calculations start with an instruction word.

Program Structure

A Fortran program consists of a main program and a number of subprograms, called subroutines. Subroutines can be called from the main program, or from other subroutines. Recursive calls from a subroutine to itself are not permitted.

Subroutines are compiled separately from each other, and from the main program. The scope of all variables is thus limited to the subroutine in which they occur, unless they are declared to be in a COMMON block. Within each routine, a program consists of a number of statements, each written on a separate line, with various columns having special purposes. Line numbers are optional, and do not have to be in order.

Data

The data types available are integer, real, double precision, complex and logical (Boolean). Variable names consist of up to six alphanumeric characters, the first of which must be alphabetic. Unless otherwise declared, variables starting with any of the letters from I to N are integers, and the rest are real. Variables do not have to be declared at the start of the routine in which they are used.

The DIMENSION statement is used to create arrays. The elements of an array may be any of the above data types. Most versions of Fortran allow at least three dimensions of arrays. For example, the statement:

```
DIMENSION LOAD (10), STRESS (10,4)
```

declares LOAD to be a one-dimensional array of ten items, and STRESS to be a two-dimensional array of forty items.

Operations

All the usual operations of arithmetic are available, with rather complicated rules for combining variables (or constants) of different types in the same expression. The standard arithmetic functions (sin, cos, tan, etc.) are available, as well as user-defined functions. Relational operators (greater than, less than, etc.) are included, for use in logical expressions which may appear in IF statements.

Input/Output

The methods of input and output provided are powerful, but rather cumbersome. They were originally designed for input data set out on punched cards. At the start of the program, all peripheral devices required are listed, together with their channel number for the duration of the program. Each input or output statement specifies a channel number, a list of variables to be transferred, and a FORMAT statement. The FORMAT statement specifies the precise layout of the data on the input, output or backing store medium. For example

```
        READ (1,100) NPART, NSTOCK, PRICE
100     FORMAT (I6, 2X, I6, 2X, F6.2)
```

inputs the integers NPART and NSTOCK and real variable PRICE from channel 1. The integers each have six digits, and the number contains six characters, with two digits after the decimal point. The data items are separated by two spaces.

Control Structure

Two types of conditional branching statement are available, namely the **arithmetic** IF and the **logical** IF. The arithmetic IF statement includes an expression and three statement numbers. The expression is evaluated. If the result is negative, control passes to the first statement, if the result is zero, control passes to the second statement, and if the result is positive, control passes to the third statement. For example:

```
IF (X+Y) 10, 20, 30
```

branches to statement:

10 if X+Y<0
20 if X+Y=0
30 if X+Y>0.

The logical IF statement includes a logical expression, and an unconditional statement. If the logical expression is true, the unconditional statement is executed, otherwise control passes to the statement after the IF statement. For example:

```
IF (AMOUNT.LE.20.00) CHARGE=5.00
```

assigns the value 5.00 to CHARGE if AMOUNT is less than 20.00. Unconditional branching (GO TO) is available, as is multi-way branching.

Program loops can be constructed by means of the DO statement. The DO statement includes the statement number of the end of the loop, a variable to be used as a counter, its initial and final values, and (optionally) a step size. For example:

```
DO 20 MONTH = 1, 12, 1
```

causes the program segment ending at statement 20 to be repeated for all values of MONTH from 1 to 12 in steps of 1. Loops controlled by DO statements are always performed at least once. This is regarded by some as a shortcoming of Fortran.

Example Program

The subprogram shown below accepts two 10x10 matrices, and multiplies them together. The formula used is as follows:

If
  $C = A \times B$ where A, B and C are matrices
then
  $$c_{ij} = a_{i1} \times b_{1j} + a_{i2} \times b_{2j} + \ldots a_{i10} \times b_{10j}$$

The subprogram uses three nested loops. The outer and middle loops work through the rows and columns of the product matrix C, the inner loop adds up the terms which form the product as shown in the formula.

```
        SUBROUTINE MATMULT (A,B,C)
        REAL A (10,10), B(10,10), C(10,10)
C       OUTER LOOP WORKS THROUGH ROWS OF PRODUCT
        DO 100 I =1,10
C       MIDDLE LOOP WORKS THROUGH COLUMNS OF PRODUCT
        DO 100 J =1,10
C       SET PRODUCT ELEMENT TO ZERO
        C(I,J)=0.0
C       INNER LOOP ADDS UP TERMS OF PRODUCT
        DO 100 K =1,10
100     C(I,J) = C(I,J)+A(I,K)*B(K,J)
        RETURN
        END
```

Notes

1 The lines starting with the letter C are comments.
2 The statement numbered 100 is the end of all three loops.
3 The dimension of the matrices are declared in the second line of the subprogram.

Assessment

Fortran was designed as a scientific and engineering language and in general it is excellent for tasks of this nature. The only major shortcoming is the difficulty experienced by many programmers with input and output. To overcome this, some versions of Fortran have simplified input/output statements.

Fortran's weaknesses become apparent when handling non-numeric data. Input, output, storage and manipulation of data in character form is extremely cumbersome, even compared to a language such as Basic. In addition, the range of data types is limited, pointers are not implemented, and user-defined data types are not allowed. Recursion is not implemented.

In spite of these shortcomings, Fortran remains as popular as ever. It has even survived attempts by its original sponsor, IBM, to replace it with a supposedly superior language, PL/1.

19.2 Algol 60

■ The name **Algol** comes from the phrase **Algo**rithmic **L**anguage. Algol 60 is a structured general-purpose language developed between 1957 and 1962.

Development

During the mid 1950s, the idea of a 'universal programming language' was expressed by a number of people, in Europe and the USA. They envisaged a language that was clearly structured, general-purpose and machine independent. Fortran, which became available at this time, did not measure up to these requirements.

During 1957, the first steps towards designing such a language were taken by the USA **Association for Computing Machinery (ACM)** and its European counterpart, **GAMM**. In October 1957 a letter from GAMM to ACM suggested a combined approach. Accordingly, during May and June 1958, a joint working conference was held in Zurich. Delegates were from computer manufacturers, users, universities and governments on both sides of the Atlantic, but did not formally represent these institutions. This conference produced a preliminary draft of the language, which became known as Algol 58.

Algol aroused considerable interest, but by 1959 it was already clear that Fortran, with IBM backing, was going to be more widely used, certainly in the USA. As the concepts of language design became clearer, it soon became evident that Algol 58 could be improved. A meeting was held in Paris, in January 1960, at which a new version of the language was drafted, to incorporate all the improvements which had been suggested. Prominent delegates at this meeting were John Backus, of Fortran fame, and Peter Naur. Naur, with assistance from Backus, devised the notation, now known as BNF, in which the syntax of the revised language, called Algol 60, was expressed.

Algol 60 was appreciated, almost immediately, as a 'rounded work of art'. Its clear, consistent structure had a significant influence on the design of subsequent high level languages, and on the architecture of many computers. Compilers were written to implement Algol 60 on a number of computers. Algol 60 was written and revised during a few short, intensive meetings attended by approximately fifteen people. There was no formal voting procedure, design decisions being reached by consensus. Algol 60 represents a degree of international co-operation hardly ever achieved in any field.

Objectives

Algol was originally conceived as a 'universal programming language'. As various drafts were written, it acquired an algebraic bias, and thus an orientation towards scientific and engineering problems. However, it is certainly more general-purpose than Fortran.

The objective of machine independence is achieved in an interesting way. No less than three versions of the language have been defined, namely a **reference language, a publication language** and various hardware **implementation languages**. The reference language is the standard 'official' version, used in the revised Algol 60 report. It forms the basis of the other versions. The publication language permits a wider range of characters and notations, and is intended for the publication of algorithms. Each hardware version is the language implemented on some computer. It contains a set of rules for translating from the reference language to the hardware representation.

The other objective which is very well achieved is that of a simple, clear structure with a minimum of special cases.

Character Set and Reserved Words

In any hardware representation of Algol 60, the character set depends on the computer being used. Unlike Fortran, most current representations permit the use of lower case letters. Algol 60 has a slightly larger set of reserved words than Fortran. For example, the pair of reserved words `begin...end` are particularly important.

Program Structure

An Algol 60 program has the following structure, called a block:

```
Label:  begin
            declarations;
            statements
        end
```

The **label** is a general form of a statement number, and is optional. **Declarations** are lists of the **types** and **identifiers** of all the variables used in the block. **Statements** are simple statements, or complete blocks, having the same structure as above. Blocks within a program are called **procedures**, and correspond roughly to the idea of subroutines in Fortran. A procedure may be called from any other procedure, or recursively from itself.

Data

Data **types** are **integer**, **real**, **Boolean** and character **strings**. Arrays may be created out of these types. Identifiers are sequences of letters or digits, starting with a letter. All variables must be declared at the start of the block in which they are used. The scope of each variable is the extent of the block in which it is declared. This includes any sub-blocks declared inside the block. Any reference to a variable which has not been declared, or is outside its scope, is invalid.

Operations

All the operations of arithmetic are available, with rules for combining different types in the same expression. Some standard functions (sin, cos, tan, etc.) are available on most hardware representations of the language. User-defined functions are written as procedures. Relational operations are available for use in logical expressions.

Input/Output

The reference language contains no provisions for input or output. Input/output operations have subsequently been standardised. These are much simpler, but less powerful, than those in Fortran.

Control Structure

Two conditional branching constructions are available:

```
if <condition> then <statement>
```
and
```
if <condition> then <statement 1> else
   <statement 2>.
```

Since each statement may be a complete block, this is an extremely powerful construction. In most cases, it eliminates the need for the `go to` statement, which is, however, available.

Loops are constructed as follows:

```
for count: = c1 step c3 until c2 do <statement>
```

where the counter variable starts at value $c1$, and is increased in steps of $c3$ until it reaches $c2$. The statement may be a complete block. The counter variable is tested before each execution of the statement, and thus the loop may be repeated no times, if c1 is greater than c2 at the start.

Sequencing of instructions is achieved by placing a semi-colon between two consecutive statements. Statements do not have to start on new lines.

Example Program

The factorial of a number n may be written as:

factorial (0)=1

factorial (n)=n x factorial(n-1).

This is a recursive definition of factorials. It is used in the following program which calculates and outputs the factorials of five input numbers.

```
begin
    integer number, fact, count;
        integer procedure factorial (n);
            value n; integer n;
            begin integer i;
                if n = 0 then factorial:= 1
                    else begin i:= factorial (n-1);
                            factorial:= n*i
                        end
            end
    for count: = 1 step 1 until 5 do
        begin ininteger (0, number);
            fact: = factorial (number);
            outinteger (1, fact)
        end
end
```

Notes

1 The variables declared in the outer block are:

number: input number
fact: factorial of input number
count: counter

Their scope is the whole program.

Working variables n and i are declared in the inner blocks. Their scope is limited to these blocks.

2 The instructions ininteger and outinteger are for input and output respectively. The numbers 0 and 1 refer to particular input and output channels of the computer.

3 The recursive call to the factorial procedure is in the statement:

i: = factorial (n-1)

Assessment

The original objective of Algol 60 was to be a 'universal programming language'. This objective has not been achieved, as Algol has turned out to be scientifically oriented, with virtually no character handling facilities. Machine independence has been well achieved by the use of a separate reference language. A specific criticism of Algol is that its input/output facilities are very clumsy and weak. Algol 60 has not been used very widely.

Algol's biggest contribution has been to the theory of the design of computer languages. Ideas which were first used in Algol, such as a block, the scope of a variable and the if..then..else construction, have been copied by many other languages. The clear structure of the language is one of its strongest points. Algol has given rise to a whole family of computer languages, notably Pascal and Ada, often referred to as **Algol-like languages**.

19.3 Cobol

■ The name **Cobol** comes from the phrase **Co**mmon **B**usiness **O**riented **L**anguage. Cobol is a language designed for commercial data processing, and was developed between 1959 and 1960.

Development

In the late 1950s, computer manufacturers and users began to realise the need for a common, machine-independent, business-oriented programming language. In April 1959 a meeting was held at the University of Pennsylvania to discuss these views. At this meeting it was agreed that the sponsorship of the new language should be independent of any computer manufacturer. Accordingly, the USA Department of Defense was asked to co-ordinate the project. In May 1959, a meeting was held at the Pentagon in Washington. Present were representatives of all major computer manufacturers, prominent users and USA government departments. The meeting agreed on the desirable characteristics of a common business language, and set up a number of committees to carry out the development work. The overall steering committee was called **Codasyl** (Conference on data systems languages).

After a short, intensive period of formal meetings, with decisions being taken by vote, the initial specification of the language was completed. It was accepted by the Codasyl committee in January 1960, and published soon afterwards under the name of Cobol 60. By the end of 1960, Cobol programs were running on several different types of computer. Various revisions of Cobol were introduced during the 1960s. A standard version was accepted in 1968 by the American National Standards Institution (ANSI). This has subsequently been revised.

Objectives

The primary objectives of Cobol are machine independence, and a correspondence with current business practices. In addition, the following 'desirable characteristics' were identified at the initial planning meetings: maximum use of simple English; ease of use, even if less powerful than other languages; and 'to broaden the base of those who can state problems to computers'.

Character Set and Reserved Words

The Cobol character set includes capital letters and digits, and is implementation dependent. The set of reserved words is very large, including 'noise' words which can be included to improve the readability of programs, but are not acted on by the computer.

Program Structure

All Cobol programs consist of four **divisions**. These are:
Identification division: This identifies the program, its author and its purpose.
Environment division: This specifies the computer environment of the program, particularly peripheral devices used.

Data division: This specifies the nature and organisation of all the data used in the program. The identifiers of data items are declared, together with certain information about the data.

Procedure division: This specifies the operations to be carried out on the data.

Each division is organised into **sections**, **paragraphs**, **sentences** and **words**.

Data

The identifiers for data items can contain up to thirty alphanumeric characters, containing hyphen (-) characters if required. For example GROSS-PAY and PAY-RATE are valid data names. Data items are declared using **picture clauses** which specify the number and type of characters in the data item. For example:

```
77 NET-INCOME  IS  PICTURE  999V99
```

declares a data item containing five digits, two of which are after the decimal point.

Arrays are declared as follows:

```
01  PRICE-LIST
    02  ITEM-PRICE  PIC  99V99  OCCURS  20
```

declares an array named PRICE-LIST of twenty ITEM-PRICEs.

Operations

Separate words (known as **verbs**) are used for each arithmetic operation. For example:

```
MULTIPLY ITEM-PRICE BY NUMBER-SOLD GIVING SALE-
VALUE
```

However, the COMPUTE verb may be used if an expression is to be evaluated. A very useful verb is the SORT verb which causes a set of data items to be sorted into numerical or alphabetical order.

Input/Output

All input and output data is structured in **files**, composed of records. The verbs READ and WRITE are used to input and output records. The layout of input and output data is carefully specified, including **filler** items for spacing.

Control Structure

Both IF..THEN and IF..THEN..ELSE constructions are available for conditional branching. The GO TO statement is available for unconditional branching.

The PERFORM verb is used for loops. A paragraph can be repeated until a certain condition is true, or a specified number of times. Examples of each type are:

```
PERFORM WAGE-CALCULATION-PARAGRAPH UNTIL END-OF-
FILE MARKER='X'
```

and

```
PERFORM PRICE-CALCULATION VARYING ITEM-NUMBER
FROM 1 BY 1 UNTIL ITEM-NUMBER =20
```

Example Program

The following program inputs a file of names, addresses and telephone numbers. The file is sorted into alphabetical order of names, and then output on a line printer.

```
        IDENTIFICATION DIVISION
        PROGRAM-1D.
           DIRECTORY-SORT.
        DATE WRITTEN.
           16 MAY 1980.

        ENVIRONMENT DIVISION.
        INPUT-OUTPUT SECTION.
        FILE CONTROL.

           SELECT DIRECTORY-FILE-IN ASSIGN TO INPUT-DISK
           SELECT DIRECTORY-FILE ASSIGN TO WORK-DISK
           SELECT DIRECTORY-FILE-OUT ASSIGN TO LINE-PRINTER.

        DATA DIVISION.
        FILE SECTION.
        SD DIRECTORY-FILE

        01 ENTRY
           05   SURNAME                  PIC X(20).
           05   INITIALS                 PIC X(5).
           05   ADDRESS                  PIC X(60).
           05   TELEPHONE-NUMBER         PIC 9(7).

        FD DIRECTORY-FILE-IN
        01 ENTRY-IN
           05   SURNAME-IN               PIC X(20).
           05   INITIALS-IN              PIC X(5).
           05   ADDRESS-IN               PIC X(60).
           05   TELEPHONE-NUMBER-IN      PIC 9(7).

        FD DIRECTORY-FILE-OUT
        01 ENTRY-OUT
           05   SURNAME-OUT              PIC X(20).
           05   INITIALS-OUT             PIC X(5).
           05   ADDRESS-OUT              PIC X(60).
           05  TELEPHONE-NUMBER-OUT      PIC 9(7).

        WORKING STORAGE SECTION.
        01 MORE-ENTRIES-REMAIN-FLAG
           88 MORE-ENTRIES-REMAIN        PIC XXX    VALUE'YES'
           88 NO-MORE-ENTRIES-REMAIN     VALUE'YES'
                                         VALUE'NO'

        PROCEDURE DIVISION.
        SORTING SECTION.
           SORT DIRECTORY-FILE
                ASCENDING KEY SURNAME
                ASCENDING KEY INITIALS
                INPUT PROCEDURE LOAD-FILE
                GIVING DIRECTORY-FILE-OUT.
           STOP RUN.

        LOAD-FILE SECTION.
           OPEN INPUT DIRECTORY-FILE-IN
                OUTPUT DIRECTORY-FILE-OUT.
           READ DIRECTORY-FILE-IN
                AT END MOVE 'NO' TO MORE-ENTRIES-
                                         REMAIN-FLAG.

           IF   MORE-ENTRIES-REMAIN
                MOVE ENTRY-IN TO ENTRY
                RELEASE ENTRY.
```

Notes

1 There are three data files: an input file, a working file used by the
   SORT verb, and an output file. All three files have the same structure.
2 The sort is in ascending order of surnames, and ascending order of
   initials for the same surname.
3 The sorting section calls the loading section to input each directory
   entry. As soon as an entry has been loaded, it is released to the sort.

Assessment

One of Cobol's stated objectives is to 'broaden the base' of the people who can write computer programs. As Cobol is one of the world's most popular programming language, there is no doubt that this objective has been achieved.

Another objective is the 'maximum use of simple English' in programs. This is indeed achieved, although it has led to criticisms that Cobol is verbose and cumbersome. Undoubtedly, the overall structure of a Cobol program is clear, though there are some awkward features, such as the construction surrounding the sort verb.

The major setback to an even wider acceptance of Cobol has been the negative view of it taken by the university-based computing science community. In spite of this, Cobol's future seems secure for the time being, partly through the enormous investment in existing software, and partly because simple versions of Cobol are available for microcomputers. The main challenge to Cobol is the increasing use of software development tools (Chapter 23).

19.4 Basic

■ The name **Basic** comes from the phrase **B**eginner's **A**ll-Purpose **S**ymbolic **I**nstruction **C**ode. Basic is designed to introduce students, particularly those not studying science or mathematics, to computer programming. Basic was first developed between 1963 and 1964, and enhanced versions have appeared ever since.

Development

Basic language was developed by Thomas E. Kurtz and John Kemeny at Dartmouth College, USA. Dartmouth College is a small institution, with the main teaching emphasis on the humanities. Computing is taught as a supporting subject to other disciplines. During the early 1960s, several attempts were made to produce a simple, introductory programming language.

Basic language was designed as part of an overall plan to make it easier for students to use the college's computer. In the summer of 1963, John Kemeny began work on a Basic compiler, for a General Electric 225 computer. On 1st May 1964, at 4a.m., the first Basic program was run.

From the outset, Basic was used on an interactive, multi-access computer system. Work continued at Dartmouth on improvements and extensions to the language. Six Dartmouth editions of Basic have been released.

Basic was well received from its first release. Over the years it has established itself as the world's most popular educational programming language. Some microcomputers use Basic as their standard language. In addition, Basic has been extended to become a powerful scientific and commercial programming language in its own right. Basic has been extensively revised over the years, and modern implementations bear little resemblance to the original. Both compilers and interpreters are available for many versions of the language.

Objectives

The prime objective of Basic is ease of use, even at the expense of machine efficiency. In the words of Thomas Kurtz: 'The system would be designed to save the time of the user, even if it appeared that the computer was being "wasted".' Those were brave words in an era when computer time was much more expensive than user time. Today, in a world of cheap microcomputers, the situation has been reversed, and the objective makes sound commercial sense.

Character Set and Reserved Words

The character set used by Basic includes capital letters, digits and a few special symbols. Early versions of Basic use a very small set of reserved words, a minimal set numbering about a dozen. Extended versions of Basic require much larger sets of reserved words. Modern versions of Basic include lower-case letters.

Program Structure

A Basic program consists of a set of numbered statements, which (in most versions) are executed in order of statement number. Subprograms may be written, but they are not clearly differentiated from the main program, with no local variables or parameter passing. Modern versions, however, include procedures and functions with local variables and parameter passing.

Data

The original data types available were **numeric** and **character** string variables and constants. Arrays may be constructed out of either variable type. Now a much larger range of types is available. Identifiers in early versions consisted of a single letter, optionally followed by a single digit. Character string variable identifiers end with a $ symbol. Thus valid identifiers were restricted to such combinations as:

```
X, A3, M$ and J3$.
```

Contemporary versions of Basic permit long identifier names. Data items need not be declared before use, and the scope of variables is the procedure in which they are declared or used, unless they are declared to be shared.

Operations

Arithmetic operations, standard functions and user-defined functions are available. Relational operators may be used in IF statements. One of the strengths of Basic is the number of character string operations and functions which are available. These make manipulation of non-numeric data extremely simple. For example, if A$ = "CAT" and B$ = "FISH", then the instruction:

```
LET C$ = A$ + B$
```

assigns to C$ the value "CATFISH", using the joining operator +.

Input/Output

The input and output operations combine simplicity with considerable power. Unless otherwise specified, printed output is automatically arranged in columns. Most versions of Basic permit data transfer to or from named data **files** on backing store. This enables programs to manipulate large sets of data, and pass this data from one program to another.

Control Structure

Conditional branching is achieved by several forms of the IF..THEN construction, including:

```
IF  <condition> THEN <statement number>
IF  <condition> THEN <statement>
```

and

```
IF <condition> THEN <statement> ELSE <statement>
```

In the first type, control passes to the statement specified if the condition is true, otherwise it passes to the statement after the IF statement. For example:

```
IF  A>5  THEN  60
```

passes control to statement 60 if A is greater than 5.

Recent versions of Basic permit compound conditions joined by AND or OR, and blocks of statements after THEN and ELSE. A GOTO statement is available for unconditional branching.

The FOR...NEXT construction is used for program loops. A counter is used to control the number of times that the loop is repeated. For example:

```
10 FOR K = 1 TO 20 STEP 1

        <part of program to be repeated twenty times>
100   NEXT K
```

In most versions of Basic, the loop is repeated zero or more times.

The DO...LOOP construction is available for loops repeated until a condition becomes true, or while a condition remains true.

Example Program

The subprogram shown below is part of a word processing program. It is written in an early version of Basic, with single-letter variable. The subprogram takes a line of text, stored as the string variable T$, and inserts the string A$ into the line, immediately before the string B$. For example, if the line of text T$ is:

```
NOW IS THE TIME FOR ALL GOOD TO COME TO THE AID OF
THE PARTY
```

and the character string A$ is MEN, and B$ is TO, then the result is:

```
NOW IS THE TIME FOR ALL GOOD MEN TO COME TO THE AID
OF THE PARTY
```

The subprogram uses some of the string manipulation functions available in Basic. Firstly, the position of the string B$ in the text is located. Then the text is split into two parts, the second starting with the characters in B$. Finally the string A$, followed by a space, is inserted between the two parts.

```
1000 REM SUBPROGRAM TO INSERT INTO LINE OF TEXT
1010 REM
1020 REM LOCATE POSITION OF STRING B$ IN TEXT T$
1030 LET P = POS (T$, B$)
1040 REM IF P = 0, STRING IS NOT IN TEXT, GO TO END
                               OF SUBPROGRAM
1050 IF P = 0 GO TO 1130
1060 REM SPLIT LINE T$ INTO TWO PARTS
1070 LET U$ = MID$ (T$, 1, P-1)
1080 LET V$ = MID$ (T$, P, LEN (T$))
1090 REM U$ IS THE FIRST PART, V$ IS FROM B$ TO THE
                                                 END
```

```
1100 REM INSERT STRING A$ BETWEEN THE TWO PARTS
1110 LET T$ = U$ + A$ + " " + V$
1120 REM
1130 RETURN
```

Notes

1 Lines starting with the word REM are remarks.
2 Most of the work is done by the Basic functions POS and MID$, and the joining operator +.
3 The line numbers of the statements go up in steps of 10. This is normal practice in writing programs in Basic.
4 In some versions of Basic, the MID$ function is called by a different name, and the joining operator is not +, but &.

Assessment

In its primary objective of simplicity, Basic has undoubtedly been extremely successful. In 1978, one of the authors of Basic, Thomas Kurtz, estimated that five million schoolchildren had learned Basic language. This simplicity is achieved through simple yet powerful instructions, particularly for character handling and input/output. Basic is particularly well suited to interactive computing, games and simulations, as well as to its original application area – teaching programming to beginners.

A number of criticisms of Basic language can be made, and as time goes by, its popularity is diminishing because of them. The most serious is that Basic, in its original form, gave very little assistance in the writing of well-structured programs. Subprograms were not clearly separated from each other, with no mechanism for parameter passing. It was quite easy to develop bad programming habits through the careless use of Basic.

Various enhanced versions of Basic have been developed to counter these criticisms, but they have worsened the problem of standardisation. In spite of these problems, Basic continues to be used as an introductory programming language, and is extensively used in the computing industry.

19.5 Pascal

■ Pascal language is named after the French mathematician and philosopher, Blaise Pascal. It was developed between 1968 and 1971.

Development

By contrast with Fortran, Algol 60, Cobol and Basic, **Pascal** is the work of one person - Niklaus Wirth, a university professor in Zurich, Switzerland. Using Algol 60 as a basis, Wirth set out to design a language suitable for teaching computer programming to university students. The first draft of the language was made in 1968. A compiler for Pascal, also written by Wirth, was operational in 1970. Pascal was first published in 1971, and a revised report appeared in 1973.

Since its publication, Pascal has gained increasingly wide acceptance at universities and for scientific and engineering applications. Pascal is available on some microcomputers. Its use is spreading to schools and to the business computing community.

Objectives

The primary objectives of Pascal are best expressed by its author, Niklaus

Wirth: 'The development of the language Pascal is based on two principal aims. The first is to make available a language suitable to teach programming as a systematic discipline based on certain fundamental concepts clearly and naturally reflected by the language. The second is to develop implementations of this language which are both reliable and efficient on presently available computers.'

Pascal is a compromise between these aims. On the one hand, it has a concise, consistent abstract structure. On the other hand, it is sufficiently close to modern computer architectures to be easily and efficiently implemented. An international standard version of the language has been agreed on, and is periodically revised.

Character Set and Reserved Words

Most implementations of Pascal use upper and lower case letters, digits and a number of special characters. Pascal has a fairly large set of reserved words, including a few not found in other programming languages.

Program Structure

Like Algol 60, Pascal is a block structured language. However, a Pascal block is slightly more restricted than one in Algol 60. In outline, the structure of a Pascal program is as follows:

A **program** is a **program heading** followed by a **block**.
A **block** is a number of **declarations** (of labels, constants, data types, variables, **procedures** and **functions**), followed by a set of **statements**.
A **procedure** is a **procedure heading** followed by a **block**.
A **function** is a **function heading** followed by a **block** .
A **statement** is a simple statement or a set of statements enclosed by the words **begin** and **end**.

Statements are separated by semi-colons, and do not have to be on separate lines. It can be seen that a program may contain a number of procedure and function blocks, which may themselves contain procedure and function blocks. A procedure or function may be called recursively from itself.

Data

One of the strengths of Pascal is the variety of **data types** available, and the provision for user-defined data types. This means that a person writing a Pascal program can construct data types, either by combining the standard types, or by listing all the values a data item can have. Pascal permits the use of **pointers**, which are data items holding the address of other data items. Pascal is unusual in having the operations **new** and **dispose** which create and delete data items pointed to in this way. In addition to individual data items, **arrays**, **sets** and **records**, Pascal language contains the concept of a **file**. All input and output takes place via a few simple operations on files. **Enumeration literals** can be used in conjunction with arrays.

Like Algol 60, Pascal includes the concept of **scope**. The scope of a data item is the block within which it is declared, and any sub-blocks contained in that block.

Operations

Pascal contains all the arithmetic (except raising to powers), relational and logical operations. In addition, the set operations **union**, **intersection** and **set difference** are available. In all cases, the types of the data items used must be compatible with the operations. In addition to the usual arithmetic functions, there are a number of functions to handle non-numeric data. For example, there are functions to find the successor and predecessor of a given data item in its set of values.

Input/Output

All input and output, as well as transfers to and from backing store, take place via files of data. A few simple operations enable data items to be transferred to or from these files. Each file is associated with a particular peripheral device.

Control Structure

Like Algol 60, Pascal has both `if..then` and `if..then..else` constructions for conditional branching. The `goto` statement is available, but its use is discouraged. Pascal has three different constructions for program loops. If a loop is to be repeated a certain number of times, the statement is:

```
for count := startvalue to endvalue do <statement>
```

The counter variable is automatically increased in steps of 1. If a loop must be repeated at least once, until a certain condition becomes true, the construction is:

```
repeat <statement> until <condition>
```

If a loop must be repeated zero or more times, while a certain condition holds, the construction is:

```
while <condition> do <statement>
```

In this case, the condition is tested before each repetition of the loop. In the previous case, the condition is tested after each repetition. In all of the above examples, 'statement' may be a set of statements, enclosed by the words `begin..end`.

Example Program

The following procedure of a program shows how a list can be constructed using pointers. The program inputs the names of twenty-five people, and stores them in a list, structured as in Figure 19.1. Note that there is a pointer called first pointing to the start of the list. The pointer at the end of the list does not point to anything – it has the value **nil**.

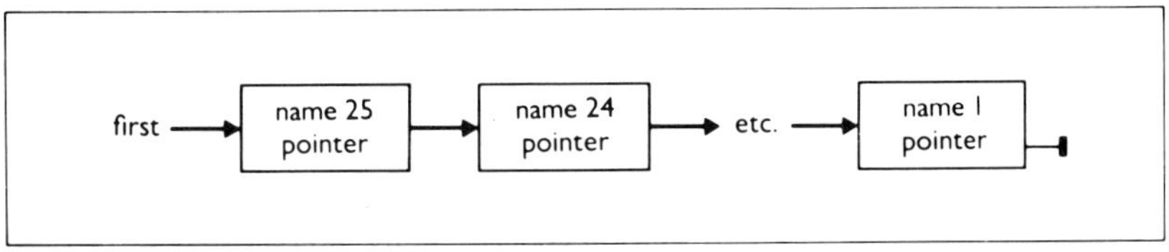

Figure 19.1

```
procedure makelist;
type
     list = ^person;        (* pointer to person *)
     person = record
          name: array [1..20] of char;
          next: list        (* pointer to next person *)
     end;
var first, newperson: list;
```

```
                                    (* front pointer and list
                                              element *)
            count: integer;        (* loop counter *)
            newname: name;
     begin
         first: = nil;
         for count:= 1 to 25 do
           begin
             readname (newname);
                                    (* procedure,not shown,to
                                            read a name *)
             new(newperson);(* create storage space for
                                    new list element *)
             newperson^.next:= first;
                                    (* link pointer to existing
                                              list *)
             newperson^.name:= newname;
                                    (* fill in name of new
                                            person *)
             first:= newperson;
                                    (* change front pointer to
                                       new list element *)
           end
     end
```

Notes

1 Diagramatically, the sequence of operations is as follows:
   Create storage space for new list element: Figure 19.2.
   Link pointer of new list element to existing list, and fill in new
   name:
   Figure 19.3.
   Change front pointer to point to new list element: Figure 19.4.

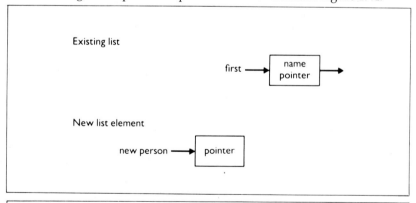

Figure 19.2

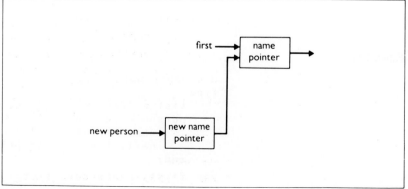

Figure 19.3

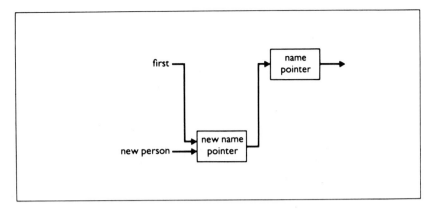

Figure 19.4

2 Notice how comments can be inserted in the program.
3 The notation 'newperson^' means 'the data item to which the
pointer newperson points'.
The notation '.next' refers to the field called 'next' in the record.
Thus 'newperson^.next' means the field called 'next' in the record
pointed to by 'newperson'.

Assessment

Pascal was designed to illustrate certain key concepts in programming,
such as structured programming, and various types and structures of
data. In general, Pascal achieves this objective very well. It combines
simplicity with considerable power. Pascal generally tries to provide one
mechanism to implement each programming concept. Short cuts are
deliberately discouraged. While this sometimes makes programs
somewhat longer than they might be in other languages, it does help
identify, isolate and eliminate program errors.

Particular strengths of Pascal are its handling of data types and
structure, and its disciplined use of pointers. Some people would criticise
its input/output facilities as being rather restrictive, but they do have the
advantage of simplicity. Pascal language has been developed in the light
of experience in other high level languages. It has already gained wide
acceptance, both in the academic world and in industry, and the number
of users continues to increase.

19.6 C

■ C is a modern, general-purpose programming language
whichcombines high level features such as block structure, the ability to
handle data types and recursion with a number of features more
commonly found in low level languages.

Development

C was designed by Dennis Ritchie in 1978, originally for use on the
Digital Equipment PDP-11 range of computers. The development of the
language has been closely associated with the development of the Unix
operating system. Both Unix and C have subsequently been implemented
on an increasingly large number of other computers, ranging from
workstations to supercomputers. They are both becoming industry
standard software items.

Objectives

The main objective of C is to provide a powerful, versatile programming language which leads to the generation of efficient object code. C has high level features such as block structures and modern control constructions, while operating on the same objects as low level languages: characters, numbers and addresses. By contemporary standards, C is a small language, and close to the architecture of a typical single-processor computer.

Character Set and Reserved Words

C uses upper and lower case letters, digits and a small number of special characters. C has a fairly small set of reserved words.

Program Structure

Like Algol 60 and Pascal, C is a block structured language. A program consists of a main program, which calls a number of functions to perform specific tasks. There are no procedures in C, and functions may not be defined within other functions. Statements are terminated by colons, and do not have to be on separate lines. A function may be called recursively from itself.

Data

C concentrates on a small range of data types. These include characters, integers (which may be short or long) and floating point numbers (which may be single or double precision). Arrays, structures (corresponding to records in most other languages) and unions may be constructed from these elementary types, and pointers can be set up to point to them. Functions may return any single-valued data type. Although every variable in a program must be declared to be of a particular data type, the rules of types are not as strict as they are in Pascal. For example, pointers may be used to access array elements, and for some purposes characters may be regarded as integers. All data items must be declared before use, and the scope of a data item is the function or program segment in which it is declared.

Operations

C contains all the arithmetic (except raising to powers), relational and logical operations. It also contains the Boolean operations AND, OR, exclusive OR and shift, and the **auto-increment** and **auto-decrement** operations commonly found in machine and assembly languages. For example, if n has the value 5, the assignment:

```
x = n++ ;
```

sets x to 5 and then adds 1 to n. If n is 9, the assignment:

```
x = --n ;
```

decreases n by 1 and then sets x to its new value (now 8). These operations enable very concise programs to be written to count through data structures. There is a 'shorthand' way of writing such expressions as:

```
i = i + 2 ;
```

which may instead be written as:

```
i += 2 ;
```

again leading to very compact code.

Input/Output

C has no built-in facilities for input and output; these are created by using the library of standard input/output facilities which is provided with every implementation of C. This library includes functions to get individual characters and numbers from the keyboard, print data with a specified format and read from and write to files on backing store.

Control Structure

C has the if..then..else constructions for conditional branching, and the case construction for multi-way branches. Statements may be bracketed into blocks for use with these constructions. The go to statement is available, but its use is contrary to the design principles of C.

There are three types of loop construction. The while construction tests the condition to continue the loop at the start of each repetition; the do ... while construction has the test at the end. The for construction is more general than that in most other languages. The loop:

```
for   (expression_1; expression_2; expression_3)
      statement ;
```

is equivalent to:

```
expression_1 ;
while (expression_2) {
       statement ;
       expression_3 ;
}
```

Example Program

The program below, consisting of a main program and a function, reads a set of words from input and sorts them in alphabetical order into a tree structure. Each node of the tree contains a pointer to the word at the node, and left and right subtree pointers. See Sections 4.9 and 16.9. The program starts with a declaration of the data structure required.

```
struct tree_node {                       /* tree node structure */
    char *word;                          /* pointer to word */
    struct tree_node *left;              /* pointer to left subtree */
    struct tree_node *right;             /* pointer to right subtree */
}
main ()                                  /* start of main program */
{
    struct tree_node *root, *load_tree();
                                         /* declares data item root and function
                                            load_tree as pointers to trees */
    char word[20];                       /* declares an array of 20 characters */
    int test_word, get_word();           /* declares integer variable test_word
and                                         function get_word */
    root = NULL;                         /* start with a null tree pointer
    while ((test_word = get_word(word)) ! = EOF)
                                         /* input next word and test for end-of
                                            file */
            root = load_tree(root, word);
                                         /* load next word into tree */
}                                        /* end of main program */
struct tree_node *load_tree(tree_ptr, wrd)
                                         /* function to load word into tree */

struct tree_node *tree_ptr;              /* tree_ptr is pointer to a tree */
char *wrd;                               /* wrd is a pointer to a character
                                            array */
```

```
{
        struct tree_node *tree_allocate();
                                        /* function tree_allocate returns a
                                           pointer to a tree */
        char *string_save();            /* function string_save returns a
                                           pointer to a character array */
        int str_compare();              /* function str_compare returns an
                                           integer */
        if (tree_ptr == NULL) {         /* a new word is to be appended */
                tree_ptr = tree_ allocate(); /* allocate a new pointer */
                tree_ptr->word = string_save(wrd);
                                        /* link wrd to the node pointer */
                tree_ptr->left = tree_ptr->right = NULL;
                                        /* make null left and right subtree
                                           pointers */
        } else if (str_compare(wrd, tree_ptr->word) < 0)
                tree_ptr->left = load_tree(tree_ptr->left, wrd);
                                        /* look at left subtree */
        else tree_ptr->right = load_tree(tree_ptr->right, wrd);
                                        /* look at right subtree */
        return (tree_ptr);
}
```

Notes

1 Brackets { } are used to create blocks of statements.
2 Notice how comments can be inserted in the program.
3 The functions get_word, string_save and str_compare are called from this program, but not defined in it.
4 The notation != is used to mean 'not equal to'.
5 The notation *var means that var is a pointer to some other object.

Assessment

C is a concise, efficient programming language with facilities for the creation of carefully-structured programs and data. It is not as elegant as Pascal, but is rapidly emerging as an alternative to it for a wide range of commercial, industrial and research applications. A particular strength of C is its suitability for the writing of systems software: almost all of the Unix operating system is written in C, as are all Unix utility programs. The association with Unix, and the availability of an international standard version, are two reasons for the rapid growth of C. It is now one of the most widely-used programming languages.

19.7 Lisp

■ Lisp (LISt Processing language) is a programming language designed for artificial intelligence work. Until quite recently its use was restricted to a small group of researchers, but at present, with the resurgence of artificial intelligence applications, Lisp is being used much more widely.

Development

Lisp originated in 1959 in the artificial intelligence group at MIT under John McCarthy. It is intended for problems which involve symbol manipulation and recursion. Most artificial intelligence work falls broadly into this category, hence the popularity of Lisp for these purposes.

Objectives

The aim of Lisp is to provide a vehicle for the writing of programs which are based on symbol manipulation. The most common programming tasks are generating and testing alternatives, and searching large bodies of information for patterns. Lisp is a small, concise language ideal for these purposes. It bears very little resemblance to any other programming language.

Character Set and Reserved Words

Lisp uses upper and lower case letters, digits and special characters, and has a small number of reserved words.

Program Structure

Lisp is a functional programming language. A top-level function calls lower-level functions in order to compute its result. Library functions may be called for elementary operations.

Data

The fundamental data element in Lisp is the **atom**, which may be an identifier or a number. Atoms are built into lists by the use of brackets. For example, (A B C) is a list of three atoms, and (A (B C) D) is a list containing two atoms and a sublist (B C). The notation (A | B) indicates a list with atom A at the head and the list B as the tail.

Operations

Processing in Lisp is in terms of functions, of which there are five elementary ones:

```
car[(A B C)] = A                        ... the head of the list
cdr[(A B C)] = (B C)                     ... the tail of the list
cons[(A; (B C)] = (A B C)               ... the constructor function
eq[A; A] = T              (for True)  ... equality of atoms
atom [(A B C)] = Nil      (for False) ... test for an atom
```

(The function names car and cdr are derived from associated assembly language instructions on the first computer on which Lisp was implemented. They are sometimes re-named head and tail respectively.)

Arithmetic operations are expressed as functions: sum [A; B] gives the sum of the atoms A and B. Arithmetic relations are expressed as Boolean-valued functions, or **predicates**: lessp[A; B] is true if A is less than B.

Control Structures

The conditional construction is:

```
[p1 -> e1; p2 -> e2 ... pn -> en]
```

where p1, p2 ... pn are predicates and e1, e2 ... en are expressions. The construction is scanned sequentially, and the first expression corresponding to a predicate which is true is evaluated. There is also a more conventional if ... then ... else construction, structured as a list:

```
(if A B C)
```

If predicate A is true then the value of B is chosen, else the value of C is selected.

A program in Lisp is written as a top-level function which invokes lower-level functions in its implementation. Functions may be processed by other functions, and giving Lisp programs unlimited possibilities for self-modification.

Example Program

The recursive function defined below tests whether the data item `elt` is a member of the list `lst`. The logic of the function is as follows:

```
if lst is non-empty
      then if elt is the head of lst
            then the function is true
            else check whether elt is a
                  member of the tail of lst
      else the function is false
```

The program is as follows:

```
(define member (elt lst)
      (if (consp (lst))
            (if eq (elt car (lst))
                  T
                  (member (elt cdr (lst))))
            Nil ))
```

Notes

1 The program code is a direct implementation of the

```
if...then...else
```

construction of the algorithm.
2 The function is recursive, calling itself in the second last line.
3 Even a short program such as this involves a large number of brackets!

Assessment

Lisp has been the mainstream artificial intelligence programming language for many years, and most AI programs of any significance have been written in Lisp. Lisp has been the starting point for a number of more recent non-procedural programming languages, notably Prolog.

An early problem with Lisp was that it did not run very efficiently on most computers. In recent years a number of dedicated Lisp workstations have appeared, with hardware and low-level software designed to support Lisp very efficiently. One possible evolution of Lisp is into an applicative language, with no destructive assignments, which will bring it into line with dataflow and graph reduction architectures.

19.8 Prolog

■ **Prolog** (**PRO**gramming in **LOG**ic) is a declarative programming language which has recently become increasingly popular. It is a logic-based language, suitable for a wide variety of database and artificial intelligence applications.

Development

Prolog was developed by Alain Colmerauer and his colleagues at Marseilles University in 1972. Research and development has continued in the UK, notably at Imperial College under Robert Kowalski, and in Japan.

Objectives

The objective of Prolog is to provide a rigorous logical basis for the development of a wide range of computer applications. Prolog allows a programmer to state a computing task in terms of a description of the data objects required, and their logical relationships, rather than a 'recipe' of processing steps which the computer must carry out. An important application area of Prolog is education, where it can be used to teach logic, problem-solving or programming, and be used with a variety of educational databases.

Character Set and Reserved Words

Prolog uses upper and lower case letters, digits and a small number of reserved words.

Features

There is no clear distinction, in Prolog, between data, processing operations and control facilities. A Prolog program consists of a set of declarations, all of which are valid simultaneously. A simple declaration, also known as a **predicate**, is of the form:

```
topic-of(Computing, Logic)
```

Predicates may be combined into **Horn clauses** of the form:

```
teaches(x, y) if topic-of(z, y) and
               assigned-to(x, z)
```

(This means that teacher x teaches topic y if y is a topic of subject z and teacher x is assigned to teach subject z.)

Because predicates can contain constants or variables, both the processing and data structuring aspects of conventional programming are expressed in Prolog in a uniform notation based on logic. The data in predicates can be single items or lists with the same rules for construction as used in Lisp (Section 19.7). For example, membership of a list is defined by the clauses:

```
member-of(x, (x | z))
member-of(x, (y | z)) if member-of(x, z)
```

(In other words, a data item x is a member of a list if it is the head of the list or if it is a member of the tail of the list. This is the Prolog equivalent of the example Lisp program.)

A Prolog program is activated by queries of the form:

```
which(x, causes-deformity(x, stunted growth))
```

This causes the Prolog interpreter to check the predicate in the query against those in the program, examining lower-level predicates and 'cancelling out' those known to be true or false, until a result is obtained, or a contradiction arises, in which case the query has no result.

Input/Output

Prolog has a number of standard predicates for input and output. Many implementations have predicates for graphics output and some include control facilities.

Example Program

An example of a Prolog program which uses a simple aircraft flight database is as follows:

```
calls-at(BA11, (London Bombay Singapore Sydney
               Melbourne))
calls-at(BA23, (London New-York))
calls-at(BA67, (London Madrid Las-Palmas
               Buenos-Aries))
```

```
calls-at(BA39, (London Berlin Moscow ))
calls-at(BA27, (London Madrid Cairo Nairobi))

member-of(x, (x | z))
member-of(x, (y | z)) if member-of(x, z)

destination-of(x, y) if calls-at(y, z)
                       and member-of(x, z)
```

The last clause is interpreted as x is a destination of flight y if y has a list of calling points z and x is a member of the list z.

A query such as:

```
which(y, destination-of(Madrid, y))
```

meaning 'Which flights have Madrid as a destination?' produces the results:

```
BA67
BA27
no (more) answers.
```

Assessment

Prolog has gone from being a fringe programming language to the mainstream of artificial intelligence work, and the basis of an increasing number of applications. There are still some problems to be ironed out, notably in the way Prolog deals with negative information. Recent work includes **Parlog**, a parallel implementation of Prolog, and various attempts to synthesise elements of Prolog and Lisp, or Prolog and a procedural language.

19.9 Conclusion

■ This small sample from the rapidly increasing population of high level programming languages illustrates some of the similarities and some of the differences that exist between these languages. Each language studied has its strengths and weaknesses, and each is best suited to a certain class of computer applications.

When choosing a high level language for a particular application, the following criteria are taken into consideration:

- The nature of the application: whether it is a commercial, industrial or scientific task, whether it is real-time, batch processing, transaction processing, an expert system or primarily a control application. In each case, there are certain special-purpose languages which may be particularly suitable.
- The computer(s) on which the application is to run, and whether the software is to be developed on these computers. The degree of portability of the language is an essential factor. If the software is not to be developed on the ultimate host computers, cross-compilers (Section 20.2) and associated software tools are needed.
- The software development tools available: if the program is a standard commercial application, for example, most of the software can probably be developed using a program generator (Section 23.7).
- Whether the software is to be developed within the company or organisation which is to use it, or whether an outside software house is to be commissioned to do the work. In the latter case, the choice of languages is wider.
- The budget for the software development, and the time allocated to do the work. If time and money are short, a language which is familiar to the company is more likely to be chosen.

Exercise 19

1 Select any two of the languages described in this chapter. Answer the following questions, comparing the selected languages.

    a) Compare the input and output facilities provided by the languages. State, with reasons, which language is simpler and which language is more powerful in this respect.

    b) Compare the provisions for calculation provided by the languages. State, with reasons, in which language complicated calculations can be expressed more concisely.

    c) Compare and contrast the provisions for conditional and unconditional branching in the languages.

    d) Compare the facilities for making decisions based on rules, and for handling data in structures such as lists.

2 Of all the languages described in the chapter, Algol 60 is probably the least widely used. In the light of your studies of the chapter, suggest some reasons for this.

3 Give your own views on the idea of a universal programming language.

4 What is the main difference between the objectives of Algol 60 and those of Pascal? What difference do you think this has made in the relative popularity of the two languages?

5 Which of the languages mentioned in this chapter come closest to being a general-purpose language, suitable for scientific, commercial and educational computing? Give reasons for your choice.

6 a) Suggest at least two reasons for the persistent popularity of Fortran, and two for that of Cobol.

    b) Give at least two reasons for the increasing popularity of C.

7 Select a programming language not discussed in this chapter. Using suitable references, write a concise account of the language, under the same headings as those used in this chapter. Some suitable languages are Algol 68, Simula, Modula, PL/1, Logo, Comal, Occam, Hope and Ada.

♦ 8 Consider the problem of printing the digits of a number in reverse order. One method is as follows:

```
reverse digits is:
        output last digit of number
        if digits remain
                then reverse remaining digits.
```

This method is recursive, because it uses itself repeatedly until there are no more digits to reverse. A procedure of a Pascal program to carry out this process is as follows:

```
procedure reverse (n:integer);
begin
        write (n mod 10);        (* the remainder when
                                 n is divided by 10 *)
        if n div 10<>0           (* the integer part
                                 of n divided by 10 *)
            then reverse (n div 10)      (* recursive
                                         call *)
end;
```

    a) Write down the steps carried out by this procedure if it is supplied with the number 8271.

A portion of a program in Basic language, to carry out the same task, is as follows:

```
1000 REM PRINT DIGITS OF NUMBER N IN REVERSE ORDER
1010 LET X = INT (N/10)        : REM INTEGER PART OF N
                               DIVIDED BY 10
```

```
1020 PRINT N-10*X          : REM REMAINDER WHEN N IS
                             DIVIDED BY 10
1030 IF X = 0 THEN RETURN
1040 LET N = X
1050 GO TO 1010
```

   b) Dry run this program segment, using the number 8271.

   c) In your opinion, which program segment is easier to understand? Give reasons for your answer.

   d) Write an equivalent program segment in one of the other languages introduced in this chapter. Comment on similarities and differences between it and the above program segments.

9 Comment on the relative emphasis on arithmetic operations in the eight languages studied.

10 Rank the case study languages in order of ease of readability of programs. Compare your ordering with that of others and comment on it.

20 Compilers and Interpreters

This chapter concerns the process of translating a program written in a high level language to an equivalent program in a machine language. The two major approaches to language translation, namely **compilation** and **interpretation**, are discussed. Also discussed are some of the other software items which are used in conjunction with language translators in the development of applications programs.

20.1 The Objectives of Language Translation

■ The main objective of a language translation program is to convert a program or part of a program in a high level language into an equivalent program in a machine language, sometimes via one or more intermediate languages. The input language is called the **source language**, and the output language the **object** or **target language**. The translation program itself is written in a **base language**. A language translation program can be represented as a **T diagram**, shown in Figure 20.1. An example of the T diagram for a Basic language compiler, written in Z80 assembly language, producing Z80 machine code, is shown in Figure 20.2.

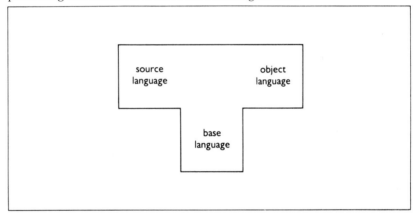

Figure 20.1
A T diagram of a language translation program

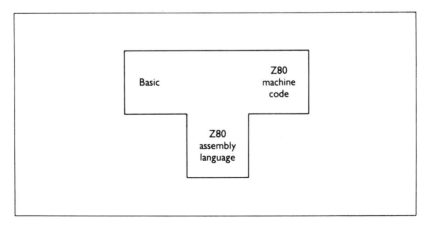

Figure 20.2
An example of a T diagram

A second objective of a translation program is to identify any errors in a source program. **Diagnostic** error messages are output, to assist the programmer to correct the errors.

Thirdly, many language translators attempt to produce object code which is as efficient as possible. The process of making the code more efficient is known as **optimisation**.

Fourthly, a language translator is a part of a set of software development tools, and one of its aims is to integrate its workings with the other tools as well as possible.

Finally, the translation program itself should be efficient. It should not take too long to translate a source program, and must not occupy too much space in the main store of the computer. This objective conflicts to some extent with the other objectives, particularly the third one. Most translation programs represent a compromise between this and the other objectives.

20.2 Principles of Compilation and Interpretation

■ **Compilers** and **interpreters** represent two different approaches to the task of enabling programs written in a high level language to be run.

A **compiler** translates a source code module (which may be a complete program, or part of one) in a high level language into an equivalent object code module in a machine language. The object code may then be linked to other object code modules to form a complete program which can be executed. The translation process is applied to the source code module as a whole. Source statements may be separated or combined, and there is not always a direct correspondence between a source program statement and one or more object program instructions.

An **interpreter** transforms a computer into a high level language machine. The computer then runs programs in a high level language. Each source program statement is analysed, and then executed. Object code is not produced. Most interpreters can only work on complete programs.

Compilers and interpreters have in common the process of analysing the source code, though the methods they use differ. Having analysed the source code, compilers then generate equivalent object code, whereas interpreters execute the source code directly. Compilers are more sophisticated than interpreters, as the latter can do little by way of optimisation. Simple languages such as Basic and Logo, and the logic language Prolog, are more commonly interpreted rather than compiled. Early microcomputers were too small to run compilers.

20.3 Extended BNF

■ One of the most useful ways of describing the syntax of a programming language is to express it as a set of rules, using a notation known as **extended BNF**. A BNF rule shows how one syntactic structure of a language is made up of other structures. For example, a small class of English sentences can be specified by the following BNF rules:

```
<sentence>   ::=  <noun> <verb>
<noun>       ::=  John | Paul | George | Ringo
<verb>       ::=  eats | sleeps | sings
```

In ordinary English, these rules are:

A sentence is a noun followed by a verb.
A noun is 'John' or 'Paul' or 'George' or 'Ringo'.
A verb is 'eats' or 'sleeps' or 'sings'.

These rules can be used to produce sentences like:

```
John eats
Paul sings
Ringo sleeps
```

On the other hand, the sentence:

```
John eats George
```

is not in accordance with the rules.

A much larger class of sentences is obtained by adding the following rules:

```
<sentence>    ::=<clause> <conjunction>
                 <sentence> | <clause>
<clause>      ::=<noun> <verb>
<conjunction> ::=and | or
```

The first of these rules is called **recursive** since the same element, namely <sentence>, appears on the left and the right of the ::= symbol. Note that the recursive element must not appear immediately to the right of the ::= symbol.

These rules allow the production of sentences such as:

John eats and Paul sings or Ringo sleeps

However, the sentence:

John or Paul sings

is not in accordance with the rules.

The following BNF rules specify the structure of a fairly wide class of decimal numbers:

```
<decimal number>   ::= <decimal point> <number>
                   |<number> <decimal point> <number>
<number>           ::= <digit> <number> | <digit>
<digit>            ::= 0 | 1 | 2 | 3 | 4 | 5 |
                       6 | 7 | 8 | 9
<decimal point>    ::= .
```

A formal way of using these rules to analyse a number is as follows:

Example I: 97.652

	9	7	.	6	5	2
rule 3	<digit>	<digit>	.	<digit>	<digit>	<digit>
rule 4:	<digit>	<digit>	<decimal point>	<digit>	<digit>	<digit>
rule 2:	<digit>	<number>	<decimal point>	<digit>	<digit>	<number>
rule 2:		<number>	<decimal point>	<digit>	<number>	
rule 2:		<number>	<decimal point>	<number>		
rule 1:			<decimal number>			

Example 2: 3.

	3	.
rules 3 and 4:	<digit>	<decimal point>

No further rules can be applied. This is not a valid decimal number as defined by the above rules.

Extended BNF Features

Two extensions are now used to the above BNF notation, hence the name extended BNF. The first is for optional elements, which are enclosed in curly brackets: { }. The second is for zero or more repetitions of an element, which is enclosed in square brackets: [ ]. For example, the syntax of a signed integer may be written as:

```
<signed integer>:={<sign>} <digit> [<digit>]
```

This means that a signed integer is an optional sign, followed by a digit, followed by zero or more additional digits. The definition of a decimal number given above may be re-written in extended BNF as:

```
<decimal number>  ::=  {<number>} <decimal point>
                                          <number>
<number>          ::=  <digit> [<digit>]
<digit>           ::=  0 | 1 | 2 | 3 | 4 | 5 | 6 |
                       7 | 8 | 9
<decimal point>   ::=  .
```

Rules in extended BNF, or **syntax diagrams**, which are a diagrammatic representation of the same constructions, are used to specify the structure of high level languages, and correspond closely to the code of the syntax analysis portions of the compilers for the languages.

20.4 Editing

■ The first stage of software development is to enter and edit the source code. For this purpose, an **editor** is used. The editor enables source code segments to be typed and amended, and has text manipulation facilities to speed up the process. To an increasing extent, word processing packages (Section 21.2) are used for editing source code.

Some compilers include an interactive editor. As soon as a line of program has been edited, it is translated into machine code, and any necessary amendments are made to the machine code version of other program lines. In this way the program remains in a compiled state during editing. It is ready to run throughout the process.

20.5 The Steps of Compilation

■ The main steps of compilation are **lexical analysis**, **syntax analysis** and **code generation**. These are now discussed, together with three other important features of compilers, namely a **dictionary**, **optimisation** and **error handling**. All compilers include these features, though in some they are more distinct than in others.

Lexical Analysis

Lexical analysis is the first stage in the processing of a source program by a compiler. It may be regarded as 'tidying up' the source program, ready for more detailed analysis. Lexical analysis generally has to perform three tasks:

- Changing the source code into a form which is independent of the input device.
- Removing redundant information such as spaces and comments.
- Dealing with reserved words and composite symbols such as ':=', replacing them with **tokens** which are used during syntax analysis.

For example, consider the following segment of a program in Basic language:

```
200 FOR I = 1 TO N STEP 1
210 LET X (I) = 0 :REM INITIALISE ARRAY
215 NEXT I
```

A lexical analysis might produce the following:

```
[L45] [T16] I = 1 [T17] N [T18] 1 \
[L46] [T09] X(I) = 0 \
[L47] [T19] I
```

where the character \ marks the end of the line, and the tokens, in square brackets, are of the following types:

L45, L46 and L47 are the internal line numbers
T16, T17, T18, T09 and T19 are the tokens for the reserved words.

Note that the comment (:REM INITIALISE ARRAY) in the source code is deleted by the lexical analyser.

Syntax Analysis

Syntax analysis is where the structure, and, to some extent, the meaning, of a source program is determined by the compiler. The overall source program is analysed into blocks, the blocks are analysed into instructions, and the individual items such as instruction words, variables and constants in each instruction are identified.

As discussed in Section 20.3, the syntax of a high level programming language can be expressed as a set of rules. Each rule specifies how one structure in a program is composed of smaller structures. The compiler applies the rules, in a systematic way, to the source program, to determine its structure. The process is known as **parsing**. For example, one of the syntax rules of Basic language can be written, in BNF notation, as follows:

```
<program line>        :: =   <line number>
                             <instruction word>
                             <rest of instruction>
```

This rule analyses the line:

```
100 LET X = 0
```

(or, strictly speaking, the tokenised form produced by the lexical analyser) as follows:

```
<line number>              : 100
<instruction word>         : LET
<rest of instruction>      : X = 0
```

and, therefore:

```
<program line>             : 100 LET X = 0
```

A common technique of syntax analysis involves the use of **state tables**. These are discussed in the exercise at the end of this chapter.

The Dictionary

A large amount of information about a program is accumulated as compilation proceeds. This information is stored in a data structure known as a **dictionary**. The information is loaded into the dictionary during the early stages of compilation and used during later stages.

Much of the information in the dictionary concerns the use of variables in the source language. As each variable in a source program is encountered, an entry for it is made in the dictionary. This entry includes the name of the variable, its type, and the address of the memory location where its value is to be stored. The dictionary entry for the variable X in the Basic program line above might be as follows:

variable name	type	address
X	N	3A2F

where N represents numeric, and the address is a hexadecimal number. The tokens for line numbers and constants generated by the lexical analyser would also be references to entries in the dictionary. For example, a Basic program might include the lines:

```
70 GO TO 100      tokenised as [L21] [T19] [L34]
. . .
100 LET X = 0     tokenised as [L34] [T09] X = [C04]
```

An entry in the dictionary is created for the line number 100. The token [L34] identifies the entry, which contains the address of the translated code for the line. It might be as follows:

source name	type	address
100	L	2B1A

where L represents line number, and the address is a hexadecimal number. This entry enables the branching instruction in line 70 to be translated completely, by providing the destination of the branching instruction.

Code Generation

Having analysed the structure of the source program, and having transformed it into an intermediate tokenised form, it is now possible to generate the object code. The intermediate code is scanned, and each token is looked up in the dictionary. The entry in the dictionary is used to form the machine code instruction. For example, if the token for a variable name is recognised, then the dictionary is used to find its address. This address is inserted into the machine code instruction being generated.

In most cases, a statement in a high level language generates more than one machine code instruction. To give an example of this, a short section of a Basic program is shown below, together with the equivalent code in AMC assembly language. It must be remembered that compilers generally produce machine code, but assembly code, together with comments is shown here for simplicity.

Basic	AMC assembly language			
200 FOR I =1 TO N		LOA X N +1		Use index as loop counter.
	NXT	CMP X	N	Compare with N.
		BGT	OUT	Exit loop if greater than N.
205 LET Y(I) = 0		CLR A		Clear accumulator.
		STO A D Y		Store contents of accumulator in Y + index.
210 NEXT I		INC X		Increment index.
		BRN	NXT	Continue loop.
	OUT			

Optimisation

One of the objections to high level languages, when they were first introduced, was that the object code they produced would be less efficient than machine code written by hand. Accordingly, much attention has been paid, especially in the early days of compilers, to increasing the efficiency of object code.

Optimisation can take place before or after code generation, and sometimes at both places. Either the source or the object code is manipulated to produce a more efficient end product. In most cases, 'more efficient' means object code which will run more quickly when it is executed. (An alternative objective is object code which is as compact as possible. This is seldom the fastest possible version.)

Optimisation can be attempted on almost any part of the code of a program, but loops are one of the most fruitful areas. Here the objective is to do as much as possible outside the loop, and reduce the number of times that the test for the end of the loop is carried out.

As an example, consider the portion of assembly code in the previous section. The instruction to clear the accumulator can be taken outside the loop. Furthermore, if the loop limit N is an even number, then the body of the loop can be performed twice before the test for the end of the loop is carried out. These optimisations lead to the following AMC code:

```
        CLR  A           Clear accumulator.
        LOA  X  N +1     Use index as loop counter.
NXT     CMP  X    N      Compare with N.
        BGT      OUT      Exit loop if greater than N.
        STO  A D Y        Store contentsof accumulator in Y+ index.
        INC  X           Increment index.
        STO  A D Y        Store contents of accumulator in Y + index.
        INC  X           Increment index.
        BRN      NXT      Continue loop.
OUT
```

Although the object code now contains more instructions, it will be executed more quickly.

One problem with optimisation is that it increases the size and complexity of the compiler. There are two solutions to this problem. One is to allow machine code instructions to be combined with high level language statements in a program. This allows the programmer to optimise crucial areas of the program, and simplifies the task of the compiler. The other technique is to allow the programmer to provide the compiler with information about the program before it is compiled. This specifies how the optimisation is to be carried out, and which modules require particular attention.

Error Handling

In all of the previous sections it has been assumed that the source program input to the compiler is correct. Unfortunately, this is not always the case. Errors detected during compilation are generally of two types. The first type are **syntax errors**, when a source program does not conform to the rules of syntax of the source language. The other type (**semantic errors**) is when there is an error in the 'meaning' of the source code, making it impossible to translate into object code. Semantic errors include transfers of control to statements which do not exist, and duplicate labels on statements.

When an error is detected, most compilers attempt to locate the position of the error and determine its cause. This process is called **diagnostics**. A message, called a **diagnostic error message**, is output, together with some indication of the position of the error.

In most cases, when an error is detected, compilation cannot be completed. The usual practice is to continue to the end of the syntax analysis phase, in case any more errors are encountered. Code generation does not take place. In some cases it is difficult to continue syntax analysis, as assumptions have to be made about the correctness of code near the error. Analysis generally re-commences from the start of the next source program statement. A few compilers make an attempt to correct certain errors such as mis-spelt instruction words. This practice does not, however, meet with widespread approval.

20.6 Linkage

■ In many cases, the output from a compiler or assembler is a set of separate modules (known as segments) of machine code, corresponding to groups of subprograms in the source code. These segments relate to each other, via call and return instructions, and may share common data. They also contain calls to library modules (Section 20.7) which are part of the software development system. The segments produced by the compiler are generally in **relocatable code** – they contain relative machine addresses, and cannot be run until these are replaced by absolute machine addresses. The task of a **linkage program**, also known as a **linkage editor**, is to plant the appropriate addresses in all the external call and return instructions so that all the modules are linked together properly. Some replace the relative addresses in the relocatable code with absolute addresses; in other cases this is done by the loader (Section 20.8). The linker also enables blocks of data, which are declared to be common to more than one segment, to be accessed by all those which use it.

Some linkage editors enable a single object program to be built up from segments which may originate from different high level languages, or a combination of high and low level languages.

20.7 Library Modules

■ Compiled code for common operations such as arithmetic, file handling, user interfacing and graphics control are kept as separate modules in the **library** associated with a compiler. The particular library modules required by an application program are linked with the other code segments by the linkage editor. Some software development systems have **indexing** and cross-reference facilities which enable new code modules to be added to the library.

These programs considerably reduce the length of applications programs, and relieve programmers of the task of writing large portions of identical code for different programs.

20.8 Loading

■ When a program has been compiled or assembled, and all the object code modules linked together, the resulting machine code program is generally written to backing store. In many cases, all the addresses in the program are relative to the start of the program. They do not yet contain the absolute addresses of the store locations to which they will refer when the program is loaded into the computer memory.

A loading program thus performs two functions. It copies the object code of a program into the main store locations in which it will reside during execution, and changes the addresses in program instructions to match the addresses into which the program has been loaded. This process is known as **relocation**. Execution of the program can then commence.

Some compilers and assemblers are called **load-and-go** systems because they include linkage and loading modules. As soon as language translation is complete, the machine language version of the program is linked, loaded and run. The language translation system remains in control throughout. In other cases, linkage and relocation are performed by the link editor, and loading is done by the operating system. Figure 20.3 shows the process of language translation, linkage and loading. For an interpretation of the symbols used, see Figure 25.1.

Figure 20.3
Language translation, linkage and loading

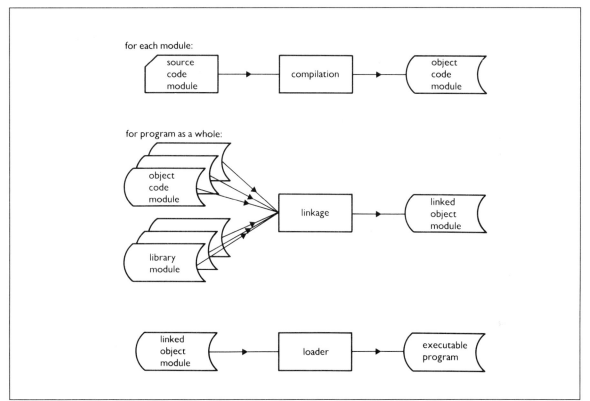

20.9
Run-Time
Diagnostics

■ During the process of developing and testing a program, it is extremely useful to know precisely what is happening at each step while it is running. Some compilers have **run-time diagnostics** packages which enable this to be achieved. The way these packages work is generally as follows.

The programmer creates a **breakpoint** at every stage where he or she wants to investigate the state of the program. This is done by inserting a special instruction or directive at each breakpoint. The program is then compiled or assembled, and run. When a breakpoint is reached, control passes to the run-time diagnostics package. The program is suspended, but the contents of all registers is preserved. The diagnostics package enables registers and store locations to be displayed and altered if necessary. Execution of the program can then be continued from the instruction following the breakpoint.

Most run-time diagnostics packages allow **single stepping**, where the program pauses after every single instruction. They allow variables to be traced, displaying their values after every instruction of the program. A run-time diagnostics facility can save one of the most expensive elements of a software development system, namely programmer's time.

20.10 Interpreters

■ An interpreter is a program which analyses and runs a source program, statement by statement. Like compilers, interpreters analyse the structure of each source program statement. However, lexical and syntax analysis are not always distinguished. Interpreters also create and maintain a dictionary of variable names and statement labels. Instead of generating object code for each source program statement, the interpreter carries out a sequence of actions equivalent to the instructions in the statement. Object code is not generated in the process.

As a consequence of this, optimisation is virtually impossible, and error diagnostics are limited, by comparison with compilers. Only one copy of the program being translated is kept, in source code. On the other hand, interpreters are generally shorter and simpler than compilers. Some interpreters have run-time diagnostic facilities. For these reasons, interpreters are particularly popular on small microcomputers.

A number of language translation packages offer both interpretation and compilation facilities. The source program is interpreted while it is being developed. When it is working satisfactorily, it is compiled.

20.11 Case Study: Prospero Pascal Compiler

■ To show how the general ideas introduced in this chapter can be put into practice, the chapter concludes with a case study of a compiler system used extensively on microcomputers, and describes the stages of the compilation of a typical program. The compiler chosen is the Pascal compiler from Prospero Software, which runs on a variety of microcomputers using the MSDOS or OS/2 operating systems. The version of Pascal is that approved by the International Standards Organisation (ISO), making it fully portable across the range of computers. The compiler system consists of the following programs:

- The compiler, Propas, which perform the three stages of compilation in a single pass of the source code. It accepts source code produced by a programmer's text editor supplied with it, or word processor such as Wordstar, and produces relocatable code segments in the machine code of the target computer. The source code can be an entire program, or a segment of a program which is to be linked to other segments at a later stage. Program segments can share common data, and call procedures and functions in other segments, or in the library modules.
- The linker, Prolink, which links the relocatable code segments from the compiler and produces executable code, ready to be loaded and run. The linker will combine segments compiled from Pascal or Fortran source code, or assembled from the assembly language of the target computer.
- A set of library modules, including Pasdos, the general-purpose library, and PasPC, the library of high-resolution graphics routines. These library modules are in relocatable machine code, ready to be

combined with segments of applications programs. Procedures and functions in the library routines may be linked selectively into other programs.

- The librarian utility, Prolib, which links relocatable code modules into library routines, and allows them to be used selectively. It can produce a set of cross-references, showing which procedures and functions are in which segments, and from which segments they are called. Prolib enables new library modules to be created by programmers for subsequent use.
- The run-time diagnostics utility, Probe. It is in the form of a relocatable code module, to be linked with the other segments of an application program before execution. It shows the source program lines as they execute, and provides a breakpoint at the start of each line. Values of all variables can be inspected and changed before running of the program continues.

To illustrate the workings of the compiler, consider a typical application program, written in Pascal, with the overall structure shown in Figure 20.4. There is a control module (the main program), three operation modules, each comprising a number of procedures and functions, and a set of service modules, which contain procedures and functions used by a number of operation modules. There are also calls to external modules for file handling and graphics operations. The program is entered as four segments: the first containing the main program and the service modules, the other three each containing an operation module.

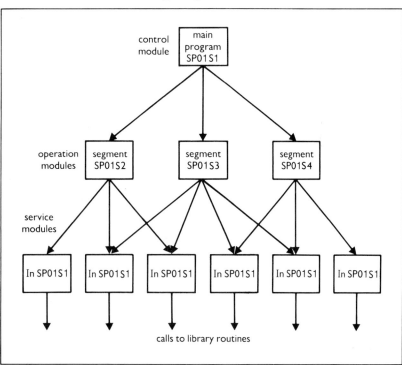

Figure 20.4
Example program: segment structure

The compiler is used to produce the relocatable object code for the four segments. The instruction to compile the first segment is:

```
PROPAS SP01S1/LN
```

where SP01S1 is the name of the program segment being compiled, and the letters L and N specify the compilation options chosen. The letter L

Compilers and Interpreters **229**

creates a listing of the source code, with line numbers added, and N causes a record of the source file and line number to be kept of each machine instruction produced. This information is written to separate files on disk, for use by the run-time diagnostic program.

When all the compilation errors have been corrected in the first segment, the others are compiled by a similar process. The instructions are:

```
PROPAS SP01S2/LN
PROPAS SP01S3/LN
PROPAS SP01S4/LN
```

When all the segments have been compiled, each has a corresponding segment of relocatable object code on disk, ready for linking. The linker is called up by the instruction:

```
PROLINK SP01S1, SP01S2, SP01S3, SP01S4, PROBE,
                            PASDOS/S, PASPC/S
```

The linker combines the four segments of the application program, the run-time diagnostic module, Probe, the general Pascal library, Pasdos, and the high-resolution graphics library, PasPC. The letter S used with the last two modules means that only procedures and functions required by the other segments will be linked from them.

The linker produces a single (large) executable module in machine code, which has the run-time diagnostic facilities built into it. This program is then run, and tested by checking the values of variables at breakpoints, etc. Changes are made to source code segments, which are then re-compiled and linked, until all the run-time errors in the program have been identified and corrected. The program is then re-compiled without the L and N options, and linked without the Probe module. The resulting machine code program is then ready for use.

This process, which in practice takes several weeks or months, shows how the facilities of the compiler system are used at the various stages of software development. The program is developed in segments, rather than as a complete entity, and the error detection facilities in the compiler, linker and run-time diagnostics package help the programmer to identify and correct errors as quickly as possible.

20.12 Conclusion

■ Over the last thirty years, language translators have become an indispensable part of computer systems. A few microcomputers go to the lengths of having a language translator permanently stored on read-only memory.

Language translation is an active area in computing research and development. Work is in progress improving existing compilers and interpreters, and writing translators for new languages, new computers and new operating systems. Much attention is currently being paid to the problem of writing translators for large languages on small computers. Optimisation and efficient compilation for parallel processors are other areas of rapid development.

The main points of this chapter are as follows:

- A compiler converts a source program or program segment in a high level language into an object code module in machine language. The compiler itself is written in a base language.
- Linkage editors combine code segments produced by compilers into single executable programs in machine code.

- Loaders replace the relative addresses in relocatable code with absolute addresses, and load these programs into memory, ready to be run. (Many linkers perform the address conversion as part of the linkage process, making separate loaders unnecessary.)
- Library modules contain compiled code for common operations such as graphics and file handling. These modules may be linked to segments in applications programs.
- Run-time diagnostics utilities enable the workings of a program to be examined while it is running.
- An interpreter analyses a source program in a high level language, and executes each instruction as it is analysed. No object code is produced.

Exercise 20

1 Briefly define the following terms: compiler; interpreter; source language object language; base language; editor; lexical analysis; token; syntax analysis; parsing; optimisation; diagnostics; dictionary; linkage editor; module library; loader; load-and-go compiler; run-time diagnostics; breakpoint; tracing; BNF.

2 Compare and contrast the processes of compilation and interpretation.

3 a) Why is interpretation more suited to small computers than compilation?
  b) Why is interpretation more suitable during program development than compilation?

4 a) Construct some more correct and incorrect English sentences according to the rules in Section 20.3. In each case, analyse the sentence using the rules, to prove whether or not it is correct.
  b) Analyse the following numbers according to the rule for a decimal number given in Section 20.3. State whether each is a valid number in terms of these rules: 469.31, .734, 4325, 45.6.7, 846.
  c) Modify the extended BNF rule for <decimal number> so that both 4325 and 846. become valid numbers.
  d) Write a set of extended BNF rules to specify the structure of a **signed decimal number**. Test each of the following numbers according to your rules: +2.345, 14.37, 456.8, +99, .543, +398.

5 Summarise the tasks performed by a load-and-go compiler.

6 An applications program, written in a high level language, requires the use of two library routines for its execution. The library routines are regarded as subprograms by the applications program. Machine code versions of the utility programs are kept on backing store. Describe in outline all the events which occur before running of the applications program can commence.

7 A simplified form of the Basic language IF...THEN statement is specified by the following syntax rules, written in BNF notation:
```
<condititional statement>::=<line number>
                                           IF <condition>
                                           THEN <line number>
<condition>::=<variable> <relation> <constant>
<relation>::= <= | < | >= | > | =
```

Using these rules to analyse a statement, the steps are as follows:

Example: 200 IF A>10 THEN 300

	200	IF	A	>	10	THEN	300
rule 3:	<line number>	IF	<variable>	<relation>	<constant>	THEN	<line number>
rule 2:	<line number>	IF		<condition>		THEN	<line number>
rule 1:			<conditional statement>				

Use these rules to analyse the following statements. Some are valid and some are invalid.

```
a)  50  IF   J=1     THEN 75
b)  95  IF   K>L     THEN 100
c) 100  IF   100=M   THEN 50
d)  30  IF   T<-5    THEN 20
```

e) Modify Rule 2 so that the statement in part (b) becomes valid.

8 A alternative method of analysing the syntax of a program is the use of **state tables**. The program is examined character by character. The state table contains a row for each state, and a column for each character which may be encountered. An entry in the table contains either a jump to another state, an exit instruction or an error condition. An exit instruction indicates that the structure defined by the table has been recognised. The state table below is for the recognition of signed decimal numbers. The symbol * indicates that the end of the number has been reached.

state			next character		
+	−	digit		*	
1	2	2	3	4	error1
2	error2	error2	3	4	error3
3	error2	error2	3	4	exit
4	error2	error2	4	error4	exit

The use of this table is illustrated by some examples:

Example 1 −59.6

	state	next character	new state
Start in state 1:	1	−	2
	2	5	3
	3	9	3
	3	.	4
	4	6	4
	4	*	exit

As an exit is reached, −59.6 is a valid signed decimal number.

Example 2 7.8.9

	state	next character	new state
Start in state 1:	1	7	3
	3	.	4
	4	8	4
	4	.	error 4

An error condition is reached. This error might carry the message 'More than one decimal point in number'.

Use the state table to analyse the following numbers:

a) 796   b) 5.2   c) +59   d) +7.3–6   e) ++8   f) –

g) Supply suitable messages for the other error conditions.

◆ h) Extend the state table to recognise floating point numbers like 3.6E9 and 4.7E-5.

9 Generate code in AMC or some other suitable assembly language for each of the following segments of Basic programs:

```
a) 100 LET L=J+K
b)  50   IF   C>10   THEN 200
c) 100 FOR K=1 TO 20
   110 LET J(K)= J(K)+1
   120 NEXTK
```

10 Consider the following portion of code, written in Basic and in AMC assembly language:

Basic	AMC assembly language	
500 FOR J=1 TO 27	LOA X N +1	Use index register as loop counter, initial value 1.

		NXT	CMP X	N +27	Compare index with 27.
			BGT	OUT	Exit loop if greater than 27.
510	LET W(J)=100		LOA A	N +100	Load 100 to accumulator.
			STB A	D W	Store contents of accumulator in W + index.
520	NEXT J		INC X		Increment index register.
			BRN	NXT	Continue loop.
		OUT			

Optimise the AMC assembly code to speed up the execution of the loop.

11 Write a short program in a high level language and compile and test it on a computer system until it is free of errors.

Run your program a number of times, in each case introducing a single, simple error. For each run, make a note of the error you have introduced and the diagnostic error message you obtain. Comment on your findings. If possible, repeat the process using exactly the same errors, on a different computer, or on a different compiler or interpreter on the same computer. Compare the error messages you receive in each case.

12 Some additional symbols used in conjunction with T diagrams are shown in Figure 20.5. Figure 20.6 shows how these symbols may be combined to depict the compilation and running of a program. The example chosen uses a source program in Pascal being compiled and run on a PDP-11 computer.

Figure 20.5
Additional symbols used with T diagrams

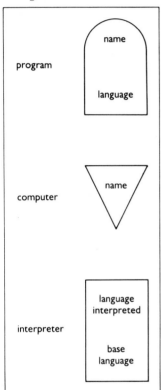

Figure 20.6
Compiling and running a Pascal program on a PDP-11 computer

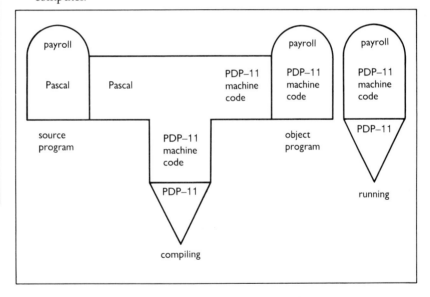

Draw similar combinations of these symbols for the following situations:
a) Compiling and running a Fortran program on an IBM 370.
b) Interpreting a Basic program on a Z80 based microcomputer.
c) Assembling a Basic compiler written in Z80 assembly language to produce a compiler written in Z80 machine language. Note that a T diagram can also be used for an assembler.
d) A Pascal compiler for an Intel 8086-based microcomputer is written in Pascal. It is **cross-compiled** on a PDP-VAX, using a Pascal compiler written in VAX machine code, producing 8086 machine language.

21 Software Packages

A software package is a ready-to-use software item, designed for a popular application such as word processing, spreadsheets or databases. Software packages run on widely-used computer systems, particularly desktop microcomputers and workstations.

This chapter discusses the general features of software packages, and then describes the commonest examples. Each type of package is presented in terms of its objectives, features, operation and an assessment. The chapter concludes with an evaluation of the benefits of software packages.

Software packages are generally developed by independent software companies, and marketed throughout the world. The same package is generally implemented on a range of computers. Competition is intense between different vendors of packages for the same application. Some of the largest and most successful software corporations are vendors of software packages.

21.1 Characteristics of Software Packages

■ Software packages are available for a wide range of applications, but they all have a number of features in common.

The distinguishing feature of software packages is that they are designed for popular applications. Any application such as word processing, where a large number of users require more or less the same facilities, is a potential market for a software package. Because they are intended for a large user population, software packages are designed to be easy to use. Much of the development work which goes into a software package is on the user interface. Ease of use is one of the ways in which purchasers distinguish between one software package and another.

Because of the wide range of potential use, software packages are designed for power and flexibility. The capabilities of the host computer, particularly if it is a microcomputer, are stretched to the limit by many software packages. The extensive programming resources which the software package vendor is able to devote to the development of the package ensure that it makes the most of the capabilities of the host hardware.

An important characteristic of software packages is machine independence, although in some cases the same operating system (Chapter 22) is required on the different computers. Packages are designed to work on a range of computer systems, and data can be transferred from one machine version of the same package to another. The user sees no difference in the operation of the package from one host system to another.

21.2 Word Processing

■ Word processing (WP) is the commonest computer application, and one which is based almost entirely on software packages. A small number of word processing packages dominate the market, and have become industry standards.

Objectives

The main objective of a word processor is to enable a user to enter and edit text simply, quickly and efficiently. Both the content and the layout of text are important. Users must be able to see the text, in its current layout, on the screen, and print it whenever required. An efficient file handling system for documents is also required.

Some WP packages allow users to check spellings, and many allow the text to be transferred to other software packages such as databases, electronic mail systems and (particularly) desktop publishing systems (Section 21.6).

Features

The main features of a word processor are its facilities for entering and correcting text. Input is from the keyboard, with a conventional typewriter layout. This makes it easy for people trained as typists to transfer to word processors. The screen is laid out as if it were a portion of a printed page. This gives rise to the notion of **WYSIWYG – what you see is what you get**. There is a cursor, an illuminated square or underline symbol, which indicates where the next typed character will appear, or from where characters will be deleted. The cursor advances as text is entered. Special key combinations, dedicated keys or a mouse are also used to move the cursor to a required position.

Text editing facilities include the ability to move, copy or delete individual letters, words or larger blocks of text. Blocks of text can be transferred to or from documents other than the one being edited at the time. Any portion of text may be marked for printing in bold or italics.

There are search facilities for finding particular words or phrases, and search and replace facilities to substitute one text item for another wherever it occurs in a document. Standard documents or paragraphs can be called up from disk, and edited to produce particular versions of the text, for example personalised letters, or standard contracts modified to particular requirements.

Some word processors can display more than one window on the screen, enabling two or more documents (or portions of the same document) to be compared, or edited together. A few word processors include typesetting facilities, enabling users to select the required typeface, size and style (bold, italic, etc.). Some allow text to be merged with graphics.

The filing system operated by most word processors is based on documents. An item of text – a letter, contract, brochure, chapter of a book, etc. – is regarded as a separate document. Each document is a separate file on backing store, identified by name. Some WPs create pure text files, others compress the files in order to reduce the space they occupy. Backup copies are often generated automatically as a file is edited, so that the user can go back to a previous version of a document if required.

Most word processors can drive a variety of printers. Dot matrix and daisy wheel printers are the most common. Either an entire document or selected pages can be printed. Some WPs have options for printing draft copies at a higher speed but lower quality than final copies. Printing is somewhat slow, but it can often take place while another document is being edited.

Operation

Most word processors start by presenting users with a menu of options: to type or edit a document, print a document, rename or copy a document, etc. The typing and editing option opens up a new document if a new file name is entered, or an existing one for editing if its name is given.

During typing and editing, some word processors rely entirely on the keyboard for text entry, formatting and control. Others use a combination of dedicated keys and menu options for this, or a combination of the keyboard and a mouse. When the typing or editing of a document is complete, control returns to the initial menu. There are detailed sub-menus to control printing, copying and re-naming operations.

Assessment

The popularity of word processing is an indication of the extent to which WP packages have achieved their objectives. Word processors are replacing typewriters for most applications in commerce, and activities such as newspaper production are now based entirely on their use. They have led to a considerable increase in productivity from typists, and a higher standard of typed work. Any errors which are noticed in printed documents can be corrected and the page re-printed very quickly. This is particularly valuable in such applications as legal work, where no corrections in the printed form of a document are permitted.

Word processing is often the access facility for applications such as desktop publishing and electronic communications, and is used during software development.

21.3 Spreadsheets

■ Spreadsheets are a relatively new computer application. They were originally developed for microcomputers, from where their use has spread to most types of system. A small number of spreadsheet packages dominate the world market, and have set industry standards.

A spreadsheet is a table of information, set out in rows and columns. Each entry in the table, called a cell, can contain a number or an item of text. Alternatively, a cell can contain a formula, to calculate the number in it from others in the spreadsheet.

Objectives

The objective of a spreadsheet is to provide a simple, uniform framework for setting out tables of numerical and associated information, and performing calculations on the numbers in the table. Spreadsheets aim to enable users manipulate large amounts of numerical data quickly and easily, in particular to do 'what if?' calculations, to see the effects of different assumptions.

Features

Spreadsheets have facilities for typing and editing the items in individual cells. Blocks of cells can be identified for moving, copying, writing to other spreadsheets or deletion.

Cells can be given properties, such as emboldening the item when printing, locking the number against changes, etc. The format of columns and individual cells can be adjusted: both the total number of characters and the number of decimal places displayed are variable.

The arithmetic facilities are based on co-ordinates to identify each cell. Some spreadsheets use row and column numbers like matrix indices: for example R3C4 is row 3, column 4. Others use letters for columns and numbers for rows: for example G5 is column G (the seventh column), row

5. Formulae use cell references of one of these forms. For example, the same formula in the two alternative forms is as follows:

```
R4C5 = R3C5/2 + 0.15*R4C4        or
E4 = E3/2 + 0.15*D4
```

The * symbol is used for multiplication, and the / symbol for division. Summation over a range of cells is specified by the notation:

```
R24C7 = sum(R2C7:R22C7)          or
G24 = sum(G2:G22)
```

Relative cell references are allowed in some spreadsheets, so that a formula can move with a block of cells. For example:

```
R9C5 = R(-1)C + RC(-1)     is the same as:
R9C5 = R8C5 + R9C4
```

Spreadsheets include facilities to sort individual rows or columns, or blocks of cells, on the data in a selected key row or column. Some enable conditional operations to take place, for example setting a number to zero if the result of a calculation is negative, or placing the larger of two numbers into a cell.

Each spreadsheet is stored as a separate file on disk, identified by a file name. A spreadsheet can be read from disk or written to disk at any time. Copying, re-naming and deletion facilities are available. Spreadsheets are generally stored in a compressed form on disk, to avoid wasting backing store space on blank cells. Links can be created between spreadsheet files, to allow information to be passed from one to another.

Some spreadsheet packages include graph facilities which enable a variety of types of graph (line graph, bar graph, pie chart, etc.) to be produced automatically from the data in selected rows or columns of the spreadsheet.

Operation

Spreadsheet packages display a portion of the spreadsheet in use on the screen, with a menu along the top or bottom lines. An individual cell or block of cells is highlighted at any time. The highlight can be moved by dedicated keys or a mouse. Control is by dedicated keys to select menu options, or by moving a highlight along the menu options using movement keys or a mouse.

Assessment

Spreadsheets gained wide popularity as soon as the idea became established. They have opened up applications to a large group of users which were previously not possible without expensive, purpose-designed software. They are a major reason for the spread of desktop computers in business, engineering and research.

The main uses of spreadsheets are in business for tables of financial information, price lists, invoices, etc. They have contributed to improved financial control, better business forecasting and tighter stock control, with all the consequent improvements in business productivity and performance.

21.4 Databases

■ A database package (not to be confused with a database system as described in Chapter 30), is the computerised equivalent of a card index system. A database package handles files of data (Chapter 27) which are collections of related records, each with the same structure in terms of a set of fields.

Objectives

The objective of a database package is to provide a range of information storage and retrieval facilities for files of information. Users are able to set up large data files, and obtain information from them quickly and easily.

Features

Database packages allow users to specify the structure of their files in terms of the fields of data in each record. Each field contains one item of information. Fields can be numeric or text, with a specified format: number of characters, number of decimal places, etc. Some packages have facilities to validate fields, for example by entering upper and lower limits for numbers. Any data item entered into a field which does not pass the validation checks is rejected.

Data entry and editing facilities include the ability to add new records, or copy, edit or delete existing records. One record, or a part of a record, is on display at any time. If the record structure is altered, the existing data must be copied into the new structure.

There are search facilities to find records with fields which satisfy given conditions. These take a variety of forms, for example:

```
Surname = 'Smith'
(Date > 1980) AND (Date <= 1990)
```

Files can be sorted on the values of one or more fields, known as key fields. Sorting can take a long time, as it requires moving records on disk, which is a slow process. An alternative is to create an index to the file, which relates key fields to the records. The index can then be sorted.

Files are identified by name on disk. One file is in use at any time. Files can be copied, re-named or deleted from disk.

Selected records, or the entire file, can be printed. The layout of the printout is similar to the layout of a record on screen.

Operation

Most database packages are either command-driven or menu-driven. In both cases, one record of the file in use (or a portion of it, if it is too large for the screen) is displayed on screen at any time.

Command-driven database packages are controlled by commands entered at a prompt at the bottom of the screen. One benefit of this type of user interface is that sequences of commands can be entered into control files, and run in batch mode, for automatic processing of data.

Menu-driven database packages have the menu on the top line of the screen or down one side, often with secondary menus being pulled down when choices are made. Control is via the mouse or dedicated keys.

Assessment

Database packages have brought facilities previously confined to large computers within reach of users of microcomputers. They have made it possible to transfer unwieldy paper files onto computer, saving time and money, and opening up new applications.

21.5 Drawing and CAD Packages

■ With the widespread availability of high-resolution graphics on microcomputers and workstations has come a number of software packages for drawing and **computer-aided design** (CAD). A range of these packages is available, from simple drawing packages suitable for book illustrations, to three-dimensional CAD packages for large-scale architectural and engineering applications. There are some differences between the two types of package, but they are similar enough to be dealt with together here.

Objectives

Both drawing and CAD packages transform the computer screen into an electronic drawing board, onto which a wide range of shapes can be drawn. They provide a range of features to assist in the production of high-quality drawings and designs much more quickly and easily than is possible with conventional drawing equipment.

Features

Both drawing and CAD packages show the current drawing, or a portion of it, on screen, sometimes in colour. A grid can be displayed, to make alignment easier. There are facilities to enter, amend, copy or erase points, lines, shapes or shaded areas. Colours are selected from a palette, in some systems a subset of a range of several millions of colours. Monochrome systems generally have a range of shades of grey, as well as black and white.

Drawing programs regard the screen image as a pattern of pixels, and store it in this form as a bit map (Section 14.6). Although a set of pixels may be drawn as a straight line, the fact that it is a line is not recorded by the system. All that is recorded are the positions of the individual pixels. The advantage of this approach is the range of 'freehand' techniques such as airbrushing that are possible. It is also possible to 'pour' colours into irregular shapes.

CAD packages regard drawings as sets of vectors, line segments which are placed on the screen and manipulated as such. This makes the drawing of structures much easier, and facilitates corrections. To make a correction, the shape concerned is highlighted and then manipulated separately from the rest of the drawing. The vectors may represent a three-dimensional object, a projection of which is shown on screen at any time, from a chosen viewpoint.

Both types of package have facilities to highlight portions of drawings and move, rotate, reflect, copy or delete them, or alter their properties in some way. Text can be entered to annotate drawings, in a range of sizes and typefaces. Drawings are saved as named files on disk, and can be copied, re-named or deleted as required.

Operation

Drawing and CAD packages are controlled by a mouse or digitising pad. This moves a pointer on the screen. A few use light pens to draw directly on screen. Some of the larger packages use two display screens, one for control, and the other to display the drawing. Control is either via a set of icons on one side of the screen, or by menu options, or a combination of both.

Assessment

Drawing and CAD packages have enabled a large number of users to take full advantage of the powerful graphics capabilities of modern computers. They are becoming the norm in the engineering and architectural professions, and on-screen drawing is rapidly gaining popularity for book, magazine and newspaper illustrations, and for film and television work. They are helping to move computing away from its traditional scientific and engineering orientation, into the world of the arts.

21.6
Desktop
Publishing
Packages

■ One of the most recent and fastest-growing computer applications is desktop publishing (DTP). A small number of DTP packages, initially designed for desktop microcomputers, dominate the market. They are now available on workstations and some larger systems. In view of the high development costs for these complex software items, the number of available DTP packages is only likely to increase slowly.

Objectives

A desktop publishing package enables a single user to deal with all aspects of the design and production of a publication in an integrated software environment. A publication typically contains a combination of text, drawings, photographs, as well as design devices such as lines, shaded areas and boxes. These are obtained from word processors, drawing packages and photograph scanners, or may be entered using built-in facilities in the DTP package. The DTP package allows the user to design pages, place objects on the page, and select typefaces, styles and sizes for the text. Pages are printed on image laser printers, or transferred on disk to high-resolution typesetting equipment for printing.

Features

DTP packages allow the user to specify the overall design of a page of the publication: the dimensions, margin widths and number of columns, and enter any common features for each page such as ruled lines, page numbers, running headings, etc. A page of the publication, or an enlarged portion of a page, is in view on the screen at any time.

Text is either entered on an in-line word processor, or obtained from documents produced on a stand-alone WP package. The text is then assigned properties, paragraph by paragraph, or even word by word. These properties include the typeface, size and style (bold, italic, superscript, subscript, all capitals, etc.), as well as the spacing between the lines, and above and below the paragraph. The spacing between individual letters can even be adjusted. The text with these properties 'flows' into the columns on the pages. This creates the various levels of heading, body text, tables, captions etc.

Drawings (either vector or bit-mapped) are brought in from separate drawing packages, or, in a few cases, produced on the in-line drawing facilities. Scanned images of photographs are obtained in a similar way. These images can be enlarged, reduced, rotated, stretched or cropped to fit spaces designated for them on the pages. Text is made to flow round the illustrations.

Lines, boxes and shaded areas are added to complete the design of each page. Some DTP packages include facilities for automatic generation of indexes and tables of contents.

Individual pages or complete publications can be printed at any time. The commonest format of the files sent to the printers is an international standard known as Postscript. This helps to ensure compatibility between DTP packages and the laser printers or high-resolution typesetting equipment they use. Publications are saved on disk as files, and may be copied, re-named or deleted as required. Because of the size of these files, Winchester disks are essential for microcomputers which run DTP packages.

Operation

At any time, one publication is open for use. Either one complete page, a pair of facing pages or an enlarged portion of a page is displayed on the screen. The display is generally of black text on a white background, conforming very closely to the WYSIWYG (Section 21.2) ideal. Most DTP packages are controlled by a combination of mouse and keyboard. Some have a set of tools – a text tool, a graphics tool, line and box drawing tools, etc. – for use as required. Others operate by highlighting an object, which may be a point in the text, or a word, paragraph, image or complete page, and then presenting a menu of options. This enables the user to call up the facility required to operate on the highlighted object.

Assessment

One problem with most DTP packages is that printing is somewhat slow. It is generally independent of editing operations, but if a number of trial prints are necessary to get a page right, it can take a long time. However, this is a minor problem compared to the great savings of time and money when DTP has replaced conventional typesetting and pasteboard page makeup.

Desktop publishing uses the power of modern computer systems to its fullest extent - utilising text and high-resolution graphics facilities with fast processing and large backing store capacity. In the few years that it has been widely available, DTP has had a great influence on the publication of corporate documents such as reports and brochures. A number of magazines and newspapers now depend entirely on the economies brought about by DTP, and book production is rapidly following suit.

21.7 Benefits of Software Packages

■ Software packages, by eliminating the need for software development by users, have been one of the main driving forces behind the rapid spread of computing during the last decade. They make the expertise and resources of a few large software development corporations available to large numbers of users at reasonable prices.

Because of the large number of users of a single package, errors are rapidly identified and eliminated. Most software packages go through an intensive testing process prior to release, and revised versions are made available at frequent intervals.

All the users of the same software package, even if they are running it on different types of host computer, are creating data files of the same format. These may be exchanged, for example by electronic mail. This compatibility of data files eases data transfer between users, and is of particular benefit to large organisations.

The high quality of the user interfaces on most packages makes training fairly straightforward. This is particularly the case with complex packages such as DTP systems, which would otherwise be prohibitively difficult to learn.

There is a move towards integration of the functions provided by separate packages, especially spreadsheets, databases and word processors. In some cases this takes the form of single integrated packages, in other cases the ability of packages to exchange information. Desktop publishing systems require a high level of integration. They can generally accept input from a large number of word processing and drawing/CAD packages. The popular packages are becoming industry standards for data interchange, further assisting the trend towards integration. Integration of packages brings about savings of time, and makes it easier to learn to operate new packages, if they work on the same principles as ones which are already familiar.

Most software packages entitle users to some measure of on-going support form the software vendor. This is generally in the form of a telephone enquiry system, often backed up by a postal reply service, and periodic user newsletters. These are of particular benefit to new users, who are often 'stuck' on relatively trivial points, which can quickly be resolved by a telephone call. Some software packages have independent users groups, which enable users to share information and experiences and, in some cases, to bring collective pressure to bear on the software vendor.

21.8 Conclusion

■ The main points of this chapter are as follows:
- A software package is a ready-to-use software item, designed for a popular application.
- Software packages are generally developed by independent software vendors. Competition in the software package market is intense.
- Most software packages are machine-independent.
- Software packages combine power and flexibility with ease of use.
- The main benefit of software packages is that they eliminate the need for software development by users.
- The availability of software packages at a reasonable cost has been a major reason for the spread of computing during the past decade.
- There is a move towards the integration of the functions provided by software packages.

Exercise 21

1 Briefly define the following terms: software package; word processing; WYSIWYG; cursor; spreadsheet; cell; database package; file; record; field; validate; file index; batch mode; computer-aided design; palette; pixel; bit map; vector; desktop publishing; Postscript.

2 Summarise the facilities provided by the following packages:
   a) word processor
   b) spreadsheet
   c) database
   d) drawing package
   e) CAD package
   f) desktop publishing system.

3 a) Find out what facilities are provided by an integrated software package, combining word processing, spreadsheet and database facilities.
   b) What benefits do an integrated software packages have over separate ones?

4 Find out what facilities are provided by two different packages in any of the categories described in this chapter. Write a short comparative description of the two, highlighting their similarities and differences.

5 a) Summarise the benefits to users of using software packages.
   b) On what grounds do users normally distinguish between software packages?

c) Why is the market for several types of software package dominated by a small number of products?

d) What has been the overall effect of the availability of software packages?

6 The annual report of a company contains the following information:
- the chairman's report
- a summary of the company's accounts
- tables of sales figures through the year
- graphs based on the sales figures
- photographs of the activities of the company.

Describe the overall stages in the production of this report, up to the point when the master copies go to the printer. State what type of software package is required at each stage.

22 Operating Systems

This chapter describes the layer of software which transforms the hardware of a computer into a useful machine: the operating system. A few of the concepts introduced in earlier chapters are re-examined here. Many of the ideas introduced in this chapter pave the way to an understanding of data processing and computer applications, which form later chapters in this book.

At the beginning of this book, a computer is defined as follows:

> A computer is a collection of resources, including digital electronic processing devices, stored programs, communications links and sets of data, which, under the control of the stored programs, automatically inputs, outputs, stores, retrieves and processes the data, and may also transmit data to and receive it from other computers. A computer is capable of drawing reasoned conclusions from the processing it carries out.

For the purposes of this chapter, it is important to emphasise the view of a computer as a set of **resources**. These resources may be hardware, software or a combination of both. Together they provide such facilities as input, processing, output, etc. For example, a compiler is a software resource which provides the facility of language translation. This concept of a resource is used extensively in this chapter.

22.1 Types of Computer Operation

■ Computers vary considerably in size, capability and type of application. Similarly, there is a wide variety of ways in which they can be operated. Each type of computer operation requires a different type of operating system.

Most desktop microcomputers can only process one program at a time, and are used by only one person at a time. This is **single program operation**, and it requires only a simple operating system. The operating system supervises the loading and running of each program, and the input and output of data. Any errors occurring are reported. A variation of this is **windows** operation, where a number of screen windows are created, each providing the interface to a program. However, there is still only one user, who is only able to interact with one window at any time.

Next in complexity is **batch processing**. A number of programs are batched together, and then run as a group. Although the programs are actually run one at a time, input and output from various programs can overlap to some extent. Programs are normally queued up for batch processing, and the operating system starts the next program in the queue as soon as sufficient computing resources are available for it. Batch processing is confined to certain applications running on mid-range and mainframe computers.

The commonest form of computer operation is **multiprogramming** (also known as **multitasking**). At any one time, a number of programs are on the computer at various stages of completion. Resources are allocated to programs according to the requirements of the programs, and in order to maximise the usage of the different resources of the computer. Computer systems from workstations to supercomputers are designed for multiprogramming.

Both batch processing and multiprogramming can permit **remote job entry**, where programs are submitted for processing at sites remote from the computer. A particular type of multiprogramming, which is becoming increasingly popular, is transaction processing. **Transaction processing** is designed for systems which must repeatedly run the same fairly small application program at frequent intervals. Each program run deals with a single transaction such as a withdrawal from a cash terminal. Transaction processing permits **multi-threading** of an application program, where a number of runs of the same code are taking place at the same time.

The most sophisticated type of computer operation is **multi-access**, an enhanced form of multitasking, where a number of users can interact, via terminals, with programs while they are all being run together on a single central processor.

Looking at computer operation in a slightly different way, one can classify some computer applications as **real-time processing**. Real-time processing requires that the computer keep pace with some external process. In many real-time systems, computers interact directly with other equipment. A common example is computers controlling machines. Real-time processing is generally restricted to computers with multiprogramming (and particularly transaction processing) or multi-access capability, though it is achieved in practice by microcomputers under single program operation. Real-time processing places an additional burden on an operating system, since there is a deadline associated with every action performed by the computer.

22.2 The Nature of an Operating System

■ Like the question 'What is a computer?', the question 'What is an operating system?' can be answered at several levels. Firstly, an operating system is a program, or set of programs. Operating systems vary in size from very small to very large, but all are pieces of software. In the past, almost all operating systems were written in a low level language. Currently, many operating systems are partly or completely written in a high level language.

Secondly, an operating system is, by virtue of its name, a system. It is a collection of parts, working together towards some common goals. The objectives of an operating system are discussed below.

Thirdly, a computer may be regarded as a set of resources, which provide a number of services, such as input, processing, storage and output. The operating system may be regarded as the manager of these resources. It controls the way in which these resources are put to work.

Finally, an operating system is the lowest layer of software on a computer. It acts directly on the 'raw' hardware of the computer. It supports other layers of software such as compilers and applications programs. Part of the task of an operating system is to 'cushion' the other layers of software from the complexities of direct use of the computer hardware.

In summary, an operating system is a program, or set of programs, driving the raw hardware of a computer, which manages the resources of the computer in accordance with certain objectives, providing a simplified hardware interface to higher layers of software.

22.3 The Development of Operating Systems

■ Operating systems are as old as electronic computers. It was realised from the start that the hardware of a computer on its own is very difficult to use. Various **supervisor**, **executive** or **monitor** programs were written to make aspects of using a computer easier. As time went by, these programs became larger, more complex, and, unfortunately, more cumbersome and less reliable.

Gradually the objectives and functions of these supervisory programs became clearer, and the term 'operating system' came into use. Better program design led to improvements in efficiency and reliability of operating systems. Sophisticated operating systems made very large computers and networks of linked computers a practical possibility. Operating systems have made different types of computer appear the same to applications software. This issue of standardisation is one of the most important in the current development of operating systems.

22.4 Objectives of Operating Systems

■ All operating systems have two major objectives. These are to make it possible for the resources of the computer to be used efficiently, and to conceal from higher levels of software the difficulties of dealing directly with the hardware of the computer. A number of industry standard operating systems have a third primary objective, namely to present a standard interface to applications software, independent of the host hardware.

The first objective, of efficient resource utilisation, is made especially difficult by the fact that some devices of a computer work much more quickly than others. Part of the task of an operating system is to ensure that fast devices such as processors are not held up by slow peripheral devices.

To achieve the second objective, of simplifying the use of the hardware of the computer, the operating system creates a **virtual machine**. A virtual machine is a simplified computer, with all difficult details taken care of by the operating system. People writing other software for the computer need only know about the virtual machine, and not about the actual hardware of the computer.

The third objective, that of a standard virtual machine, is gaining importance. It means that applications software can be developed to run on a particular operating system, and may only require re-compilation to be transferred from one type of host hardware to another. This brings about a great saving in software development time and costs. It benefits both software developers and users, as the latter are able to run the same software in the same way on different types of hardware.

22.5 The Functions of an Operating System

■ The tasks performed by an operating system depend to some extent on the type of computer operation in question. The functions of a multi-tasking operating system on a large computer are somewhat different from those of a single program operation monitor on a microcomputer. Nevertheless, some general points can be made. These apply to a greater or a lesser extent depending on the type of computer operation.

The functions of an operating system may be loosely classified as **time allocation**, **resource control**, **input/output control**, **error handling** and **protection**, **operator interface** and **accounting**. These are outlined below, and described in more detail in the context of the structure of a typical operating system, later in the chapter.

Time allocation involves the scheduling of all the various activities going on in the computer. Resource control is the allocation of the resources of the computer in a rational way. Major resource control tasks include partitioning the computer memory between programs, allocating disk space to programs and data and queuing output for printers. Input/output control involves channelling data to and from the peripherals of the computer. Error handling and protection involves the detection and reporting of errors, and minimising their effect. Accounting involves charging users, according to a scale of costs, for their use of the resources of the computer.

The operator interface is the communication with the person operating the computer. On desktop computers and workstations, the person using the computer is also the operator, starting and stopping programs, loading data disks, etc. On larger computer systems, there is a computer operator (or a team of operators) whose job it is to start up and shut down the computer system, load programs and data disks as required, allocate resources to users, and respond to any problems which arise. Computer networks often have a system manager whose job it is to keep the network operating efficiently, mainly by controlling the shared resources such as file servers and printers. These computer operators and system managers work directly with the operating system of the computer.

This is a diverse list of functions for an operating system. At this stage it is worth remembering that they must all be performed in accordance with the objectives of the operating system, outlined in the previous section.

22.6 Desirable Features

■ Operating systems have certain objectives, and must perform a number of functions. In addition, they must have some desirable features. These include **efficiency**, **reliability**, **maintainability** and **small size**.

Efficiency implies that an operating system must carry out its tasks quickly, with minimum disruption to the running of applications software. Much of the time spent on operating system functions is productive computing time wasted. Reliability is crucial, as a failure in an operating system can lose operational data and, in some situations, render the host computer useless. Maintainability means that modifications to the operating system are easy to make. A clearly written, well structured program for the operating system is essential for this.

Finally, in spite of all the things it must do, and all the other desirable features it must have, the program for an operating system must be as small as possible. A small operating system does not occupy very much main or backing store on the computer, is less error prone, and runs more quickly. Other desirable features tend to increase the size of an operating system. In practice, a compromise has to be reached between these and the requirements of small size.

22.7 The Structure of a Typical Operating System

■ This section gives a description of the structure of the program for a typical, or perhaps ideal, operating system. It must be emphasised that in practice the program structure varies according to the size and complexity of the operating system. Nevertheless, the features mentioned here are all present in some form.

The program structure is presented as a series of modules. The first module, called the **nucleus**, is a service module for the others. Each of the other modules performs one or more of the operating system functions mentioned previously. The other modules are **memory management**, **input/output control**, **backing store management**, **resource allocation and scheduling**, and **protection**.

The Nucleus

The lowest-level module of an operating system is known as the **nucleus**. It is supported directly by the hardware of the computer, and provides a number of services required by the other layers of the system. Tasks carried out by the nucleus include handling interrupts (Section 12.8), allocation of work to the processor and providing a communication mechanism between different programs.

When the hardware of the computer detects that an interrupt has occurred, control is transferred to the interrupt handler in the nucleus of the operating system. The interrupt handler determines the cause of the interrupt and then takes appropriate action. This action may be to transfer control to another module of the operating system, to start up some other program, or to resume the program that was interrupted. As many interrupts are caused by requests for input or output, the input/output handler is one of the modules most commonly called.

In allocating work to the processor, the nucleus transfers control to the program which the scheduler has determined should be the next to run. Communication between programs is achieved by maintaining a queue of messages waiting for each program in the system. The nucleus receives a message from a program, and adds it to the queue of its destination program.

Most computers have certain machine instructions whose use is restricted to the nucleus of the operating system. These restricted instructions include ones which transfer control from one program to another, and ones which access restricted registers. Restricting these instructions in this way is a very efficient means of controlling the overall running of the computer, and limiting the effects of errors.

Memory Management

The main store of most computers is too small to handle all the programs and data on the computer at any one time. The memory management module of an operating system allocates main store to programs or parts of programs which need it most. Everything else is kept on backing store. When main store is allocated, it is done so in a structured, orderly way.

The commonest memory management policy is to create a **virtual memory**. This is the memory of the computer as seen by a particular application, and is much larger than the actual main store of the computer. The operating system takes care of all transfers between main and backing store in order to support this virtual memory. Virtual memory means that applications do not have to transfer working sets of data to temporary files, and do not have to have different versions written for different memory sizes.

Input/Output Control

The problem with input and output is that different input/output devices have different characteristics, and run at different speeds. For example, a line printer outputs characters one line at a time, whereas a keyboard accepts input one character at a time. A line printer transfers characters more than one hundred times as fast as a keyboard.

The input/output control module of an operating system deals with these problems by making input and output **device independent** from the point of view of the application. To an application, all devices have the same characteristics, and are instructed in exactly the same way. The operating system deals with the special characteristics of each type of device. For example, many operating systems regard all transfers to and from backing store, peripherals or communications links in terms of reading from and writing to files. The operating system deals with the physical aspects of the transfer - the blocks and sectors of the disks, etc. - leaving the applications programmer free to concentrate on the logical aspects of the data structure transferred - the records and fields.

These operating system facilities are activated by means of calls from applications programs. There is a particular call for each type of operating system function, and each call is accompanied by a set of **parameters** describing the data to be handled by the call. For example, a call to read a file from disk will have the file name as its parameter.

A very common technique, especially useful for output, is **spooling**. Data for output is held on a spool, or queue, on backing store, until the output device is ready for it. There are calls to the operating system to add an output file to the spool, and to delete files from it. Figure 22.1 illustrates this procedure.

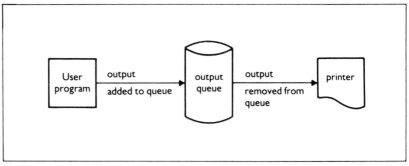

Figure 22.1
Spooling

Backing Store Management

The backing store of a computer is where the bulk of the data and programs being processed are kept. The backing store management of an operating system has the task of maintaining the structure of all this information, and ensuring that the backing store of the computer is used efficiently.

Data and programs on backing store are kept in **files**. The backing store management supervises the creation, updating and deletion of files. A directory is kept of all the files on each backing store device at any time. Many file systems are in a tree structure, with a directory at each node of the tree, containing either files or sub-directories. If a system of virtual memory is implemented, transfers between main store and backing store are co-ordinated between memory and backing store management in order to maintain the virtual memory.

The files on backing store have very different purposes. Some contain information which may be shared. Others are private, or even secret. Other files contain program code, which may be run by certain users, but not others. Accordingly, each file has a set of access privileges which indicate to what extent the information in the file may be shared, or who is able to run the code in the file. The operating system checks that these privileges are not violated.

Resource Allocation and Scheduling

Most of the time that a computer is running, the demand for its resources is greater than their availability. To deal with this problem, an operating system generally has a **resource allocation policy**. The resource allocation mechanism puts this policy into practice.

Matters would be very simple if a straightforward policy like 'first come, first served' could be implemented. The problem is that such policies can lead to a situation known as **deadlock**. This is when two programs prevent each other from continuing because each has claimed a resource which the other one possesses. Deadlock is analogous to the situation of two wide vehicles meeting half way across a narrow bridge, shown in Figure 22.2. Various resource allocation policies have been evolved, either to prevent deadlock, or to recover from it should it occur.

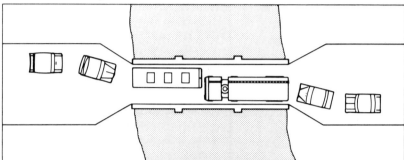

Figure 22.2
Deadlock

The **scheduler** is mainly concerned with the allocation of processor time to programs. This is done in accordance with some **scheduling policy**. Scheduling policies vary considerably from one operating system to another. Some involve the allocation of a level of priority to each program.

A very common scheduling policy on multiprogramming and multi-access systems is known as **time slicing**. Each program on the computer is allocated a short slice of processor time. If the program is not completed during its time slice, then it returns to a queue of programs waiting their turn. Figure 22.3 illustrates this method of scheduling. Scheduling policies cannot be too complicated, otherwise the computer spends far too much of its time deciding what to do next.

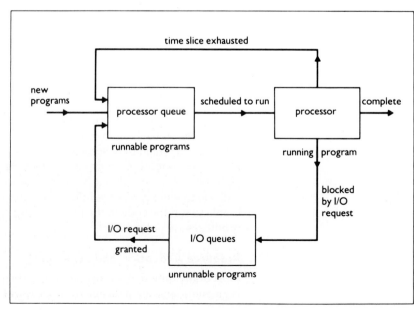

Figure 22.3
Time slicing

Protection

When a computer contains a number of active items of software, accessing a common memory and peripheral devices, these must be protected from interfering with each other. The most essential piece of software to protect is the operating system itself.

Protecting is generally needed against two eventualities, namely errors and deliberate abuse of the system. Although it is impossible for the operating system to prevent errors in applications programs, it is essential to detect and diagnose them as early as possible, and to limit their effects. Deliberate abuse of the system is rather more difficult to deal with. Although protection mechanisms are designed to prevent unauthorised activities from succeeding, few operating systems are regarded as completely foolproof.

Protection mechanisms are distributed throughout most operating systems, with most attention being paid to main store and backing store. Files on backing store are protected by the system of access privileges mentioned previously. Main store protection is regarded as the most important aspect of a computer, because everything that a computer does is via code or data resident in main store. The memory management system allocates portions of main store for various purposes, and then assigns these portions various levels of protection, depending on their nature. Checks are carried out to ensure that the protection of a portion of memory is not violated. The most common memory protection violation is when a program tries to read or write data outside the area of memory allocated to it.

Some operating systems allocate **levels of privilege** to all programs on the computer. The nucleus of the operating system has the highest level of privilege, while applications programs have the lowest level. The use of certain machine instructions, and access to main store and backing store, is governed by the level of privilege of the program concerned.

Accounting

One of the more mundane tasks that some operating systems must perform is to keep a record of the charges incurred by each user program. The most significant portion of the cost is generally for processor time. Information is passed to the accounting module from the scheduler, to establish how much processor time a program has used. Other charges are for the use of backing store media and printer paper.

User and Operator Interface

Communication between an operating system and the outside world takes the form of two interfaces, namely that between the operating system and a user of the computer, and that between the operating system and the person operating the computer.

In a batch processing system, the user interface is the **job control language (JCL)**. This is the language in which instructions to the operating system are placed at the front of each program. These instructions specify, among other things, the maximum running time of the program, how much main store is required, and what peripherals are to be used. In some cases the operating system may be instructed what to do if an error is encountered in the program. Certain job control languages permit the user to define **macro-instructions**. These are single instructions which are interpreted as a group of instructions, defined in Chapter 16. An example of some job control instructions is shown in

Figure 22.4. They instruct an operating system to compile and run a program written in Pascal.

```
#job testprog umace07 lines 600 time 10
#password s021suf
#deck myfile pascal


   [program]


/*
pascal myfile
exec myfile print
#eoj
```

Figure 22.4
Job control language

In reply to these job control language instructions, the operating system outputs a series of messages, indicating the progress of various stages of the program.

In a desktop computer or workstation, or a larger multi-access system, communication between the user and the operating system is interactive. The user can issue **commands** to the operating system from a terminal. These commands are for such operations as running a program, listing the contents of a directory, or moving, copying, re-naming or deleting a file. The operating system responds to these commands, and sends messages to the user.

The interface between an operating system and the person operating the computer is also one of commands and messages. Many of the functions of the operating system can be over-ridden by the operator if necessary. This applies particularly to scheduling and resource allocation. At all times the operator is in ultimate control of the computer. A typical section of a **console log**, showing commands from the operator and messages from the operating system, appears in Figure 22.

```
1804 26 batch queue = 37
1804 51 job asp3 umach09 started
1804 53 job asp3 umach09 error 57
1804 55 job asp3 umach09 abandoned
1905 02 job testprog umace07 started
batch queue? 39
1905 12 job testlog umace07 time limit exceeded
1905 14 job testprog umace07 abandoned
1905 23 job at47 umach01 started
1905 25 disk vol 3721 allocated
1905 31 disk vol 3721 free
1905 37 job at47 umach01 ended
1905 39 batch queue = 38
disk vol 3721? free
```

Figure 22.5
A console log

22.8 Bootstrap Loaders

■ A very important item of systems software on every computer is the one which loads the first program into the computer after it has been started up. These programs have been given the name **bootstrap loaders**, from the phase 'to pull oneself up by one's bootstraps'. The origin of this name is explained below. In some computer systems, the bootstrap loader is part of the operating system; in others it is part of the **firmware** of the computer, at a lower level than the operating system.

In the early days of computing, a bootstrap loader worked in the following manner. Hand keys on the operator's console of the computer were used to load a very short, simple program into a few memory locations. This program was sufficient to activate a peripheral device, often a paper tape reader, and to load a longer, more sophisticated loading program. This loading program would then be run, to load other items of software, generally starting with the operating system.

The advent of semiconductor memories, containing portions of read-only store, has put an end to the early morning routine of hand keyed instructions and paper tape. In most modern computer systems, including microprocessor-based systems, a sophisticated program loader is permanently stored in ROM. When the processor is switched on, control passes automatically to this loader. By the time that the visual display screen in the operator's console has warmed up, all systems software has been loaded, and the computer is ready to start work. Most computers include a **reset button** which may be pushed as a last resort when things have gone wrong. The initial loading program is again activated, and the system is able to start afresh.

22.9 An Assessment of Operating Systems

■ Having read this chapter, and reflected a moment, you will realise the magnitude of the task undertaken by the operating system on a medium or large sized computer. An operating system must perform a number of different tasks, in an integrated way, under very difficult circumstances. Some of the largest and most complex pieces of computer software ever written are operating systems.

Because operating systems evolved in a haphazard way, without clearly defined objectives or a respectable program structure, some of the early large systems were slow, clumsy and error prone. Job control language and operating system messages were almost incomprehensible. Time and experience have brought about a new generation of smaller, simpler and more efficient operating systems, with much better user and operator interfaces.

As mentioned at the beginning of this chapter, one of the biggest challenges to large operating systems comes from microcomputers. Most microcomputers have a small operating system, in some cases permanently stored on read-only memory. Almost all microcomputers and workstations use one of a small number of machine-independent, industry standard operating systems. This makes it easy to transfer software and data between them. Microcomputer salesmen never tire of pointing out the fact that medium and large size computers spend a considerable proportion of time (often more than thirty per cent) running their operating systems. Their effective processing power is thus much less than it appears. A few microcomputers, at a small fraction of the price, would be just as powerful.... Over the next few years the marketplace will no doubt resolve this question.

22.10 Conclusion

■ The main points in the chapter are as follows:
- An operating system is a program, driving the raw hardware of a computer, which manages the resources of the computer in accordance with certain objectives. The three major objectives of an operating

system are to utilise the resources of the computer efficiently, to conceal the difficulties of dealing directly with the hardware of the computer and to present a standard hardware interface to applications programs.

- A standard hardware interface presented by different types of computer is of great benefit to applications software developers and users.
- The tasks performed by an operating system include time allocation, resource control, input/output control, error handling and protection, operator interface and accounting. Desirable features include efficiency, reliability, maintainability and small size.
- A typical operating system program is structured into the following modules: nucleus, memory management, input/output control, backing store management, resource allocation and scheduling, protection, accounting and user and operator interface.
- In practice, operating systems attain their objectives with varying degrees of success. It remains to be seen whether microcomputers will erode the market for medium and large sized computers with sophisticated operating systems.

Exercise 22

1 Briefly define the following terms: resource; single program operation; batch processing; multiprogramming; remote job entry; transaction processing; multi-access; real-time processing; interrupt; directory; spooling; deadlock; time sharing; job control language; console log; bootstrap loader.

2 The phrase 'running under an operating system' is used to describe a computer using a particular operating system. For example, one might say 'an 80286 microcomputer running under OS/2'.
Use the concept of a virtual machine to explain the significance of this phrase for a person writing a program for the computer concerned.

3 a) In your own words, give a brief answer to the question 'What is an operating system?'.
b) Summarise the structure of a typical operating system.

4 Name a significant feature which modern microcomputers have in common with early electronic computers.

5 State some advantages of the concept of a virtual machine.

6 Operating systems are described in the text as 'some of the largest and most complex pieces of computer software ever written'. Explain why this is the case.

7 A software developer produces an applications software package for two different types of microcomputer, both of which use the same operating system. The package is written in a portable high-level language. It is developed on a workstation which also runs under the operating system used by the microcomputers.
a) Explain what steps are required to produce ready-to-run packages on the two types of microcomputer.
b) What difficulties would be encountered if the two microcomputers, and the workstation on which the software is developed, all used different operating systems?

8 a) Why is the nucleus the most privileged part of an operating system?
b) Why is the concept of virtual memory so useful to a programmer?
c) Why is it essential for an operator to have ultimate control of a computer, rather than an operating system?

9 A microcomputer has a single program operation monitor as its operating system. Summarise the objectives of this system and the features you would expect it to have.

23 Operating Systems Case Studies

This chapter presents surveys of three operating systems currently in use. The intention is to consolidate the general ideas introduced in the previous chapter, and to give some idea of how the principles of operating systems are put into practice. Each of the operating systems outlined here is designed for use on one of the computers whose hardware is described in Chapter 15. Like their host computers, these operating systems are representative of the range of systems currently available, and are generally regarded as being well designed. The operating systems are as follows:

MS-DOS used by the Research Machines Nimbus microcomputer.
Unix used by Digital Equipment VAX minicomputers and by the Cray-2 supercomputer.
VME/B used by ICL 2900 series mainframe computers.

23.1 MS-DOS

■ The MS-DOS operating system is a single-user operating system developed for 16-bit microcomputers. It is particularly suited to computers using the Intel 8086 family of microprocessors (which includes the 80386) and their associated co-processors, or the Motorola 68000 series. It has been implemented on a wide variety of computers, including the IBM PC, where it is known as PC-DOS, and the Research Machines Nimbus.

MS-DOS was developed in 1979 by Tim Paterson, working for Seattle Computer Products. It was purchased by Microsoft Corporation, which now develops and distributes it. The second and subsequent versions of MS-DOS have been extended to include certain features which are similar to Unix, notably hierarchical disk directories, which are discussed below.

General Features

The aim of MS-DOS is to provide a powerful, flexible layer of systems software to control all the aspects of the operation of a microcomputer. In particular it controls the disk filing system, the transfer of data to and from all other peripherals, and the loading and running of user programs. It provides a simple interface to the user of the computer.

The overall structure of MS-DOS is illustrated in Figure 23.1. It has a **command processor** which calls the **input/output system** and the **utilities**. The input/output system has three levels: the **filing system** (MS-DOS), the **basic input/output system** (BIOS) and the **firmware input/output routines**. The filing system is in overall control of all input and output. Detailed operations, in particular the transformation from logical to physical structures, are carried out by BIOS. The firmware routines deal with the machine-dependent aspects of input and output, and provide a standard interface for the operating system routines.

The input/output system has two sets of facilities: one set for peripherals which transfer individual characters, and one set for the disk drives, which transfer data in blocks. The latter is the disk filing system.

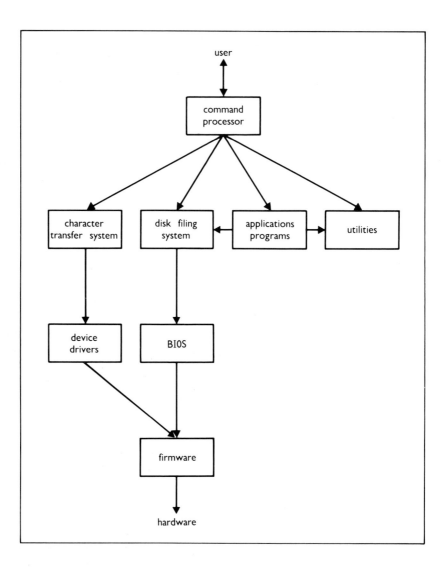

Figure 23.1
MS-DOS overall structure

Command Processor

The command processor has four functions: interaction with the user, interrupt handling, error handling and running the internal MS-DOS system calls.

The user interface of the operating system is a set of prompts and messages displayed by the command processor, and a set of commands which it accepts from the user. MS-DOS has a simple command line editor to enable users to correct commands they are typing. It also enables users to create files of commands. These **batch files** are a sequence of MS-DOS commands which are executed one at a time when the batch file is called. The command processor transfers control to the input/output system, one of the MS-DOS utilities, or (via the disk filing system) a user program, as required.

The interrupt handler has a simple priority system for dealing with interrupts from peripherals. When an interrupt has been dealt with, control is returned to the program which was running when the interrupt occurred. The error handling system works in a similar way, returning control to the program in which the error arose, if possible; if not, to MS-DOS.

A number of MS-DOS commands are dealt with directly by the command processor. These include the command which displays a disk directory, and commands to erase, rename and copy files. MS-DOS keeps track of the date and the time: the command processor allows the user to set or reset these.

Backing Store Management

The most important task performed by MS-DOS is managing the filing system of the computer. Each disk is given a **directory** which has details of every file on the disk, as well as the names of any **sub-directories**. In this way, the directories form a hierarchy, with a tree structure. See Figure 23.2. At any time, the user is 'logged on' to a particular directory, and

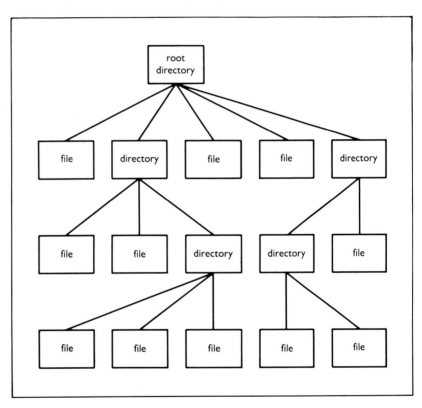

Figure 23.2
MS-DOS directory structure

unless otherwise specified, all files used are in the logged on directory. If a file outside the current directory is required, a **pathname** is used to locate the file. This contains, in order, the names of all the directories required to locate the file. For example, a letter with a filename PBA9107.TXT, in the LETTERS sub-directory of the ADMIN directory of the disk in drive B has the pathname:

```
B:\ADMIN\LETTERS\PBA9107.TXT
```

The disk filing system handles this hierarchical directory system. It responds to user commands from the command processor, and system calls from within applications programs. It has facilities to create a file, open one for reading or writing, transfer information to or from files and indicate how much free space there is on a disk. Transfers take place in terms of one disk sector (512 bytes) at a time, via two or more disk **buffers** in memory. Records in files may be accessed sequentially or randomly: the programmer is concerned only with the logical structure of the files; MS-DOS deals with the physical aspects. The disk filing system takes care of the details of loading and running user programs, and deals with most of the operating system calls from them.

File space in a disk is allocated by taking the next free sectors available. When a file is erased or reduced in length, unwanted sectors are freed. There is no 'tidying up' mechanism, and some files, particularly those used for word processing which change length every time they are edited, can become very fragmented. If sectors of a file are distributed throughout the disk, reading and writing can be somewhat slow.

Character-Oriented Input/Output

With the exception of the disk drives, all peripheral devices transfer data one character at a time. These include the keyboard, display screen, printer and communications links. MS-DOS has a set of **device drivers**, one for each of the above types of device, which present a standard interface to the programmer. In this way, all of these devices appear to the programmer to have the same characteristics. The character-oriented input/output facilities check whether devices are ready to get or send a character, and transfer the characters.

Utilities

The MS-DOS utilities are a set of programs which carry out various 'housekeeping' tasks. These include formatting disks, copying and checking disks, recovering corrupt files and a line-oriented text editor. A set of programming utilities is provided, to locate errors in assembly language programs and to link relocatable modules into executable code. There is also a sorting program to arrange lines in a text file in alphabetic order.

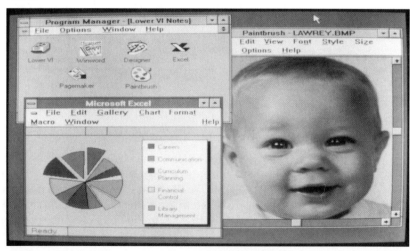

A typical MS windows screen.

Extended Features

MS-DOS now supports an additional layer of systems software which allows users to interact with any one of several operational programs at any time. This software, **MS Windows**, creates a window on screen for each program which is active. Using a mouse, the user moves a pointer to a particular window in order to interact with the program running in the window. Windows may be re-sized or moved about the screen, and arranged one in front of another.

Programs running under MS Windows have standard user interfaces, in terms of pull-down menus. Data can be transferred from one program to another, for example a portion of a spreadsheet may be cut out and pasted into a word processor document.

Assessment

MS-DOS has become the standard operating system for 16-bit microcomputers. It is powerful and flexible, and makes good use of all the hardware features of micros of this size. However, it is compact, and fast in its own operation. The standardisation of a large number of microcomputers from different manufacturers on MS-DOS makes it easy to develop machine-independent software, and to transfer data between them. In spite of the withdrawal of support from MS-DOS by its original sponsor IBM, a consortium of other prominent microcomputer manufacturers has agreed to continue development of a common operating system which is compatible with it.

MS Windows is an implementation of the most advanced concepts of user interfacing, with substantial benefits to software developers and users alike. By providing the support functions for a state-of-the-art user interface of this nature, and by an increasing similarity in concept to Unix, MS-DOS seems assured of a central place in microcomputer systems software for some time to come.

23.2 Unix

■ The **Unix** operating system was originally designed for use with Digital Equipment computers. It was designed and is still supported by a team at the Bell Laboratories of the American Telephone and Telegraph Corporation (AT&T). The first version went into operation in 1971. Unix has subsequently been updated several times, and is now available for use on a wide range of mid-range systems, workstations and some 16 bit microcomputers. Its implementation on the Cray-2 and other supercomputers means that it is now regarded as suitable for a wide range of host machines, from microcomputers to supercomputers.

General Features

Unix is a general-purpose, multi-user, interactive operating system. It supports both multiprogramming and multi-access. An assembler, a number of compilers for high level languages and a text editor are among the items of systems software available under Unix. Unix itself is written in the high level language C (Section 19.6).

Unix is designed for a number of users accessing a single processor via terminals. No single user is regarded as the operator of the computer. All users may submit commands to the operating system in the course of their work. Responses to these commands are sent to the users by the system.

Memory Management

Unix implements the concept of virtual memory. Each user appears to have access to the entire memory of the computer.

Input/Output Control

Each peripheral device in the system is accessed via one or more **files**. These files are treated in exactly the same way as ordinary data files. In other words, to display an item of data, the data is written to the file associated with the VDU. This simplifies the input and output of data, and conceals all the peculiarities of the various peripheral devices from the user. Facilities also exist for the spooling of output for a line printer.

Backing Store Management

All backing store space is regarded as being partitioned into files. The contents of a file may be structured according to the wishes of a user, but the relationships between files are controlled at system level by **directories**. Directories enable files to be grouped together, and permission to be given by a user for other users to share his or her files. The operating system maintains a **root directory** via which every file in the system may be accessed. The filing system is regarded as one of the most important features of Unix.

Protection

Protection within the system is achieved via **protection bits** associated with each file. These enable **read**, **write** and **execute** permission to be established for a file, both for its owner and for other users. Different users have different levels of privilege, which determine the extent to which they may access files, and thereby use the resources of the computer. If an error is detected during the running of a program, the operating system jumps to a simple error handling subroutine. A facility is also available for a user to interrupt a program which appears to be going wrong.

User Interface

All commands to the operating system are interpreted by a program called the **shell**. One notable feature of the shell is that it enables a user to control the extent of multitasking carried out by the computer. In normal circumstances, the operating system completes its response to one command before prompting a user to input another command. However, a user may instruct the system to start work on a command, and then accept another command straight away. Actions resulting from both commands are multiprogrammed together.

Assessment

Unix combines the features of simplicity, ease of use and small size with considerable flexibility and power. It is a small, conventional operating system which has met with a wide measure of acceptance. Although it is some years old, its popularity is still on the increase. Efforts are being made to produce an internationally-agreed standard version of Unix, as there are differences between the versions for different computers. Although it was originally designed for mid-range systems, Unix is being implemented on the majority of workstations and some of the more powerful 16 bit microcomputers currently becoming available.

The most significant feature of Unix is that it has become an industry standard. It dominates the mid range of the computing industry, and its use is spreading both upwards and downwards. It provides a standard platform for the development of a wide range of applications software, and ensures the portability of this software between hardware hosts.

■ The **VME/B** (for **virtual machine environment**) operating system is used by the computers in the ICL 2900 series. It was designed and developed at the same time as the computers which support it.

General Features

VME/B is a sophisticated, general-purpose operating system, incorporating a number of advanced features. It supports transaction processing, multi-access and batch processing simultaneously. One of its prime objectives is to provide a simple, consistent high level interface to all users. It is flexible, in the sense that it can be tailored to the requirements of a particular installation. VME/B is written in a high level language, specially designed for the purpose. Communication with VME/B is via a language called **system control language (SCL)** which is a block structured high level language.

Virtual Machine Concept

As its name implies, VME/B is centred on the virtual machine concept. The virtual machine available to each user includes that user's program and data, and all the operating system facilities and utility programs needed by the user. To a user, a virtual machine appears completely self-contained, yet VME/B allows certain segments of data and code to be shared, to prevent unnecessary duplication of software. See Figure 23.3. A sophisticated protection mechanism is used to ensure the security of each virtual machine, and of shared segments.

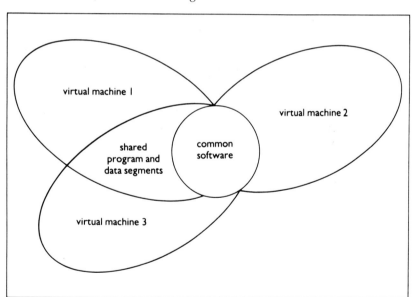

Figure 23.3
Virtual machines under
VME/B

Program Structure

Like many operating systems, VME/B is built up of a number of layers. See Figure 23.4. At the centre is the **kernel**, which transforms the hardware of the computer into a number of virtual machines. Next is a layer of systems software which manages the resources of the virtual machines. The outer layer contains applications programs. Unlike older operating systems, VME/B does not have a completely rigid boundary between systems and application software.

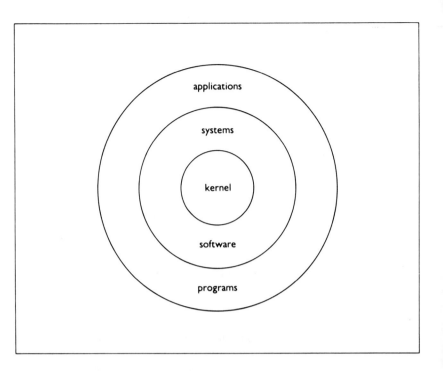

Figure 23.4
VME/B program structure

Memory Management

Each virtual machine running under VME/B is provided with a virtual store which can be much larger than the main store of the computer. VME/B manages all transfers of segments of programs and data to and from backing store in order to implement this policy.

Each virtual machine makes extensive use of a hardware-driven stack. The stack simplifies the processing of programs originally written in a high level language.

Communications Management

One of the overall objectives of the 2900 series is the efficient handling of data communications. On the hardware side, a number of input/output controllers are used to link peripheral devices to processing units and main store. On the systems software side, VME/B supervises and schedules all input and output. This relieves users of this burden, and makes the best use of the hardware resources.

Backing Store Management

All aspects of the use and security of files are handled by VME/B through the use of an integrated filestore. The user may be responsible for the placement of his or her files on backing store, or may choose to leave this task to the operating system.

Scheduling

Scheduling of applications takes place at several levels within the software. At the highest level, there are separate schedules for the transaction processing, batch and multi-access streams. At an intermediate level there is a scheduler for virtual machine resources, and at the lowest level the scheduler allocates the real hardware resources of the computer.

Protection

One of the most important aspects of the VME/B operating system is its protection mechanism. It is based on the concept of **levels of privilege**. Every process in the computer has associated with it a level of privilege in the range 0 to 15, 0 being the highest level, and 15 the lowest. Levels 0 to 2 are reserved for the kernel, levels 3 to 9 are for other systems software, and levels 10 to 15 are for applications programs. See Figure 23.5.

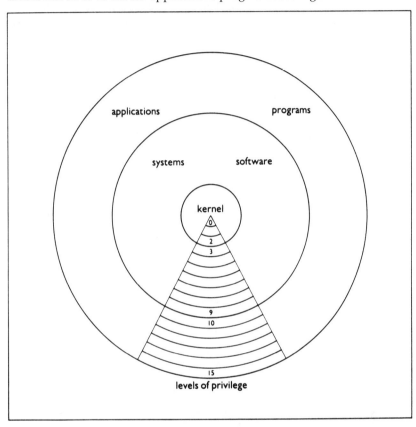

Figure 23.5
VME/B levels of privilege

When a process is running, a register called the **access control register** contains its level of privilege. Each segment of data that the process may wish to access contains a **read access key** and a **write access key**. Each key has a value between 0 and 15. Access is only permitted if the level of privilege in the access control register is less than or equal to that of the particular key. For example, a process with privilege level 11 may read from a segment with read access key 14, but may not write to a segment with write access key 8. Furthermore, each segment has an **execute permission bit**. Only if this bit is set may the code in the segment be executed.

This is a powerful and versatile protection system. It enables portions of the operating system to be protected from other portions, and users to create levels of protection within their own applications programs. It minimises the damage caused by an error at any level, and prevents the kernel from being corrupted by an error at any other level of systems or applications software.

Software Supported by VME/B

Among the systems software supported by VME/B are a Basic

interpreter, Fortran, Algol and Cobol compilers, and data management software. The Basic interpreter is an interactive system which allows online syntax checking editing and alteration of the flow of a program during execution. The Fortran, Algol and Cobol compilers share a number of modules, and produce object code in the same format. High level language programs may be written in a mixture of these three languages. The data management software is a flexible facility which allows a range of data structures to be constructed and developed by users. In particular, it provides a feature known as **data independence** (Section 28.3), which is a vital property of all large stores of data.

Assessment

VME/B is a large, complex and sophisticated operating system. Many of its design concepts are based on experience with the Atlas computer which, in its time, was the most powerful computing system in the world.

Although there have been some initial problems, these have now been resolved. Many features, especially the protection mechanism and the high level system control language, are highly regarded. In general, VME/B is considered to be a 'state of the art' system, and a model for the development of other operating systems.

23.4 Conclusion

■ Although few in number, the operating systems outlined in this chapter are representative of the range of systems currently in use. Each is designed for a particular type of computer, and a particular area of application. The systems vary considerably in size and complexity, from the sophistication of VME/B to the straightforward simplicity of MS-DOS. Nevertheless, they all have a number of features in common.

These operating systems represent some of the more successful attempts to write programs to the extremely demanding requirements outlined in the previous chapter. Each in its own way transforms the raw hardware of its host computer into a machine which can be put to useful work.

Exercise 23

1 Which of the case study operating systems support:
   a) Multiprogramming?
   b) Multi-access?
   c) Transaction Processing?
2 Which of the case study operating systems implement the concept of virtual memory?
3 Compare and contrast the protection mechanisms provided by Unix and VME/B.
4 Summarise the features provided by each operating system for the controlling of programs by users.
5 VM and OS/2 from IBM, RTL2 and Pick are the names of a few more well-known operating systems. Investigate one of these systems (or another of your choice), and summarise its features, using the same headings as contained in this chapter.
6 Discuss the significance of a single operating system which is implemented on a range of computers for:
   a) Computer manufacturers
   b) Software developers
   c) Computer users.

24 Fourth Generation Languages

This chapter covers the most recent development in programming - the use of integrated software development tools to specify, design and generate applications software. Software tools of this nature are known as **fourth generation languages** (4GLs), to distinguish them from the three previous generation of computers and their associated programming languages. Fourth generation techniques are beginning to replace the use of high level languages for the development of applications, for reasons which are discussed below.

24.1 Limitations of High Level Languages

■ High level languages were first developed in order to simplify and speed up the process of developing computer applications, and to broaden the base of the people who were able to design and program these applications. They have achieved these objectives to a great extent, but it is now becoming clear that they have certain limitations. In particular:

- High level languages are still too close to the way of working of acomputer, and not close enough to the needs of the user. Although they are problem-oriented, they specify the steps of the solution to a problem in terms of the elementary processing capabilities of a computer.
- The use of high level languages, at the end of a systems analysis and design process (Section 26.5), is far too slow in today's business environment.
- The long time taken to develop software means that, in view of the costs of programmer's time, software is very expensive.
- Software developed using high level languages is not always of a very high standard. There are no automatic checks of the correctness of program modules, and software maintenance (Section 26.10) is haphazard and can introduce new errors while correcting others.

Taken together, these shortcomings are leading many computer users, particularly commercial users, to investigate alternative techniques for software development. The majority of commercial data processing is stereotyped: an interlocking set of applications based on large files of data, or an integrated database. The software records all transactions, and enables the transaction data to be analysed and reports prepared from it. What is needed is a set of software development tools which enable applications of this sort to be developed quickly and cost-effectively.

24.2 The Objectives of Fourth Generation Languages

■ The objectives of fourth generation languages are complementary to the limitations of high level languages:

- To bring about a substantial improvement in the productivity of software development.
- To allow users to have more influence on the design of applications software.
- To assist in the development of integrated suites of applications software, accessing a common set of data files, or a database.
- To allow the rapid production of **prototypes** of applications from their initial specification, so that users can check whether they are actually

what is needed. A prototype is a rough first draft of the software which runs on test data.

- To assist with software maintenance. The same software tools which are used to develop an application in the first place are used to modify it. This reduces the possibility of introducing errors during modification.

24.3 Fourth Generation Languages: General Structure

■ Figure 24.1 shows the overall structure of a typical fourth generation language. It is not a programming language in the conventional sense, although parts of it may include statements in a specification language. Instead, it is an integrated set of facilities, with a common data access mechanism. It enables applications to be developed using the same data access mechanism. The data is in the form of files, or (more commonly) a relational database (Section 30.3). The fourth generation language has links to '' : file management layer of the operating system, or the database management system which maintains the database.

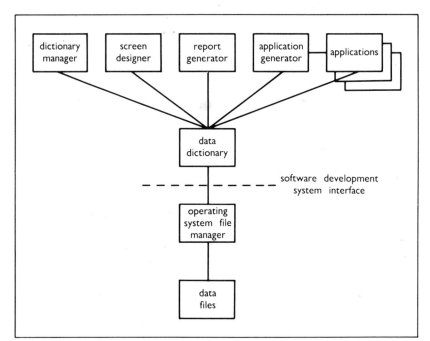

Figure 24.1
Fourth generation language: overall structure

The common interface between the fourth generation language (and any applications generated by it) and the filing system is the **data dictionary**. This is a layer of software which maintains, for each file in the system, a dictionary (also known as a descriptor file) which describes the structure of the file as records, and the nature of each data item in a record.

There is a **screen design** module which enables the layout of the screen display for each operation to be specified, as well as the layouts of printed output. There is a **report generator** which enables summaries of the data to be extracted, analysed (by adding up totals, etc.), displayed and printed. There are **application generators**, often one for each type of application, which enable the processing of the data to be specified. Once an application has been generated, it becomes another element in the system, using the same data access mechanism as the fourth generation language. This is shown in Figure 24.1.

There are two broad approaches to the design of fourth generation languages. One requires the applications designer to fill in a set of forms, on the computer screen, to specify how an application is to work. The other uses a programming language, at specification level, in order to describe how the processing is to take place. Some fourth generation languages use a mixture of the approaches: the form-filling approach for the data dictionary and screen designs, and the specification language for the report generators and application generators.

24.4 Data Dictionary

■ The data dictionary mechanism is the link between the fourth generation language and the applications generated by it, and the data files on which they operate. By channelling all access to data through this single mechanism, it is possible to ensure that the data is always in a consistent state, and that the rules specifying the structure of the various files are always adhered to.

The data dictionary enables the structure of each data file in the system to be specified. A file, which may, for example, contain all the invoices raised by the company, is structured as a set of records (one for each invoice in the example), each of which has a set of fields (such as the invoice number, date, etc). The type of each field is specified. Types generally include characters, numbers (which may be divided into integers, fractions, currency, etc) and dates, in the format chosen. **Attributes** of each data item may also be set. For example, numbers may be in a certain range, or codes may have to be unique in the file (no duplicate invoice numbers, for example). Data items in one file may be codes for references in another file. For example, the invoice file may contain customer codes which are looked up in the client file to obtain the full name and address of the customer. These attributes are used to check data items as they are entered into the records of the file. **Default values** may also be specified in the dictionary. These are values which a field will assume if no data is entered. For example, a date may default to the current date unless the user types another.

The data dictionary facility is used to create a descriptor file for each data file in the system. One descriptor may apply to a set of data files. For example, the invoice file may hold all the invoices for a year. At the end of the year a new invoice file with the same structure, is created. The data dictionary allows these descriptor files to be amended, for example by the inclusion of additional fields in each record. It then supervises the conversion of the associated data files from the old format to the new format. The data dictionary is also used when data is entered into the files. It checks each entry according to the conditions for the field, and supplies default values. If an entry is a reference to another file, it checks that it is present in the other file.

24.5 Screen Design Facilities

■ The screen design facilities enable the layout of the screens used for each aspect of an application to be specified. If a screen is to be used for the entry of the fields in a record, the facilities enable the fields, and their associated labels, to be positioned on the screen, and additional headings, prompts and error messages to be included. If the screen is for a report, the data may be arranged in columns, with headings and footnotes. On some systems, the same design facilities are used to specify the layout of printed output.

In some fourth generation languages, the screen design facilities are a separate module; in others they are an integral part of one of the applications generators.

24.6 Report Generator

■ One of the commonest types of commercial programs extracts data from a file and displays or prints the extracted data. For example, a program may be required to calculate and display the monthly totals of the invoices raised by a company, or the breakdown of invoices by department. The report generation module enables applications of this sort to be specified very simply.

The stages of the specification are to list the data files from which the report is to be derived, state what processing is required, and specify the format of the output. Processing includes selection of certain records in the file if fields match stated conditions, calculating totals of the records, and including only some of the records in the report. In most cases a sort is required, either before or after selection of the required records. The format of the output is specified either by reference to a screen already designed, or by formatting instructions included in the report generator.

24.7 Application Generator

■ Application generators are used to specify the processing which is to be carried out on the data files. Most fourth generation languages have more than one application generator, for example one for transaction processing, which updates individual records, and one for batch processing, which updates all the records in a file.

An application generator allows a software designer to describe what processes are to be carried out on the data, without becoming involved in the detailed processing steps. The steps of the specification of each application are generally similar to those of report generation, but are much more flexible. The input and output files are specified, as well as any temporary files for intermediate data. The interaction with users at terminals is described, in terms of screen designs already established, or by designing the screens as part of the specification. The nature and format of any displayed or printed output is also specified. The processing operations - sorting, selection, performing calculations and carrying out conditional operations - are described. Calls to software modules written in a high level language may also be included.

When the steps of an application have been entered and checked, they are compiled, and become an integral part of the software system. The compiled application uses the data dictionary to access files, and the screen layout designs to display data. If the application is to be modified, the application generator is again used to carry out the modifications.

24.8 Case Study: Powerhouse Software Development System

■ Powerhouse is an integrated set of development tools for business software, designed and marketed by the Canadian company, Cognos Incorporated. It is implemented on a number of mid-range computers, including the Digital Equipment VAX series.

Objectives

The principal aims of Powerhouse are the cost-effective development of error-free commercial software, with a productivity improvement from software development staff of anything up to a factor of ten. Powerhouse

specification language it uses has many statements in common with Quick, with additional facilities to create and delete data files, and to update all the records in a file systematically. QTP does not have a screen interface, but can be used in conjunction with Quiz for report generation. QTP has locking facilities for files, either for the whole of the updating run, or during access, and for individual records during processing.

Example Software Specification

As an example of the use of Powerhouse, suppose that the structure of an invoice file had been entered in the dictionary. An invoice contains an invoice number, date, client reference, and a series of item lines, each containing a stock reference and number ordered. The client and stock references are codes which refer to items in the client file and the stock file respectively. An application program to raise invoices might be specified as follows, using the screen design facility of Quick:

`SCREEN RAISE-INVOICE`	gives the application a name
`FILE INVOICES`	use the invoices file
`FILE CLIENTS REFERENCE`	also refer to the clients file
`FILE STOCK REFERENCE`	also refer to the stock file
`TITLE "Invoice Entry" CENTRED`	gives the screen a title
`GENERATE`	generate the screen design
`BUILD`	compile the application

The Quick screen designer takes this specification, together with the descriptions of the data from the dictionaries for the invoices, clients and stock files, and generates a screen design for invoice entry.

To run the application, Quick is called, and the name of the application (`RAISE-INVOICE`) is supplied. A screen showing the fields of an invoice, as specified in the data dictionary, is displayed. The data for an invoice is then entered and may be edited before being written to disk and printed.

To generate a report of all the invoices raised during a particular month, with totals analysed by department, the following specification is supplied to Quiz:

`ACCESS INVOICES`	use the invoices file
`SELECT IF DATE GT 851031 &`	select invoices raised
`    AND DATE LT 851201`	during November 1985
`SORT ON DEPT`	sort by department
`REPORT DEPT INV-NO DATE &`	include these fields
`    INV-AMOUNT`	
`FOOTING AT DEPT`	include department
`    "Department Total" &`	totals
`    INV-AMOUNT SUBTOTAL SKIP 2`	and skip two lines
`GO`	

Note that the & symbol is used if a statement is to be continued on another line, and that the continuation line is indented.

Assessment

Powerhouse, and fourth generation specification languages like it, are presenting designers of business software with software development tools of unprecedented power. They are restricted to one class of applications, but this class is very broad, and software modules written in applications, but this class is very broad, and software modules written in a conventional programming language can be called from generated software if necessary. Fourth generation languages are gaining acceptance very rapidly, hindered only by the lack of knowledge of business software developers and their managers, and by the general reluctance to change from established software development practices.

24.9
Conclusion

■ The main points of this chapter are as follows:
- Software development tools, also known as fourth generation languages, are integrated sets of facilities which enable certain types of software to be developed very rapidly.
- Most fourth generation languages are designed for the generation of commercial applications.
- Software development systems use a data dictionary to access the file management facilities of the operating system or database management system which supports them.
- There are modules for screen design, report generation and the generation of various types of application. Once an application has been compiled, it uses the same data access mechanisms as the fourth generation language itself.
- The benefits of fourth generation languages include greatly increased productivity of software developers, rapid prototyping and an increased involvement of users in the software development process.

Exercise 24

1 Briefly define the following terms: fourth generation language; prototype; specification language; data dictionary; descriptor file; report generator; application generator; attribute; default value; usage.

2 For each of the following types of application, state whether fourth generation languages of the types described in this chapter, would be suitable:
a) stock control
b) cinema seat reservations
c) keeping accounts
d) aircraft flight simulators
e) controlling a factory robot
f) recording and analysing examination results.

3 a) How do fourth generation languages enable users to be more closely involved in the process of software development?
b) What are the consequences of the closer involvement of users in software development?

4 How do fourth generation languages bring about an improvement in the productivity of programmers and others involved in software development?

5 Find out about other fourth generation languages which are now in use. Write a report on one of these, using the same headings as those in the Powerhouse case study.

6 a) Give your views on the extent to which fourth generation languages will replace the use of high level languages such as Cobol for the development of business software.
b) Do you think that fourth generation languages will come into use for other types of computer application? If so, list the application areas where you think this will happen.

25 Software Engineering

A number of far-reaching changes are taking place at present in the way in which computer software is developed. The causes of these changes include the following:

- The increasing costs of software development.
- Dissatisfaction from users with the quality and suitability of software.
- The increasing length and complexity of software: commercial programs have tens of thousands of lines of source code; real-time software often has hundreds of thousands of lines.
- The increased dependence of many organisations on their computer systems, with no manual backup. Banks, insurance companies and most large commercial organisations are entirely dependent on computers for their business transactions, and many scientific, engineering and, above all, military systems are now entirely computerised. A hardware or software failure in any of these systems could have serious consequences.
- The requirement for standard interfaces, both to users and to other software.

These pressures are causing a re-assessment of the methods used for the development of computer software. What is needed is a technique for the development of large, complex software items, which satisfy strict standards of performance and correctness, in a controlled, scheduled, budgeted and cost-effective way. The approach which is evolving in response to these requirements is known as **software engineering**.

25.1 The Objectives of Software Engineering

■ Software engineering is the profession which is replacing programming and systems analysis. The objectives of software engineering are as stated above: the development of large, complex software items, which satisfy strict standards of performance and correctness, in a controlled, scheduled, budgeted and cost-effective way. Software engineers require, in addition to a proficiency in programming, a knowledge of formal mathematics and logic, computing science, economics and management.

Software engineering is carried out by teams of people. When a software development project is started, the teams are set up with a management structure corresponding to the structure of the software itself. A schedule is drawn up for the project, and costs are allocated to the various portions and stages. Each team has a team leader, whose task is to make sure that the software developed by the team is correct, properly structured, has the right interfaces to the software being developed by the other teams, and is on schedule and within budget. This is a difficult task, which requires a wide range of technical and management skills.

Software engineering is concerned with the entire life cycle of a software project: design, development, testing, use and maintenance. All the work done is aimed at the highest possible standards at the lowest possible costs throughout this life cycle.

25.2 Program Structure

■ It is now quite clear that the only way of achieving the required standards of correctness, performance and reliability of software is through the careful design of the structure of a program. A well-structured program must satisfy the following conditions:

- The programs must have a clear overall structure in terms of **modules**, with each module carrying out a specific task. Modules may be implemented as functions or procedures, depending on the programming language used.
- There must be a clearly defined interface between modules. This is particularly important when interfaces are between modules written by different software engineers.
- Each module should be a simple combination of the elementary constructions of the programming language. Modules should be easy to read by people other than their original programmer.
- There must be a close correspondence between the structure of a module and the structure of the data on which it operates.
- Each module should leave the data structures on which it operates in a state which is consistent with their defining properties. This is particularly important with pointers: they should not be left 'hanging loose' by one module, on the assumption that another module will tidy them up.
- A module must have no **side effects**: it must not make any changes to data values, or to the state of the program, apart from those it is intended to make.

Achieving a program structure which satisfies these conditions is a difficult task. Some help is given by the program structuring properties of the language, as discussed in Section 18.5.

25.3 Program Design

■ Program design is the means by which proper program structure and function are achieved. It is the technique for going from the initial statement of the requirements of a program, which is generally vague, incomplete and contradictory, to the final structured, tested and approved code. See Figure 25.1. It is a long and difficult process, made more so by the lack of widely-accepted, tested techniques of program design. However, a number of methods of program design do exist, and their use is increasing all the time. In the foreseeable future, it is likely that most software development will be based on a formal technique of program design.

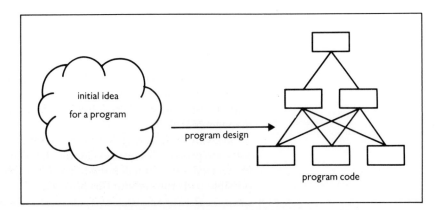

Figure 25.1
Program design

The simplest and one of the most popular methods of program design is **stepwise refinement**. It is based on the use of **algorithms**, which are written in a language (known as **pseudo-code**) somewhere between

English and a programming language such as Pascal. The process itself may be described by an algorithm of this nature:

State the overall steps of a program in a brief, top-level algorithm.
Repeat
>Expand each statement of the algorithm as a detailed algorithm which describes the steps required to implement the statement.
Until the task has been task has been specified in sufficient detail for the code of the program to be written.

Stepwise refinement is a **top-down** process, with details being added in an orderly fashion as the design progresses. If an algorithm turns out to be incorrect, it can be 'unplugged' and replaced by another without too much effect on the program structure as a whole.

Although stepwise refinement can bring about a great improvement in the structure of a program , it is not formal enough for many applications. In particular, there is no guarantee that data structures are left in a consistent state by the various modules. It is very difficult to prove the correctness of program modules developed in this way (Section 25.4).

A number of more formal methods of program design are coming into use, the most popular being **functional decomposition**. Like stepwise refinement, functional decomposition is a top-down method, starting with the overall requirements of a program, and adding detail in an orderly way. The difference is that at every stage, the essential properties of the data structures are specified, and each algorithm is expressed as a mathematical function which transforms these data structures. Each algorithm can be tested by various mathematical techniques, in order to prove that the propertiers of the data structures are not altered by the operations it performs on the data.

25.4 Proving the Correctness of Programs

■ At present, programs are tested by supplying them with a large amount of test data, in order to check that they work properly with every type of data that they are likely to encounter in practice. However, this process can never establish for certain that a program is correct, no matter how many different sets of test data are used. If a program is of critical importance, as so many commercial, industrial and military applications now are, every possible precaution needs to be taken to ensure that there are no errors in it.

The technique which is beginning to be used to ensure that program modules (and algorithms used in program design) are correct is to regard them as mathematical theorems, and apply the same methods of proof to them as are used to prove the correctness of theorems. Two types of proof are required for each algorithm or program module: the first determines that it carries out the required transformations on the data correctly, and the second checks that it leaves the defining properties of the data structures intact. This is an extremely difficult and time-consuming process, bearing in mind the length and complexity of operational software, and the complexity of the data structures commonly used. It can only be applied to software written in certain programming languages, or algorithms using a precisely-defined mathematical notation. Research is currently under way to develop semi-automatic methods of carrying out these proofs.

25.5 Computer-aided Software Engineering

■ Traditionally, computer programming is almost entirely a manual task. A programmer takes the specification of the program, which has been designed by one of the techniques discussed above, and writes the code to create a program which corresponds to the specification. One change which is beginning to occur to this practice is the use of software development tools for certain types of application, as described in Chapter 24. However, the demands of software engineering, as discussed at the beginning of this chapter, mean that the traditional methods of writing programs by hand are not adequate.

What are required are **computer-aided software engineering (Case)** tools, also known as **software development environments** which form the basis of all stages of the design, development, testing and maintenance of software. These have some features in common with fourth generation languages, such as data dictionaries, but are more powerful, and are required for all types of computer application. Typical features of a set of Case tools are as follows:

- A **central database** which includes all modules of all software under development, module libraries, and the specifications and algorithms written during software design. This includes an administration system to keep track of the different versions of each module which are developed.
- A **data dictionary** system giving access to all the data files for each application.
- Facilities to check specifications for completeness and correctness, and to assist in the proofs of correctness of program modules.
- **Compilers** and **cross-compilers** so that the most suitable programming language can be used for each code module, and that programs can be linked from modules written in a variety of source languages. In many cases the object code will be for different computers or electronic systems from the one on which the software development system runs.
- **Program generators** for routine modules such as file handling and screen input/output. User interfaces increasingly conform to industry standards, and are developed using standard software modules.
- **Run-time diagnostic facilities** and simulators for other computers, so that linked object code can be tested before it is transferred to its ultimate host computer.
- Word processing or desktop publishing facilities for the production and maintenance of documentation.

Case tools of this sort require a powerful computer system to support them, with network links for communication between software engineers. Links are also required to a range of target computers so that the final versions of the software can be transferred to them. Workstations are the most popular platforms for Case tools.

The **Ada program support environment (Apse)** is an example of a set of Case tools for the support of a single high level language. A number of other Case systems are now available, and computer-aided software engineering is a major growth area in the computing industry.

25.6 Conclusion

■ Software engineering is an approach to software development which is steadily gaining acceptance in the computing industry. It is quite likely that, during the current decade, techniques of software engineering become the norm, and **information systems factories** are set up for software development. The method of writing programs entirely by hand may go the way of the valve and the punched card.

The main points of this chapter are as follows:

- Conventional methods of designing and writing programs are becoming inadequate as programs get longer, more complex and more expensive, and computer applications become increasingly important.
- Software engineering is an approach to the development of large, complex software items, which satisfy strict standards of performance and correctness, in a controlled, scheduled, budgeted and cost-effective way.
- Software engineering is concerned with the entire lifecycle of a software project: design, development, documentation, testing, use and maintenance. All the work done is aimed at the highest possible standards at the lowest possible costs throughout this lifecycle.
- The proper design of the structure of a program is essential if the program is to meet the software standards now required.
- Program design is a technique for going from the initial specification of a program, which may be vague, incomplete and contradictory, to the final structured, tested and approved code.
- In order to establish beyond reasonable doubt that a program module or specification algorithm is correct, mathematical techniques of theorem proving are beginning to be applied.
- A computer-aided software engineering toolset is a set of development tools including data dictionaries, cross-compilers, theorem provers, module libraries, module generators and run-time diagnostic aids used to assist in the development of software by methods of software engineering.

Exercise 25

1 Briefly define the following terms: software engineering; software lifecycle; program structure; side effect; program design; stepwise refinement; top-down method; functional decomposition; proof of correctness; computer-aided software engineering.

2 Discuss the similarities and differences between the fourth generation languages described in Chapter 24 and the Case tools described in this chapter.

3 Why is it so important to try to develop methods of proving the correctness of programs by mathematical techniques?

4 Describe the significance of cross-compilers for software development environments.

5 Examine the source code of a program in a high level language that you have written, or one obtained from elsewhere, and state the extent to which it satisfies each of the requirements of a well-structured program given in Section 25.2.

6 In what ways do introductory programming languages such as Basic make it difficult to satisfy the requirements for a well-structured program?

7 Give your views on the consequences for the programming profession of the trend towards software engineering.

26 Information System Design

This chapter describes the sequence of steps required to plan, design, implement and maintain a computer application. It describes how this work is done within the computing industry, and should enable you to carry out the steps yourself for simple information systems. To assist in this process, an example application is developed throughout the chapter. It is not a case study, but is nevertheless a realistic application. The example is a computer system used by the distributor of a monthly magazine for subscriber records.

The **data processing cycle** is the sequence of actions carried out during the development of a new information system. Depending on the application, the cycle can take anything from a few weeks to more than a year. The person, or team of people, most actively involved in all stages of the data processing cycle have the job title of **systems analyst**. If the design of the system, and the writing of the software are done by the same people (as is increasingly the case), the job title is **software engineer**.

26.1 The Need for Information Systems

■ Before studying the methods of designing and implementing computerised information systems, it is important to clarify the reasons for introducing such systems into an organisation. These need to be kept in mind while a system is being developed.

The commonest reasons for introducing a computer system into a company are to reduce costs, to increase productivity, to take advantage of the facilities offered by computers, and to increase the volume of business. In addition, computers can supply better management information, and enable long-term forecasts and plans to be made. Also, computers enable some operations to be carried out which would otherwise be impossible. In many cases, companies are obliged to introduce information technology because their competitors have done so. Without the benefits of computerisation, they would be unable to compete.

A computer system must satisfy the general requirements of a business or administrative environment. This is characterised by large quantities of data, usually requiring similar forms of processing, within tight time schedules. The cost of various operations are important, and it is vital that deadlines are met. Computerised systems must run smoothly, with adequate backup if anything should go wrong.

A selection of these factors is the motivation for each particular application. These reasons for introducing an information system are also some of the general objectives of the system.

26.2 Types of Information System

■ Although no two information systems are quite the same, it is possible to identify a number of distinct classes of them. Broadly speaking, data processing systems are of three types: **systems where processing is done periodically**, **real-time systems**, and **database systems**. There is a correspondence between these classes and the types of operating system discussed in Section 22.1

Systems Where Processing is Done Periodically

These systems are characterised by large volumes of data of identical type. From time to time, batches of such data are processed in one operation, hence their name: **batch processing systems**. The commonest example of a batch processing system is a payroll system. Once a week or once a month, a payroll system is put into action to produce the payslips for all the employees of a company. The volume of data processed is large, and each employee receives identical treatment by the system. Batch processing systems are regarded as 'traditional' data processing systems. They closely resemble manual methods of data processing.

Real-time Systems

Real-time processing is data processing 'while you wait'. In other words, the computer must keep pace with some external process. Small quantities of data are processed in one operation. The delay in processing the data, which varies from a fraction of a second to a couple of minutes, is acceptable to the user of the system. Three types of real-time systems may be identified, though the distinction between them is fairly fine. The types are **process control, information storage and retrieval** and **transaction processing**.

Process control is an industrial application of computers. It is the continuous monitoring and controlling of an operational process by a computer. Measurements taken from the process are sent to the computer at frequent intervals, often many times a second. Control instructions are issued by the computer in response to this data. The time taken to process the data and issue the control instructions is short. An example of process control is the automatic control of several aspects of oil refining. The temperature, pressure and composition of substances in various reactor vessels are monitored, and control instructions are issued accordingly.

Information storage and retrieval systems are concerned with accessing and updating data stored in files. Small quantities of data are handled in one operation, and calculations or other operations on the data are minimal. An example of an information storage and retrieval system is a medical records system. The medical record of a patient can be accessed or updated by doctors, nurses or administrators from a terminal.

A **transaction processing system** is one which handles specifically defined transactions one at a time. Each transaction is processed to its conclusion before work on the next transaction commences. The amount of data supplied for a transaction is small, fitting into predefined categories. Processing may include a certain amount of calculation, as well as updating files. The commonest example of transaction processing is airline seat reservations. All the information required to make a reservation is supplied to the system, which then checks whether one can be made. If so, various files are updated, and passenger totals are adjusted. Other examples of transaction processing are withdrawals of money at bank cash terminals and most stock control systems. Transaction processing systems are becoming the commonest type of information system.

Database Systems

Database systems use one store of information (the database) to support all the data processing activities of a particular company. The database is independent of any individual application. Applications may be of any of the types of data processing described in the previous sections. Database systems are described in detail in Chapter 30.

Data Communications Systems

Several of the types of data processing system mentioned in the previous sections involve the transmission of data from one place to another. This aspect of data processing is discussed in Chapter 31.

26.3 Feasibility Study

■ In a variety of ways, and for various reasons, the need to computerise one aspect of the work of a company becomes apparent. Reasons for the introduction of computerised working are discussed in Section 26.1. The desire for computerisation is generally expressed by one of two groups of people within the company, namely the management or the users. Managers are concerned with turnover, efficiency, productivity, profits and growth. The users are the people whose work will be done, partially or completely, by computer. They have detailed knowledge and experience of how the work is done at present.

The decision to investigate the possibility of changing to computerised working is generally taken at the appropriate level of management, in consultation with the users. But the way ahead is fraught with difficulties. How will the work be done by computer? What equipment will be needed? What changes will there be in staffing? What effects will the change to computers have on the company as a whole?

The first step towards answering these questions is a **feasibility study**. This is a preliminary survey, carried out by a manager or systems analyst, to determine whether a full scale system analysis should be carried out. The survey is generally conducted by consultation with management and users. A feasibility report is prepared, outlining the objectives and constraints of the proposed system, estimating the costs involved, and recommending whether or not to continue with the project.

Magazine Subscription System: Feasibility Report

For the example magazine subscription application, the feasibility report might identify the main features of the system as follows:

Overall System Structure
A single integrated database of subscriber details.
Tasks
1 Enter new subscriber details.
2 Update existing subscriber details.
3 Locate subscriber details.
4 Print address labels for magazine issues.
5 Print reminders when subscriptions are due or overdue.
6 Record payment of subscriptions.
Software
Implement systems using database package.
Hardware
System to run on existing desktop microcomputers, with data stored on existing Winchester disk.
Operation
System to be operated by existing clerical staff after a training course.
The study also gives cost estimates and an overall implementation schedule.

26.4 System Analysis

■ If the feasibility report is favourable, and approved by the managers, then a detailed system analysis is undertaken. This takes the form of interviews, surveys, questionnaires and sometimes the systems analyst working with the users for a while. The two objectives are to gain a thorough knowledge of the current way of working, and analyse, in a fair amount of detail, the requirements of the computerised system. The outcome from the system analysis phase is a **requirements specification** of the proposed system. This states the detailed objectives of each task, in terms of the required inputs, processing and outputs.

Magazine Subscriptions System: Requirements Specification

For the example system, the systems analyst works with the clerical staff to see how they deal with subscriptions using the existing card index. The tasks involved are studied carefully, to ensure that the computer system will adequately cover all aspects of the work. The requirements specification is written in terms of the tasks identified in the feasibility study. For example, the task of printing the address labels is described as follows:

4   Print Address Labels: Requirements
      Information for each subscriber:
                  Full name: Title, initials, surname
                  Address: Five lines
                  Postcode
                  Number of copies
                  Whether subscription valid
      Information printed to fit in standard adhesive labels
      Labels to be printed in batches of variable size

The other tasks are described at a similar level of detail. From the task requirements, the overall information requirement of the database can be given. This is as follows:

      For each subscriber:
                  Identification Code (for internal use only)
                  Surname
                  Initials
                  Address (five lines)
                  Postcode
                  Number of copies
                  Subscription Validity Code (Valid, Lapsed, Cancelled)
                  Subscription Expiry Date (Month and Year)
                  Date of Last Payment (Day, Month and Year)

Records are never deleted from the database. They either become lapsed (because the subscription is not renewed) or are cancelled by the subscriber. Experience indicates that many lapsed or cancelled subscribers re-subscribe later, and mailshots can be addressed to them with some success.

26.5 System Design

■ The requirement specification from the system analysis phase is used to plan the structure of the data, and the operations carried out by the computer system. This system design phase is the central stage of the entire data processing cycle. Applying their knowledge of the capabilities of a computer system to the requirements of the particular application, the systems analysts produce a **functional specification** of the new application.

This includes an outline of each task to be performed, with detailed descriptions of the input and output data at each stage, the processing carried out, and the file formats involved. The task specifications may be written as algorithms. The functional specification generally includes a **system flowchart**, which is a diagram showing the overall flow of data through the system, and the various operations carried out. The functional specification is submitted to the managers for approval. It may be accepted, modified or rejected. When agreement has been reached (often after modifications have been made to the specification), it marks the end of the system design phase of the data processing cycle.

System Flowcharts

The aim of a system flowchart is to present a clear picture of the overall tasks and flows of data in a computer application. It is precise enough to form the basis of software development, but simple enough to be understood by people who are not computer experts (such as managers).

System flowcharts are based on an internationally agreed set of symbols (though they do not always follow them strictly). Figure 26.1 shows the system flowchart symbols in common use. Notice that there is one set of symbols for stored data, and another set for various types of processing.

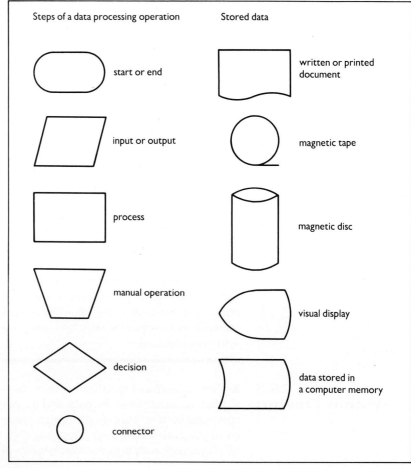

Figure 26.1
System flowchart symbols

Many data processing operations are concerned with files. A file is a large collection of data, with a definite logical structure, held on a physical medium such as magnetic tape or magnetic disks. Chapters 27 and 28 deal with file structures and file processing in detail. System flowchart segments are discussed below for a few common operations on files.

File Creation

Data is transferred from an external medium, such as OCR forms, to a file on a magnetic tape or disk. Alternatively, in may data processing systems, data is typed directly from data entry terminals to a file. See Figure 26.2.

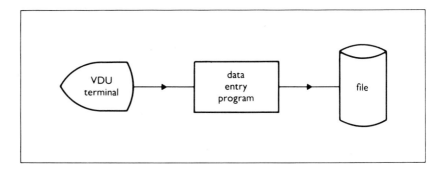

Figure 26.2
File creation

Data Validation

The data in a file is subjected to various tests. This process is called **validation**. In batch systems, incorrect data is printed on an error report; correct data is stored on another file. See Figure 26.3. In transaction processing systems, input data is validated as it is entered. Invalid items are rejected and must be retyped.

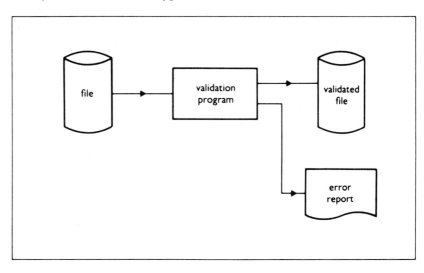

Figure 26.3
File validation

Updating a File

In batch systems, a file of amendments is used to bring the data on another file up-to-date. A new file is produced of the updated information. See Figure 26.4. In transaction processing systems, updating is done for each transaction as soon as it is entered.

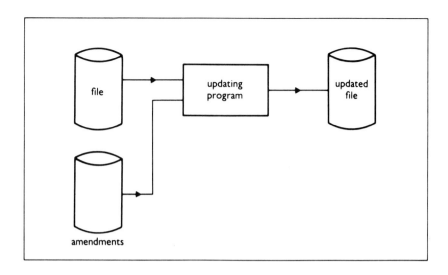

Figure 26.4
File updating

Output and Report Generation

Data selected from a file is output, and, if required, a report is generated, summarising the information contained in the file. See Figure 26.5.

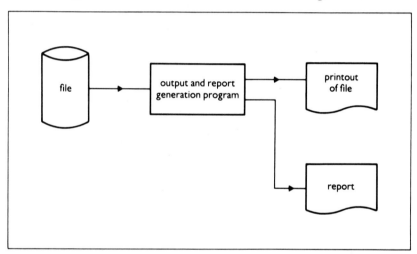

Figure 26.5
Output and report generation

Magazine Subscription System: System Flowchart

Figure 26.6 shows the system flowchart for the magazine subscription system. Note how all the processing operations relate to the single central database.

The file format for the subscriber database is specified as follows:

Identification Code:	Year/sequence, eg 91/0001
Surname:	Alphabetic, max 20 characters
Initials:	Alphabetic, max 6 characters
Address: 5 lines, each:	Alphanumeric, max 15 characters
Postcode:	Alphanumeric, max 7 characters
Number of copies:	Integer, 2 digits
Subscription Validity Code:	V: Valid, L: Lapsed, C: Cancelled
Subscription Expiry Date:	Month and Year, eg 08/92
Date of Last Payment:	Day, Month and Year, eg 22/08/91

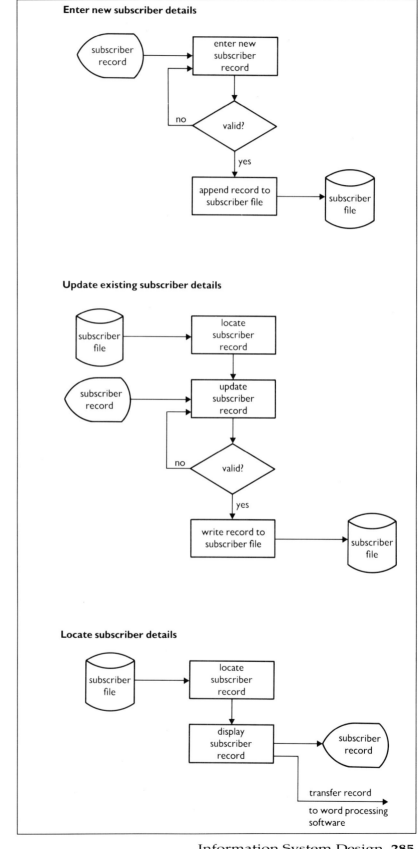

Figure 26.6
Magazine subscription system flowchart

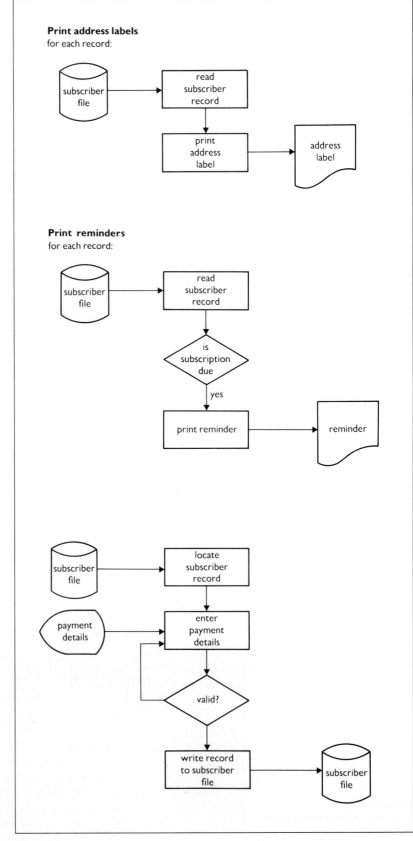

Figure 26.6
Magazine subscription system
flowchart (continued)

This file format is entered into the database package when the system is implemented. The specification for each field is used to validate each data item as it is entered. The algorithm for the task of entering new subscribers is specified as follows:

```
For each new subscriber, repeat:
        Issue database package append command
        For each field, repeat:
                Repeat
                        Enter field
                        Validate field
                        If not valid, reject field and display message
                Until field is valid.
```

Algorithms for the other tasks are written at the same level of detail in the functional specification.

26.6 System Development

■ Once the specification of a new data processing system has been accepted, the detailed work on the development of the system can begin. System development is concerned with specifying, writing, testing and documenting the programs for the new system, or configuring an existing software package for the tasks required. This is done by a team of software engineers (programmers) reporting to a team leader.

Writing Software

Using the relevant portion of the system flowchart, together with various file specifications, the specification of each program required is set out in detail. Several programs are generally needed, and these are further broken down into modules, each module performing a specific task. It is usual to specify what must be done by each module of each program, without stating how it is to be done. The method used in each module is at the discretion of the programmer writing the module.

When the program specifications have been agreed with the software team leader, the programmers set to work, writing each module of each program. For the majority of applications, either a high-level language or a fourth generation language is used. Modules are written separately, often by different programmers, and combined at a later stage. Libraries are developed of common code modules, which are accessed by operational modules as required. The modules of the new programs are tested separately and then combined, or built, into complete programs.

Selecting and Configuring a Software Package

An increasing number of information systems are implemented using standard software packages. These include such tasks as word processing, accounting, stock control, payroll processing, database applications and spreadsheets. If a software package is to be used, the system flow chart and functional specification for the proposed application provide the criteria for selection of a particular package. Common types of application are covered by a number of competing software packages, the most suitable of which must be selected.

The general criteria for selection of a software package are as follows:
• The extent to which the package can match the system flowcharts and functional specification for the proposed application. In most cases, a compromise has to be reached between the requirements of the

application and the capabilities of the software pack. Most packages can be configured by users to meet the particular needs of an application.

- The degree of compatibility of the software package with existing software used by the company. Aspects of this include whether the package will run on the existing computers used by the company, and whether any hardware modifications are required. In many cases the new software must be able to use existing data files, or transfer data to and from existing data files. The user interface of the package must not be too different from those of existing software.
- The level of support and user training offered by the supplier of the software package. The users must be convinced that problems will receive prompt attention, and that training manuals and courses provided with the software package are adequate.
- The costs of the package. Most business software packages are purchased for an initial fee, together with an annual maintenance charge. The costs have to be weighed against the benefits of the particular software package.
- The business prospects of the software supplier. Regrettably, many software packages are developed by small, independent software houses, whose prospects of staying in business are sometimes uncertain. If a software supplier goes out of business, users of the software package are left with no support.

In spite of some of the problems described above, the use of software packages for commercial computer applications is on the increase. Most small businesses base all their computer applications on such packages, and many larger companies are beginning to follow the trend. The main reason is cost: the cost of developing a commercial data processing system internally is very much higher than that of purchasing and, if necessary, adapting an existing software package. Furthermore, established software packages have been proved in use by all their other users, and modified in the light of any problems that have occurred.

When a software package has been selected, it is **configured** to meet the functional specification of the application. Configuration includes specifying file formats, input validation, and the user interface for particular operations. Many software packages have facilities which resemble high-level programming langugages for configuration purposes.

Magazine Subscription System: Implementation

The feasibility study for the magazine subscription system specified that, for reasons of cost, the system should be implemented by means of a database package. Using the criteria given above, a suitable database package from the many available for desktop microcomputers is selected. Required features include data validation facilities, and a configuration language powerful enough to create the screen formats for data entry and display, and the output formats for printed labels.

The configuration phase includes specifying the required file format, giving the data type and field width for each field, and specifying any additional validation requirements. A screen layout is defined for each task performed on the data, and a menu system is created to allow users to select the task they require.

The file structure on backing store is created and maintained by the database software. It does not have to be specified explicitly during system configuration. Records are stored in the order in which they are entered. Instead of sorting them into alphabetical order of surnames, an index is created of the surnames. This is sorted, and allows an entry to be located on a surname key very rapidly. The index is updated and re-sorted each time a new record is entered. Figure 26.7 shows an the screen layout for entering a subscriber record. Figure 26.8 shows the layout of a printed address label.

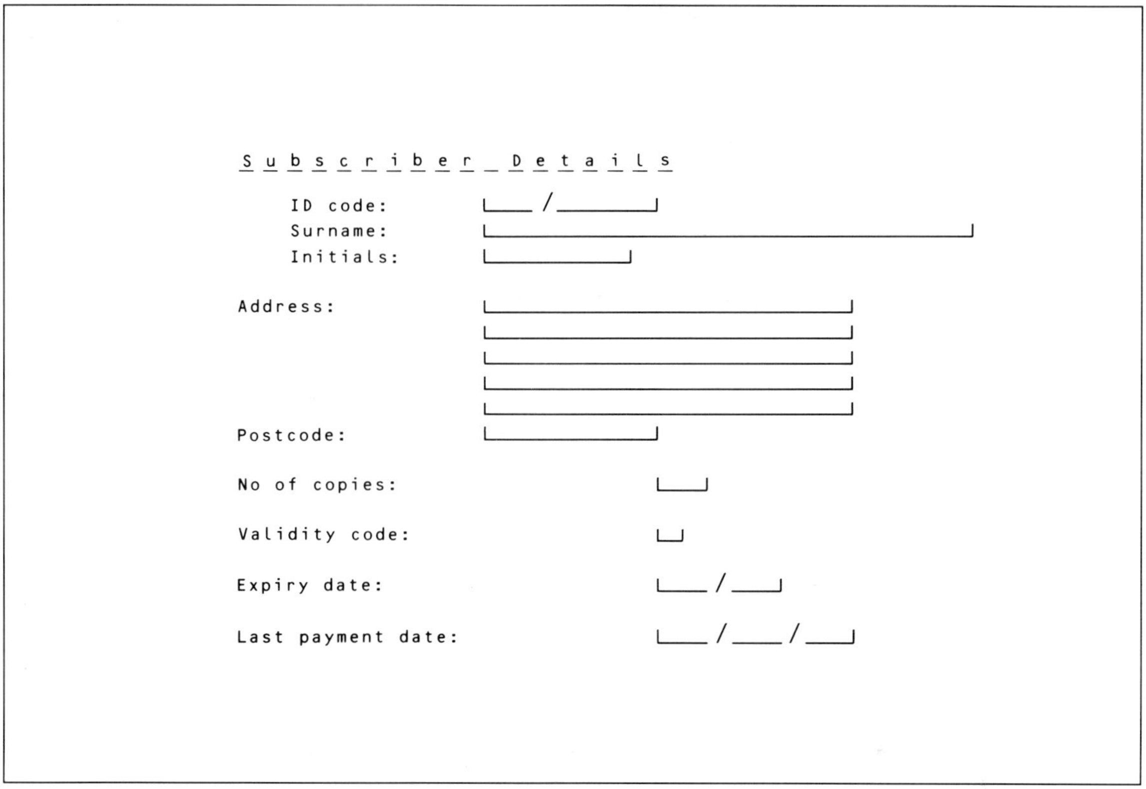

Figure 26.7
Magazine subscriber record screen layout

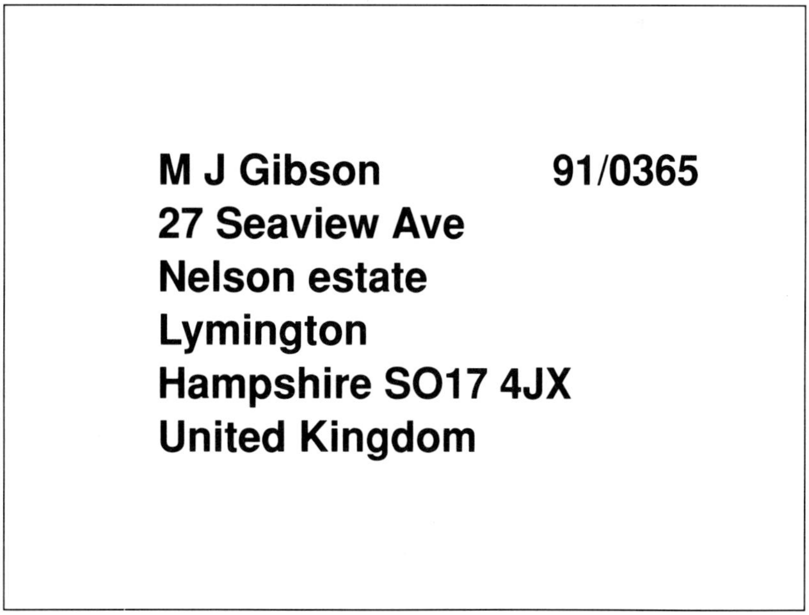

Figure 26.8
Magazine subscriber address label

26.7
System Testing

■ Testing is an integral part of the development of an information system. It takes place at a number of stages of the development cycle. There are four major test points: module testing, program testing, system testing and acceptance testing. In each case, the objects are tested against their specifications produced during the system design stage, or the start of the software development stage.

Module Testing

This is the lowest level of testing, carried out by the programmers themselves as they complete each module. Modules are tested with typical data, as well as extreme cases and invalid data, which should be rejected without causing the module to fail.

Program Testing

Program testing takes place when modules have been built into programs, or software packages configured to perform specific tasks. It generally uses specially prepared test data. This contains all the data errors and awkward cases that are likely to arise in practice, and is designed to try to make the new programs fail. Program testing continues until all the errors in the programs have been identified and corrected, and the programmers and systems analysts are satisfied.

System Testing

System testing tries out the running of the information system as a whole. The programs are run in their intended sequence, and the various manual parts of the operation are carried out. The passing of data from one stage to the next is checked, as are security and backup features. System testing is the last stage of testing carried out by the programmers themselves. When these tests are satisfactory, the system is ready to be tried out by the users.

Acceptance Testing

Acceptance testing is carried out by the users, generally after some initially training. They see if the system performs to their satisfaction, and again try to 'break' the system with awkward cases and incorrect data. One of the main areas to be tested is the user interface. It is essential that the users are able to operate the system properly, and make use of all the facilities it offers. Modifications are made to the system until the users are satisfied.

26.8
System Implementation

■ The final phase of the data processing cycle concerns putting the new system to work. Pilot running, with the new system doing part of the work alongside the old system, is often used for a transition period. It is also common, though not always possible, to run the new and the old system parallel for a while. Finally, often a year or more after the new system was proposed, it is in full productive operation.

26.9
System Documentation

■ Documentaton is a written description of how a program works, how it is to be used, or how it is to be run on a computer. Several types of documentation are prepared during the development of an information system.

The feasibility study leads to a **feasibility report**, giving an outline of the proposed system. The system analysis phase results in a **requirement specification**, setting out the objectives of the system. The **functional specification** is a written description of the operation of a system, and its overall data structures, produced by the systems analysts at the end of the system design phase. This is the central document used during the system implementation phase.

Program documentation is an account of how each module of a program works, written by the programmer. It is for the use of anyone who wishes to understand the detailed working of a program, in order to test it or modify it. Operator documentation (if it is required) is a description, for computer operators, of how the application is to be run. It states which devices are needed and which data files must be loaded, and any special stationery required. It also specifies what is to be done should the program fail.

User documentation is an account of how the system is to be used. It contains step-by-step instructions, often accompanied by worked examples. It is written in non-technical language, and does not contain any details of the internal workings of programs, or of data structures. User documentation is usually written by technical authors who are trained in the art of explaining complex systems in a simple way.

**26.10
System
Maintenance**

■ Once a system is in operation, it is unlikely that it remains entirely satisfactory for long. On the one hand, experience in using the system brings to light shortcomings and suggests improvements. On the other hand, the requirements of the system change as time goes by. For these reasons, the system requires periodic maintenance. Maintenance requires re-specification of portions of the system, and amendments to programs and documentation accordingly. A certain amount of testing is also involved.

**26.11
System
Troubleshooting**

■ The above description of the data processing cycle makes it sound like a textbook operation, with no problems likely to arise. In practice this is seldom the case. A few of the commonest sources of problems are outlined below.

Changing Specifications

For a variety of reasons, it is often necessary to change the specification of a system while it is under development. Changes can arise from altered business circumstances, new hardware becoming available, or because someone has thought of an 'improvement' to the system. The amount of disruption caused by a change depends on the nature of the change. In some cases, large amounts of detailed work have to be done again.

Increasing Costs

At current levels of inflation, it is certain that almost all costs will increase. Estimates of these increased costs are generally made at the start of a project, but they can never be totally accurate. Unforeseen costs almost always arise. Occassionally, increased costs lead to the abandoning of a new system. However, in most cases, cost increases tend to trip the balance in favour of a computerised system, where greater efficiency and productivity offets rising costs. Furthermore, hardware prices are continually reducing for systems of the same capability.

Delays

The feasibility report generally contains estimates of the duration of the various stages of the data processing cycle. A series of deadlines (known as **project milestones**) is usually set up. Depending on the circumstances surrounding the project, these are or are not met. In general, the computing industry has quite a good record for meeting deadlines. (There are, however, a few notorious exceptions to this.) Delays can be a nuisance or a disaster, depending on how vital it is to have the new system in operation. Delays always have the effect of increasing the development cost of the system.

Resistance to Change

Changing to computerised working implies new work practices, new equipment to operate, and, in some cases, transfers to different jobs or redundancies. Most people, familiar with one way of doing a job, are reluctant to change their working habits. Very few people are happy about being made redundant. Trade unions are likely to raise objections if the welfare of their members is being threatened. Inter-union disputes over new work practices are particularly difficult to resolve. All these factors must be taken into account when a new data processing system is being planned. Unfortunately, lack of consideration of the welfare of employees, lack of consultation and inflexible attitudes have sometimes led to serious problems in this area.

26.12 Conclusion

■ This chapter is intended to give a 'feel' for the way in which computers are put to work in commerce and industry. It is worth stressing that data processing in this area is strongly influenced by business practices, and that a relatively small proportion of the data processing cycle is spent actually writing programs.

The main points of the chapter are as follows:

- Information systems are generally set up in order to reduce costs, increase the volume of business of the company and to take advantage of the facilities offered by computers.
- Information systems may be classified as batch processing systems and real-time systems. Real-time systems include process control systems, information storage and retrieval systems and transaction processing systems. Some of these systems use databases, some involve data communication.
- The data processing cycle is the sequence of activities required to bring a new information system into operation.
- The overall steps of a data processing cycle are feasibility study, system analysis, system design, system development, system implementation and system maintenance. Each of these steps can be broken down into more detailed steps.
- A system flowchart is used to illustrate the overall steps of a data processing system.
- In spite of carefull planning, a number of things can go wrong during a data processing cycle. Common problems include changing specifications, increasing costs, delays and resistance to change.

Exercise 26

1 Briefly define the following terms: data processing; batch processing system; real-time system; process control system; information storage and retrieval system; transaction processing system; database system; data communications system; data processing cycle; systems analyst; user; system design; system development; system implementation; feasibility study; system investigation; system specification; system flowchart; program specification; module testing; program testing; test data; system testing; acceptance testing; system maintenance; validation; report generation; documentation; program documentation; user documentation; operator documentation; software package.

2 a) Summarise the general objectives of a data processing system.
  b) What are the characteristics of the environment of a commercial data processing system:

3 Classify the following data processing system according to the types of data processing described in the chapter:
  a) An accounting system, where accounts are brought up-to-date once a month.
  b) An order processing system, where each order is processed as soon as it is received.
  c) A bank accounting system, where accounts are brought up-to-date every night.
  d) The on-board navigation system on a rocket.
  e) The book index at a library.

4 Summarise, in about 100 words, the most significant features of the data processing cycle.

5 At what stages may a data processing cycle be terminated before the new system is put into operation?

6 A small company, which already has a computer, intends to computerise another part of its operations. It intends to buy an applications package to run the new work on its computer. Outline an approach which could be used by managers in dealing with this problem.

7 Why is it not adequate only to use sets of real data during program testing?

8 State some effects of delays in meeting deadlines during a project.

9 At which point in the data processing cycle is it most likely that resistance to change on the part of employees will become apparent? Discuss some approaches which could be used by managers in dealing with the problem.

10 Complete the requirement specification and the functional specification for the magazine subscriber system used as an example in this chapter.

11 A chain of retail shops wishes to implement a point-of-sale transaction recording system. The overall specification of the system is as follows:
  i) Cash registers are to be replaced by data entry terminals, linked to a microcomputer within each shop.
  ii) When a sale is registered, the stock number for each item sold is read from a bar code on the item. The price of the item is displayed. The total for the sale is displayed and the amount paid by cash, cheque or credit card is entered. The amount of change is displayed.
  iii) At the end of each day, the microcomputer produces a printout showing the total cash, cheques and credit card slips collected at each till. This is checked against the cash, cheques and credit card slips in each till. A file is produced on a floppy disk, showing the number sold of each stock item. This file can be inspected on the display screen.
  iv) The file of stock movements is then transmitted via a telephone link to a central mainframe computer.
  a) Draw one or more system flowcharts showing the overall steps of this system.
  b) Identify the applications programs required for this system.
  c) Write out a specification for each application program.
  d) Identify any potential problems in the implementation of this system.

27 File Structure

This chapter is concerned with the way in which data files are structured on backing store. It is concerned with the logical structure of the data, as opposed to the physical structure which is discussed in Section 14.4. Users and programmers are concerned only with the logical structure of files; the conversion between logical and physical structure is done by the operating system.

27.1 Files, Records, Fields and Keys

■ Computers inherited files and file processing from manual data processing systems. Many of the ideas and terms used in connection with computer files are derived from the terminology of manual files. Whether it is stored in a filing cabinet, on a magnetic disk or on any other form of storage, a **file** is an organised collection of data. Files are generally large, contain related items of information, and are strictly arranged according to some structure.

The unit of data which makes up a file is a **record**. A record corresponds to a card in a card index, or a single sheet of paper in a manual file. A record contains a number of related data items, and each record in a file generally has the same structure. Records are not always the same length: in a file of invoices, for example, the number of item lines in an invoice (one record) is not constant. However, if the file is a random-access file (Section 14.4), where records can be accessed and updated individually, then a fixed amount of space must be allocated on the backing store medium for each record. In most computer systems, there must be an integral number of records on each physical block or sector on the backing store medium.

Individual data items occupy **fields** within a record. A field may be of fixed or variable width. The term **fieldwidth** refers to the number of characters in a field. Fields may be of different **type**: numeric, text, currency, date or codes where each character has a special significance.

The commonest way of identifying a record is by means of a chosen field within the record. This field is referred to as the **key** of the record. The only restriction on keys is that all the records in a file have distinct keys. For this and other reasons, more than one field is sometimes used as the key of a record. The fields are then called the **primary key**, **secondary key**, etc.

For example, consider the information in a city telephone directory as a file. A record is the entry for one person. A record comprises four fields, namely surname, initials, address and telephone number. The primary key is the surname field, the secondary key is the initials and the tertiary key is the address. The three keys together are required to identify each person uniquely, whereas a surname on its own is not enough.

27.2 File Structures

■ In the early days of computing, the structure of a file was largely determined by the storage medium available. Today the situation has been reversed. The nature of the computer application determines the structure of the files, which in turn determines the type of storage medium used. The commonest types of file structure are **serial** files, **sequential** files, **indexed sequential** files and **random files**. The following sections discuss these types of files.

Text Files

Many files are structured simply as lines of text, with the end of each line indicated by a carriage return character. These text files have one record per line, with no subdivision of the record into fields. The commonest application for text files is word processing. Program code is also stored in text files, but the structure of the code is not known to the file system.

Serial Files

A serial file is one in which the records are in no particular order. Serial files are mainly used for temporary storage of data, until a more highly structured file is created. Magnetic tapes and magnetic disks are equally suitable for storing serial files.

Sequential Files

A sequential file is one in which records are in order of one or more keys. The order may be numeric or alphabetic. For example, a file of examination results may be sorted in order of class of pass (primary key) and, within each class, alphabetic order of surnames (secondary key). Sequential files may be stored on magnetic tapes or magnetic disks, and are the backbone of the 'traditional' file processing systems discussed in the previous chapter.

Indexed Sequential Files

Indexed sequential files are the commonest types of files in current use. As their name suggests, indexed sequential files are ordered files which also have an index. The **index** is a set of data which enables the key of a record to be associated with its physical disk address (Section 14.4). It is very similar to an index of a book, which relates words and phrases to page numbers. The index of a file is generally stored at the beginning or the end of the file, or, more commonly, as a separate file. If more than one level of index is used, as is often the case, different parts of the index may be stored throughout the file.

Since indexed sequential files require that records be located by address, they must be stored on magnetic disks. A number of different indexing techniques are in use, but only one is discussed here. It is the simplest, and relates directly to the structure of a magnetic disk pack. It is called **cylinder-surface-sector** indexing.

For each disk pack of the file, there is a cylinder index, which relates each cylinder number to the highest key value stored in that cylinder. Once a cylinder has been selected, its **surface index** is used. This index relates each surface of the cylinder to the highest key value in that surface. Once a surface has been selected, its **sector index** is used. This relates each sector number to the highest key value within the sector. The required sector is then copied from the disk, and the required record located within it.

For example, consider a file which stores records of motor car parts. Each record concerns one part , with the part number being the key. Part numbers are in the range 00001 to 99999. The following table contains a portion of the cylinder index of the file, together with one surface and one sector index.

Cylinder Index		Surface Index for Cylinder 106		Sector Index for Surface 4	
Cylinder	Highest Key	Surface	Highest Key	Sector	Highest Key
1	00396	1	41077	1	41079
2	00785	2	41124	2	41186
...		3	41171	3	41194
105	41027	4	41223	4	41200
106	41421	5	41269	5	41207
107	41803	6	41318	6	41214
...		7	41368	7	41219
256	99999	8	41421	8	41223

Suppose it is required to access the record for part number 41192. Inspection of the cylinder index shows that this record is in cylinder 106. The surface index for this cylinder is then accessed. Inspection of this index shows that the record is on surface 4. The sector index for this surface is then accessed. This index shows that the required record is in sector 3. This sector is then copied from the disk, and searched for the required record.

It can be seen that locating this record required four accesses to the disk, once for each of the three indexes, and one for the data sector. After each disk access, the index or data sector is searched in the memory of the computer.

One advantage of indexed sequential files is that it is easy to leave spaces in sectors, surfaces or cylinders for the insertion of new records. This allows a file to grow without having to be copied onto another disk, and re-indexed, too frequently.

Random Files

Random files are ones in which records are scattered at random on the storage medium. In order to access a record, there is a function which relates the key of the record to its address on the storage medium. This process is known as **address generation**. As in the case of indexed sequential files, this requires that magnetic disks be used to store the data.

It is occasionally possible to use the backing store address of a record as its key. In this case, accessing the record is extremely simple. More frequently, some calculation or manipulation must be carried out on the key of the record in order to produce its backing store address. One technique for this is called **hashing**, and the file structure is called a **hash table**. Problems arise when two different key values produce the same backing store address. Address generation techniques are investigated in more detail in the exercise at the end of the chapter.

Random files are most suited to applications where rapid access is required to individual records. If access to groups of records with consecutive keys is required, then indexed sequential files are much more useful. Random files are less common than indexed sequential files.

27.3 Blocking Strategy

■ The way in which the logical structure of a file – its records and fields – are arranged on the physical blocks of the backing store medium is the **blocking strategy** of the file management system. Blocking strategies vary according to the nature and structure of the file, and whether the backing store medium is disk or tape. The objectives are the same in all cases:

- To make the most efficient use of the backing store medium.
- To make access to files as quick as possible.
- To deal with enlargements and reductions in the file size in an orderly manner.

In almost all cases, an integral number of records is stored on a physical block. This usually leaves some blank space in each block, and many blocking strategies leave more than this minimum to allow for growth of the file. The term **packing density** refers to the ratio of backing store space used by a file at any time to the total space available. If files are expected to change in size very frequently, space is left in every block for new records. An alternative is to reserve overflow blocks at suitable positions on the medium for new records. If records are a variable length, then there are two possibilities: to allow the maximum possible record space for each actual record, or to reposition all the records on a block (and update the appropriate indexes) every time one changes in length. If space is short, the packing density is kept as high as possible, and new records are inserted wherever there is a large enough space. This leads to fragmentation of the file, and slows access to records.

27.4 Conclusion

■ This chapter has discussed some of the general principles of files and file structure. It prepares the way for the discussion of file processing, in the next chapter. The main points of the chapter are as follows:

- A file is a large collection of related data items, strictly organised as records and fields.
- The commonest types of file structure are text files, serial files, sequential files, indexed sequential files and random files.
- In a text file, records are one line of text, delimited by carriage return characters.
- In a serial file, records are stored one after another, with no ordering.
- In a sequential file, records are stored in order of one or more keys.
- An indexed sequential file has a separate index relating the physical disk address of each record to its key(s).
- A random file has its records stored in random order, with an address generation technique for locating each record from its key(s).
- A common address generation technique is hashing.
- The technique for allocating records to physical blocks of backing store is the blocking strategy of the file management system.

Exercise 27

1 Briefly define the following terms: file; record; field; fieldwidth; text file; serial file; sequential file; indexed sequential file; random file; address generation; hashing; packing density; blocking strategy.

2 A word processing system includes a file which contains an index to the letters sent by the user of the system. There is a record for each letter, containing the name and address of the person to whom the letter was sent, the date and a reference to a separate file containing the text of the letter.
   a) Why is the index in a separate file from the text of the letters?
   b) What is the most suitable structure for the files of the letters?
   c) Suggest one or more keys for a record in the index file, and justify your choice.

d) Suggest a suitable structure for the index file. Consider likely uses of the file in making your choice, Include these uses in reasons for your choice of structure.

e) State, with reasons, the storage medium you would use for the file.

3 A form of index sometimes used on indexed sequential files is a **hierarchical index**. Like cylinder-surface-sector indexing, this has several levels of indexing. However, each level of index does not correspond to a physical aspect of the layout of the file on the disk.

The top level index relates each index number of the next level of indexes to the highest key value contained in that index. Each of the next level of indexes has a similar structure, relating to a third level of indexes. Each of these indexes relates a set of block addresses to the highest keys within the block. For example:

Top level index		Second level index 11		Third level index 531	
Second level index number	Highest Key	Third level index number	Highest Key	Block Address	Highest Key
1	12509	501	125254	26501	132504
2	25038	502	125517	26502	132510
...	...	...	...	...	...
10	125250	530	132500	26543	132712
11	137503	531	132758	26544	132719
...	...	...	...	...	...
0	625341	550	137503	26550	132758

a) Describe the steps in locating the record with key 132714, using these indexes.

◆ b) Suggest why this method is slightly slower than cylinder-surface-sector indexing.

4 A technique for calculating the backing store address from the key, in random files, is called **folding**. For example, if the key is 9 digits long, then the three sets of three digits are added up to obtain the backing store address, as follows:

```
Key :  396 421 608        396
                          421
                    +     608
                        _____
Backing store address:   1425
```

a) Use this technique to calculate the backing store addresses of these keys: 492 117 503, 625 417 902.

b) If the address thus calculated is already occupied, then the next available address is used instead. This principle is called **open hashing**. Assuming an initially empty file, use this principle to load records with the following keys: 462 803 906, 341 915 916, 638 702 831, 594 913 666.

c) Load the records from part (b) in a different order. Comment on your findings.

28 File Processing

The great majority of computer applications involve the processing of data files. In many commercial systems, file processing is the main activity performed by the computer.

This chapter discusses some of the commonest ways in which files are processed in computer applications. These operations are: data capture, validation, sorting (both in a computer memory and on backing store). merging, searching and updating files. To conclude the chapter, some techniques to ensure the security of data files are introduced. The file processing techniques are described in general terms, and implementation-dependent features are avoided. This helps to keep the descriptions as simple as possible. It must, however, be borne in mind that when these techniques are put into use, the software required can become extremely complicated.

28.1 Data Capture

■ The first step in any file processing operation is to get the data onto the computer. This is done either by direct reading from source documents, reading from bar codes, or by entering the data at a terminal. See Section 14.2 for details of the media and devices used.

In a number of data processing systems, a document which is the output from one process becomes the input to another. Such documents are known as **turnaround documents**. For example, most gas, electricity, water and telephone bills are printed by computer. They include a tearoff slip which is returned with the payment. The slip has a row of optical character recognition (OCR) characters printed along the bottom. When the slip is returned, some additional characters may be printed giving details of the payment. The slip then becomes the input source document for the program which records the payment of the bills.

28.2 Validation

■ Validation is the process of checking input data, before storing or processing it. A number of checks can be carried out; the ones used in each case depend on the application. As far as possible, validation is interactive. Checks are carried out as the data item is entered, and, if they fail, the item is rejected immediately. This greatly reduces the chances of errors occurring at later stages.

The simplest checks are **type** and **range** checks. Type checks determine whether the data is of the correct type (alphabetic, numeric or conforming to a particular format such as that for a date). Range checks determine whether numeric data is within an acceptable range. Various totals can be used to check input data. If batches of data are input, items in each batch can be added up, and the **batch total** (or **control total**) entered. The total is re-calculated by the program, and compared with the one input. If the totals are different, an error has occurred. The same principle applies to **hash totals**, which are totals of data items within the same record.

Numeric data items of particular importance, such as the keys of records, often have **check digits** attached to them. The value of the check digit can be determined from the other digits in the number. The check digit is tested from time to time, to see if an error has arisen during copying of the data item. Examples of data items which include check digits are account numbers, credit card numbers, international standard book numbers and the numbers encoded by bar codes. There are several ways of calculating check digits in common use. Some of them are introduced in the exercise at the end of the chapter.

28.3
Sorting in Main
Store

■ Sorting is a very common data processing technique. Some programming languages, notably Cobol, and most program generators have a single instruction to cause a file of data to be sorted. Many operating systems have built-in sorting facilities. Much attention has been devoted to developing efficient ways of sorting, as it can be an extremely slow process.

For a set of data to be sorted, all the data must be in the main store of a computer. If the set of data is too large for this, it is sorted in portions, each of which can be accommodated in the available main store. This section is concerned with the part of the process which takes place in the main store of a computer, using data which has already been loaded. A later section examines the problem of sorting larger sets of data.

An informal algorithm for a common sorting technique is now introduced. The technique is called **quicksort**, as it is one of the fastest sorting out methods. Others include the **insertion sort**, **tree sort**, **selection sort**, **Shell sort** and **bubble sort**. Some of these are covered in the exercise at the end of the chapter.

Algorithm for Quicksort

If the set contains more than one record
then select the first record,
        partition the remaining records into two subsets:
                a **left subset**, with keys less than that of the first record
                a **right subset**, with keys greater than that of the first record,
        place the first record between the two subsets,
        quicksort the left subset,
        quicksort the right subset
else the set is sorted.

Note that the algorithm is recursive, in other words it calls itself repeatedly, for smaller and smaller subsets of the set of data. The example below shows the steps of quicksort applied to the keys of eight records in a file. The square brackets show which elements have not yet been sorted.

Original order of keys:
    [11 9 23 7 31 5 2 17]

Select first key (11) and partition the set:
    [9 7 5 2] 11 [23 31 17]

Quicksort left subset:
    Select first key (9) and partition the set:
    [7 5 2] 9 11 [23 31 17]

Quicksort right subset:
    Select first key (23) and partition the set:
    [7 5 2] 9 11 [17] 23 [31]

Quicksort the first remaining subset:
    Select first key (7) and partition the set:
    [5 2] 7 9 11 [17] 23 [31]

Quicksort the first remaining subset:
    Select first key (5) and partition the set:

[2] 5 7 9 11 [17] 23 [31]

All remaining subsets are of length one element, and are therefore already sorted:

2 5 7 9 11 17 23 31

Although this process appears anything but quick, it is in fact better than most of its rivals for larger sets of data. The reason for its speed is that data items are moved quickly to positions close to their final ordering. The last few sort passes are to tidy up the final ordering.

28.4 Merging

■ Merging is the process of combining two ordered files of data to produce a single ordered file. The method is quite simple, and is outlined in the algorithm below.

Algorithm for Merging

Records from ordered files A and B are to be merged to form ordered file C.
Repeat
　　if all records from A have been removed
　　　　then copy remaining records in file B to file C
　　else if all records from B have been removed
　　　　then copy remaining records in file A to file C
　　else compare next records in files A and B
　　　　copy the record with lower key to file C
Until all records from files A and B have been merged.

The important fact about this process is that it does not require that all the data be in the main store of the computer. One record from each input file is, in fact, sufficient. Thus files can be merged which are much larger than the capacity of the main store of the computer doing the merging.

Although merging is an important file processing operation in its own right, its most common use is to form part of a sorting process for files which are much larger than the capacity of the main store of the computer which is sorting them.

28.5 Sorting Large Files

■ A number of techniques are used to sort files which are too large for the main store of the computer. They are generally based on combinations of sorting and merging. The file which is to be sorted is divided into **strings**, each of which can be accommodated in the main store of the computer. Each string is sorted, and the sorted string copied to backing store. These strings are merged, creating successively larger strings, until the whole file has been merged into a single string.

The following sequence of merges illustrates this technique, though it is not actually used in practice. Consider a file which has been divided into eight strings. The strings have been sorted, and copied onto two magnetic tapes, as follows:

Tape A:	String 1	String 3	String 5	String 7
Tape B:	String 2	String 4	String 6	String 8

The strings are merged in pairs, the resulting strings being placed alternately on two further tapes.

Tape C:	String 9 (String 1 + String 2)	String 11 (String 5 + String 6)
Tape D:	String 10 (String 3 + String 4)	String 12 (String 7 + String 8)

These strings are again merged in pairs, and the resulting strings copied onto alternate tapes:

Tape A: String 13 (String 9 + String 10)
Tape B: String 14 (String 11 + String 12)

These two strings are merged to form a single string, which is the entire file, in order. The merging techniques used in practice are more complicated. They reduce the number of merges needed for a given number of strings. Nevertheless sorting a large file on a small computer is frequently the slowest step of the entire data processing operation.

28.6 Searching

■ Searching is the process of locating a record in a file, given the key of the record. If the file has an index, then the index is used to locate the record. If the file is randomly organised, then the process used to load a record is also used to access it. Otherwise, the file must be searched. Three common file searching techniques are discussed here, namely the **sequential search**, the **binary search** and the **tree search**.

Sequential Search

A sequential search involves starting at the beginning of a file and examining every record file until the required one is found. It is only used if a small number of records are present, or if the file is not ordered. On average, half the records in the file have to be examined before the required record is located.

Binary Search

A binary search involves partitioning the file into smaller and smaller subsets, each of which is known to contain the required record, and each of which is half the size of the previous subset. An informal algorithm for a binary search is as follows:

Algorithm for Binary Search

If the set contains at least one record
then select the middle record
    partition the remaining records into two subsets:
        a **left subset**, with keys less than
            that of the middle record
        a **right subset**, with keys greater than
            that of the middle record,
    if the middle record is the required record
    then **the required record has been found**
    else if the key of the required record is
        less than that of the middle record
        then **binary search** the left subset
        else **binary search** the right subset
else **the required record is not in the set**.

Notice that this algorithm is similar in structure to that for a quicksort. like the quicksort, it is recursive. The example below shows the steps of a binary search applied to the keys of eight records in a file. The required record has key value 7.

Initial situation:
   2 5 7 9 11 17 23 31

Select middle record (key 9), partition set:
   [2 5 7] 9 [11 17 23 31]

Required key is less than that of middle record, so binary search left subset:
   2 5 7

Select middle record (key 5), partition set:
   [2] 5 [7]

Required key is greater than that of middle record, so binary search left subset:
   7

Select middle record (key 7), which is the required record.

It can be seen that the process of dividing the set into two subsets is carried out three times to locate the required record. In general, the maximum number of steps, for a file of N records, is $\log_2 N$. A binary search is much quicker than a sequential search. A binary search does not require that all the records of a file be in the main store of the computer. The backing store addresses of records can be used to locate the middle element of each set. This element must be copied into main store for examination. However, the requirement of backing store addresses does rule out the use of magnetic tapes.

Tree Search

A tree search is a systematic scan, or traversal, of a set of data stored in a tree structure. It is gaining importance because of its frequent use in artificial intelligence work. In some cases, the data to be searched exists before the search starts; in others the data is created before being tested, a process known as **generate-and-test**. For example, when a computer is playing chess, it generates a set of possible moves from the current state of the game, and tests each possibility to determine how advantageous it would be. The most favourable move generated is the one selected.

There are two types of tree search: the **depth-first** search where the search is carried out as far 'down' each branch of the tree as possible

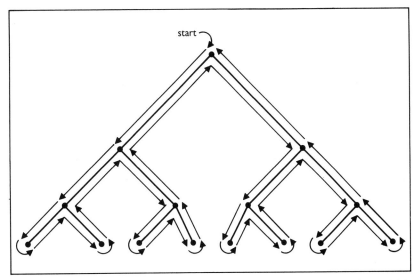

Figure 28.1
Depth-first tree search

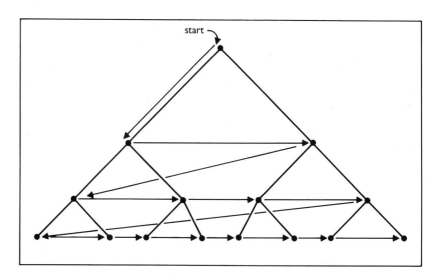

Figure 28.2
Breadth-first tree search

before looking at another branch, and the **breadth-first** search which scans across all branches, one level at a time. See Figures 28.1 and 28.2. In practice, tree searches are often a combination of these two approaches. Tree searching can also be used as part of the process of sorting data, as investigated in the exercise at the end of this chapter.

28.7 Updating

■ Updating a file involves amending, deleting, inserting and appending records so as to bring the information in the file up to date. If the file to be updated is a sequential file, then the amendments data is sorted into the same order as the ordering of the sequential file. The systems flow diagram, Figure 26.4, in the previous chapter shows the process of updating a sequential file. The process forms a cycle, since the up-to-date file produced on one occasion forms the file to be updated on the next occasion. In transaction processing systems, files are updated one record at a time: the new record overwrites the old one in its position on backing store, or is placed at the end of the file.

A common problem during file updating is **overflow**. This occurs when the updated version of the file is larger than the original, and too large for the backing store space allocated. The response to an overflow problem depends to a large extent on the operating system in use. Some will simply abort the updating process, while others will allow a file to be stored on more than one physical medium, at least temporarily. Others will suspend the operation so that the disk or tape can be 'cleaned up' by deleting redundant files or records from it. There are only two permanent solutions to file overflow problems: either reduce the size of the file, or increase the amount of backing store allocated to it.

28.8 Report Generation

■ Most active files in a data processing system contain large amounts of data. In order to provide an accurate, up-to-date picture of the system, it is important to generate **reports** at regular intervals. These reports summarise the data on one or more files, and are intended for the information of managers at various levels of the organisation. One of the facilities of the fourth generation programming languages discussed in Chapter 24 is report generation.

As an example, consider a file containing records of all the sales by a particular company during the current financial year. A report might be generated from this file once a week, showing the total number of sales, the total value of the sales, and breakdowns of these figures by salesman, product group, area and method of payment. This report could be used by the sales manager. The total sales figures could be included in reports to managers at higher levels.

28.9 Data Security

■ The files used by most data processing systems are vital to the system. Any loss or corruption of data can lead to delays, loss of business or legal action being taken against the company. For these reasons it is essential that files be guarded against computer failures, program errors, human errors and malicious interference.

If files are stored on magnetic tapes, and updated regularly, it is common practice to keep the previous two versions of the file, together with the amendments used to update them. This is called the **grandfather-father-son** principle, each version being a **generation** of the file. If the current generation of the file is lost, it can be re-created from the previous generations.

If magnetic disks are used to store a file, then these are periodically copied, or **backed up** onto another magnetic disk or **dumped** onto a magnetic tape. All the data used to update the file since the last dump is kept. Alternatively, incremental dumps are made, containing only those files which have been updated since the last dump. Complete dumps are made after a certain number of incremental dumps. Dumping is often done as part of a **housekeeping** process, during which files are 'tidied up', with out-of-date records being deleted and gaps closed up.

It is essential to keep a **log** of all operations carried out on a file. The log shows the dates on which various updates and backups took place, and includes identification numbers of the various disks and tapes used. Additional security precautions include keeping magnetic disks and tapes in fireproof safes, and storing copies at sites away from the computer.

Protection against deliberate data corruption is much more difficult, as it ultimately involves the trustworthiness of staff members. Some of the security precautions which are taken include restriction of access to computer and data preparation rooms, the use of passwords when logging on at terminals, and strict job segregation – programmers may not operate the computer, etc. Files are protected from access by anyone but their owner. The data in many secure files is **encrypted** – stored in a code which can only be deciphered by the software which handles the files. In some cases a special hardware 'key' must be attached to the computer before it can read encrypted files.

Good data security is achieved by constant vigilance, and strict adherence to specified procedures, in other words, 'working by the book'. Unfortunately, this tends to make some computing jobs rather tedious.

28.10 Conclusion

■ This chapter has covered the most common ways in which files of data are processed, and some of the problems which can arise during processing. The main points of the chapter are as follows:
- The main file processing operations are data capture, validation, sorting, merging, searching and updating.
- Validation techniques include type checks, range checks, hash totals, batch totals and the use of check digits.

- Problems which can occur during file processing are overflow, and the long time taken to sort files which are larger than the size of the computer memory.
- Steps must be taken to ensure the security of data against accidental or deliberate corruption. These include keeping up-to-date copies of the data, restricting access to the computer, passwords and data encryption.

Exercise 28

1 Briefly define the following terms: data capture; turnaround document; validation; batch total; hash total; check digit; sorting; merging; searching; sequential search; binary search; tree search; generate-and-test; depth-first search; breadth-first search; updating; file overflow; report generation; data security; grandfather-father-son principle; file dump; incremental dump; file processing log; data encryption.

2 A monthly payroll program requires the input of the following data for each employee: name, employee number, days worked, days on leave, days ill and days absent for any other reason.
   a) Suggest a suitable field layout for the input data, if it is to form one line on a VDU screen.
   b) Which data item is likely to include a check digit?
   c) What additional check(s) can be carried out on the data as it is input?

3 The batch total of a set of data is checked after the data has been input, and is found not to match the batch total which was input with the data. Later checks show that all data items are in fact correct.
   Explain where the error must be, and discuss the limitations on the usefulness of batch totals imposed by this situation.

4 A common method of calculating check digits is as follows: multiply each digit of the number, including the check digit, by a **weighting factor**, and add up the products. The check digit is chosen so that the total thus formed is exactly divisible by a suitable number, usually 11. For example:

number:	3	7	4	6	5	check digit
weighting factor:	9	5	3	7	1	
products:	27	+ 35	+ 12	+ 42	+ 5 =121,	exactly divisible by 11

Using the same set of weighting factors, calculate the check digits for the numbers 6297 and 5116. Use the symbol X if a check digit of 10 is required.

5 Carry out the steps of a quicksort on the following sets of numbers:

a)	6	14	18	23	5	9	11	12,
b)	5	9	1	3	14	19	2	27,
c)	18	16	10	11	8	4	3	7,
d)	8	15	9	16	10	17	11	18.

Comment on any effects of initial ordering, or partial ordering, on the steps of the process.

6 Assume that a computer memory can only contain four records of a particular file. Use the method outlined in Section 28.5 to sort a file with key values as follows:

17 4 9 21 8 5 20 2 7 11 15 6 3 1 19 13.

7 An informal algorithm for an **insertion sort** in ascending order is as follows:

Partition the file into two strings, the unsorted string followed by the sorted string.
For each record in the unsorted string, repeat
   Scan the sorted string until the first record is found with a key greater than that of the record from the unsorted string.
   Move the record from the unsorted string to the position in front of the

record located in the sorted string, moving the records in between forward by one position. (This also moves the boundary between the sorted and unsorted strings forward.)

For example, the steps to sort a string of four records are as follows. The boundary between the sorted and unsorted strings is marked |.

Initial situation:	35	11	47	18		
Insert 35:	11	47	18		35
Insert 11	47	18		11	35
Insert 47:	18		11	35	47
Insert 18		11	18	35	47

a) Carry out the steps of an insertion sort in ascending order on each of the following sets of data:

79	43	12	82	23	47	
45	34	56	23	18	14	12
23	34	43	18	56	67	78

b) Comment on the extent to which the data is 'shuffled' in each case, relative to the degree of ordering already present.

8 An informal algorithm for a **selection sort** in ascending order is as follows:

Partition the file into two strings, the unsorted string followed by the sorted string.
Repeat
Select the record with the highest key in the unsorted string. Move this record to the front of the sorted string, moving the intervening records forward by one place. This moves the boundary of the sorted string forward by one place.
Until all records have been placed in the sorted string.

For example, the steps to sort a string of four records are as follows. The boundary between the sorted and unsorted strings is marked |.

Initial situation:	35	11	47	18		
First pass:	35	11	18		47
Second pass:	11	18		35	47
Third pass:	11		18	35	47
Fourth pass:		11	18	35	47

a) Carry out the steps of a selection sort in ascending order on each of the following sets of data:

79	43	12	82	23	47	
45	34	56	23	18	14	12
23	34	43	18	56	67	78

b) Comment on the extent to which the data is 'shuffled' in each case, relative to the degree of ordering already present.
c) Compare the efficiency of the insertion and selection sort techniques.

9 Outline the steps of a binary search to locate the record with key 19 from a file with keys as follows:

4 7 8   10 11 19 23 31.

10 During the updating of a file, stored on magnetic tape, a power failure occurs. Both the source and the updated copies of the file are corrupted. Outline the steps involved in re-creating the up-to-date version of the file.

11 During the updating of a file stored on a magnetic disk, a **disk crash** occurs. The read-write head comes into contact with the surface of the disk, destroying the disk and damaging the disk drive. Outline the steps involved in re-creating the file.

12 Outline some of the measures taken to protect data from deliberate interference. Give your opinion on the effectiveness of these measures, and the wider implications of their use.

29 User Interfacing

The user interface is the point of contact between a computer system - hardware or software - and the person using it. All communication between the user and the system is via the user interface.

In the early days of computing, little thought was given to the design of user interfaces. They reflected the internal workings of the system, and paid scant attention to the requirements of the user. Today this situation has been reversed. The user interface is recognised as an essential component of a computer system. In the case of software packages, the quality of the user interface is a key factor in determining the success or failure of the package in the market. Extensive research, by psychologists as well as computer scientists, has been undertaken into the principles of user interface design. There are also moves towards standard user interfaces, common to ranges of software items, to simplify the task of learning to use new packages.

29.1 Principles of User Interfacing

■ The majority of computer systems in use today are interactive. Communication between the system and a user is in the form of a dialogue, an alternation of inputs from the user and responses by the system. A number of general principles have evolved which set out the 'ground rules' for this type of dialogue. These are:

- The user interface should be based on ideas which a user would naturally associate with the system. For example, word processors present the text on the screen in the same layout as on the printed page. This idea of 'what you see is what you get' (Wysiwyg) is what users expect. It forms the basis of the user interface of the word processor.
- A user interface should be as simple as possible. This is difficult to achieve in practice. Options must be carefully grouped, messages must be clear, errors easy to recover from and special cases must be avoided.
- A user interface must be consistent its operation. A few general principles must be applied throughout, making it easy for a user to remember them.
- Operations performed by the user should be quick. This sometimes conflicts with the requirement for consistency. A number of user interfaces have alternative 'short cuts' for experienced users, which enable them to by-pass longer sequences of operations.
- In some systems, it is desirable to build in an element of flexibility, to enable users to configure the user interface to their own requirements. This is particularly important for large, complex systems such as CAD packages.

29.2 Command-driven Interfaces

■ The first widespread form of user interface was based on a set of commands to control the system. In a command-driven user interface, the system displays or prints a prompt when it is ready to accept an input. The user responds by typing a command.

The advantages of command-driven interfaces include the large repertoire of commands which can be used, and the fact that commands can have qualifiers which modify the way they operate. Commands can be entered into a file, and run as a batch, in a non-interactive mode of operation. For example, the Unix operating system has a command-driven user interface. A typical command with a qualifier is:

$ cp -r /user1/designs/multchip .

The parts of this command are interpreted as follows:

$	Unix prompt
cp	command: copy
r	qualifier: copy directory and its contents
/user1/designs/multchip	directory to be copied destination: current directory

This example illustrates the strengths and weaknesses of command-driven user interfaces. It is a powerful and versatile command, but it is almost impossible for someone without specialised training to understand it. This is the case in general: command-driven user interfaces are powerful and flexible, but difficult to use. The larger the set of commands and qualifiers, the more difficult they are to remember. These interfaces often involve excessive amounts of typing.

29.3 Menu-driven Interfaces

■ Menu-driven interfaces display a set of options at each stage of the operation of the system. The user chooses an option, either by typing a number or an initial letter, or by using arrow keys or a mouse to highlight the required option. Some interfaces have a hierarchy of menus, with each option at the top-level menu opening up a secondary menu. Menu interfaces also use text boxes or forms to fill in on the screen for the times when users need to enter details of an operation in text form.

For example, the top-level menu of the WordStar word processing package includes the options:

Change logged disk drive
File directory on/off
Set help level
Open a document file
Print a file
Rename a file
Copy a file
Delete a file
Exit from WordStar

The user chooses an option with a single keystroke, or by means of the mouse. For some of the options, further information, such as the name of a file, is then typed at a prompt.

The benefits of a menu-driven interface are speed of operation, simplicity and keyboard or mouse control, with the minimum number of keystrokes or mouse button depressions. The limitation is the number of options available: if a system has a large number of operations, several levels of menu are required to provide access to them all. If operations have various optional ways of working, this requires forms to complete, which complicates matters further. Batching of menu choices is not possible.

29.4
Windows
Environments

■ In an attempt to get away from keyboard-based user interfaces, and provide a natural way of operating a computer, particularly for users who are not computer experts, user interfaces based on windows, icons, mice and pointers have been developed. These are also known as **Wimp** environments.

In a **windows** environment, the computer screen is presented as a desktop on which reside icons representing the objects on which the system operates. For example, a word processor might have icons representing folders, documents, a wastepaper basket, etc. The mouse moves a pointer on the screen, which can be used to open up icons. Opening a folder displays the documents in it, opening a document displays its text. Some icons open as pull-down menus, giving choices to be highlighted with the pointer. Some choices open up forms, into which details concerning the operation are entered.

The text is viewed in a window - several windows may be open at any time. To delete a folder or a document, its icon is placed in the icon for the waste paper basket.

Windows environments were first made popular by the Apple Macintosh range of computers in the mid-1980s. All applications running on these computers conform to the same standards of user interface. This makes it easy for users to learn to use a new application. They can be sure that it works in the same way as the other applications they already know. The ease of use of Wimp environments, and the standard interfaces built up on them, have been one of the main reasons for the rapid spread of desktop computer systems during the last decade.

Windows-based environments are becoming the norm for software packages on desktop microcomputers and workstations, and further standardisation of these user interfaces is taking place. The windows facilities are generally provided by the operating system, and used in a uniform way by all applications running under it.

29.5
Intelligent User
Interfaces

■ The next phase in the development of user interfaces is to bring a certain amount of artificial intelligence into them. This is already starting to happen with conventional menu-based systems: previous choices are taken into account when determining a default option in a menu. This is the option which is selected if the user does not move the highlight on the menu. Intelligent defaulting enables the user to carry out a sequence of operations without having to make repeated menu choices. Other user interfaces have a set of rules, against which all menu choices are evaluated. Any combination which violates the rules is not permitted. This gives greater flexibility in choice of operation, but prevents the user from making errors.

Further into the future, two main channels of communication are being emphasised: the use of natural language (Section 7.7), and image processing (Section 7.8). Although interaction in a complete natural language is beyond the capabilities of even the most advanced computer system, the intention is to enable them to use a large enough subset to make a number of voice-driven applications possible. Image processing requires the computer to be able to accept video pictures as input, and generate output of the same quality. Some approximation to three-dimensional vision is required.

29.6 Conclusion

■ The user interface of a computer system is the means of communication between it and the person using the system. The quality of a user interface is a determining factor in the acceptability of the system to its users, and the extent to which the system is used to benefit the users. Designing an appropriate user interface is a major aspect of the development of a computer system.

The main points of this chapter are as follows:

- The general requirements of a user interface are simplicity, consistency, use of natural concepts and speed of operation.
- Command-driven systems have the advantages of power and flexibility, and the ability to run operations in batches. The disadvantage is the difficulty of use.
- Menu-driven systems are easy to use, with a minimum of keystrokes, but are somewhat inflexible.
- Windows systems use icons, mice and pointers to present a visual interface, minimising the use of the keyboard.
- Current developments include the use of artificial intelligence in user interfaces.

Exercise 29

1 Briefly define the following terms: user interface; command-driven interface; prompt; qualifier; menu-driven interface; default option; Wimp environment; Wysiwyg; desktop; icon; pointer.

2 Discuss, with examples, the advantages and disadvantages of:
(a) command-driven interfaces
(b) menu-driven interfaces
(c) Wimp interfaces.

3 In your opinion, how useful would a word processor be without a Wysiwyg interface?

4 Choose a menu-based software package with which you are familiar.
(a) Draw a diagram showing the structure of the menus.
(b) Discuss the advantages and disadvantages of this structure, using specific operations as examples.
(c) Suggest any improvements which you think could be made to the user interface.

5 Suggest some potential applications for voice-activated user interfaces. In each case, state the advantages voice activation has over a conventional user interface.

30 Database Systems

This chapter introduces one of the fastest growth areas in computing, namely **database systems**. It explains the nature of a database, and discusses some of the advantages of using one. The topic is presented in broad outline only, as a detailed study involves concepts which are beyond the scope of this course.

One example is used to illustrate several of the points raised in the chapter. This example concerns a typical user of a database, namely a mail order retailer, selling a wide variety of goods from a number of warehouses to customers throughout the country. Although this example is not a case study, it is nevertheless a realistic application of a database system.

30.1 What is a Database System ?

■ This question is first investigated in an informal way, before a precise definition of a database is given. Note that it is important to distinguish between a database system, which supports a number of applications, and a database package (Section 21.4), which provides information storage and retrieval facilities.

Most organisations which use a computer base all their operational systems on it. In the case of the mail order retailer, these operational systems might include customer accounts, stock control and payroll systems. Each of these applications requires a large volume of stored data.

The traditional approach to the storage of this data is to use files, as described in two previous chapters. Each application has its own set of files, containing the data it needs, and structured according to its method of processing. In most cases, because all the applications are for the same organisation, there is a large degree of overlap of data between the files

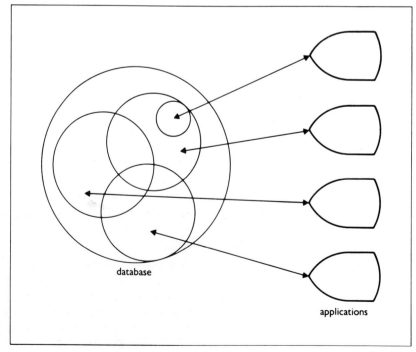

database

applications

Figure 30.1
A database: general concept

for the various applications. For example, a transaction recorded in the customer accounts file includes details of the goods, which are also recorded in the stock file.

If these files are replaced by a single, large, suitably organised collection of data, accessed by all the applications, then this collection of data is a **database**. In the case of the mail order retailer, the database is a single collection of data used for customer accounts, stock control and payroll applications.

A concise definition of a database is as follows:

A database is a collection of stored operational data used by all the application systems of an organisation.

A database system is a layer of software which maintains the database, and provides an interface to the data for the applications programs which use it. The general idea of a database is illustrated in Figure 30.1.

30.2 Advantages of Databases

■ Using a single, centralised store of data for all applications has a number of advantages. These include:

- Consistency of data: when a data item is updated, its up-to-date value is available to all applications. This ensures that the data used by all the applications is consistent.
- Less data proliferation: because only one copy of each data item is kept, duplication of data is eliminated.
- Ease of setting up of new applications: when a new application is contemplated, much of the data it needs is probably already on the database. Extending the database and providing a new interface is generally quicker than starting the new application from scratch.
- Easier security monitoring: because all access to data is via a centralised system, a uniform system of security monitoring can be implemented. In most cases this is more effective than a number of separate security systems.

Databases do also have disadvantages. These are discussed in the assessment at the end at the chapter.

To get a more concrete idea of the advantages of using a database, consider again the example of the mail order retailer. Before the introduction of the database, every sale of goods to a customer required both stock control files and customer account files to be updated. This involved a duplication of effort, and any errors could lead to inconsistencies between the two files. With a database, only one update is required.

30.3 Database Concepts

■ There are two concepts essential to an understanding of databases: the ideas of **data models** and **data independence**.

Data Models

Although a database is a single collection of data, the data must appear to be different when viewed by the different applications which use the database system. Each application which uses the database must see a set of data structured according to its requirements. Furthermore, the logical structure of the data might be different from the way it is physically represented on backing store media.

The way around these problems is the idea of a **data model**. A data model is the logical structure of the data as it appears at a particular level of the database system. Each application which uses the database has a different data model. For the example of the mail order retailer, consider the stock control and accounting applications.

The data model for the stock control application might be a set of item records, each containing an item number and a supplier. Associated with each item record is a set of stock movements, each comprising a date and a quantity supplied or dispatched. This data model is illustrated in Figure 30.2.

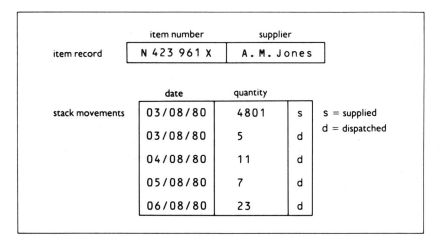

Figure 30.2
Stock control data model

On the other hand, the data model for the customer accounting application might be a set of **customer records**, each containing a customer number and customer details. Associated with each customer record is a set of transactions. Each transaction includes a date, item number, quantity and price. This data model is illustrated in Figure 30.3.

customer record	customer number	customer details		
	C 491 267 4	P. Sharp 4 Elm Street Ashton		

transactions	date	item number	quantity	price
	04/08/80	N 436 215 4	1	10.45
	04/08/80	N 391 204 9	1	23.16
	05/08/80	N 423 961 x	3	9.95
	10/08/80	N 104 723 5	2	38.47

Figure 30.3
Accounting data model

In addition, there is the data model associated with the database as a whole. This model depicts the ideal, logical structure of the data, independent of the media on which the data is stored. All other data models are derived from this central model. It is the task of the various layers of the database system software to create and maintain these data models. The words **transformation** or **mapping** are used for the process of creating one data model from another.

Data Independence

You will recall that a database is a large store of operational data. Because it is operational, it is changing all the time. Data items are constantly being updated, and new data is being added. In most cases, the total volume of data is increasing. On the other hand, new and improved data storage media are constantly becoming available. These are generally cheaper, more compact and quicker to access than before.

For these reasons, it is necessary from time to time to replace the media on which the data is stored. If applications referred directly to the storage media, this would require amendments to every applications program. These amendments would be slow, error-prone and costly.

Accordingly, the central data model of the database, and the application data models derived from it, are independent of the physical storage of the data. One level of the database system software is devoted to mapping the central data model onto the physical representation of the data. If the storage media are changed, only this layer of software needs to be altered.

This discussion gives rise to the idea of **data independence**. Data independence is when the logical structure of the data, i.e. the central data model, and associated application data models, are distinct from the arrangement of the data on any particular backing store medium. The data models are unaffected by any changes in techniques of storing the data.

30.4 Database System Elements

■ The elements of a database system have now been introduced. It consists of the stored data, the various data models, the layer of software which maintains the data (often called a **database management system**), and also a person working as a **database administrator**. Figure 30.4 illustrates all the elements of a database system.

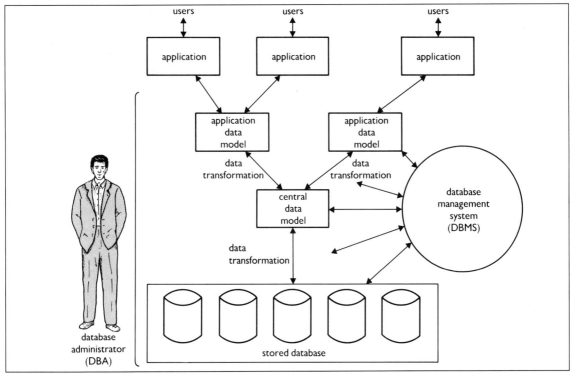

Figure 30.4 A database system

The **database management system (DBMS)** is a large and complex piece of software, responsible for all aspects of the creation, accessing and updating of the database. Tasks it performs include transforming or mapping the data from one model to another, or between the central data model and the stored database. All interactions between users and the database are dealt with by the DBMS. This includes carrying out various security checks. A database management system is a real-time system, and has much in common with an operating system.

The **database administrator (DBA)** is the person in charge of the overall running of the database system. Duties of a database administrator include deciding on the information content of the database and the structure of the various data models, deciding how the data is to be stored, liaising with users, and defining a strategy for back-up storage and recovery from breakdown. This job requires a combination of software and managerial skills.

30.5 Structuring the Data Model

■ The central decision in the design of a database system is the structure of the data model. Almost every other aspect of database system depends on this structure. Because the database is large, and there are many relationships existing between individual data items, a satisfactory structuring of the data is difficult to achieve. Objectives of a well structured data model include efficiency of storage, ease of transformation to application models, speed of access to data and ease of modification of the model.

The three common approaches to the structuring of data models are discussed. These are the **hierarchical**, **network** and **relational** approaches. Historically, these approaches have been developed in this order, with relational databases being the most recent, and rapidly becoming the most popular.

customer supplier record

identification number	details
C 491 267 4	P. Sharp 4 Elm Street Ashton

trading records

date	item number	quantity	price	p = purchased
04/08/80	N 436 215 4	1	10.45	p
04/08/80	N 391 204 9	1	23.16	p
05/08/80	N 423 262 X	3	9.95	p
20/08/80	N 104 723 5	2	38.47	p

customer/ supplier record

identification number	details
S 437 261 5	A. M. Jones PO Box 194 Ely

trading records

date	item number	quantity	price	s = supplied
03/08/80	N 423 961 X	480	9.95	s

Figure 30.5
Hierarchical data model

The Hierarchical Approach

The hierarchical approach involves creating a tree structure for the data. Different data items are stored at different levels, with some levels being 'below' others in the tree. The problem with the hierarchical approach is that not all databases fit naturally into a tree structure.

Figure 30.5 shows an attempt to create a hierarchical model of the data for the mail order retailer's database. Two levels of the hierarchy are shown, namely the customer/supplier record level, below which is a level of trading records. Each customer/supplier record has one or more trading records associated with it.

The Network Approach

In an attempt to overcome the rigidity of the hierarchical approach, the network approach to structuring a data model has been developed. In this approach, data items are linked to other data items by pointers, forming a network. Information is extracted by traversing the network in various ways.

Figure 30.6 shows a network data model for the mail order retailer's database. Notice how information is extracted by following various arrows through the network.

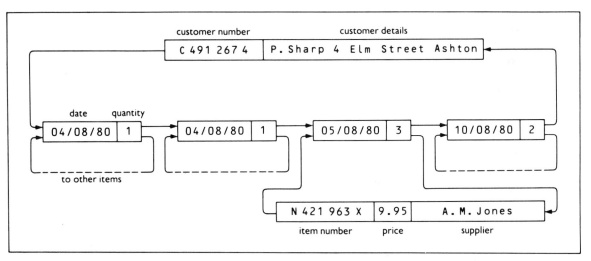

Figure 30.6
Network data model

The Relational Approach

The relational approach is the newest and most promising method of structuring a data model. Using this approach, the data is presented as a set of tables, each table representing a relationship existing between two or more data items. The model can be transformed by combining relationships via a common data item and deleting unwanted data items.

Figure 30.7 shows a relational data model for the mail order retailer's database. The tables can be joined to produce invoices and purchase orders. The item numbers and identification numbers are common columns.

The relational data model has the benefits of simplicity of concept, economy of storage, and a wide variety of applications which seem to fit naturally onto its structure. It is being used as the basis of fourth generation software development tools (Chapter 24).

identification/details relation

C 491 267 4	P. Sharp 4 Elm Street Ashton
S 437 262 5	A. M. Jones PO Box 194 Ely

item number/supplier/price relation

N 423 961 X	S 436 261 5	9.95

date/item numbers/identification number/quantity/transaction type relation

03/08/80	N 423 961 X	S 437 262 5	480	s
04/08/80	N 436 225 4	C 491 267 4	1	p
04/08/80	N 391 204 9	C 491 267 4	1	p
05/08/80	N 423 961 X	C 491 267 4	3	p
10/08/80	N 104 723 5	C 491 267 4	2	p

Figure 30.7
Relational data model

30.6 An Assessment of Databases

■ This chapter has outlined how large centralised data structures can be constructed to contain all the operational data of an organisation. The advantages of these databases are discussed earlier in the chapter. Experience has shown that databases do indeed have the advantages mentioned earlier, but they also have two major disadvantages.

The first disadvantage is that a database requires a large software system to create and maintain it, and a fairly large computer to support it. This is in contrast to the current tendency towards small, cheap microcomputers with small software overheads, and distributed processing. However, as microcomputers become more powerful, and database management software becomes more compact, this problem is becoming less serious. In particular, the availability of distributed relational databases is helping to overcome it.

The second disadvantage is that a database is an example of putting all one's eggs in the same basket. A failure of a database system, through a hardware or software failure, or deliberate damage or industrial action, can have serious consequences for an organisation with all its data processing dependent on the database.

30.7 Conclusion

■ The main points of this chapter are as follows:
- A database is a structured collection of stored operational data used by all the application systems in an organisation.
- A data model is the logical structure of a database as it appears at a particular level of the database system. Each application which uses a database has its own data model.
- Data independence is when the logical structure of the data model is independent of its physical structure on any particular backing store medium.
- A database management system is the software which maintains the database and supports all the applications which use the data.

- The three common methods of constructing data models are the hierarchical, network and relational techniques.

Exercise 30

1 Briefly define the following terms: database; data model; data independence; database system; DBMS; DBA; hierarchical data model; network data model; relational data model.

2 You will recall that a system is a collection of parts working together towards some common objectives. List the objectives of a database system.

3 Explain, in your own words, the significance of the concept of data independence.

4 Summarise the advantages and disadvantages of the use of databases.

5 A news reporting agency uses a database system to store the text of all news items. News reports are supplied, by telex, by a number of correspondents, and then purchased by a number of newspapers and magazines.

   The model of the data, from the correspondents' point of view, is as follows:

Correspondent record

Identity	Name

```
K  347  P JOHN   GREGGOROWSKI
```

News items supplied

Date	Text

```
05/11/80  TODAY RUSSIAN TANKS....
07/11/80  STRIKES IN POLAND....
08/11/80  URGENT DISCUSSIONS ARE....
11/11/80  THE SITUATION IS DETERIORATING....
12/11/80  NO SIGN OF AN END....
```

The model of the data, from the newspapers' point of view, is as follows:

Newspaper record

Identity	Name

```
N   417    WASHINGTON STAR
```

News items purchased

Date	Correspondent Identity	Text

```
04/11/80  K 007 L   LONDON EXPERIENCED....
07/11/80  K 347 P   STRIKES IN POLAND....
07/11/80  K 007 L   MISS WORLD....
09/11/80  K 291 A   ARGENTINA'S DICTATOR....
12/11/80  K 347 P   NO SIGN OF AN END....
```

   a) Using either the relational or the hierarchical or the network approach, draw up a central data model for this system.

   b) Explain how your data model can be used to determine which newspapers have brought any particular news item.

6 Design in outline a suitable simple database system of your own. State the data model for each application, and also the central data model of the system.

7 **Oracle** is a relational database system developed by Oracle Limited. It can be used on a wide variety of workstations, mid-range and mainframe computers. Find out about the system, specifically how concepts introduced in this chapter are implemented.

31 Data Communications Systems

Left A fibre optic cable. This is one of the many items of data communication equipment which we take for granted today.
Right An electronic telephone exchange, switching telephone calls and digital data.

Over the past century, a number of communications networks have been developed, to the stage where they now encircle the globe and reach into space. Radio, television and telephone links enable hundreds of millions of people to keep in contact with each other, often over distances of thousands of miles.

Although one of the earliest forms of communication systems used a digital code (the Morse code) for information transmission, the bulk of the development of these networks has been based on analogue signals, for voice and picture transmission (with the important exception of the telex system). With the advent of computers, the situation is changing again. Information is being sent, in digital form, in increasing quantities, as more and more computers are being linked to the local and global communications networks. The telecommunications networks in all industrial countries are in the process of changing from analogue to digital transmission. The combination of computers and communications systems is one of the major areas of technological development at present. It may yet have as profound an impact on the lifestyles of millions of people as the advent of computers, or of telephones, radio or television had in their time.

This chapter is a brief introduction to the field of data communication. The topic is discussed from several angles. The first part of the chapter concerns the way in which data is transmitted between two computers, or between a peripheral device and a computer. The second part of the chapter outlines some of the hardware configurations which can be built up around a data communication network. The use of computers as exchanges in digital telecommunications network is also discussed. The chapter concludes with a case study of an electronic mail system.

31.1 Concepts of Data Transmission

■ This section discusses some concepts relating to the transmission of data, in digital form, along a communications medium. These concepts are much the same whether the communication medium is a wire, a radio or a fibre optics link.

Bit Serial Transmission

Just as data is always stored and processed in a computer in binary form, so is it transmitted between computers in a binary form. Individual bits are grouped together to code characters, and characters are grouped together to form larger data structures.

If two digital devices are very close to each other, it is possible to connect them by a multi-strand cable which can transmit a number of bits simultaneously. This is **parallel** data transmission. It is a common form of connection between a computer and a local printer, for example. In the majority of cases, where data is to be transmitted over any distance, a single carrier is used. In these circumstances, only one bit at a time is transmitted. This is called **bit serial transmission**.

Broadband and Baseband Communication

It is possible to transmit the binary values 0 and 1 over short distances using the presence or absence of a voltage, or a positive and a negative voltage to represent these values. When a fibre optics link of any distance is used, the situation is also very simple: a pulse of light signals a 1; no pulse signals a 0. Data transmission where the presence or the absence of a signal signifies a 0 or a 1 is known as **baseband** transmission.

For long distance communications by wire or by radio, a more sophisticated technique known as **broadband** transmission is required. There is a carrier signal of a high frequency, on top of which the data signals are sent. In most cases, variations in the carrier frequency are used, one type for a 0 and the other for a 1. Broadband communications systems allow a higher throughput of data than baseband systems, and are less prone to noise. The details of broadband and baseband techniques are beyond the scope of this course. It is sufficient to know that an **interfacing** device is placed at each end of the transmission line, to transmit and receive the appropriate signals for 0 and 1. Interfaces generally deal with the conversion of parallel data from the computer or peripheral device to serial data for the transmission line.

One of the commonest types of communications interfaces is called a **modem** (for **mod**ulator/**dem**odulator). Another device, which links with

Figure 31.1
Bit serial data transmission

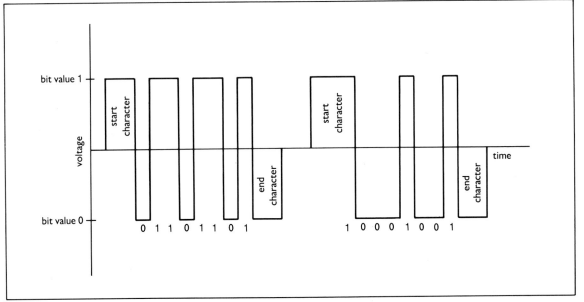

an ordinary telephone, is called an **acoustic coupler**. Both transmit and receive serial data along telephone lines, and convert it to or from the internal coding used by the computer.

The serial transmission of a set of characters is illustrated in Figure 31.1. Notice how the beginning and end of the bits for each character is marked.

Simplex and Duplex Communication

Verbal communication between people is not possible if both talk at once, or if each waits for the other to speak. Similarly, in data communication, there must be ways of establishing in which direction transmission is taking place at any one time. There are three approaches to this problem, as outlined below.

Simplex communication is where transmission is in one direction only. This may be used, for example, for transmission of data from a remote input device to a processor.

Half duplex communication is where transmission may be in either direction, but not in both directions simultaneously. In other words, at any given instant, transmission is in one direction only. Ways of indicating that transmission is complete, and that the direction may therefore be reversed, are dealt with in the next section.

Full duplex communication is where transmission may proceed in both directions at the same time. This is the most sophisticated form of data communication.

Data Transmission Codes

Data transmission is an area where standardisation is very important. Any two items of equipment which adopt the same standards of data communication can be linked together.

One of the essential standards in data communications is a code for the binary representation of characters. Fortunately there has been a very wide measure of agreement on this matter. Only a few character codes are used in data transmission, and one code, the **American Standard Code for Information Interchange** (**ASCII**), has become an international standard. An increasing proportion of data communication is in this code. (As mentioned in Chapter 3, this code is becoming increasingly popular for the internal representation of data in computers.)

Data transmission codes include representations of letters, digits and punctuation marks, as well as a number of **control characters**. These characters only have relevance to the transmission of data, and are not used for the storage or processing of data. For example, there are characters to signal the end of transmission, or the start of a block of data. The codes for some of the ASCII control characters are shown in Figure 31.2.

hexadecimal	binary	interpretation
01	00000001	start of header
02	00000010	start of text
03	00000011	end of text
04	00000100	end of transmission
05	00000101	enquire, who are you?
06	00000110	acknowledge
07	00000111	ring bell
08	00001000	backspace

Figure 31.2
ASCII control characters

Speeds of Data Transmission

Speeds of data transmission vary considerably, depending on the application, and the data communication medium. The unit of measurement of data transmission rates is the **baud**. The precise definition of the baud is rather complicated, but it may, for practical purposes, be regarded as one bit per second.

On an ordinary telephone line, a data transmission rate of 1200 or 2400 baud is generally used. On special lines, this rate may increase to 9600 baud (9.6K baud). Even higher rates are possible on other communication media.

Packets

When one writes a letter, the pages are placed in an envelope, which is generally of a standard size. A similar principle is used in many data communication systems. Data is transmitted, not in single characters, or groups of characters, but in **packets**.

A packet is a set of transmitted data, enclosed by strings of control characters. The control characters at the start and end of the packet follow a strict set of rules. The data within the packet is of a standard structure. A packet is the unit of transmission and reception within a particular data communication network. All devices connected to the network send and receive data in packets of the same type.

Communication Protocols

When one sends a letter, one must follow a number of rules imposed by the Post Office. For example, the address must be set out in a certain way, and the stamp must be in the top right hand corner of the envelope. Similar rules apply in the case of data transmission. These rules are called communication **protocols**.

Among other things, a protocol specifies the structure of a packet of data, what control characters are used and what procedures are followed for the transmission and reception of data. For half duplex transmission, the protocol specifies the procedure for changing the direction of transmission. Many communications protocols permit the data in packets to be **compressed**. Compression aims to reduce the number of characters which actually need to be transmitted, for example, by representing repeated characters as a counter followed by the character.

The advantage of a communication protocol is this: any two devices which use the same communication protocol can be linked together. For this reason, communication protocols are designed very carefully, in order to be as widely applicable as possible. At present, there are only a small number of protocols in widespread use.

Errors in Data Transmission

We all have experience of bad telephone lines, poor radio reception and erratic television pictures. These are all caused by interference, or **noise**, in the communications medium. Although careful design and higher quality (and more expensive) equipment can reduce the amount of noise, it can never be eliminated entirely.

Data communication is not immune to the problem of noise, although the situation benefits from the nature of digital transmission. As long as the signal for a 0 can be distinguished from that for a 1, a bit is correctly received. However, there is always a small probability that noise will cause the wrong bit value to be detected.

As it is impossible to prevent bits from being detected wrongly, the best that can be done is to try to detect when an error has occurred, and, in some cases, locate and correct the error. Most data transmission codes incorporate checks on the data transmitted. The commonest check is the inclusion of a **parity bit** in the code for each character. The question of parity is discussed in Section 3.12. Other checks include the insertion of **check characters**, or groups of check characters, as discussed in Section 14.7. One type of error correcting code, called the **Hamming code**, is discussed in the exercise at the end of this chapter.

31.2 Communications Networks

■ This section describes the commonest types of data communications networks at present in operation. The different types of network introduced here are not to be regarded as rigid stereotypes, but merely as examples of common communications configurations.

Central Processor with Terminals

A large central processor linked to a number of remote-access terminals is the 'traditional' approach to data communication. This arrangement is illustrated in Figure 31.3. A refinement of this idea is to collect the lines to a number of terminals together at a suitable point, and connect this point to the processor by a single high volume data link. The device at the linking site is called a **multiplexer** or **cluster adaptor**. This technique is illustrated in Figure 31.4.

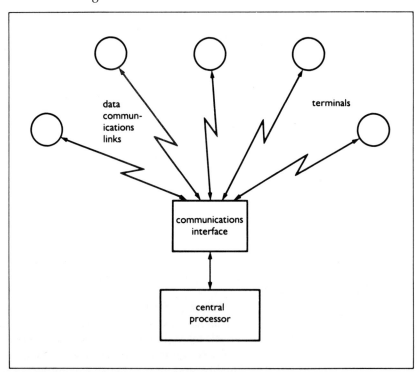

Figure 31.3
A terminal network

Intelligent Terminals

Instead of centralising all the processing in a computer network at a single processor, an increasingly common configuration makes use of **intelligent terminals**. Microcomputers or special-purpose devices such as cash terminals are the commonest types of intelligent terminals. A cash

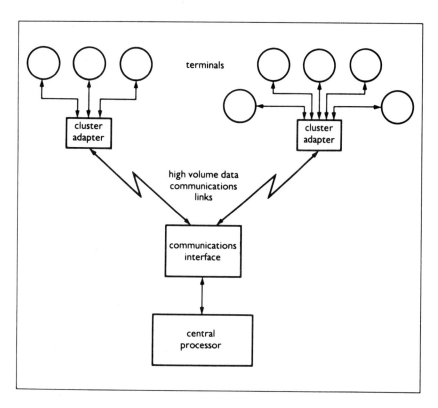

Figure 31.4
Multiplexing

terminal handles cash withdrawals from bank accounts, and similar transactions. When processing a transaction, the required information about the account in question is requested from a central computer over the communications network, and the details of the transaction are handled by the terminal.

The structure of a network of intelligent terminals is the same as that shown in Figures 31.3 and 31.4, but processing is shared between the central processor and the terminals. If communication fails between an intelligent terminal and the central computer, the terminal is usually able to continue work for a certain time.

Computer Networks

Computer networks can include more than one processor, as shown in Figure 31.5. The processors can be long distances apart, connected by radio, telephone or satellite communication links, or they can be close together, often in the same building. The latter situation is known as a **local area network**. Local area networks are an increasingly popular computer configuration. They generally consist of a number of **network stations** and one or more **file servers**. The network stations are microcomputers with network interfaces, and the file servers have the disk drives which are shared by all the workstations.

There are several advantages of processors linked in this way. Resources such as disk drives and printers can be shared amongst the processors. The processing load is shared evenly between the processors. This is particularly significant if the processors are in different time zones, where off-peak times at one processor correspond to busy periods at others. The other major advantage is that a breakdown at one processor does not put the whole system out of action.

A network in a busy office. The combination of desktop processing and data communications enables office workers to be much more productive than before.

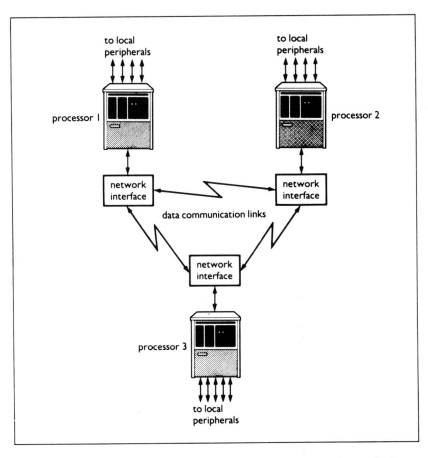

Figure 31.5
A computer network

The major disadvantage of such a network is the size and complexity of the operating system required to control the network. A significant proportion of the time of each processor is spent doing 'housekeeping' tasks, in order to keep the network as a whole functioning smoothly.

31.3 Local Area Network Architectures

■ There are two approaches to local area network architecture: **common carrier cables**, and **ring architecture**.

Common Carrier Architecture

The majority of local area networks are connected by coaxial cable like that used for television aerials. See Figure 31.6. The communications protocol is very simple: when a station has data to transmit, it waits until the carrier is quiet, and then sends its packets of data. The data is addressed to one or more destination stations. Every station receives the data, but only those to which it is addressed retain it. If two stations start transmitting at the same time, they detect a **collision** and stop sending. They wait for a short random interval of time before starting again. The technical name for this system is **carrier sense multi-access with collision detection (CSMA/CD)**. It was pioneered by the **Ethernet** local area network system.

Ring Architecture

A type of local area network currently under development is based on the idea of a **ring**. As illustrated in Figure 31.7, the ring connects all the

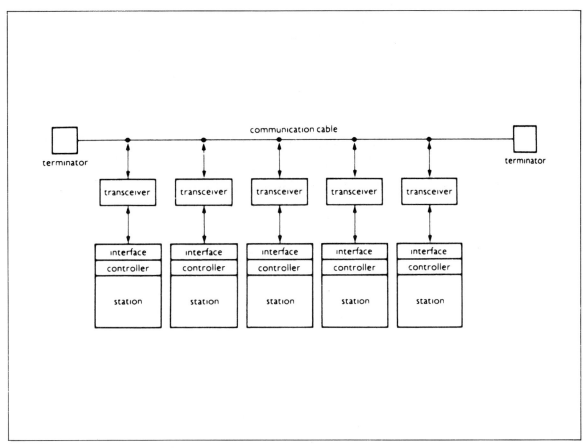

Figure 31.6 An Ethernet network

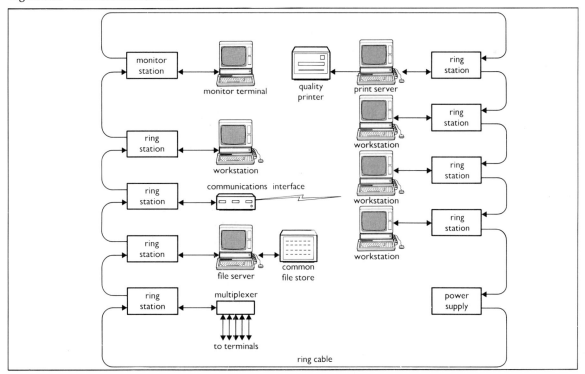

Figure 31.7 Ring architecture

processors and peripheral devices in the network. It consists of a number of ring stations, joined by a cable in a continuous loop. Data travels in one direction only around the ring. Each station has storage for a few bits of data, and the signal delay in the cable creates storage for additional bits in transit. The stations and the cable may be thought of as a circular shift register, around which bits circulate at high speed, generally 10 megabits per second.

The circulating bits are organised into one or more slots, and a gap. Slots generally comprise about 40 bits. Any station may insert a mini-packet of data into a free slot as it passes. The mini-packet contains the address of the sending station, the address of receiving station, two bytes of data, some control bits and a parity bit.

The mini-packet circulates around the ring until it reaches the station to which it is addressed. If the station is ready to receive, it copies the mini-packet into its internal registers, and marks the packet as accepted. The mini-packet continues around the ring until it again reaches the station which transmitted it. The station notes whether or not the mini-packet has been accepted, and marks it as free. To prevent one station from dominating the ring, a station must skip a slot before it can use another slot.

The monitor station is responsible for starting up the ring, determining the number of slots in circulation and detecting and recovering from errors. Each station checks the parity of all passing mini-packets. If a parity error is noted, an error mini-packet is sent to the monitor station. The monitor station fills all empty slots with random bits, and checks them if they return still empty. If the ring breaks, the first station 'downstream' of the break sends a continuous stream of fault packets to the monitor station. In these ways, a number of error checks are built into the ring. The monitor station plays an important part in the error detection process.

Power for the running of the ring itself is supplied from the monitor station and from one or more ring power supply stations in the ring. Each ring station requires local power for its registers, but the ring itself is not affected if the local power is switched off.

A ring station provides a simple interface between the ring and a wide variety of connected devices. More sophisticated interfaces to certain processors are provided by access logic, which is placed between the ring station and the processor.

A ring local area network is faster and more resilient than a CSMA/CD system. However, it is much more expensive to install.

31.4 Message and Packet Switching

■ **Message switching** is the work performed by a telephone exchange. It involves establishing a link between the originator of a call and the receiver of the call. The equipment interprets the digits of a dialled number by setting a series of switches. When all the switches have been set, the call is linked to its destination. The traditional mechanical apparatus still in use in a few areas is slow, cumbersome and requires extensive maintenance to keep it in operation.

The modern technique of message switching involves the use of computers and digital telecommunications. Using specially designed hardware and software, these **electronic exchanges** can link lines extremely rapidly, keep records of which numbers have been connected, and supply the information necessary for the preparation of telephone bills. Digital electronic exchanges are software controlled, making them very flexible in use. Most circuits are duplicated, giving them a high level of **redundancy** to be able to cope with component failures. Digital electronic exchanges are being introduced into the telephone systems of most industrial countries. Examples include the **System X** developed for British Telecom.

Similar to message switching, but used for computer data only, is **packet switching**. A packet switching network is a long-distance communications network between computers, using a combination of high-speed telephone lines, satellite links and microwave radio channels. See Figure 31.8. All data is sent in packets, as described in Section 31.1. The 'exchanges' on the system are **packet switching computers**. These receive incoming packets and route them according to their addresses. They may store the packets if the destination computer is not ready to accept them. They also act as an interface between communications links which may have different data transmission speeds. An example of a packet switching network is the **Swift** system for electronic funds transfer between banks.

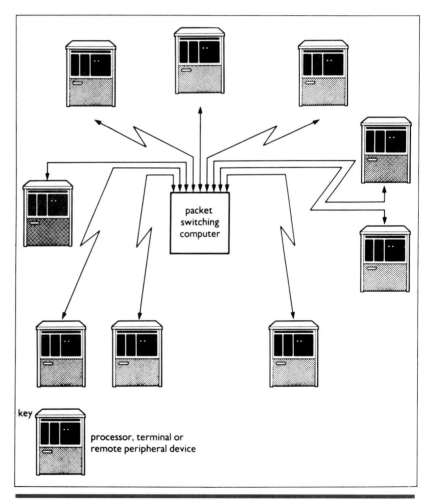

key

processor, terminal or
remote peripheral device

Figure 31.8
A packet switching network

■ **Vaxmail** is an electronic mail (**E-mail**) system for users of Digital Equipment Vax computers. It is typical of a number of similar services, and can interlink with many of them. It provides both local and long-distance communications. Local services are carried on Ethernet networks; long-distance communications are via a packet switching network. Users do not need to know whether a message is being sent locally or long-distance: routing of messages is taken care of by the mail system.

Each person using Vaxmail has a **user identity**, possibly suffixed by the name of the computer via which their mail is routed. For example, a user named Roger Jones on a computer named Summit would have a Vaxmail address jones@summit. Each user has a **mailbox** to which all incoming messages are sent.

To use the mail system, a user logs in by typing the command 'mail' from the operating system. The interactive Vaxmail prompt is then displayed. The user can then enter any of the Vaxmail commands. These include:

Directory

This lists the messages currently in the user's mailbox. All incoming messages are automatically placed in the mailbox.

Read

Read a message from the mailbox. The message is displayed on screen. Messages are identified by number, in the order in which they appear in the directory listing.

Extract

Extract a message from the mailbox and save it as a text file. This is the way of getting messages out of the mail system.

Send

Send a message to another user. The mail address of the destination user is entered, together with the subject of the message. The text of the message is either typed or taken from an existing file.

Reply

Reply to the message just read. The name of the sender is looked up in the incoming message, and used as the destination of the reply.

Exit

Leave the mail system and return to the operating system.

The above are the most commonly used of the Vaxmail commands, but by no means all of them. The benefits of the system include its versatility, the fact that it can be used to transfer any files, whether or not they were typed within the mail system, its speed and its low cost. Many organisations depend on an electronic mail system like this for all their internal communications, both local and long-distance. There are some problems due to the incompatibility of different electronic mail systems, but gateways are provided to link different systems. The volume of information sent by E-mail is growing rapidly.

31.6
Conclusion

■ This chapter has provided a brief introduction to the field of data communications. It must be emphasised that this is currently one of the major growth areas of computing. For example, during the current decade it is intended to replace all the mechanical telephone exchanges in Britain with electronic equipment. Local area networks are another area of rapid development: stand-alone computers in commercial and industrial organisations are rare. The convergence of computing, communications and electronic control systems is the basis of **information technology** which is rapidly becoming the basic support technology of industrial countries.

The main points of this chapter are as follows:

- Most data communications systems use bit serial transmission.
- Baseband systems send pulses of light or electricity corresponding to the 0's and 1's being transmitted; broadband systems use a carrier wave which is modulated to send the signals for 0 and 1.
- Simplex data transmission is in one direction only; half duplex is in either direction at any one time; full duplex is in both directions simultaneously.
- The rules for the transmission and reception of data on a particular type of network are called a communication protocol.
- Types of communication network include computer terminal networks, local area networks and long-distance networks.
- Digital telephone exchanges carry out message switching; packet switching networks are used for long-distance computer links.

Exercise 31

1 Briefly define the following terms: serial and parallel data transmission; broadband; baseband; modem; simplex; half duplex; full duplex; control character; packet; protocol; noise; local area network; packet switching; interface; E- mail; gateway.

2 Why is standardisation important in data communication?

◆ 3 The screen of a visual display unit shows 20 lines each of 40 characters. Data is transmitted to the VDU in packets, each packet containing the characters for one screen display, in order from the leftmost character of the top line, line by line, to the rightmost character of the bottom line. New-line characters are not required after each line.

Data is compressed by representing repeated characters as a counter (occupying one byte, with most significant bit 1), followed by the character. For example, a blank line is represented as follows:

	first byte		second byte	
Binary	1010	1000	0110	0000
Hexadecimal	A	B	6	0
ASCII	Count=40		space	

a) Write down, in binary, hexadecimal and ASCII, the string of characters needed to transmit a screen display containing the following characters:

A row of dots (Hexadecimal 2E) on the second and nineteenth lines.

The characters **MESSAGE ENDS** starting at the left side of the fourth line, the rest of which is blank.

All other lines blank.

b) Count the number of bytes transmitted, and comment on the effectiveness of the compression system.

(Use Figure 3.1 for the ASCII codes of the characters.)

4 Vaxmail is one of a number of electronic mail systems available at present. Most large computer manufacturers market a system. Investigate one of these systems and compare it with the case study in this chapter.

5 A cluster adapter combines a number of 1200 baud lines into a single 9.6K baud line. If multiplexing information accounts for 10 per cent of the data on the high speed line, how many low speed lines can the cluster adapter accept?

6 The Prestel viewdata system, marketed by British Telecom in the UK and a number of other countries, is an early example of a data communications system available to the public. The user interface of the system is a microcomputer or specially adapted television set which connects to an ordinary telephone line. The system is supported by a number of minicomputers, one in each major population centre. Having dialled into the system, users can access 'pages' of information on a wide variety of topics, using a simple hand-held keypad for control.

a) Find out more about the services provided by Prestel.

b) Draw a diagram showing the configuration of the Prestel network.

c) Find out how information is supplied to the system.

d) Write a report on your findings, and comment on likely development areas of the Prestel system.

7 A code which will detect and correct single-bit errors is the **Hamming code**. This code requires a number of even parity check bits in a data item. They are distributed in such a way that they do not check on each other. Three check bits are required for a four bit data item, as shown in the table below:

			B1		B2	B3	B4
Data bits:			B1		B2	B3	B4
Check bits:	C1	C2		C3			
Digit numbers:	D1	D	D3	D4	D5	D6	D7
Example	1	0	1	1	0	1	0
Check	*		*		*		*
Check 2		*	*			*	*
Check 3				*	*	*	*

In the example, the data bits are 1010 and the check bits are 101.

The digits are numbered from left to right, and the checks are determined by the binary equivalent of these digit numbers, expressed in the pattern of asterisks in the last three lines.

Each row of asterisks starts with a check bit. The remaining asterisks in the row indicate the data bits whose parity is indicated by the check bit. For example, the check bit C2 tests the parity of data bits B1,B3 and B4.

If a single bit error occurs, the three checks are sufficient to locate and thus correct the error.

For example, if the data is corrupted to 1011110, the checks are as follows:

Data:	1	0	1	1	1	1	0	
Check 1:	1		1		1		0	fail (value 1)
Check 2:		0	1			1	0	pass (value 0)
Check 3:				1	1	1	0	fail (value 1)

If a check fails, it is given the value 1, and if it passes, the value 0. The binary number thus formed indicates the position of the digit which is wrong. In the above example, the number is 101, indicating that the fifth digit is in error, which is in fact the case.

a) Locate and correct the errors in each of the following data items, which Hamming check digits as above.

```
1 0 1 1 1 0 1
0 0 1 1 0 0 0
1 1 1 1 1 0 1
```

◆ b) An eight bit data item requires four Hamming check bits. Draw up a table, similar to the one above, showing the positions of the data and check bits, and the four checks to be carried out. (Hint: Start by drawing
the binary pattern of asterisks.)

◆ c) Write down some correctly encoded eight bit data items. In each case, introduce a single-bit error. Then perform the four checks, to ensure that they locate the error.

◆ d) Repeat part (b) and (c) for 16 and 32 bit data items.

32 Control Systems

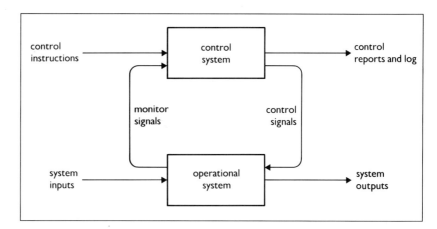

Figure 32.1
A control system and an
operational system

A **control system** is a system which regulates the behaviour of another
system (in this context, the operational system). The control system senses
the state of the operational system, decides what controls to apply, and
sends control signals to the operational system. If the control system is
self-contained, receiving only occasional external inputs, then control is
automatic. Figure 32.1 is a general system diagram of a control system
and an operational system.

This chapter discusses the need for control systems, the principles of
automatic control and the two main types of control system: analogue
and digital control systems, and concludes with a section on electronic
control systems. Electronic control systems are one of the three branches
of information technology.

32.1 The Need for Automatic Control

■ One of the pioneering devices of the industrial revolution was the
steam-driven pumping engine, used to pump water out of mines. These
used large pistons which were moved slowly in and out by low-pressure
steam. The first models of these engines required an operator (usually a
young boy) to open and close the steam valves at the end of each stroke.
This was a tedious and dangerous job, and limited the speed at which the
engine could operate. This task was soon replaced by levers driven by the
piston itself which opened and closed the steam valves automatically.
This led to the development of the high-speed steam engine which was
the main source of power for the first century of the industrial revolution.

In addition to highlighting the need for automatic control, this
example demonstrates a number of advantages of automatic control
systems over manual ones. These include the elimination of tedious jobs,
improvements in safety, and the ability to operate equipment at a higher
speed than previously. Domestic automatic washing machines are
another example which emphasises these benefits: they do not require
constant attention, and produce better results than the manual machines
they have replaced.

Today we take automatic control for granted. Its applications range
from simple domestic refrigerators to advanced industrial systems such
as nuclear reactors.

32.2
Principles of Automatic Control

■ As illustrated in Figure 32.1, control systems are based on a cycle:

- sense the state of the operational system
- decide what controls to apply
- act to apply control signals.

Automatic control systems use a **control algorithm** in deciding what controls to apply. For example, a domestic central heating system uses a thermostat (temperature sensor) to control the pump which transports the hot water to the radiators. The algorithm for the pump control may be expressed as follows:

If the temperature is below the preset level
then turn the pump on
else turn the pump off

Alternatively, in Boolean terms, if the thermostat sends a signal when the temperature is above the preset level, the control algorithm is:

Control signal to pump = NOT (thermostat signal)

If, furthermore, the central heating has a time switch, and a main on/off switch, the Boolean expression for the signal to the pump becomes:

Control signal to pump = (NOT (thermostat signal)) AND
(timer signal) AND (on/off signal)

32.3
Analogue and Digital Control Systems

■ The auto-pilot on a ship compares the course of the vessel with a preset course, and measures the difference between them. It turns the ship's wheel by an amount which is proportional to this difference, but in the opposite direction. It has a simple control algorithm:

turn on wheel = $-K \times$ deviation in course

where K is a suitable constant, determined by the way the ship responds to the helm.

This is an example of an **analogue control system**. The signal sensed from the operational system (the deviation in course) is a continuous signal, in the range -180 to $+180$ degrees. The control applied is also continuous, in the same range. Sensing takes place all the time, as does the application of the control signal.

This is also an example of a characteristic of many control systems, namely **feedback**. The control affects the behaviour of the operational system, which in turn affects the inputs sensed by the control system.

Control and sensing form a cycle. The feedback in the above example is negative in that the control signal is in the opposite direction to the sensed signal. Negative feedback is applied by most control systems.

The algorithms for analogue control systems can generally be expressed as mathematical equations like the one above. If they involve rates of change (speeds, accelerations, etc.) they are often of the type known as **differential equations**.

By contrast, **digital control systems** are based on signals which are either on or off. Inputs from sensors are on if a measured quantity is above a reference level, or off if it is below it. Control signals are on if a device is to be activated, or off if it is not. The central heating control system in the previous section is an example of a digital control system.

The control algorithms for many digital systems can be expressed as Boolean equations, as in the previous section. More complex digital systems sample signals from sensors at regular intervals, and then use an algorithm which resembles that for a computer program to determine the controls.

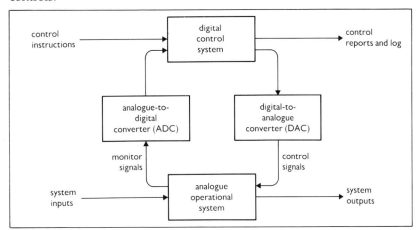

Figure 32.2
A digital control system with
analogue inputs
and outputs

Hybrid control systems have analogue inputs and control signals, but use digital electronics to implement the control algorithm. These sample the analogue signals, convert the values from analogue to digital, and apply the control algorithm. The digital control signal is then converted back to an analogue quantity. Figure 32.2 shows a hybrid control system, with analogue sense and control signals, and digital processing.

32.4 Electronic Control Systems

■ Electronic control systems are based on the same integrated circuit technology as computers. They fall roughly into three classes: **hard-wired systems, programmable systems** and **computer-based systems**.

Hard-wired electronic control systems are used when the control algorithms can be expressed directly as Boolean functions. These functions are implemented using standard logic gates mounted on printed circuit boards, or, increasingly, as **application-specific integrated circuits (Asics)**. An Asic implements the entire logical function of a digital control system in a single integrated circuit. Asics can deal with analogue interfacing as well as digital processing. They are small, cheap, reliable and use little electricity. Their savings in cost and space are some of the main reasons for the widespread use of electronic control systems in devices ranging from cameras and compact discs to guided missiles.

Hard-wired control systems have their control algorithms implemented directly in silicon. Once fabricated, these algorithms cannot be changed. Programmable electronic control systems are based on dedicated microprocessors, running control programs stored in **erasable programmable read-only memory (EPROM)**.

The commonest example of programmable electronic control systems are industrial robots. They are based on dedicated microprocessors, or linked arrays of microprocessors. These are programmed with the details of the task which they are to perform. Some can store a number of programs at any one time, and select one as required. Revised programs can be downloaded into them whenever the task they are required to do changes. The benefit of programmable control is flexibility. The operational system can perform a wide range of tasks, directed by a single control system. Programmable control systems are generally more expensive than hard-wired control systems.

The third category of control systems use general-purpose computers

Industrial robots are examples
of programmable control
systems.

to implement their control algorithms. These computers have special-purpose input and output devices to act as interfaces to the operational systems. The control programs are complex real-time software modules. Computer-based control is required for the most complex of control systems, and those where safety is critical, such as control systems for nuclear reactors. They can deal with input data from a large number of sensors simultaneously, and can support a number of control outputs. Processors are sometimes duplicated as a precaution against system failure. The data storage facilities make it easy to keep a log of the state of the system and the control actions performed. **Control logs** are important when analysing the performance of a system, or re-constructing situations when something has gone wrong.

32.5 Conclusion

■ The main points of this chapter are as follows:
- A control system senses the state of an operational system, decides what controls to apply, and acts to apply these controls.
- A control system applies a control algorithm. Control algorithms may be expressed as mathematical equations, Boolean expressions or as program algorithms.
- Control systems may be analogue, digital or hybrid (usually with analogue sense and control signals, and digital implementation of the control algorithm).
- Electronic control systems are based on integrated circuit technology. They can be classified as hard-wired, programmable or computer-based control systems.
- The cycle of interaction between a control system and an operational system is known as feedback.

Exercise 32

1 Briefly define the following terms: control system; control algorithm; analogue control system; digital control system; hard-wired control; programmable control; computer-based control; feedback.
2 Write control algorithms in Boolean form for:
   a) a domestic refrigerator
   b) an engine cooling system
   c) a domestic hot water system.
   d) the signal which opens the door of a bank vault when:
      a time switch has reached the correct time
      a valid pass card is placed in a slot
      a password corresponding to the card ID is entered.
3 a) Distinguish between hard-wired, programmable and computer-based control systems.
   b) Give two applications suited to each type.
4 Give two reasons for keeping a control log of a system.
5 List three safety-critical applications of electronic control systems. Choose one of these and state:
   a) What the consequences are of a system failure.
   b) What automatic safety precautions are implemented (or should be implemented).
   c) What role human operators play (or should play) in the event of an emergency.
6 Discuss the benefits and any disadvantages of the introduction of automatic control systems in:
   a) the home
   b) industry
   c) transport.

33 Expert and Knowledge-Based Systems

Expert and knowledge-based systems are some of the first concrete results to emerge from the work in artificial intelligence. The first few sections of this chapter deal with expert systems; knowledge-based systems are introduced in Section 33.3.

An **expert system** is one which provides a computer with a certain measure of intelligence in a particular field. In areas such as medicine, geology and engineering, it has proved possible to transfer a certain amount of knowledge from expert practitioners to a computer. The computer can then be consulted, in most cases by other experts, to give advice in particular cases.

A definition of an expert system is as follows:

> An expert system is a computer system which is able to draw reasoned conclusions from a body of knowledge in a particular field, and communicate to the user the line of reasoning by which it has reached a conclusion.

The first expert system went into operation in 1965, but it is only since the mid-1980s that they have begun to be used on a significant scale. Expert systems are likely to be a major application area of computers in the 1990s.

33.1 Objectives of Expert Systems

■ The purpose of an expert system is to provide reasoned advice at a comparable level to that provided by a human expert. This capability has two main aims: to enhance the abilities of leading experts in certain fields, and to make a high level of expertise available to less highly qualified practitioners.

The first aim takes note of the fact that some areas of human expertise, such as the diagnosis and treatment of cancer, are so complex that even the leading experts can benefit from the systematic, logical approach provided by a computer. A computer system will take into consideration all the knowledge at its disposal in the consideration of every case, and will follow known lines of reasoning exhaustively, no matter how complex they are. These capabilities complement the skills of a human expert, which are generally based on a mixture of knowledge, experience, insight and intuition.

The second aim attempts to raise the level of skill of professionals who are not themselves leading experts. A large number of medical practitioners fall into this category, particularly in developing countries. When expert systems become widely available, the skills of these practitioners could be significantly enhanced.

33.2 Techniques of Expert System Design

■ Expert systems draw reasoned conclusions from a knowledge base in a particular field. When designing an expert system, the structure of the knowledge base, and how the knowledge is represented, are two of the main considerations. Factors taken into consideration are the size of the knowledge base, the completeness of the knowledge, and how precise it is. If the knowledge is in any way uncertain, a method of representation which includes some form of probability is used. One of the techniques of knowledge representation discussed in Section 7.3 is used in most cases.

In some expert systems, the expert knowledge is fixed into the system when it is constructed. In others, there is a built-in ability to learn from experience, including from mistakes made by the system. This latter approach is more complex, but generally leads to more useful systems. In many expert systems, the knowledge is completely separate from the rules for its manipulation. These are initially built as expert system **shells**. They are then supplied with the knowledge they require for their particular applications.

Most expert systems are programmed in Lisp (Section 19.7), but Prolog (Section 19.8) is being used to an increasing extent.

33.3 Intelligent Knowledge-Based Systems

■ **Intelligent knowledge-based systems (IKBS)** have more general capabilities than expert systems. They use inference to apply knowledge to perform a task. The knowledge base on which they operate can be in a broad or a narrow field. They require at least the following capabilities: classification, concept formation, summarising, selection, searching, reasoning, planning, modelling, the use of 'common sense' rules, and the ability to learn. These are at the very limit of the capabilities of present-day computers.

Research and development work is under way on various aspects of these problems, the most important - and the most difficult - being an adequate method of knowledge representation. See Section 7.2. A number of techniques of knowledge processing are being tried out. These include evidential reasoning, based on the way people draw conclusions from bodies of evidence, such as that presented at a trial, and procedural learning, based on the way expert learn to solve difficult problems. Efficient methods of searching large databases are also being investigated.

Knowledge-based systems are still at the research and development stage. The next few years will tell if they are able to provide useful and cost-effective services.

33.4 Applications of Expert Systems

■ A small number of expert systems are in use at present. These are mainly in the following fields:

- Medicine: Expert systems are in use for diagnosis and the planning of treatment in specialised fields. These include certain types of cancer, kidney diseases and some viral infections. Expert systems are also used to plan and monitor experiments, particularly in genetics. Expert systems for use by general practitioners in diagnosis and treatment are under development, but none are in widespread use at present.
- Geological Prospecting: Expert systems have already proved their worth in oil prospecting, and are now being used for other minerals.
- Designing Computer Configurations: Digital Equipment Corporation uses an expert system to design the computer configuration required when an order for a VAX minicomputer is placed. The expert system ensures that a compatible set of equipment is delivered, which meets the requirements of the customer.
- Chemistry: The analysis of chemical structures from mass spectrometer data is often done with the aid of an expert system.
- Legal Advice: Expert systems which give general legal advice, and assist in such matters as making Social Security claims, are at present under development.

33.5 Case Study 1: Mycin

■ The expert system **Mycin** was developed at Stanford University in the USA to assist doctors with advice on diagnosis and treatment of infectious diseases. The body of medical knowledge is stored in a form which includes a certainty value. This is a number in the range –1 to +1, where –1 means a negative association, and +1 means a definite positive association. A value near zero means that no correlation is known. For example:

Aids   HIV 1.0

which means that the virus HIV is associated with the disease Aids, with a certainty factor of 1.0.

The knowledge is processed by a set of **production rules** of the form:

if <condition> then <action>

At the start of a diagnosis, many of the items of knowledge are incomplete, or the certainty factors in them are near zero. During a diagnosis, additional knowledge is accumulated, and certainty factors move towards –1 or +1. The process is interactive. The physician enters background information and symptoms, and is then asked to give further information by the computer, as it requires it. At the end of the diagnosis, the conclusions are displayed, together with their certainty factors. At any stage, the line of reasoning and intermediate conclusions may be examined by the physician.

The approach pioneered by Mycin has been extended and modified for use in other medical expert systems. Mycin is available as an expert system shell – **Emycin** – which may be used in other medical fields.

33.6 Case Study 2: Prospector

■ **Prospector** was developed by SRI International in association with the US Geological Survey. It performs three tasks: the evaluation of geological resources in a region, checking for certain deposits at a site, and selecting the best sites for drilling.

Prospector does not draw as clear a distinction between knowledge and the rules for its processing as Mycin does. Prospector uses a set of **models**, one for each investigation. Items of knowledge are stored as spaces in a model, with an associated probability. The spaces are connected by rules, which have two numerical factors which determine their strength.

An analysis starts with the construction of a model to suit the situation. At the outset, many of the probabilities are unknown or very low. As the analysis proceeds, the values of the probabilities are updated. An inference mechanism, consisting of a set of **production rules** is used. It refers to a **semantic network** of basic geological knowledge in order to decide the sequence of rules to apply. The user interface is interactive: either the user or the expert system can initiate steps, by asking questions or supplying information. At any stage the user can ask Prospector to explain its current line of reasoning or intermediate conclusions.

Prospector, and expert systems like it, have proved their worth many times over in exploration, notably for oil. The cost of the computer system is a very small fraction of the costs of drilling a test well, and improved siting of production wells brings in greatly increased revenue.

33.7 Conclusion

■ The main points of this chapter are as follows:
- An expert system is the application of artificial intelligence to a

particular field of human expertise. A knowledge-based system draws inferences from a broad base of knowledge.

- Expert and knowledge-based systems deal with vague and incomplete knowledge, and must be able to explain their line of reasoning to users.
- Some expert systems have their expert knowledge fixed in them when they are constructed; others have a self-learning capacity.
- Application of expert systems include medicine, geological prospecting, chemical analysis, legal advice and computer-aided design.

Exercise 33

1 Briefly define the following terms: expert system; knowledge-based system; expert system shell; production rule; semantic network.

2 Give reasons for the use of programming languages such as Lisp and Prolog for expert and knowledge-based systems, rather than Pascal or Cobol.

3 Comment on the slow rate of acceptance of expert systems over the last twenty-five years.

4 Discuss the consequences of the widespread availability of medical expert systems for:
a) industrial countries
b) developing countries.

5 Discuss the consequences of the use of expert systems for the number of expert jobs available, and the nature of these jobs.

6 Significant expert systems in addition to those described in the text are:
Internist: general internal medicine
Dendral: analysis of chemical structures from mass spectrometer data
R1: configuration of minicomputer systems
Apes: general-purpose expert system shell.
Find out about one of these systems, and write a case study of it at the same level of detail as those in the chapter.

34 Applications Case Studies

This chapter covers five case studies of the application of computing in practice. They are:

- Rolls Royce Advanced Integrated Manufacturing System (Aims)
- Sony Music Manufacturing System
- Meteorological Office Atmospheric Model
- Solo 1400 Asic Design System
- London Underground Ticketing System (UTS)

These case studies have been chosen to illustrate the wide range of current computer applications, and to show how the general principles introduced in the rest of this book can be applied. They illustrate the benefits of the use of computers, in terms of improved productivity, efficiency and quality.

34.1 Rolls Royce Advanced Integrated Manufacturing System

■ The gas turbine engines which power commercial and military aircraft must satisfy the highest standards of manufacturing quality. They contain large numbers of components machined to fine tolerances. They operate for long periods, at extreme internal temperatures and in any kind of weather condition that may be encountered anywhere in the world, at any flying altitude. The lives of hundreds of passengers and crew depend on their safe running.

There are only three manufacturers of aviation gas turbine engines in the Western world. Competition between them is intense, in a market which is large and growing, as airlines expand to meet increasing demands for air travel. Manufacturers are under pressure to deliver large numbers of jet engines to tight schedules, at competitive prices, without any compromise on quality.

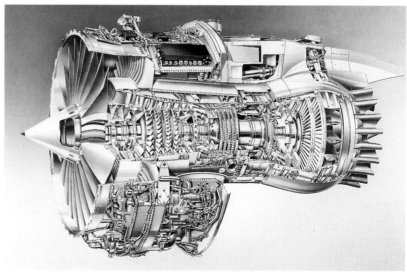

A cutaway view of a gas turbine, showing the turbine blades mounted on discs

Background

Rolls Royce is one of the three gas turbine manufacturers, the only one based in the UK. During the mid-1970s, it became apparent that its traditional manufacturing processes were too inefficient and time-consuming to allow it to continue to compete effectively in the international market. The long production cycle (around 26 weeks per engine) meant that large sums of money were tied up in work-in-progress. Forged raw materials were being supplied unnecessarily large, wasting time and money in machining away the surplus metal. Above all, it was not possible to respond in a flexible way to varying patterns of orders.

A gas turbine engine consists of a central shaft, on which rotate a number of rings of turbine blades. A key component of the assembly is the set of discs on which the blades are mounted. As shown in Figure 34.1, an engine has around eighteen discs, no two of which are identical. They are high-precision components, made from costly metal alloy forgings, and must withstand extremes of temperature and pressure with no distortion. Efficient production of these discs is essential for the cost-effectiveness of the whole engine production cycle.

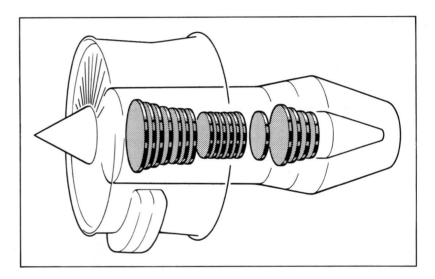

Figure 34.1
Schematic diagram of discs in gas turbine assembly

As a key element in its overall modernisation strategy, Rolls Royce decided to replace its existing production system for these discs with an **advanced integrated manufacturing system (Aims)**. This involved rationalisation of the machine tools, and bringing the entire disc production cycle under centralised computer control.

Objectives

The objectives of the Aims project were as follows:
1 To reduce the production cycle time from 26 to six weeks.
2 To increase productivity by over 40%
3 To reduce the value of work-in-progress by two thirds.
4 To achieve sufficent savings in the first full year of operation to cover the investment costs of the project.
5 To achieve a 'batch-of-one' production capability in order to respond quickly to customer requirements.

Strategy for Implementation

The means of achieving the above objectives were as follows:

1 Parts should be organised into family groups.
2 The number of machining operations should be reduced, and machine tools rationalised and standardised. Setting-up time for the machines should be greatly reduced.
3 All manufacturing processes should be integrated into a computer-controlled workflow and handling system.
4 Routine inspection should be automated as far as possible.
5 The new manufacturing facility should be built in existing workshops without disruption to on-going production.

This ambitious strategy was implemented in a number of phases, with Aims fully operatioinal by early 1986.

The Aims Installation

The Aims plant (Figure 34.2) is a self-contained manufacturing facility formed by merging a number of existing workshops. It consists of a number of processing cells, each with a computer-controlled machine for one stage of the disc shaping operation. Other areas are for electron beam welding, quality control inspections and tool storage. There is an automated rack storage system to hold parts between operations as required. Parts are transported by **automatically guided vehicles (AGVs)** between cells, and to or from the rack.

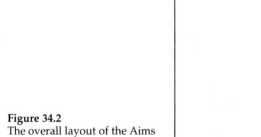

A general view of Aims installation.

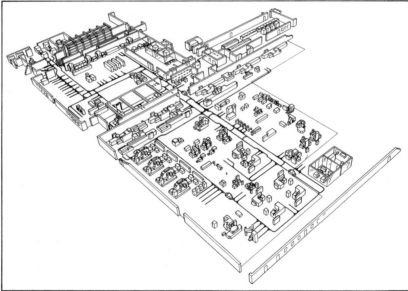

Figure 34.2
The overall layout of the Aims plant

The **numerically controlled (NC)** machine tools in the cells use fewer tools than the previous equipment, and can perform several operations simultaneously. They enable the metal forgings from which the discs are machined to be produced only slightly over-size, lowering raw material costs, and reducing the amount of waste which needs to be machined away.

Hardware Configuration

The real-time control and monitoring system for Aims (Figure 34.3) is based on a **central control system (CCS)** running on an IBM 8100 mid-

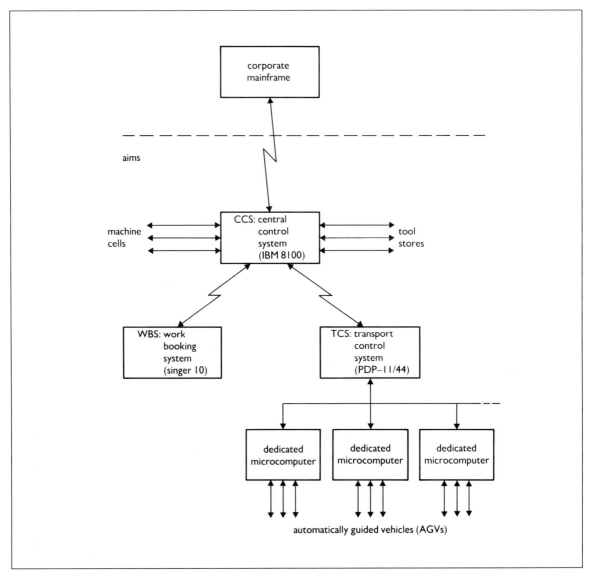

Figure 34.3
The configuration of the Aims computer hardware.

range computer. It has network links to the production cells and tool stores. It also has links to the **mechanised work booking (MWB)** system, running on a Singer 10 computer. The AGVs are controlled by the **transport control system (TCS)** running on a PDP-11/44, which connects to a number of dedicated microcomputers. These in turn communicate with the AGVs through wires buried in the floor. There are also network links with the corporate mainframe computer system.

System Software

The software for the control system was developed entirely in-house by a Rolls Royce team of software engineers. It is designed for real-time, non-stop operation, and was subjected to exhaustive tests before going live.

Operation of the System

The overall operation of Aims is illustrated in Figure 34.4.

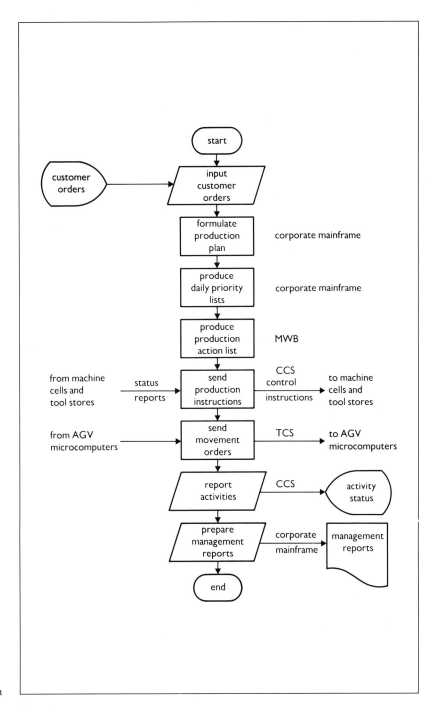

Figure 34.4
The Aims system flow diagram

Inputs

The primary inputs to the system are orders from customers for engines.
These are processed by the corporate mainframe, which takes into
account stock levels, available production capacity and the status of work
in progress. The mainframe produces a production plan, which is
translated into daily priority lists for Aims.

Processing

The daily priority lists are sent from the mainframe to the Aims central
control system, which passes them on to the MWB system. The

mechanised work booking system produces a detailed list of production actions, which is returned to the CCS. The CCS controls the implementation of this action list in real time. It sends instructions to the production cells, and movement orders to the transport control system. It provides details of tool requirements to the tool stores. The CCS receives status reports from the procesing cells, tools stores and TCS, which enable it to keep track of work in progress.

Outputs

In addition to the control instructions to the equipment, the CCS outputs details of production activities to terminals, for operators to check. It also feeds action reports back to the corporate mainframe, which summarises them into management reports. Reports are automatically generated of any equipment malfunctions, or any other problem which has interfered with the production schedules.

Assessment

Aims represents a major re-organisation of a key element in Rolls Royce's production facilities. It was necessary to ensure the continued commercial viability of the company. It required a change to flexible, automated production techniques as well as the introduction of computerised control and monitoring systems.

Aims was implemented on schedule, within budget and without interrupting on-going production. Although it involved major changes to working practices, it was achieved with the full co-operation of the workforce. The entire development and integration cost was repaid through efficiencies achieved within the first year of operation. Aims is an on-going process, with expansion of facilities and further integration of other parts of the manufacturing process taking place all the time.

Aims is an example of the three branches of information technology - computers, communications and control systems - being put to work to achieve a major enhancement to the capabilities of a world-standard industrial manufacturer.

34.2 Sony Music Manufacturing System

■ Sony is a worldwide organisation, dealing in a wide range of products and services. These include electronic consumer goods, manufacture and marketing of CDs, records and cassette tapes, and film production through its subsidiary company, Columbia Pictures. Sony Music is responsible for the manufacture and marketing of audio products worldwide. It operates in a very large, but very competitive market, where demands change extremely rapidly. An efficient, flexible business approach, capable of rapid response to changing circumstances, is essential.

Sony Music UK carries on the operations of the company in Britain, and is closely linked to the company's European operation. One of the major aspects of its work is record production. In addition to producing records and tapes carrying their own labels, Sony Music UK does the production and packaging for a number of other record companies. Production and distribution take place at a large facility in Aylesbury. Planning and overall management of the company is centred at the UK headquarters in London.

Computers in Sony Music

Computers play a vital part in the work of Sony Music. There is a large mainframe configuration in Aylesbury, linked to a microprocessor and other peripheral equipment in London, and to a number of peripheral devices at the manufacturing plant in Haarlem, Holland. In addition, there are terminals at several of the other companies for whom Sony Music produces records.

The computer system is designed for continuous operation, and supports a number of real-time transaction processing applications. The application chosen for this case study is the European Manufacturing

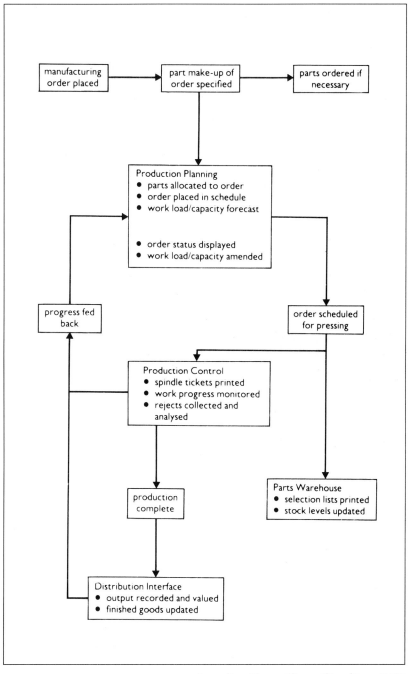

Figure 34.5
Sony Music manufacturing
order flow

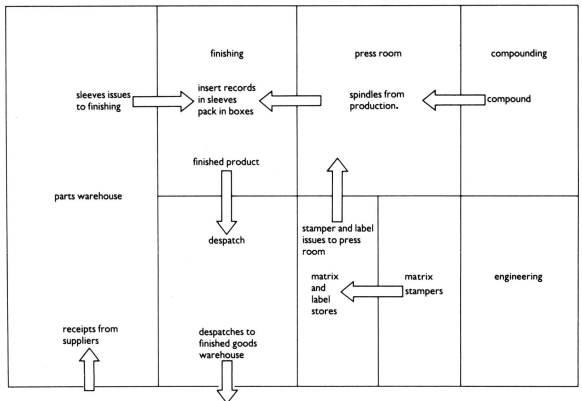

Figure 34.6
Sony Music stages of record
production

System. This system monitors all aspects of record and cassette production and CD finishing in the UK and Holland.

The detailed study of the system, presented in the following sections, refers to the computer applications centred at the Aylesbury manufacturing plant.

Objectives of the System

The system has a number of objectives, many of which are inter-related. The most significant objectives are as follows:

1 To provide an up-to-the-minute picture of the manufacturing situation, at a number of levels of detail:
   in broad outline, for central management and marketing personnel;
   at an intermediate level of detail, for production plant managers;
   in great detail for plant operators.
2 To monitor the progress of each batch of records through the various stages of production.
3 To monitor the performance of a number of key items of equipment, notably record presses.
4 To provide a comprehensive information service for the parts warehouse, which stores labels, posters, bags, inserts and sleeves for the records. This information enables all the parts required for a particular batch of records to be collected together as efficiently as possible.

Manufacturing Overview

In order to understand the role of the computer in record production, it is necessary to gain some idea of the operation as a whole. Figure 34.5 shows the overall flow of events during the manufacture of a batch of

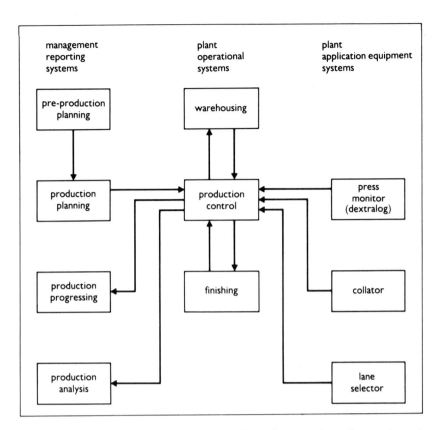

Figure 34.7
Sony Music computerised
monitoring system

records or cassette tapes. Notice that each product consists of a number of parts, such as the sleeve, the record label and any special promotional material, etc. Figure 34.6 shows the stages of the production of a record. The unit of production is a spindle of records (60 seven-inch singles or 30 LP's). A batch consists of a number of spindles.

The role of the computerised monitoring system is shown in Figure 34.7. Corresponding to the three levels of information mentioned in the objectives of the system, there are three aspects of the operation of the system. These are referred to as the Management Reporting Systems, the Plant Operational System and the Plant Application Equipment System in the diagram.

Four aspects of this system are discussed in more detail. These are the printing of spindle tickets (part of the production control operation), press monitoring (the Dextralog system), collating and lane selection, and warehousing.

Printing Spindle Tickets

When a batch of records is scheduled for pressing, a set of spindle tickets is printed for the batch. These tickets contain items of information to be entered manually as the spindle progresses through the various stages of production. They also contain the bar code used in collating the spindles into batches before finishing.

Spindle tickets are the means of recording all the data relating to the production planning, monitoring and control.

Record Press Monitoring: The Dextralog System

The Dextralog press monitoring system provides a number of services, including:

1 The allocation of batches to record presses.
2 Counting the records produced by each press.
3 If a press is idle, recording the reasons for its stoppage.
4 Forecasting when the end of a batch will be reached.
5 Receiving information about rejected records, and updating pressing quantities accordingly.
6 Providing real-time statistics on the progress of batches and the status of presses.

The hardware of the system includes sensors in each record press, a device on each press for entering the reason for stoppages, a colour monitor in the production control room showing the status of each press, nine terminals with simple keypads for displaying real-time statistics, and two multiplexers. Processing is carried out on a dedicated Nova 3 minicomputer, with 32K of main store. The Nova 3 has a data link to the IBM mainframe which processes the job and shift information.

Software consists of a module for each function of the system, synchronised by a simple transaction processing operating system. Each record press is polled by the operating system once every 20 seconds, to determine its status, and whether it has pressed a record since it was last polled. Various modules are then invoked to process the data thus obtained.

Requests from the terminals are treated with interrupts. Modules are invoked to deal with these requests, and to display the required information on the screen. All nine terminals work together, in other words a request from any terminal alters the display on all of them.

In general, the Dextralog system works extremely well. Its only shortcoming is the lack of data validation built into the system.

Collating and Lane Selection

When spindles of records have been pressed, they are loaded onto a ski-lift type conveyor belt to be transported to the finishing area. When the spindles arrive, they are collated (all the spindles of the same batch are collected together) and diverted to a lane for finishing.

Collating and lane selection is done on an automated racking system, together with controls on nearby conveyor belts. The control panel of this racking system is connected to a dedicated microprocessor, which controls the allocation of batches to racks, and the routing of incoming spindles accordingly, as well as the allocation of finishing lanes to batches, and the routing of outgoing spindles. Identifying data is read from the bar codes on the spindle tickets.

Warehousing

The real-time warehousing system provides the following services:

1 Allocating rack positions to stocks.
2 Locating stock items.
3 Producing lists of stocks to be dispatched for a particular batch of records, in such a way as to minimise the movements of the unloading hoists.
4 Updating stock levels.
5 Reporting all stock movements to the mainframe computers.

The system is based on an IBM mainframe and runs within the CICS tele-

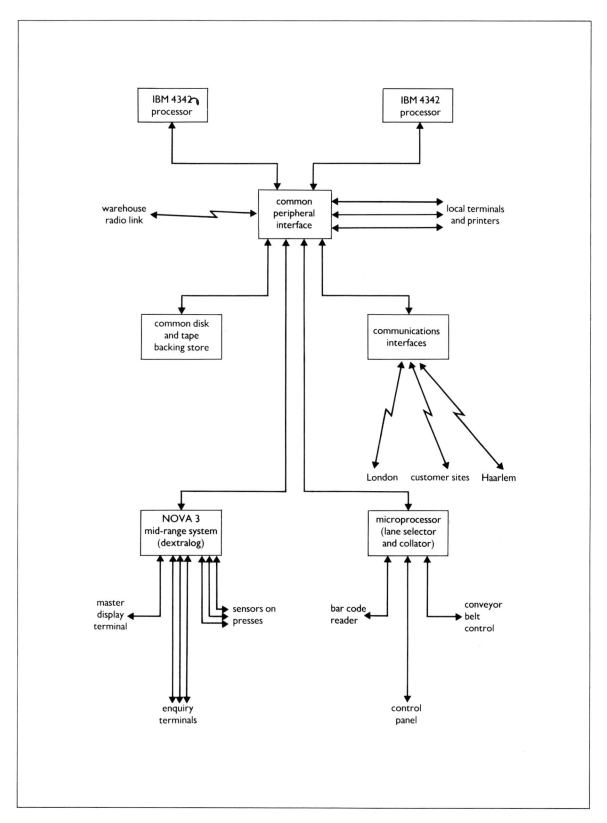

Figure 34.8
Sony Music hardware
configuration

processing operating system. All data is entered on-line in real time.

There are six trucks operating in the warehouse, which communicate with the mainframe computer by radio frequency channels. In this way instructions can be passed directly from the mainframe to operators within the warehouse.

Instructions are displayed on a two-row, 40-column vacuum flourescent display. Warehouse operators are able to reply to instructions on an alphanumeric keypad. In addition, requests for stock may be printed on a small side printer.

System Hardware

Figure 34.8 gives an overview of the hardware used by the Sony Music European manufacturing system. The hardware is designed for uninterrupted 24-hour-per-day operation. Accordingly, several essential components, including the central processing units and many communications links are duplicated. This spreads the processing load more evenly, and enables the system as a whole to continue to operate in the event of a failure of any single element.

Assessment

The computer system is an integral part of the workings of Sony Music. Should the system fail completely, there is no manual backup. In this event, record production and a number of other activities of the company are severely curtailed. The record of the computer system in this matter is very impressive. The system as a whole has been operational for more than 99 per cent of the time over the last few years.

The computer system enables Sony Music to maintain an extremely rapid, flexible and efficient record production process. The productivity per worker is very high. The computer system plays an essential part in maintaining Sony Music's leading position in a highly competitive field.

Postscript

The system described above was implemented in 1980 and ran until the closure of the vinyl record production unit in 1991. The warehouse and management system are still in use, for cassette production in Aylesbury and record and cassette production in Haarlem. At the time of closure, the system was still effective, providing up-to-the minute manufacturing information.

34.3 Meteorological Office Atmospheric Model

■ Computers are being used to an increasing extent to assist in weather forecasting. The computers receive and analyse weather reports from all over the world, and then run a simulation of the main trends in the atmosphere over a period of a few days ahead. The output from this simulation are used by the forecasters. In Britain, computer-assisted weather forecasting is done at two centres, the Meteorological Office at Bracknell and the European Centre for Medium Range Weather Forecasts at Reading. This case study is based on the work at the Meteorological Office, but the methods used at the medium range forecasting centre are very similar.

Objectives of Computer-Assisted Weather Forecasting

Computers are being used in weather forecasting in order to achieve the following aims:

- To improve the accuracy and reliability of weather forecasts, and enable then to cover a longer period into the future.
- To provide a wider range of weather forecasting services than was previously possible.
- To reduce costs by taking over most of the routine work of logging incoming weather reports, producing maps and maintaining weather records.

In order to achieve these aims, the computers carry out the following tasks:

- Receiving all incoming weather reports on a global data communications network, and storing this information in a database.
- Validating incoming data and transforming it into a form which is compatible with the atmospheric model.
- Using a complex mathematical model to run a simulation of the main physical processes in the earth's atmosphere, in order to predict the overall behaviour of the atmosphere for some days ahead.
- Communicating the results of the simulation to forecasters, regional weather centre computers and other users of the data.
- Preparing maps of weather reports and forecasts.

These tasks require a combination of data communications, graphics for the maps, database management for the reports and numerical processing to carry out the actual simulation. The whole cycle of events must take place quickly, in order to meet the deadlines required by he users of the forecasts.

Mathematical Models of the Earth's Atmosphere

The behaviour of the earth's atmosphere may be described by a **mathematical model**. A mathematical model is a set of equations which describes, in a simplified way, the behaviour of a physical system. The

Figure 34.9
The Meteorological Office atmospheric model

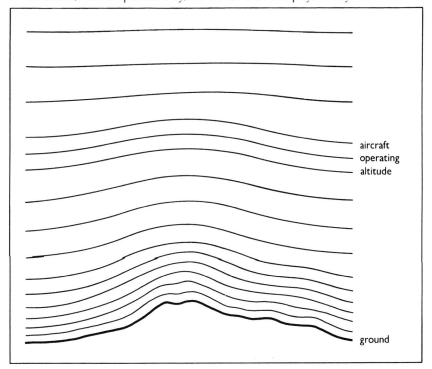

aircraft
operating
altitude

ground

equations in the atmospheric model enable the future state of the atmosphere to be calculated if its present state is known. They use the mathematical technique of **differential equations**. The basis of the model is as follows:

The earth's atmosphere is a continuous, approximately spherical layer of gas. It is bounded on one side by the earth's surface, which is of an irregular height and composition, and on the other side by space, with no definite edge. The most effective way to represent the atmosphere in a mathematical model is to regard it as a series of layers. The layers are not determined by altitude, but by the atmospheric pressure in the layer and that at the ground, in such a way that the layers follow the contours of the ground. See Figure 34.9. The Met Office atmospheric models use twenty layers, more closely spaced near the ground and at the commonest operating altitude of aircraft.

Within each layer, the atmosphere is regarded as a grid of points. The Met Office uses two models, the global model, which covers the whole world, and the regional model, which covers Europe and the North Atlantic. In the regional model (Figure 34.10), the grid points are spaced about 50 km apart. In the global model, the points at 5/6 of a degree of latitude and 5/4 of a degree of longitude, about 90 km apart on average, covering the entire surface of the earth.

At each point, the computer stores values of the wind speed and direction, temperature and humidity for each of the twenty layers, as well as the atmospheric pressure at ground (or sea) level. When these values are established for all the points on the grid at a certain time, a complex set of mathematical equations is used to calculate new values a short time later. The equations calculate the movements of air and the flows of energy between the grid points. In this way the model steps forward in small time intervals from the present state of the atmosphere into the future. Because of the large number of grid points, and the complexity of the equations, millions of calculations are needed to advance by each time step. Sophisticated numerical techniques have been developed by

Figure 34.10
Grid points in the Met Office regional model

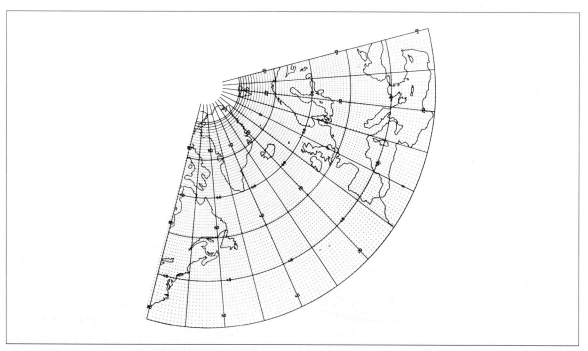

meteorologists in order to solve the equations as efficiently and precisely as possible. The same mathematical model is now used at Bracknell for forecasting and for research into climate.

Weather Forecasting Hardware and Software

Figure 34.11 shows the network of computers used to assist in weather forecasting at the Met Office in Bracknell. There are three types of computer in the network: communications processors, the front-end procesor and the main numerical processor.

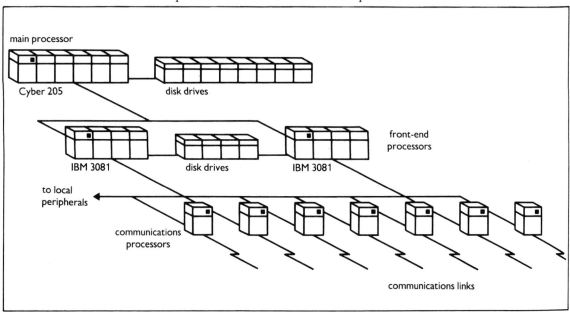

Figure 34.11
Meteorological Office
computer network

Communications processors

A number of small communications processors are used to handle the huge volume of incoming weather reports received at the Met Office. These reports come on the **Global Telecommunication System** run by the World Meteorological Organisation from weather stations, lighthouses, weather balloons, ships, aircraft and satellites. The communications processors also re-transmit received data and forecasts to other computers on the network. The communications processors pass on received data to the front-end processor.

Front-end processor

The IBM 3084 front-end processor receives the data from the communications processors, and validates it in several ways. In addition to the usual range checks, any data which differs too much from earlier values at the same place is rejected, as is any which differs by too much from adjacent reports. Any dubious reports are displayed on a screen for the meteorologists to decide whether or not to accept them.

The front-end processor then selects data in order to prepare a synoptic database for use by the main processor. Synoptic data is all measured at or very close to a certain time.

Another task of the front-end processor is to produce maps of observed and predicted data. These are either printed or appear as screen displays. The front-end processor has communications links to regional Met Office computers, which can also produce maps.

Main processor

The main processor at the Met Office is a Cray Y-MP/8 supercomputer. It is a very large mainframe computer designed for scientific work. It has eight processors, thus enabling different parts of the mathematical model to be calculated in parallel to achieve very rapid computations. The main memory of the Cray Y-MP/8 can hold 32 million items of data, each item occupying 64 bits. (The European Centre for Medium Range Weather Forecasts also has a Cray Y-MP/8 main processor.)

The main processor has two functions. The first is to use the synoptic database prepared by the front-end processor to work out the initial data values at the grid points. The second task is to step through the calculations of the mathematical model, and calculate new data values at the grid points. The results are returned to the front-end processor for maps to be drawn.

Software

The software controlling the three types of computer has been developed by the staff of the Meteorological Office over the years. It is based on sophisticated techniques for solving large numbers of complex equations as efficiently as possible. The computers must operate much faster than real time, in order to project the calculations into the future.

Computer-Assisted Weather Forecasting in Operation

The Met Office in Bracknell follows a fixed six-hourly cycle of operation to receive and analyse incoming weather reports, run the atmospheric simulations and produce weather forecasts. The cycles start at midnight, 0600, 1200 and 1800 GMT. The stages of a cycle are described below, using the timings for the one which starts at midnight GMT.

At midnight GMT, weather readings are taken by weather stations, high altitude balloons, ships, lighthouses and buoys all over the world. Readings taken by aircraft and satellites at times close to midnight GMT are used along with this synoptic data. The readings are relayed to the Met Office via the Global Telecommunications System. The data is received by the communications processors and passed on to the front-end processor. Here it is validated and added to the synoptic database.

At 0200 hours is the cut-off point for incoming data for the regional model. The main processor starts work on the synoptic database, analysing the data and working out the starting values for the grid points. None of the incoming reports are actually measured at the grid points. The first task of the main processor is to examine the available information near each grid point and obtain the values for each of the twenty layers at the point from it. The method of weighted averages is used. Some data (for example weather station or weather balloon data) is regarded as more accurate than other data (such as satellite data). When the analysis is complete, the results are returned to the front-end processors for maps of the reported weather to be drawn.

The main processor then starts work on the regional mathematical model. It moves forwards in steps of five minutes, and takes ten minutes of real time to advance the simulation by 36 hours. The state of the model at every three hours from the start is returned to the front-end processor for further maps to be drawn. One of the maps produced in this way is shown in Figure 34.12. It shows the central area of the regional model.

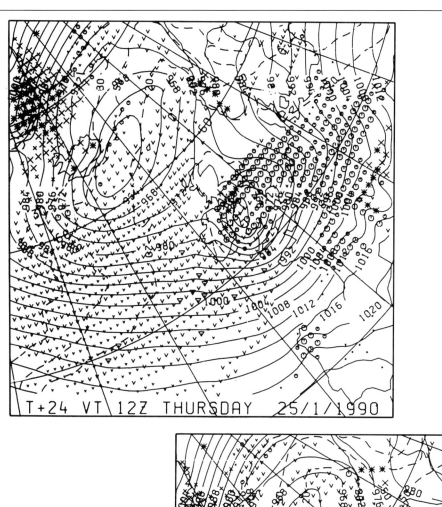

T+24 VT 12Z THURSDAY 25/1/1990

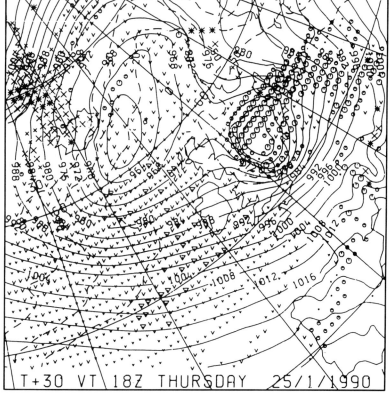

T+30 VT 18Z THURSDAY 25/1/1990

Figure 34.12
Output from the Met Office atmospheric model

The Chief Forecaster on duty uses these maps to produce the weather forecasts. He uses his knowledge and experience of meteorology to interpret the maps, and to decide to what extent to rely on the computer output. The first map (for 0300 hours) is checked against the latest weather reports and satellite photographs to see if the general trends predicted are actually occurring. When the overall weather situation has been decided by the forecaster, the details of the forecast are added to the computer results. For example, the regional model does not at present take account of fog, and does not distinguish all the various forms of precipitation such as rain, hail or snow. Thunderstorms are also not adequately predicted by the computer. However, the forecaster can also refer to a more detailed model, covering the United Kingdom, for guidance on these details. When this work has been done, the official Met Office forecast is issued.

In the meantime, at 0320 hours, the cutoff point for incoming reports for the global simulation model is reached. This data originates from all over the world, hence the longer collection time. The data is added to the synoptic database for midnight, and is checked and analysed as before. The main processor sets to work on the global model, this time advancing in time intervals of ten minutes. The global model is run for a period of six days ahead, taking 40 minutes for the actual processing. At regular intervals, results are transferred to the front-end processor for maps to be drawn. These maps are used by the forecasters on duty in the preparation of longer term forecasts. They are compared with similar maps from the computers at the European Centre for Medium Range Weather Forecasts.

The output from the regional and global models is transmitted to regional Met Office computers. These centres have facilities for producing maps, and issue their own regional forecasts. The output is also transmitted directly to several computers belonging to airlines. The data is used in the preparation of flight plans by the airlines' computers. There are direct links with computers belonging to the BBC and other television companies, which enable some of the weather maps seen on television to be produced from the Met Office computer output.

Assessment

The nature of the earth's atmosphere is such that completely accurate weather forecasts are impossible in practice. In spite of the complexity of the mathematical models, they are inevitably a simplified description of the physical processes involved. More significantly, the weather reports on which the models are based are incomplete. The best that can be hoped for is a continuing improvement in the reliability of forecasts with the introduction of more powerful computers.

The Met Office mathematical models in use at present, and the computers which run them, are the fourth generation in operational service. They replaced a simpler model and a less powerful main computer in 1990. There is no doubt that the new computers are helping to produce more accurate and longer term forecasts. Most runs of the global model provide useful information up to five days ahead. The range of forecasting services which can be provided is also increasing. Detailed forecasts can now be requested for specific events where the weather is critical, such as the assembly of a North Sea oil platform.

There was criticism of the Met Office when it failed to give adequate warning of the severe storm which struck the UK in October 1987. Since that time, the mathematical models have been updated to improve their representation of storm situations, and the computer system has been upgraded with the replacement of the main and front-end processors. An improved performance was evident in early 1990, when a sequence of severe storms was accurately forecast, but much still depends on the availability of crucial obeservations on any particular occasion.

Although the costs of the forecasting computers are very high, the savings brought about by improvements in weather forecasting are higher. An increase of only a few percent in the value of a harvest is worth a very large sum of money. Aircraft flight paths are planned on the basis of weather forecasts, and the saving of fuel and time resulting from more accurate forecasts is significant. Improvements in safety of motoring, shipping and aviation have undoubtedly saved many lives. Better weather forecasts have led to great savings in the costs of North Sea oil production. Severe storms are a feature of some British winters, and accurate forecasting of them will limit damage and save lives.

34.4 Solo 1400 Asic Design System

■ Integrated circuits are some of the most complex artefacts ever produced. The complexity of a VLSI chip is comparable to that of the road network of a large city - condensed into an area of about 10 mm square. Designing a device of this complexity, with any degree of assurance that it will function correctly, is impossible without the aid of computer systems.

Computer-aided design (CAD) systems for the design of silicon chips have evolved over the years, to the point where they are now able to transform a design automatically from an input as a logic schematic (Section 6.4) to a layout of transistors which will implement the logic function in silicon. This process of **silicon compilation** is the key facility in the CAD systems now in use for integrated circuit design.

The silicon CAD system chosen for this case study is the Solo 1400 system produced by European Silicon Structures (ES2), a pan-European company which has a silicon fabrication plant in the south of France. ES2 specialises in application-specific integrated circuits (Asics), manufactured in small or large batches. Solo 1400 combines all the facilities required for the design of an integrated circuit in a single software package. It is intended for use by a single engineer, taking a design through all its stages from initial schematic entry to submission for fabrication.

Objectives

Solo 1400 has the following objectives:

1 To enable design engineers to enter the logical specification of an application-specific integrated circuit as a set of schematics. The design may include on-chip RAM, ROM, multiplier and **PLA (programmed logic array)** blocks.
2 To simulate the behaviour of the device in response to a set of input stimuli provided by the designer. Simulation results are provided as truth tables and as waveforms, showing the states of inputs, outputs and any selected internal signals.
3 To transform the logical specification of the device into a physical arrangement of transistors in rows and columns, incorporating the blocks into the arrangement. The connections between the elements are established automatically, using routing channels between the rows and columns of transistors.

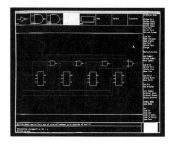

A logic schematic on a Solo 1400 display screen.

4 To provide facilities for the design engineer to modify the automatic layout of the device if required.

5 To check that the design matches the requirements of the fabrication plant before it is submitted for fabrication.

These specific objectives have an underlying aim in common:

To enable electronic system designers, who in the past have used standard integrated circuits to construct electronic systems on printed circuit boards, to move to Asic-based designs. A single Asic replaces a large number of standard chips, and leads to major reductions in the size and cost of an electronic system.

Operation of the System

Figure 34.13 shows the overall stages of an Asic design. Note that the order of certain steps is not significant, but that both simlation and physical design must be complete before the final validation step.

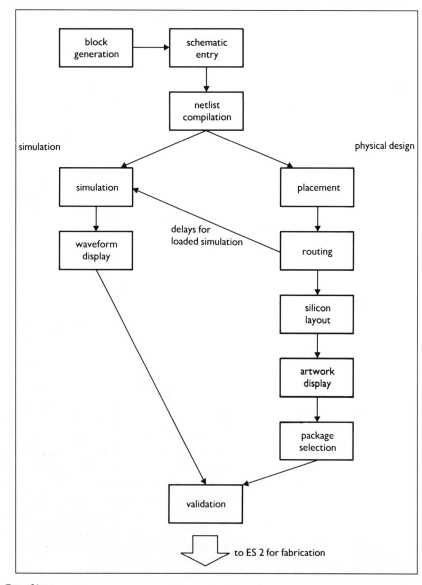

Figure 34.13
Solo 1400 Asic design flow

360 Applications Case Studies

Design Entry

The logical function of an integrated circuit is entered at the start of the design cycle. If the design includes any ROM, RAM, multiplier or PLA blocks, these are first generated. To do this, the required inputs and outputs are specified, and a truth table is entered which specifies the contents of a ROM or the function of a PLA.

The **schematics** forming the design as a whole are then entered. These form a hierarchy. At the lowest level are the basic logic gates (AND, OR, NOT, etc.) and flip-flops (D-type flip-flop, etc.) which are implemented directly in silicon. These are selected from the libraries provided with Solo 1400, placed in logic schematics, and connected together as required. Generated blocks are also included. The inputs and outputs of the schematic are marked and given names.

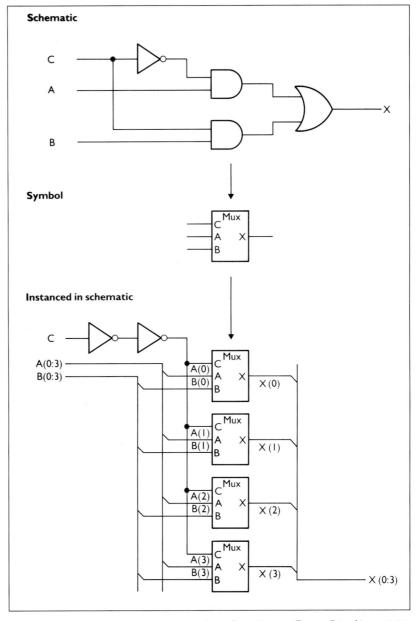

Figure 34.14
Hierarchy of schematics and symbols

A **symbol** is then generated from the schematic. This has the same inputs and outputs as the schematic, but none of the internal logic. The symbol may then be placed in a higher-level schematic, where it represents the logical function specified in its schematic. In this way, a hierarchy is built up, with lower-level schematics (which represent simple functional units such as registers) implemented in higher-level schematics for the more complex operations performed by the device. The top-level schematic includes the primary input/output connections which are placed around the perimeter of the chip.

Figure 34.14 illustrates the idea of a hierarchy of schematics and symbols. The benefits of this hierarchical approach include the elimination of duplicated elements, and a reduction in the complexity of the design. Instead of having to understand (and locate errors in) a single, very large schematic, the design engineer has a set of schematics, each specifying one aspect of the function of the device. The complexity of each individual schematic is manageable.

Schematic entry is done entirely on-screen. The screen represents a sheet of drawing paper, with a grid of points added to assist alignment. Schematics may be printed on a digital plotter or laser printer.

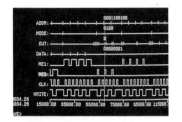

A solo set of 1400 simulation results displayed as a waveform.

Design Compilation

When schematic entry is complete, the design is transformed into an equivalent text form, which is then compiled into a **netlist**. The netlist itemises all the elements in the design, and the connections between them. It is the central representation of the design, used for both simulation and physical layout.

Simulation

In order to check that the device, as entered, will function correctly when fabricated, its behaviour is **simulated**. The engineer makes up a set of **stimuli**, which is a table of input values at different times or a concise equivalent written in a programming language. These are supplied to the simulator, which uses the netlist and the properties of the library elements to calculate the state of each signal in the circuit over the time period of the simulation. The simulator works quickly, but not nearly as fast as the actual device will work. Times are expressed in nanoseconds (one thousand million nanoseconds is one second).

The states of input, output and selected internal signals can be viewed in graphical form as a **waveform**. The waveform has time as the horizontal axis, and each wave showing as a high, low or (occasionally) unknown state as a function of time. The same waveform would be obtained by connecting the fabricated device to an oscilloscope. Alternatively, the simulation outputs may be produced in the form of a truth table.

Simulation results are checked against the required operation of the circuit. The schematic is modified, re-compiled and re-simulated until the circuit behaves precisely as intended.

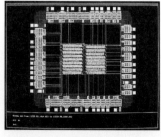

The physical layout of an integrated circuit as displayed by the solo 1400 artwork viewing facility.

Physical Design

When the simulation results are satisfactory, the device is taken through the automatic placement and routing steps to obtain the layout of transistors, ROM, RAM, multiplier and PLA blocks, and input/output connections. This process may be fully automatic, or the design engineer may intervene at various points to alter the arrangement produced

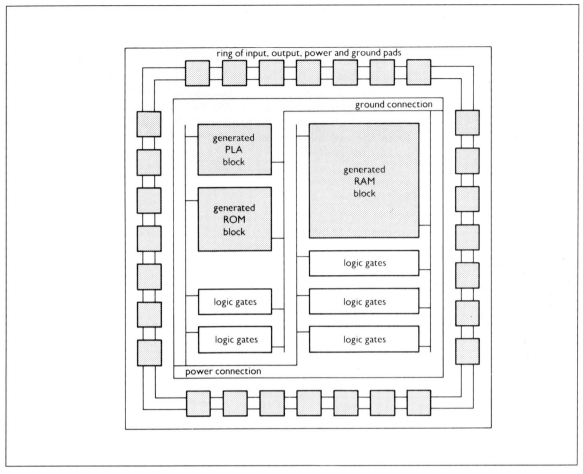

ring of input, output, power and ground pads

ground connection

generated
PLA
block

generated
RAM
block

generated
ROM
block

logic gates

logic gates

logic gates

logic gates

logic gates

power connection

Figure 34.15
Solo 1400 silicon layout

automatically. The device is set out in rows and columns of transistors, with row widths adjusted if necessary to match any ROM, RAM, multiplier or PLA blocks. See Figure 34.15.

The objective of physical design is to obtain a layout in the minimum area, and as nearly square as possible. An additional constraint is the cavity in the package selected for the device. The silicon must fit into this cavity, with the correct number of input/output connections along each side.

The final artwork showing the arrangement of the layers of treated silicon and metal interconnections is displayed on the screen. The artwork viewing facility has zoom features to examine selected portions of the artwork, and selected layers may also be examined on their own.

The input/output connections are arranged around the periphery of the device. The engineer may interchange these, in order to match the connections on the selected package. Once the input/output configuration has been established, and the internal layout completed, a **bonding diagram**, specifying the wiring between the input/output connections and the package, is produced.

If any problems become evident during physical design, modifications are made to the schematic to correct them. The simulation must be re-run to check the functionality of the modified design, and the physical design steps repeated. When the physical design is complete, the simulation is repeated, taking into account the additional signal delays due to the routing channels.

Validation and Fabrication

When both physical design and simulation are satisfactory, the design is put through a number of **validation routines**, to ensure that it is suitable for fabrication, and that the simulation stimuli can be used to test the devices when they have been fabricated.

When all these checks have been passed, the design is copied onto a magnetic tape for submission to ES2. ES2 engineers perform additional checks and carry out certain preparatory work before sending the design to the fabrication plant. Silicon is delivered within a few weeks of the submission of the design.

Software Structure

Solo 1400 is an integrated suite of separate programs, each performing one step of the design cycle. A large number of files are built up, describing various aspects of the device. These include the schematics, netlist, simulation inputs and results, physical layout, bonding diagram, etc. Programs read from and write to these files as required. The complete database of files is submitted to ES2 when the device is fabricated.

User Interface

Solo 1400 has a user interface which incorporates a certain measure of artificial intelligence. Details of the design are contained in a large number of variables, which are assigend values as a design progresses. Each facility is invoked by issuing a command. The facility uses the variables which apply to it in order to locate the required files, and determine the conditions under which it should operate. Additional variables may be set during the process. A log is kept of every operation, recording whether it succeeded or failed, and noting the values of the variables used.

There are a number of rules governing the values of variables, and which values (or combinations of values) are valid for a design to be fabricated. These rules may be checked at any time, and are all checked during the final validation phase.

The intelligent user interface gives the engineer facilities to check the outcome of design operations that have already been performed. The current values of all variables can be examined, and the rule checking capability makes it possible to see what design phases remain to be completed. These facilities are of great assistance during the complex procedure of designing and integrated circuit.

Hardware

Solo 1400 can be run on an IBM PC fitted with an additional graphics control card, running under MS-DOS. The commonest hardware configuration is a Sun or Hewlett-Packard workstation, running under Unix. In all cases, a Winchester disk is required to hold the software and design database, as well as a high-resolution graphics screen. A variety of types of plotter is supported.

Assessment

Solo 1400 provides a complete range of facilities for the design of VLSI chip. It is powerful, but straightforward to use. It is intended for use by engineers who may have little previous experience of silicon chip design, having used ready-made integrated circuits in the past to build up designs on printed circuit boards.

The widespread acceptance of Solo 1400, both in the electronics industry and at universities, indicates that its approach is sound. There is evidence of a move away from electronic systems designed using standard chips on a printed circuit board to custom-designed Asics, such as those designed using Solo 1400. Solo 1400 is making a substantial contribution to the number of designs submitted for fabrication at the ES2 plant.

34.5 London Underground Ticketing System

■ The London Underground is one of the busiest public transport networks in the world. During the last decade, passenger journeys have increased steadily, to the point where the system is overloaded at certain stations during peak hours. Concerns have been expressed over passenger safety, and staff shortages are an on-going problem. Ticket fraud - passengers travelling without tickets, with invalid tickets, or beyond the validity of their tickets – is another major concern.

In response to the growth in usage, and to the problems noted above, London Underground has undertaken a major programme of re-furbishment and extension, covering all the stations in the central area. At the same time, an automated ticketing system has been introduced for the entire network.

Backgound

A prototype for the new system was tested at a trial station (Vauxhall) during 1982/1983. The full **Underground Ticketing System (UTS)** was developed and implemented during the next five years. It is based on a highly distributed network of computers and dedicated electronic devices at Underground stations and at the operational centre in Baker Street. The UTS and the tickets it issues are compatible with a similar system introduced by British Rail at the same time.

Objectives

The UTS has the following objectives:

1 To speed up the sale and checking of tickets.
2 To reduce ticket fraud.
3 To improve staff security when handling money from fares.
4 To provide individual accountability for booking clerks.
5 To provide centralised accounting of ticket sales.
6 To provide centralised reporting of management statistics.

Strategy for Implementation

The UTS is based on credit-card sized tickets, printed at the time of issue on the front, and with a magnetic strip on their reverse side, encoded with corresponding information. These are issued by booking clerks using ticket office machines, or by passenger-operated ticket machines. They are read by automatic gates on entry to or exit from a station, and by hand-held machines operated by ticket inspectors. Season tickets are printed on more durable paper than that used for single-journey tickets.

All the electronic devices in the system are connected by a network, but are capable of operating stand-alone for a considerable period of time if the network link fails. In a system which collects large sums of money in cash, security is critical. Access to equipment is strictly controlled by

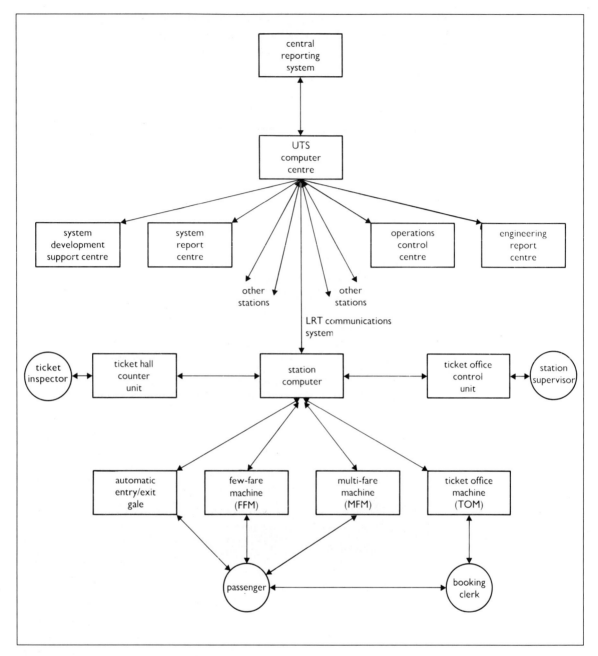

Figure 34.16
London Transport UTS
configuration

means of magnetically encoded staff identity cards and personal identity numbers **(PINs)**.

System Configuration

The UTS consists of a set of electronic equipment at each station, linked via the London Regional Transport (LRT) communications network to the UTS computer centre at Baker Street. This is in turn linked to the LRT central reporting system at Newmann Street.

Station Equipment

The equipment at each station is centred around a station computer which acts as the communications interface with the LRT network. It

A passenger using an
automatic ticket machine

receives information such as revised fares and operating policies from the UTS computer centre, and sends back reports on the status of all equipment at the station, and accounting information.

Within the ticket office there is a ticket office control unit for use by the station supervisor, and externally there is a ticket hall control unit for use by travelling ticket inspectors. These can be used to send commands to devices, and to access account information from the ticket issuing machines. They can also be used to send and receive messages to and from the central computer.

There are three types of ticket issuing machine:

- **Ticket office machines (TOMs)** are used by booking clerks to issue all types of tickets, including season tickets. These may have an automatic change dispenser attached.
- **Multi-fare machines** are operated by passengers. They sell tickets for any journey on the Undergound system, and for a selected number of British rail destinations. They can accept coins and £5.00 notes, and give change.
- **Few-fare machines** are quicker for passengers to operate than multi-fare machines, but sell a limited range of tickets. They accept coins only in payment.

All types of ticket vending machines keep records of all transactions, and can produce accounting and other reports when requested by an authorised member of staff. Reports are also transmitted electronically via the communications network. They can operate in stand-alone mode until their internal transaction memories become full.

Each station in the central area contains an array of automatic gates appropriate to the layout of the station, and to the volume of passengers. Gate are entry-only, exit-only or reversible. Gates allow passengers to move into or out of the station.

A gate is activated by a passenger inserting a ticket into the slot. The magnetic strip on the ticket is read. If the ticket is valid, a record is added to the strip, the gate opens, and the ticket is returned to the passenger. If the validity of the ticket expires at the station, the gate opens but the ticket is retained. If the ticket is not valid, a message is displayed, the gate remains closed, and the ticket is returned to the passenger unaltered. The gates have a number of infra-red detectors to check the movement of the passenger through them.

Each gate records details of all tickets which pass through it. This information is transmitted to the station computer, from which the gate receives tables of fares and operating policies. The gate can operate in stand-alone mode if the data link fails. In the event of a power failure, the gate opens, and internal data is retained by battery reserve power.

Each station also has at least one manual gate for use by passengers who are unable to operate the automatic gates. These gates are operated by staff members.

Central Computers

The UTS computer centre has three central processors, designed for non-stop operation. If one breaks down, its processing load can be shared by the other two. The three processors are networked to the station computers, and support four report and control centres:

- The system report centre handles all operational data coming from the stations: transactions details, accounting reports, etc.

- The operations control centre consists of five pairs of terminals. Four are for the operating divisions, the fifth is for overall control, and to provide a backup. This centre receives status reports of the equipment, and can send messages to all stations, as well as downloading information onto ticket machines and gates.
- The engineering report centre deals with fault information from anywhere in the system. Faults are logged and repairs initiated from this centre.
- The system development report centre is responsible for updating fares and operational policies, and sending this information via the network to the stations. It also handles updates to the software.

The UTS central computers are linked to the LRT central reporting system which is based on an IBM mainframe. This sends all accounting information to the LRT revenue accounts office, and reports to management of rail operations, planning and maintenance.

System Software

The UTS system is based on a number of special-purpose devices, based on dedicated microprocessors. The software for the system was developed under a turnkey contract by a software house, using its own equipment. The cross-compiled code was then downloaded onto the dedicated microprocessors. The software is all transaction processing code, running in real time. It is designed for a large volume of similar transactions, each of which is completed quickly.

The software was tested exhaustively before the system became operational, as a serious software failure could put the system out of action. However, the local nature of the processing makes the system resilient against hardware or software failures.

System Operation

The UTS system operates in real time for about 20 out of every 24 hours. It has a peak throughput of thousands of transactions per minute. It records several million items of data in every daily cycle.

Every passenger journey is monitored, from the sale of the ticket, to entry and exit through the gates, until the ticket is captured when its validity expires. Equipment responds within a few seconds to an input. Failures are reported automatically, and most items are able to operate stand-alone if they become isolated from the network.

An audit trail is maintained of all transactions. This means that accounts are created and stored at several levels of the system, and then summarised to higher levels. Accounts are reconciled against bank statements which give details of the cash banked. Any errors can be traced back to the point where they first occurred.

Assessment

The UTS represents a changeover from a manual to a large, complex computerised system running an integral part of the operation of London Underground. Initial reaction by passengers was mixed: the automatic gates were perceived as somewhat hostile, and concern has been expressed over evacuation of a station in the event of a fire or other emergency.

However, passengers appreciate the improved ticket purchase facilities, and the generally faster passage into and out of stations. The compatibility with British Rail tickets, and the availability of through tickets covering rail and Undergound journeys saves a lot of time. Fewer staff are needed to operate the system than previously, which has helped to solve the problem of staff shortages. One of the major objectives of the system, the reduction of ticket fraud, has undoubtedly been achieved.

Exercise 34

1 Identify the hardware and software elements of the Rolls Royce Aims system which can be classified as:
   a) computers
   b) communications systems
   c) control systems.
2 a) What were the business reasons for introducing the Aims system at Rolls Royce?
   b) What were the benefits to the company when the system was in operation?
   c) What would the consequences have been if the new system had not been installed?
3 Briefly describe the progress of a batch of records through the Sony Music manufacturing system. Mention each interaction of the batch of records with the computer system.
4 What are the consequences to Sony Music of a breakdown in its computerised manufacturing system?
5 What is the main source of errors in the Met Office atmospheric model? Give some suggestions for reducing the errors from this source.
6 What are the advantages and disadvantages of representing the state of the earth's atmosphere by values of variables at a finite set of grid points?
7 Discuss the benefits of a vector processing computer architecture when processing a complex mathematical model such as that used for weather forecasting.
8 Discuss the consequences of the availablility of reliable long-term weather forecasts for each of the following activities:
   a) agriculture
   b) civil aviation
   c) merchant shipping
   d) off-shore oil production
   e) gas and electricity supply systems
   f) tourism.
9 Assume that it is possible to link a home or school microcomputer to the Met Office computer network. State what information could usefully be transferred to the micro, how the information could be processed, and how it would be displayed or printed. Sketch some examples of the screen displays and printouts which would be produced.
10 What are the benefits of using a single application-specific integrated circuit over a number of standard circuits on a printed circuit board?
11 Summarise the main stages of the design of an Asic using Solo 1400.
12 Explain what is meant by silicon compilation, using Solo 1400 as an example.
13 a) What is meant by a hierarchy of schematics and symbols in specifying the function of an integrated circuit?
   b) What are the benefits of hierarchical design?
14 Explain the operation of a simulator in a silicon CAD system such as Solo 1400. Why is it esential to include a simulator in such a system?
15 Which objectives of the London Underground automated ticket system relate to services to the passengers, and which relate to administrative improvements? Comment on your answers.
16 The London Underground ticket system is an example of a system which can continue to operate when parts of it are disabled. Give examples of this capability, and discuss its importance in a system of this nature.

17 Give some examples of special-purpose computers and control systems in use in the London Underground ticket system. Discuss the advantages (and any disadvantages) of using special-purpose equipment rather than general-purpose computers with special-purpose software.

18 Comment on the degree of dependence of the organisations mentioned in these case studies on their computer systems.

19 Using a computer application of your choice, conduct a study of the workings of the system. Use the same general approach as in this chapter, and write a report of your findings.

35 The Computing Industry

A modern industrial estate, showing the premises of a number of IT companies. Sites like this are becoming a major source of industrial activity

It has been widely predicted that by the year 2000, information technology will have become the world's largest single industry. As a whole, the computing industry encompasses a wide range of activities. It provides employment for a large number of people, and is becoming an increasingly important element in the economy of all developed countries. In spite of upheavals from time to time, computing is one of the few industries which is growing steadily through economic cycles of growth, inflation and recession.

This chapter describes, in outline, the current state of the computing industry. As far as possible, a worldwide perspective is maintained. Various aspects of the manufacture and use of computer systems are covered, as well as some of the service industries which have grown up around computing. The principal types of work in the industry are discussed.

35.1 The World Computing Situation

■ From a world viewpoint, the computing industry is currently dominated by a struggle between the USA and Japan for the leading position. There are big readjustments taking place in Europe, as companies in the region attempt to keep their places in the world IT league, and to make a common market for IT goods and services.

The leading organisations in information technology are all transnational companies, with research and development sites, production plants, sales offices and support centres all over the world. A computer system purchased by a user is likely to have been designed in one country, and assembled in another using components brought in from all over the world. When assessing the world computing situation on a regional basis, the international nature of the major IT companies needs to be borne in mind.

The USA – the Centre of Gravity

The centre of gravity of the computing industry is undoubtedly the United States of America. Here, computer systems and software are designed, produced and used in the greatest numbers. The USA has the most highly developed user market for IT products in administration, commerce and industry. It is the home of a number of multinational computer manufacturing companies.

The USA is a world leader in one of the most important aspects of computer development, namely the design and production of VLSI chips. Much of this activity is centred in California, in an area known as Silicon Valley. Integrated circuit development and manufacture tends to be a cyclic business, with years of expansion followed by cutbacks and recession. A number of silicon vendors have flourished, only to go out of business or be taken over.

The UK and Europe – Software Expertise

Although a certain amount of design and manufacture of integrated circuits and computers takes place in the UK and Europe, the strength in this region is in the software area. Program language design, and systems and applications software development are the subjects of intense activity at universities, software houses, computer manufacturers and user installations.

Concern has been expressed in recent years over the worsening balance of trade in IT goods and services in the UK, and the fact that an increasing proportion of the IT companies which are based there are subsidiaries of American or Japanese multinational corporations. In Europe there is increasing emphasis on collaborative projects involving academics and companies from more than one country. These are helping to strengthen the position of the European IT community against competition from the USA and Japan.

Japan and the Pacific Rim – Significant Growth

Japan's proven ability to produce large volumes of high quality manufactured goods is extending into the computing field. A number of Japanese manufacturers are now producing a wide range of computing equipment. Production of electronic components for computers is an extension of the country's established electronics manufacturing capability.

Japan is now advancing from its traditional role as a perfector and mass producer of high-technology goods to that of an innovator. An increasing amount of new product development is taking place in Japan in all areas of information technology, and Japan's share of the world IT market is increasing. Japan's weakest area is software, but rapid progress is being made in that field.

Japan is the leading member of an emerging industrial bloc - the Pacific Rim, including countries such as Singapore, Hong Kong, Malaysia and South Korea. In these countries, the combination of relatively low wages and access to information technology is helping to create a base of high-technology industries, and associated banking and financial services, which is becoming significant on the world scale.

OPEC Countries – Rapid Implementation

The shift of wealth to oil producing countries in recent years has led to many of these nations embarking on ambitious development programmes. Many of these programmes include the importation of large, sophisticated computing systems, usually from the UK, Europe or the USA. Particularly strong application areas include defence, civil administration, hospitals and industrial production. The oil industry itself is a major user of computers. Many computer workers have been enticed to these areas by large, tax-free salaries and extremely attractive fringe benefits. However, the political and social instability in these regions is a major hindrance to their development, both in the computing field and in other areas.

The rate of growth of IT in this region is now slowing down, as the price of oil fluctuates, and the political problems and frequent conflicts between countries in these areas have their effects.

Developing Countries – A Slow Start

Most developing countries have made an extremely slow start in the use of computers. The point has been made that computers are helping to widen the gap between industrial and developing nations.

There are a number of reasons for the lack of widespread use of computers in the Third World. The most significant reason is a lack of applications. Most work in developing countries is labour-intensive, and little would be gained by the use of computers. Other reasons include a lack of expertise, minimal service and support facilities, political and social factors which lead to a distrust of Western products, and a chronic shortage of finance. The poor quality of the basic infrastructure, particularly power supplies and telecommunications, is an additional problem.

How this situation will change in the future is the subject of debate. It seems fairly likely that a number of factors will combine to keep the spread of computers in these countries to a very slow pace. However, should this pace increase, the Third World will become an enormous market for the whole range of computer products and services. The first major change is likely to be in telecommunications. A number of developing countries are in the process of planning or installing advanced digital telecommunications networks. These may help to create the infrastructure needed for further technological advances.

The USSR, Eastern Europe and China – Opening Doors

Although research and development in computing takes place in Communist countries on a large scale, in the past there has been little co-operation between these countries and the West in the field of information technology.

The USSR and Eastern Europe have had a policy of producing a unified range of computer equipment, with each country responsible for the development and production of certain units in the range. It appears that hardware development in these countries is several years behind that in the West. Microprocessors are just beginning to be produced, while such devices as floppy disk drives still have to be imported from the West. However, on the software side, particularly in scientific and mathematical programming, these countries are second to none.

Since the breakdown of relations between the USSR and China in 1961, China has pursued an independent course in computer development. For a variety of reasons, including political pressure, development has, until recently, been slow. Emphasis is on scientific, military and industrial applications. In recent years, pressure has been exerted within China to introduce new methods of working in all fields, including the use of new technology. This change of policy is taking some time to take effect, but it could lead to a significant increase in the use of computers. The takeover of Hong Kong by China in 1997 will give China access to some of the most sophisticated computers in existence.

There were a number of reasons for the lack of co-operation between East and West in the field of computers. By far the most prominent was mutual distrust, as computers are a vital part of modern military systems, particularly nuclear weapons systems. Computer sales from most Western nations to Communist countries have to be approved by government agencies. The regulations which govern these transactions were tightened a few years ago, to include software and even manuals. There was a desire in Communist countries to develop their own high technology products, and not to be dependent on imports from the West. There was also a lack of Western currency with which to pay for the computers.

How this situation will change with improving relations between East and West remains to be seen, but early indications are of a relaxation of export restrictions, improved collaboration at academic and research level, and joint training schemes. The next stage is likely to be joint production ventures, using Western technology under licence to produce IT equipment in the East.

35.2 The Computing Industry by Activities

■ One of the most significant activities within the computing industry is the manufacture of computer systems. The next few sections examine various aspects of hardware and software development.

Research

The importance of research to computing can be seen by the amount of money allocated to it, both by governments and by companies. All computer manufacturers, and many computer service companies, have research divisions. A large proportion of the income of these companies is allocated to these divisions. Some of the research is at the most fundamental level of semiconductor technology and computing theory, looking many years into the future.

Most universities, colleges and polytechnics have Computing Science departments. These departments have both a teaching and a research function. Unlike the situation in many other fields, there is generally close co-operation between the academic world and the industrial and commercial world in computing research. This has proved fruitful in the past, and will no doubt continue to be so.

Original Equipment Manufacture

The raw materials of computers are integrated circuits and other electronic components, cathode ray tubes for VDU screens, keyboards, plugs, casings and a large number of other components. Companies which make these components are called **original equipment manufacturers (OEMs)**. There are many of these firms, but the most significant of them are the manufacturers of microprocessors, RAMs, ROMs and other very large scale integrated circuits. Among the leading companies in this field are Motorola, Intel, Zilog, Rockwell and Texas Instruments in the USA, Fujistu, Hitachi and NEC in Japan, and Ferranti, Mullard, Inmos and European Silicon Structures (ES2) in Europe.

Mainframes

Some of the largest corporations in the computing industry are those engaged in the design, development and manufacture of mainframe computers and associated software. A few of these manufacturers rank among the largest corporations of any kind in the world.

The leading company in this area, in terms of income, number of computers sold, number of employees and profit, is **International Business Machines (IBM)**. Based in the USA, but with branches all over the world, including agencies in Moscow and Peking, IBM has built up a sales and support network second to none. When electronic computers were first developed, during and after the Second World War, IBM was already an established manufacturer of office equipment. Although it was somewhat slow in moving into computers, once it entered the market, it soon reached a position of dominance which has never been challenged. It is the leading corporation in both the mainframe and the microcomputer markets.

Other prominent USA-based computer manufacturers are **Unisys**, **Honeywell**, **Cray**, **NCR**, **Amdahl** and **Control Data Corporation**. The leading UK firm in this field is **International Computers Limited** (ICL) (now under Japanese ownership). In Japan IT companies include **Fujitsu**, **Hitachi** and **Nippon Electric Company** (NEC).

Although the strength of the companies mentioned in this section is in mainframe manufacture, many of them also supply mid-range systems and microcomputers, as well as systems and applications software. The tendency is also increasing to sell a computer as part of a hardware-plus-software package.

Mid-range Systems

In spite of the pressure from workstations and microcomputers, the market for mid-range systems does not appear to be declining significantly. Mid-range systems are also benefiting from the availability of cheap VLSI chips. They are now able to provide facilities which a few years ago were confined to mainframes.

As in the case of mainframes, the most significant manufacturers of mid-range systems are based in the USA. **Digital Equipment Corporation (DEC)**, producer of VAX computers, is the most prominent. **Hewlett-Packard** and **Data General** are other important mid-range system manufacturers.

Workstations

Workstations are the most recent class of computers to enter the market, and their growth in numbers has been the most rapid as the market establishes itself. The leading supplier is the USA-based **Sun Microsystems**, with competition from Hewlett-Packard.

Microcomputers

Another rapid growth area in the field of computing is microcomputers. Performances are increasing and prices keep low as a number of manufacturers compete in a potentially huge market. All the companies engaged in this area are far too numerous to mention, and a number have only stayed in business for a short time. A few of the significant ones are as follows: **IBM**, **Compaq**, **Apple**, **Atari**, **Commodore** and **Radio Shack** in the USA; **Research Machines**, **Amstrad**, **Apricot** and **Acorn** in the UK; and **Toshiba**, **Sharp**, **Canon**, **Epson** and **Sony** in Japan.

Dedicated Microprocessors

In addition to being used in microcomputers, microprocessors are being incorporated into a growing number of other products. These products include calculators, watches, cameras, automatic production equipment, industrial robots, word processors, banking terminals, motor vehicles, satellites, ships, aircraft, railway locomotives and juke boxes. Some of these products are produced by computer manufacturers. The rest are helping to keep a large number of other companies in business. This is a rapidly expanding field, with enormous potential for further development.

Peripherals

In the early days of computing, it was the usual practice for all the units of a computer system to be produced by the same manufacturer. These days it is becoming increasingly common for a computer installation to be assembled from units made by a number of different manufacturers. The peripherals used in these systems are **plug-compatible** with the processors. In other words, they can be connected directly to the processors, without any interfacing adjustments needing to be made. The widespread use of standard interfaces is accelerating this trend.

The continued growth of computing, and the introduction of new types of peripherals, is creating a large market for peripheral equipment and media. A number of manufacturers are currently engaged in this area. Among the most prominent are **Memorex**, the USA-based magnetic disk manufacturer, **Amdahl**, a producer of plug-compatible processors which link to IBM equipment, and **Epson**, a Japanese manufacturer of printers and other peripherals.

Software Development

In terms of the number of people employed and the revenue generated, software development is comparable to that of OEM and hardware development. Broadly speaking, software is developed by three categories of organisation: hardware developers, independent software vendors and users.

Hardware developers are responsible mainly for the systems software which is an integral part of the systems they supply. Independent software developers are in two groups: suppliers of custom-designed software to individual clients, and software package developers. The former fall into the category of computer services.

Computer Services

A large number of companies are engaged in some form of computer services. These companies are also known as **software houses**, **systems houses** and **computer bureaux**. Although the individual companies tend to be smaller than hardware manufacturers, together they form a substantial industry in their own right.

These companies provide a wide range of services, including standard software packages, consultancy, custom-built software and the hire of computing equipment. The phrase **turnkey contract** is used to describe the arrangement whereby a computer service company provides a complete, ready-to-use computer system, designed to the specifications of a customer. Consultancy is provided in such areas as computer systems design, management of projects, office automation, program design, purchase of computer equipment, marketing and the forecasting of future trends. Prominent UK software houses include **Logica** and **CMG**.

Software Package Suppliers

The main share of the vast market for software packages has been captured by a small number of prominent, USA-based corporations. Most are based on a single range of products, which is updated regularly. Large teams of software engineers and marketing staff work to develop and support each release of the package, which is generally sold through chains of distributors worldwide. Examples of software package vendors include **Ashton Tate** (databases), **Lotus** (integrated packages), **WordStar** (word processing), **Aldus** (desktop publishing) and, the largest of them all, **Microsoft** (operating systems and a range of applications packages).

Computer Media Suppliers

The computing industry supports a large number of suppliers of computer media. Traditional media such as printer paper are still in demand, though their market is beginning to dwindle. However, there is an increasing demand for magnetic disks and tapes, microfiches, OCR stationary, pre-printed stationery for computer output, and a large number of other products. As new devices come into use, a market is created for media to supply these devices. The majority of disk and tape suppliers are Japanese companies, such as **Maxell** and **Dysan**.

**35.3
Working in the
Computing
Industry**

■ The various branches of the computing industry described in previous sections are significant employers. The majority of the jobs are for highly skilled engineers, sales and marketing staff, managers and other professionals. An increasing number of jobs related to the application of computing require a combination of technical and business skills.

Integrated Circuit Manufacture

Integrated circuits designed and developed by electronics engineers, and fabricated by highly skilled workers using sophisticated equipment. Computers are used in the design, manufacture and testing of these circuits.

Computer System Manufacture

The complete process of designing and constructing a computer is extremely complex, and involves the work of a number of people. The stages are generally as described in the following sections.

Research

Most computer manufacturers have a research department, investigating new computer architectures, new hardware devices, new software techniques and new computer applications. Scientists, research engineers and technicians, as well as highly skilled software engineers are among the staff of these departments.

Design

The overall design of a new computer, or series of computers, is in the hands of computer architects. Detailed circuit design is in the hands of electronics engineers. Computers are designed from both the hardware and the software point of view. Accordingly, systems programmers, who write the systems software for the computer, are also involved in the design process.

Construction

Highly skilled production workers are responsible for the various stages of construction and assembly of units. Production lines are only used for small systems. Generally, a team of workers is assigned to take a unit through all stages of construction and exhaustive testing.

Sales

This computer sales rep. is giving a presentation to potential customers.

One of the highest paid jobs in computing is that of computer salesman. Salesmen operate in an intensely competitive environment, where their level of pay depends to some extent on their sales figures. The process of selling a large computer system can take several months.

Installation and Maintenance

Field engineers are responsible for the installation and commissioning of new computer units, and the maintenance and repair of systems in operation. With many computers running 24 hours a day, this type of work often involves calls at unsocial hours.

A Data Processing Department

Traditionally, an organisation which uses a computer has a data processing department, containing all the staff who work directly with the computer. A typical reporting structure for a large data processing department is shown in Figure 35.1. Other departments and individuals in an organisation relate to the data processing department as users of the computing equipment. The description of a data processing department given here applies in particular to large user organisations such as banks, insurance companies, airlines and many central and local government departments.

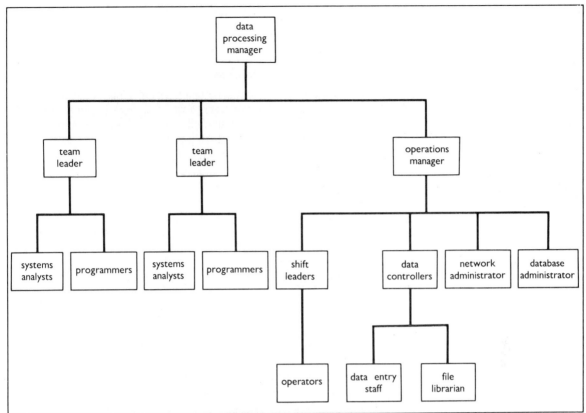

Figure 35.1
A data processing department

In overall charge of a data processing department is a **data processing manager**. Responsibilities of a data processing manager include formulation of policy, approval of projects, staff recruitment and maintaining the relationship of the department with the rest of the company.

The work of a data processing department has two aspects, namely the program development aspect, and the operations aspect. On the program development side, **systems analysts** are responsible for steering each project through the software design cycle, as described in Chapter 26. **Programmers**, more properly called **applications programmers** in this context, are responsible for writing, correcting and maintaining programs, and producing various items of documentation, explaining how programs are used. However, the work of systems analysis and programmers is gradually merging into the profession of **software engineering**, as described in Chapter 25.

On the operation side, there is an **operations manager** in charge of scheduling the use of the computer, arranging for maintenance and ordering supplies. A team of **operators** man the computer room, often working in shifts under shift leaders. More about the work of a computer operator is to be found in Section 22.5.

The flow of data to and from the computer is sometimes supervised by **data controllers**, who ensure that the right data is available at the right time. **Data entry staff** operate data entry terminals to keep up the supply of data to the computer. In some large computer systems, **file librarians** are responsible for the large numbers of magnetic tapes and magnetic disks used.

If the computer supports a database, then a **database administrator** is in charge of this aspect of the work. The responsibilities of a database administrator are discussed in Section 30.4. If a data communication network is used, this is often under the overall charge of a network administrator.

New Directions in Job Definitions

In many user organisations, computers have become such an integral part of their operations that a separate data processing department is not required. This applies particularly to medium-sized companies in insurance, finance, engineering, architecture and the travel industry. The majority of the employees in such organisations make some use of the computer. They are trained to use the software they require, either in-house, or on courses provided by the hardware or software manufacturers. Programming and systems design is contracted out to software houses, or standard software packages are purchased. Overall responsibility for the computer system is assigned to a **system manager**.

Software Houses

Many software houses have extremely flexible working arrangements, falling broadly under the heading of software engineering. Most of their employees are skilled in a variety of areas, including systems and applications programming, system analysis, project management and computer design. A team of software engineers is assigned to each project which is undertaken. Work is shared among the members of the team according to their interests, capabilities and experience. There is no strict demarcation of jobs. When a project has been completed, the team is disbanded. Engineers are assigned to other projects.

35.4 Users and User Groups

■ The majority of industrial and commercial organisations in the Western world are computer users. Most of these organisations are irrevocably committed to computers. In other words, they would be unable to continue to operate without their computer systems.

Many computer users are members of user groups. Each group generally represents the users of a particular type of computer. These groups enable users to discuss problems of mutual concern, and enable them to bring pressure on computer manufacturers to rectify faults which the users have found with their systems.

35.5 Professional Associations

■ As computing has spread to involve the work of more and more people, a number of associations have been formed to represent the interests of people who work with computers in various ways. Most prominent of these organisations are the **British Computer Society (BCS)** and **National Computing Centre (NCC)**, in the UK, the **Association for Computing Machinery (ACM)** in the USA and the **International Federation for Information Processing (IFIP)**.

Although each of these organisations has a unique character, their activities cover similar areas. Their most significant activities include the following:

1 Holding conferences, meetings and seminars on a variety of topics relating to computing. Some of these topics are very specialised, others are much broader issues, such as computers and privacy.

2 Publishing journals, weekly and monthly bulletins and newsletters, as

well as books and pamphlets on matter relating to computers. Some of these publications are the accepted means of communicating new developments in computer research. Others contain news, editorial comments, product advertisements and advertisements of job vacancies in the computing field.

3 The creation and maintenance of standards and codes of practice for the computing industry.

4 Promoting debate on issues relating to the use of computers, such as privacy and unemployment, and giving evidence to Commissions of Enquiry into these issues.

5 Providing an informal meeting place for their members.

These organisations have helped to enhance the status of the computing industry, and provide an invaluable internal safeguard against abuses of the power of computers.

35.6 Conclusion

■ This chapter has provided a survey of the most significant aspects of the computing industry. It is an industry which includes a number of different activities. Indeed, much of its strength is in its diversity. Although it has reached the age of maturity, it retains its youthful optimism, and is still growing vigorously.

The main points of this chapter are as follows:

- IT is a worldwide activity, with all the leading organisations involved being transnational companies.
- The USA is the world leader in information technology, but its position is being increasingly challenged by Japan.
- Britain and the rest of Europe are struggling to maintain their position as a front-rank IT region.
- The rapid pace of IT implementation in OPEC countries is now slowing down.
- IT is gradually gaining acceptance in the Third World.
- The Eastern Bloc is striving to keep up with the West in IT, but the level of co-operation between the two regions has until recently been low.
- The IT industry can be divided into the following areas of activity: original equipment manufacture, user product manufacture (mainframes, minis, micros and peripherals), software development, computer services and computer media supplies.
- Contact between IT professionals is maintained through professional associations.

Exercise 35

1 Briefly define the following terms: OEM; plug-compatible; turnkey contract.

2 Outline the work done by each of the following: electronics engineer; systems programmer; computer architect; field engineer; data processing manager; systems analyst; applications programmer; operations manager; data controller; file librarian; database administrator; software engineer; network administrator; system manager.

3 a) Compare and contrast the computing situations in the USA and the USSR.

b) Suggest some reasons for the emergence of the USA as the world leader in computer manufacture.

c) Suggest some reasons for the rapid Japanese penetration into the computer market.

d) Give your views on the role of computers in Third World countries.

e) How have improving relations between Eastern and Western countries influenced the development of computing in the East?

4 Summarise, in about 100 words, the most significant activities in the computing industry.

5 Investigate one or more of the professional associations mentioned in Section 35.5. Write a report listing its activities, publications and areas of interest.

6 Select a major industrial activity such as motor car production, steel making or nuclear energy. Write an overview of the industry, using similar categories to the ones in this chapter. Then compare the industry with the computing industry, mentioning in particular relative rates of growth and future prospects.

7 A small number of computer architects are responsible for the majority of the computer designs in use today. These include Gene Amdahl (IBM 360 and 370 series), Seymore Cray (Cray-1 and Cray-2) and Stephen Jobs (Apple II and Apple Macintosh). Find out more about the work of one or more of these computer architects.

8 Suggest one or more possible career paths for someone who starts working in the computing field as an applications programmer.

9 The list of data processing jobs mentioned in this chapter is not exhaustive. By studying the computer press, or some other suitable source, identify some jobs not described here. Write brief accounts of the nature of these jobs.

10 One of the prime requirements for a job in the computing field is experience. This makes it difficult for new graduates, or people transferring from other areas of work, to obtain their first job in computing. Investigate this situation and comment on it.

11 The computing industry has the lowest membership of Trade Unions of any industrial sector in the UK and other countries. Find out more about this situation, and comment on it.

36 Computing in Perspective

This chapter investigates the economic and social consequences of the widespread acceptance of information technology since the end of the Second World War. It draws some general conclusions from specific information given in a number of previous chapters, notably the various case studies. Where possible, a worldwide point of view is maintained, though the situation in the United Kingdom is often used as an example.

Some of the material introduced here is contentious, and may become increasingly so in the future. It is impossible to be completely unbiased in presenting such material. The best that can be done is, wherever possible, to present both sides of an argument. Several questions in the exercise at the end of the chapter invite you to form and clarify your own opinions on the topics presented.

Industrial plants like this, using computerised production techniques, have the benefits of quality, flexibilty and lower costs.

36.1 Economic Reasons for Computerisation

■ Computers, communications equipment and control systems are installed in commercial and industrial organisations for reasons of quality, profitability and growth, and in administrations for reasons of efficiency and cost savings. In many cases, the change to IT represents a risk to the viability of the company: without the introduction of new techniques, the company will no longer be competitive in its markets, and if the IT strategy fails, the company will be unable to recover its investment in the new equipment. The future success of the company depends on its successful transition to information technology.

As is made clear in several case studies, the substantial investment in IT equipment has a limited payback period for it to be cost-effective. For a successful project, such as the Rolls Royce Aims system, the payback period is short – less than a year. Most IT investment is expected to pay off in under five years, and then generate significant revenues in subsequent years.

36.2 Effects on Organisations and Individuals

Reporters and editorial staff at work in the offices of a newspaper. They are using a network of word processors and page makeup terminals. The introduction of IT has resulted in completely new working practices in the newspaper industry

■ The introduction of IT generally has a profound effect on the way an organisation operates. Experience has shown that it is seldom useful to automate existing methods of working. What is required is to re-evaluate the entire business operation, and plan a new method of operation in order to make the most of the introduction of new technology.

This can involve changes in work practices, new reporting structures, new management styles, and new methods of accounting. One of the most significant examples of this change in work practices was the change to word processors and desktop publishing by all the national UK newspapers. This involved new premises, equipment, work practices and management structures, the disappearance of large numbers of jobs, and, after a period of industrial unrest, new relationships between management and Trade Unions. Motor vehicle manufacturers and steelworks have also undergone changes as far-reaching and sometimes as disruptive as these. Banks, insurance companies, building societies and travel companies are some examples where similar, though somewhat less disruptive, changes have accompanied the introduction of IT.

For the individuals involved, these changes have meant re-training, learning to use new equipment, understanding new management techniques and, in some cases, working different hours. In other cases, these changes have meant redundancy, particularly for staff near to retiring age.

These changes in working practices in turn have caused changes in education and training courses. There is no point in training people to jobs which no longer exist, or to use obsolete equipment. The increased flexibility of working hours which new technology brings to many jobs, as well as the overall reduction in working time, has led to new patterns of work and leisure. Much of the employment created by IT is (or can be) part-time, opening up new opportunities for mothers of young children to return to work. Another consequence is that people are taking far more short holidays (over a long weekend, for example) than was the case a few years ago. Activity-based holidays are becoming increasingly popular.

36.3 Employment and Unemployment

■ It is an inescapable fact that computers and electronic control systems put people out of work. The motor vehicle industry is a significant example of this. But on the other hand, computers create jobs, both directly and indirectly. Jobs created directly include those of all the people who design, construct, program and operate computers. They form a large, prosperous and growing industry. By their contribution to efficiency and productivity, computers create and preserve jobs in an indirect way. Again, the motor industry is an example: without the introduction of new technology, many motor vehicle manufacturers would have gone out of business.

The net effect of this is that computers are changing the nature of employment. Jobs have been lost in manual and semi-skilled areas, and created in skilled and professional areas. Jobs have been lost in traditional manufacturing industries, and being created in service industries. This implies that a shift in training patterns, and considerable retraining of displaced workers is necessary, as one attempt to cope with the problem.

In the present economic climate, computers are not the only cause of unemployment. Inflation, recession, changes in interest rates, currency fluctuations and changing patterns of demand are far bigger causes. For these reasons, studies of the unemployment that has been caused by computers, and projections of the unemployment that computers will cause, are contradictory. Few firm conclusions can be drawn from them.

Each application of computers must be judged on its merits, from the point of view of employment and unemployment. In all cases, it is necessary to take a broad view of the situation, in an attempt to see the long term effects, and wider implications, of the introduction of computers for a particular application.

36.4 Privacy of Personal Data

■ It has been estimated that the average citizen of a Western country has personal data stored about him/herself on about 25 different computer systems. These include computers at banks, hospitals, tax offices, employers, driving and television licence centres and, in some cases, the police. This raises a number of questions: Who should have access to this information? How safe is this information against unauthorised disclosure?

Although manual methods of storing personal information have been in operation for a long time, the widespread use of computers for this purpose makes the problem of unauthorised disclosure potentially far more serious. In theory, it is now possible to obtain millions of items of personal information in a few seconds.

There are in fact two aspects to this problem: the deliberate disclosure of information by the people or organisations which store it, and the 'theft' of this information by outsiders. The latter issue comes under the heading of data security.

With regard to the first aspect of the problem, most Western countries now have legislation regulating the storage and dissemination of personal information. Countries in the European Community are obliged to pass laws in accordance with a set of guidelines on the subject. In Britain, the Data Protection Act of 1984 is now fully implemented. It created a register of all users of computerised personal information. In terms of the Act, users must declare all the purposes for which they intend to use the data, and data subjects have a right of access to their records. Certain police and national security systems are exempt from the Act. Although there have been only a handful of prosecutions under the Data Protection Act, most of the concern on this issue has been centred on the disclosure of personal information by police forces. There have been calls for the Act to be extended to cover data held on police computers.

36.5 Security of Data

■ In recent years, the press has been full of stories of 'hackers' who have managed to break into supposedly secure computer systems and extract or alter information in them. Although the scale of this problem is possibly less than these stories would suggest, security of stored data is a serious problem. Various attempts have been made to provide adequate security for stored data. These include 'scrambling' the data into a code, limiting access to computers and terminals, and systems of passwords for people 'logging on' to the system. Systems with direct access by users to computers with sensitive information, such as cash terminals linked to bank computers, have generally proved to be secure.

A related and more serious problem is that of 'virus' software. A virus is a program which is introduced into a computer system surreptitiously. A virus program is activated when a certain date (such as Friday 13th) is reached, or a certain sequence of instructions is entered. When the virus runs, it can have a number of effects, such as erasure of data or disabling the operating system of the computer. The virus also makes copies of itself, hence its name. Virus software can be spread when disks are passed from one computer to another, or via networks.

Security software which attempts to detect and erase viruses in a computer system is available, but new and better-hidden viruses are being developed all the time. There have been a number of prosecutions of programmers responsible for serious damage to computer systems by virus software.

The accident at the Chernobyl nuclear reactor highlights the potential consequences of the failure of an electronic control system.

36.6 Consequences of System Failures

■ The accident at the Chernobyl nuclear reactor in the USSR in 1986, which caused at least 300 deaths and devastating consequences to the surrounding area, is the worst example to date of the failure of a control system. It was not caused by a computer failure, but by the deliberate over-riding of the automatic control and safety system by operators. However, it serves as a warning of the possible consequences of the failure of a computer system. All nuclear reactors in Western countries have computer-based control systems, supervised by operators.

Nuclear reactors are not the only computer-controlled systems where safety is critical. Aircraft such as the Airbus A330 use 'fly-by-wire' control systems, with no mechanical linkage between the pilots and the control surfaces or engines. All control is via a network of microprocessor-based control units, with a high level of redundancy. The automatic landing systems used in reduced visibility are another example of safety-critical electronic systems in the aviation industry.

The hardware and software used in safety-critical systems is tested with utmost rigour during development. Formal methods of software development are often used for these applications. Nevertheless, there is concern whether the required standards are high enough when large numbers of people's lives are at stake.

36.7 Computer Crime

■ Almost all financial information held by banks, building societies and other financial institutions is stored on computers. The majority of transactions, especially those involving large sums of money, take place by electronic funds transfer (EFT). The benefit of EFT is the speed and simplicity of transactions, and the lack of paperwork; the disadvantage is the reduced level of security. When transactions required documents to be completed and sent by post or messenger, there was time for careful, independent checks. When transactions are done on-screen in a few seconds, checks are less thorough.

This lower level of security is providing opportunities for a new breed of criminal: the computer fraudster. Computer fraud involves the theft of money by setting up illicit transactions via EFT. Sums of money can be large, and dishonest employees are sometimes involved.

Financial institutions are reluctant to give details of the amounts of money involved, or the methods used for these transactions, for fear of highlighting weaknesses in their computer security. It is also difficult for police forces, unused to EFT systems and practices, to identify the criminals, and present sufficient evidence to a court to secure a conviction. In spite of these problems, there have been a number of convictions for computer fraud in recent years.

36.8 Computers and Political Control

■ One of the most sinister applications of computers is their use by security forces of a number of states, to store and process information about terrorists, spies, subversives and other 'persons of interest' to these forces. Indirect evidence suggests that this is a widespread computer application, though official confirmation of the existence of these computers is rare.

The problem is that there are no public safeguards on the use of such computers. Most people would agree that every available resource needs to be used against spies and terrorists, but where does one draw the line? There is also evidence that so much information is gathered by some of these systems that it is impossible to sort out the vital from the trivial.

36.9 Political Consequences of Computerisation

■ The widespread use of information technology in industry, commerce and public administration leads to significant improvements in efficiency and productivity. It makes a substantial contribution to the prosperity and economic strength of a country. At the same time, the use of IT in its armed forces gives the country a substantial military advantage.

This combination of industrial and military strength arising from the use of advanced information technology has political consequences. It is one of the reasons for the dominance of a small number of industrial countries over the world economic and political situation, and for the wide gap between the influence of industrial and Third World countries. It lies behind the emergence of nations on the Pacific rim as economic powers. It is also one of the underlying reasons for the rejection of socialist policies by East European countries during the late 1980s, and their moves towards market economies.

36.10 Computers in a World of Change

■ It has been pointed out since the days of ancient China that the only constant fact about civilisation is that it is changing. This section is an attempt to give a very brief assessment of the forces of change which are currently in operation, and identify the place of information technology among these forces.

It seems that the pressure for change currently at work fall into five very broad categories. These are political and religious pressure, resource pressure, population pressure, pollution pressure and technological pressure. Each of these is briefly discussed below.

Political and Religious Pressure

Both religious and political views incline people to have visions of the kind of society in which they want to live. In some countries, these pressures have their outlet in the political institutions of the state. Changes occur from time to time, but without too much dislocation or upheaval.

However, there are also numerous instances where political and/or religious motivation has led to terrorism, civil wars, forcible changes of government and conflicts of all types between and within states. Many such conflicts remain unresolved today, and in many parts of the world, no stable solutions are in sight. The ever-increasing power of available weapons, including nuclear weapons, is an additional factor which compounds the seriousness of these problems.

Political and religious pressure is the oldest and most visible force for change at present in operation. But it must now take its place among other pressures, and be affected by them.

Resource Pressure

Over the last few decades it has become apparent that a number of the earth's natural resources are becoming seriously depleted, and some will be completely used up in the foreseeable future if present trends in the consumption of these resources continue.

The most obvious resource in this category is oil. Oil producing countries have realised the degree of dependence of industrialised nations on their output, and the fact that their reserves are limited. In spite of new discoveries and reductions in demand, the price of oil is being pushed gradually higher, with a number of consequences for both producers and consumers.

Other minerals, including a number of metals, are being depleted at an alarming rate. Renewable resources like timber and fish stocks are being used up faster than they can replenish themselves. Species of plants and animals are becoming extinct, depleting once and for all the 'pool' of genetic material available on earth.

The deliberate destruction of rainforests in South America is causing the irreplaceable loss of a natural resource.

Resource pressure is forcing a change in the way of life of many people. Its worst effects are being felt by poor and underprivileged individuals and nations at the present time, but it will begin to affect everyone in the near future.

Population Pressure

In spite of a number of efforts to control it, the global population is increasing at a disturbing rate. The largest increases are occurring in the poorest countries. It is almost impossible for world food production to keep pace with population growth. The result is that North America and Europe have grain surpluses, wine lakes and butter mountains, while much of the rest of the world has malnutrition and famine.

Population pressure is a factor in the miserable way of life of a significant proportion of the people of the world. It may yet demand a change in the way of life of the rest before a more satisfactory state of affairs is reached.

Pollution Pressure

It is becoming increasingly clear that harmful substances are being released, by a number of industrial processes, into the air, water and ground which are beyond the capacity of the environment to absorb. In spite of considerable success in some areas, notably the control of air pollution in certain European cities, the problem of pollution is becoming worse. Certain enclosed seas such as the Baltic and the Mediterranean are in danger of losing their capacity to support marine life. A number of European forests are in danger of destruction by acid rain. An increasing number of poisons are present in air, water and food supplies. The percentage of carbon dioxide in the atmosphere is slowly but steadily increasing.

Most pollution is being caused by industrial nations. The ex-socialist countries of Eastern Europe have particularly bad records. Pollution pressure is forcing these countries to change in a number of ways. Industrial, agricultural and domestic practices are having to adjust to increasingly stringent regulations. If certain types of air and water pollution are not brought under control in the fairly near future, the consequences could be extremely serious.

Technology has a profound influence on the lives of people with access to it.

Technological Pressure

Ever since the industrial revolution two centuries ago, technology has been the driving force in the evolution of Western societies. Each major breakthrough has had profound social repercussions. Furthermore, it appears that the pace of technological innovation is quickening.

Since the Second World War, we have seen jet engines revolutionise long distance transport, transistors lead to a multiplicity of cheap, high quality electronic devices, television create a global village, nuclear energy provide a significant proportion of electric power, nuclear weapons transform war into a potential global catastrophe, and computers become an essential aspect of industrial and commercial activity. Advanced telecommunications have made worldwide communication of speech, pictures and information a practical possibility. Genetic engineering is poised to become a significant technology in medicine and chemical production. Each of these changes has had beneficial and detrimental effects. One of the disadvantages is the upheaval caused by constant change, a phenomenon becoming known as future shock.

Information technology must take its place amongst the technological innovations which are propelling societies forward. Although computers are a major influence, they are not the only influence in this field. Technological pressures must, in turn, take their place amongst the other pressures mentioned in previous sections. It very seldom happens that all these pressures are acting in the same direction. One reason for the complexity and lack of cohesion of contemporary societies is that they are at the mercy of a number of different forces, none of which is very clearly understood, pushing the societies in different directions.

36.11 Conclusion

■ This chapter has presented, in a condensed form, an overview of the effects information technology is having on the societies in which it is used. The place of IT among the many pressures determining the course of these societies has also been discussed.

This chapter has skirted round the question 'Are computers a good thing?' Occasionally, rather extreme answers, in one direction or the other, are given to this question. This chapter makes the case that the answer to this question must lie between the extremes.

On the one hand, consider the situation where computers are used worldwide to the maximum extent which is technically possible. The result would be an economic and social disaster, with massive unemployment, widespread discontent and disorder amongst large sections of the population, a highly regimented way of life and repressive governments.

On the other hand, consider the situation where computers are phased out completely. This would result in the collapse of the financial systems and of most industrial and commercial organisations in all developed countries. Supplies of food, gas, electricity and water would be adversely affected. Standards of local and national administration, policing and medical services would suffer. The high standard of life which many people have come to expect would no longer be possible.

The practical alternative is to steer a middle course, judging each computer application on its merits, and taking into account both the immediate and the wider implications of the situation. In the future, the further spread of computers, particularly in the Third World, could become a political issue. The more people there are who know something about computers, the better are the chances of reaching a satisfactory consensus on these issues.

Exercise 36

1 Find out what happened when information technology was introduced into the UK newspaper industry during the late 1980s.
   a) Write a brief account of the main sequence of events.
   b) Why was IT introduced in the industry?
   c) What types of jobs disappeared entirely?
   d) What changes were there in the jobs which continued?
   e) What were the effects on the Trade Unions involved?
   f) What effects were there on the management of the newspapers?
   g) What have been the long-term effects on the newspaper industry as a whole?

2 Give your views on the general issue of information technology and unemployment. Include your comments on the following topics:
   a) Whether computers are in any way related to other major causes of unemployment, such as changes in industries like steelmaking, shipbuilding and motor car manufacture.
   b) Whether you think that the increased job opportunities created by computers offsets the unemployment they cause.
   c) What the effect of computers on unemployment will be in the future.

3 Name some areas in which you think computers should not be introduced because of the unemployment which would be caused.

4 Find out the policies of some Trade Unions towards the introduction of computers.

5 a) Make a list of all the computer systems which would store personal information about someone living in the UK who has a bank account, credit card, house mortgage, medical records, works for a large company and pays income tax and the community charge.
   b) Choose one of these systems, and describe the potential consequences of an unauthorised disclosure of this information.

6 Give your views on the issue of computers and the privacy of personal information. Include your comments on the following topics:
   a) The extent to which privacy is already being abused by various computer applications.
   b) The potential for abuse of privacy in the future, by computer applications.

c) Whether further legislation should be introduced in this area and, if so, what form the legislation should take.

7 Find out about the privacy laws existing in some countries. Briefly describe each situation you investigate, and identify similarities and differences between them.

8 At present breaking into a computer system is, in itself, not a crime under UK law. (It is against the law to destroy, damage or alter data having broken in.) State, with reasons, your opinion on the issue: whether unauthorised access to a computer system should, in itself, be outlawed.

9 Give your views on the issue of computers and political control. Mention what (if any) safeguards you think should be placed on the use of computers in this area.

10 Outline some of the most significant changes which, in your view, have been brought about by the introduction of the following technologies: telephone; radio; television; motor cars; jet passenger aeroplanes; nuclear weapons.

11 Give your own views on the most significant factors causing change in societies today. Identify the relative importance of information technology among these factors.

37 Revision Exercises

This Revision Exercise contains questions from past examinations in Computing or Computer Science at Advanced Level. Examination Boards are identified by the following abbreviations:

AEB   Associated Examining Board
JMB   Joint Matriculation Board
NISEC Northern Ireland Schools Examinations Council
OLE   University of Oxford Delegacy of Local Examinations
UCLES University of Cambridge Local Examinations Syndicate
UL   University of London School Examinations Board
WJEC Welsh Joint Education Committee

1 A bank has installed cash dispensing machines at its provincial branches. Each dispenser has a fairly powerful processing capability and is also connected to a central computer by telephone lines. Each customer has a plastic card and can withdraw cash as well as ask for the current balances to be displayed or full statements to be sent by post.

    The machines consist of a number of sub-systems including card-reader, keyboard, display system and dispensing drawers. Messages to be displayed on the screen are kept in a set of standard messages, which contains a number of text messages interspersed with control characters. Data to be sent to the central computer is to be spooled with either high or low priority. Requests for statements will be sent with low priority whilst validation requests and transactions such as balance enquiries and withdrawal requests, will have high priority.

a) What is meant by a control character? Give two examples of the use of control characters in this application.

b) What is meant by spooling? State two advantages of spooling in this application.

c) Explain the processes which must be carried out when data is to be transferred from the dispenser to the central computer.

d) Prior to the selection of a service, the customer must insert the plastic card and key in a personal identification number. Explain the processes carried out by the system.

e) Which other sub-system would be needed if customers are to receive a record of the transactions? Explain briefly how this sub-system would produce output.

AEB 89 Paper 1 Q13

2 a) i) With the aid of examples, distinguish between machine code and assembly language programs.

    ii) In assembly language, what is meant by a directive? Give an example of a directive.

b) The central processing unit of a particular computer contains 8 general purpose registers of 8 bit word length labelled A, B.....H. A simple assembly language is used, which allows the following instructions and predefined macros:

Function	Operands	Description
MOV	R1, R2	Move into register R1 the contents of register R2
LD	R, N	Load register R with the number N
ADD	R1, R2	Add to register R1 the contents of register R2 and set the carry flag if overflow
DEC	R	Decrement register R. If register R=0 then zero flag is set
NEG	R	Branch to label if Zero flag is set
BN	NZ, label	Branch to label if Zero flag is not set
BN	C, label	Branch to label if Carry flag is set,
BN	NC, label	Branch to label if Carry flag is not set

Registers can be paired together, eg. AB, CD... to form 16 bit single registers. For example, ADD GH, GH will add the contents of GH to itself with the carry flag set only if there is a carry from the G register, which is equivalent to shifting GH one place to the left.

All numbers are binary.

Macro TEST with parameter N is defined as

```
MACRO      TEST      N
           LD        G,   N
           LD        H,   0
           LD        C,   0
           LD        E,   1000
START:     ADD       GH,  GH
           BN        NC,  NOADD
           ADD       GH,  CD
NOADD:     DEC       E
           BN        NZ,  START
           MOV       CD,  GH
ENDMACRO
```

i) If register D contains the binary number 00111011, list the contents of registers G and H at the end of each of the iterations when the macro is called by TEST 1011.

ii) Describe the function of this macro.

iii) If N is a negative number, stored in two's complement format, describe the additional steps which will be needed.

AEB 89 Paper 1 Q14

3 Two systems store numbers in 16 bit words. The first system uses a fixed point representation with the point assumed to be after the tenth bit (from the left). The second system uses a normalised floating binary point representation with a ten bit mantissa and six bit exponent. Both systems store negative numbers and use two's complement notation.
Example: The floating point representation of 4 is
0100000000 000011
  i) Compare the range of positive numbers in each system and examine the accuracy of the floating point representation of the largest number in the fixed point system.
  ii) If in the fixed point system, two successive 16 bit memory locations contain the hexadecimal numbers 00DC and FD40, write down the denary equivalent of both numbers.

iii) In the floating point system write down the binary equivalent of the denary numbers 7/32 and -24.

iv) Outline the main steps needed to multiply two numbers in the floating point system. Include in your answer the steps required to normalise the result.

AEB 89 Paper 1 Q15

4 a) The system nucleus in an operating system consists of program modules which include the interrupt handler and the dispatcher. List the steps involved, including the functions of the interrupt handler and the dispatcher when an interrupt occurs, which will alter the status of the current process.

b) Describe three of the main duties of a job scheduler in an operating system which supports multi-programming and multi-access.

c) In such an environment it is possible for a situation to arise in which no process can continue because the resources each process requires is held by another, with the resources being unshareable.
  i) Give an example of one shareable resource and one unshareable resource.
  ii) Describe a strategy for resolving this difficulty.

AEB 89 Paper 1 Q17

5 The process of compilation involves a number of stages (or phases). Give the name of the stage at which each of the following errors would be detected:

a) The compiler cannot recognise the structure of an arithmetic expression due to a missing bracket.

b) A keyword in the source program is misspelt.

c) An arithmetic operator has operands of incompatible types.

d) A compiler created constant is too large to fit into a word of the target machine.

e) The name of a variable contains more characters than are permitted in the language definition.

AEB 89 Paper 2 Q12

6 a) Explain what is meant by "top down design" of programs. Give two advantages of designing programs this way.

b) A program is required to enter a set of students' examination marks, to count the number of students who obtained each mark and to output the count for each mark. Examination marks are integers in the range 0 to 500.

  Use the method of top down design to produce a pseudo-code description of an efficient algorithm. Give just two design levels, the first using a suitable graphical method or ordinary English, the second in pseudocode. Give also the design of a suitable data structure to process the examination marks. Discuss briefly the efficiency of your design.

c) Suggest two different application packages in which the program described in (b) may be contained as one of the number of modules.

d) It is proposed to add a validation module to the program described in (b) in order to avoid errors due to erroneous input. Give a high level design for a suitable module and explain at what point it is called by the program in (b).

AEB 89 Paper 2 Q14

7 a) Compare the file based approach to data management with the database approach and hence illustrate the advantages and disadvantages of each approach.

b) An on-line database system supports a number of concurrent data enquiry applications. The whole system is closed down at infrequent intervals in order to update the database. What precautions are needed to maintain data integrity and data security in the data enquiry system?

c) One of the applications given in (b) was developed from an older batch processing system. In the old system the input of a key field was validated using a check digit system. This feature was not implemented in the new system. Discuss reasons why this change may have been made. In your judgement was it wise to drop the check digit system?

AEB 89 Paper 2 Q16

8 A local telephone area office uses a computer based system to invoice telephone subscribers every quarter. Three files are used in the invoicing system. The first file is the Charges File which stores rarely changing data such as the cost of dialled telephone units, the rate of VAT, quarterly charges for equipment on hire, etc.

The second file is the Subscriber File which is maintained in telephone number order and stores the following data for each subscriber. (The key field is telephone number):

Telephone number; Subscriber name; Subscriber address;

Quarterly rental charge; Last meter reading; Current meter reading; Number of units dialled; Cost per unit;

Cost of units used; Balance outstanding of unpaid bills; Total of all charges; VAT; Total payable.

a) Write down the data required in the Transactions File for each subscriber.

b) The invoicing system updates two of the fields in the Subscriber File. Which are they?

c) Payment of invoices by subscribers is handled by a separate system which also access and updates the Subscriber File. What is changed in this file when the subscriber's payment is processed?

d) Which of the items on the subscriber's invoice are calculated at the time the invoicing program is run?

e) The data in the Charges File could equally well have been incorporated in the programs which process the other files. Give two advantages of keeping this data in a file rather than as part of the program.

f) The system was designed to take account of a variety of possible changes. Write down four different types of change that may be required and describe what needs to be done in each case in order to update the system.

g) The invoicing system uses a batch processing method, thus providing the opportunity to incorporate control totals. Suggest a control total which would be useful in this application and describe briefly its purpose.

AEB 89 Paper 2 Q17

9 A manufacturing company has a large number of representatives who each travel an area of the country promoting the company's products to customers.

An electronic mail system, based on the company's mainframe computer, is used to provide a communication link between the representatives and their managers. The representatives contact the company from their own homes or directly from customer's premises.

    i) Indicate, with reasons, the hardware required by the representatives.

    ii) Suggest the content of the electronic mail that is likely to pass between the representatives and their managers and vice versa.

    iii) The mail is stored in one large file. A second file indicates the location of messages for each user. Describe suitable organisations and access methods for these files. Describe the record structure of each of the files.

    iv) Give three disadvantages of electronic mail as a means of communication.

JMB 88 Paper 1 Q14

10 a) A large modern multiprogramming operating system can often provide both batch processing and real time multiaccess facilities apparently at the same time. Explain how this is possible including a description of the use of priorities and foreground/background tasks.

    b) A multiprogramming operating system adopts the approach that a program must request all resources at the start and can only start once all the resources it requires have been allocated.

    The computer has 100K of memory of which 20K is ocupied by the operating system. At the start of the day the following peripherals are available for use.

       3 Tape Decks
       3 Disc Drives
       2 Line Printers

    The priority of the programs waiting to start and the peripherals and memory they require are shown in the table below. (Priority 1 is highest.)

Program	A	B	C	D	E
Priority	1	2	3	4	5
Tape Deck	2	2	1	1	0
Disc Drive	0	1	2	1	0
Line Printer	1	0	0	0	1
Memory (K)	48	33	11	20	10

    Explain which programs will be loaded initially, assuming program priority takes precedence over other considerations. Describe what happens to allow multiprogramming to take place.
    Under what circumstances will the next program be loaded? Explain which of the remaining programs will then be selected.

JMB 88 Paper 1 Q16

11 A computer system has been installed to control the temperature in a chicken rearing shed. The system has 16 temperature sensors located equidistantly along its length.

    Associated with each sensor is

    i) an extractor fan which must be switched on when the temperature rises above 21 deg C and off when the temperature reaches 20 deg C,

ii) a fan heater which must be switched on when the temperature falls below 19 deg C and off when the temperature reaches 20 deg C.

The temperature sensor has three outputs indicating

i) temperature at 20 deg C,

ii) temperature below 19 deg C,

iii) temperature above 21 deg C.

a) Construct an algorithm which will test the temperature sensors every 10 seconds and will take the appropriate action as indicated by each sensor.

b) In order to provide management information about the environment, data is to be stored about the usage of each of the extractor and heater fans. The external temperature, windspeed and wind direction information is also available from other sensors close to the chicken shed. Suggest a suitable record and file structure which could be used to store the above information efficiently for subsequent analysis.

JMB 88 Paper 1 Q18

12 A small museum has a room set aside which it uses for showing a short video programme. The video recorder is controlled by a microcomputer. It is only possible to enter the room by one door and leave by the other as part of the one-way flow round the museum. The two doors each have a sensor which detects a person entering or leaving the room. The video recorder is started when someone enters the room provided the video is off. If the room becomes empty during the showing of the video programme the video recorder is stopped and immediately rewound. At the end of the video programme the video is rewound and is started again 30 seconds later if anyone is still in the room.

i) Construct an algorithm for the control of the video recorder.

ii) How could the computer program produced from the algorithm be tested without actually wiring up the room?

iii) Suggest four different sequences of entry and exit by people which could be used to test the computer program.

JMB 88 Paper 2 Q1

13 a) Explain the difference between syntax errors and runtime errors, giving two different examples of each type of error. Define the term 'data type' as used in high-level languages and give two examples of how the use of data types can help in debugging programs.

b) i) Explain how an array and pointers may be used to implement a queue. Two procedures are used; one to add and one to remove an item from a queue. Explain in detail the parameters to these procedures and how they would be used by a calling program.

ii) It is required to add and remove elements from either end of this queue. What changes are needed to implement this data structure?

JMB 88 Paper 2 Q4

14 Figure 37.1 is a diagram of the structure of a 16-bit central processing unit (CPU) and memory system. The register IN is an input buffer for data from the memory. The register OUT is an output buffer for the arithmetic and logic unit (ALU). An instruction comprises an 8-bit function code (F) and an 8-bit operand field (O).

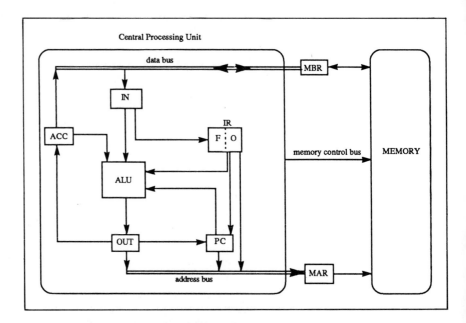

Figure 37.1

a) Explain the use of the following registers:
   i) IR – Instruction Register,
   ii) ACC – Accumulator,
   iii) PC – Program Counter,
   iv) MBR – Memory Buffer Register,
   v) MAR – Memory Address Register.
b) What signals will be required on the memory control bus?
c) From the diagram construct the sequence of register transfers and memory control signals that carry out the following instructions:

   i) Jump Relative   – the program counter is to be incremented by the value in the operand field,

   ii) Add Direct   – the address of the value to be added is contained in the operand field,

   iii) Load ACC Indexed   – the value to be loaded has the base address of the table initially stored in the accumulator and the offset stored in the operand field.

   Explain your notation.

JMB 88 Paper 2 Q7

15 A mail order firm maintains its order entry and dispatch system by means of a computerised database.

Two of the files maintained by the database are an order-file and a customer-details-file.

The order-file has the following fields:
   customer-number
   order-number
   order-date
   order-ready
   dispatch-date.

The customer-details-file has the following fields:
   customer-number
   customer-name
   customer-address
   customer-telephone.

Within the customer-details-file the key-field customer-number is unique. Whereas, within the order-file the same customer-number may occur in several records, once for each order placed by a customer. Neither file is sorted into any particular order.

    i) Construct an algorithm for the following label printing process. Each day the customer-details-file is processed against the order-file to produce address labels for each order that is ready. An address label comprises the customer-name and customer-address together with the customer-number and order-number along the top of the label. Orders which are ready have the order-ready field set to true, otherwise it is set to false. Once the label has been produced the dispatch-date field is set to the current date.

    ii) Discuss two independent modifications which could make the system more efficient.

JMB 88 Paper 2 Q8

16 Given below are the contents of several locations in a computer's memory containing a linked list. The linked list is used as an efficient method of storing a sparse array (i.e. an array with few locations used) of dimensions (1..8, 1..10). The data associated with each node of the linked list is stored in four consecutive memory locations. One contains the pointer and the other three contain the value of the array element and its indices. The pointer points at the first of the four memory locations associated with a particular node.

Location	Contents	Location	Contents
99	100	112	4
100	1	113	9
101	3	114	−12
102	−28	115	−999
103	104	116	3
104	2	117	6
105	2	118	46
106	31	119	120
107	108	120	4
108	2	121	7
109	7	122	24
110	−83	123	112
111	116		

a) Given that the start pointer is held in location 99 draw a diagram of the linked list making clear the items of data held at each node.

b) Draw a diagram of this sparse array.

c) What is the purpose of the −999 stored in location 115?

d) Give a disadvantage of using this method of storing the sparse array.

e) The data item 84 is to be stored in the array in element (4,6). Indicate how this element would be added to the linked list in its correct position by showing the locations which would need to be changed, and their new contents.

f) In mathematical calculations involving arrays it is frequently necessary to multiply all the elements of one row by a particular value. Explain how you would carry out this type of operation when the array was stored using the method indicated above.

JMB 89 Paper 1 Q16

17 Many financial institutions now issue plastic cards which can be used at cash dispensers to withdraw money and, if requested, give details of the holder's account.

These cash dispensers are available 24 hours a day, 7 days a week. When issued with a card the holder is given a PIN (Personal Identification Number). On the back of the card there is a thin strip containing magnetically encoded information relating to the holder's account. This strip has three rows on which information can be stored. The financial institutions have adopted two main ways of using the information on these strips.

> Method 1 Stores the holder's account number on row 2, and on row 3 a coded version of the PIN together with that account holder's weekly cash withdrawal limit and the money removed so far that week. The system is normally on-line during the day and off-line at night.
>
> Method 2 Stores only the holder's account number on row 2 and leaves row 3 empty. This method requires the system to be on-line at all times. The cash dispensers hold no information of the transactions which have been carried out.

To use the card it has to be inserted into the machine and the PIN entered when requested.

a) i) Why must method 2 be an on-line system?
    ii) Why must the PIN on the card in method 1 be held in coded form?
b) Give an example of a potential invasion of privacy in this application.
c) Give an example of a potential breach of security in this application.
d) Describe how the security of each of these systems could be broken by the following people and in each case indicate what measures could be taken to prevent that breach of security.
    i) members of the general public,
    ii) the bank's computer staff.
e) Describe two checks which could be held in the rows of the magnetic strip to ensure the data has been read correctly.
f) Using method 2, when the card holder enters the PIN, what is it checked against?
g) Suggest what information could be held in row 1 of the card in both methods.

JMB 89 Paper 1 Q19

18 Text prepared using a wordprocessor can have its spelling checked using a spellchecking facility. When this is activated each word in the prepared text is checked against a dictionary of over 50,000 words held in ROM.

a) In principle, how can a spellchecker confirm the correct spelling of a word?
b) Certain rejected words may be correctly spelt. Describe, with examples, two distinct cases when this could occur and describe how a spellchecker could accommodate such words for future reference.
c) When may a spellchecker not be able to recognise a misspelling? Give an example.

d) Once any misspelt words have been found and isolated, describe what might be done in order to correct them. Describe any other facilities that a spellchecker might provide to assist the wordprocessor operator.

e) Describe, using diagrams, an appropriate data structure to hold the dictionary in order to provide a fast access route to any given word. Explain how the dictionary is accessed.

JMB 89 Paper 2 Q1

19 A company has a mailing list of over 10,000 of its customers. This customer file is kept as a serial disc file ordered sequentially on the customer number. The record format is:

field name	fixed length/variable length	field length
customer number (key)	fixed	7
name	variable	–
first address line	variable	–
second address line	variable	–
town	variable	–
postcode	fixed	9

a) i) Suggest why variable length fields have been specified.
   ii) Draw a diagram showing how the following data can be stored in the record described above, introducing any additional characters and/or fields that may be necessary.

    1073562
    Mrs D Smith
    The Elms
    Moss Drive
    Sandbach
    CW7 3ST

   iii) State the validation checks which would be appropriate for each field on data entry.

b) The company, in developing an on-line file update system, has opted for the binary search technique for accessing a record.
   i) State why it is inappropriate to perform this technique on the customer file as it stands.
   ii) Given that the customer file is not to be altered, describe how, through the introduction of an additional file, the binary search technique could be implemented. Illustrate your answer with an example.
   iii) Why has the system designer insisted on keeping the customer file sequentially organised?
   iv) State what problem might arise in amending a record and suggest a remedy. Describe how a deletion would be handled.

c) In keeping the customer file, what are the statutory obligations that the company has to its customers under the Data Protection Act?

JMB 89 Paper 2 Q3

20 An arithmetic processor handles floating point numbers in 12 bit registers consisting of a 4 bit exponent in bits 0-3 (bit 0 is the least significant bit) and an 8 bit normalised mantissa in bits 4-11. The binary point of the mantissa is between bits 10 and 11. Both exponent and mantissa are in two's complement notation.

The calculation $(9.2) + (-0.375)$ is to be performed by this arithmetic processor.

a) Show how the two numbers, 9.2 and -0.375, are held by the above processor. Explain any rounding used.

b) Show how the processor would add together the representation of the two numbers, arrived at in part (a). What is the decimal equivalent of your answer?

c) The calculation $(9.2) + (-0.375)$ has the exact arithmetical result 8.825.

Explain any difference between this and your answer obtained in part (b).

d) Explain the precautions that should be taken to avoid errors when using conditional statements that involve testing floating point numbers.

JMB 89 Paper 2 Q5

21 A company intends storing details of its products on computer. At any time the company has a maximum of 1000 products. Each product has a unique four digit code associated with it. The systems analyst has decided that the file will require 500 blocks and will be organised randomly with each block in the file capable of holding two records. The location of the record on disc is obtained by a hashing algorithm which involves the following processes:

1 take the last three digits of the product code
2 divide this number by two
3 take the integer value of the result of this division.

Using this algorithm the record for the product with code number 1427 will generate a block address of 213. However products with code numbers 4426 and 2427 will also generate 213 as the block address even though each block is only capable of holding 2 records. When a block is full and the algorithm generates that block address again for the record being added, the next block is tested, and so on, until a free area is found into which the record is written.

a) Records with the following product numbers are submitted in the sequence indicated. Into which blocks will they be written, assuming the file is initially empty?

0462   3464   1465   1463   4462

b) Write an algorithm for locating a record in the file.

c) If product 1465 is discontinued how would the record be deleted without reorganising the file?

d) Write an algorithm for adding a record to the file.

e) Every six months the company performs a stock check and this requires the file to be printed out in product number order. Describe an efficient method of producing a tape file which could be used for this print-out.

JMB 89 Paper 2 Q8

22 a) Describe the principal features of each of the following:
   i) system design documentation,
   ii) the user manual.

b) "An interactive program should behave in a way meaningful to the end user for any type or volume of input."
Discuss the implications of this objective for program design.

NISEC 88 Paper 1 Q17

23 a) In computer based systems, code numbers are often used primarily in order to identify items. Describe briefly four requirements which code numbers should satisfy.

b) What is a check digit? Which of the following are valid ISBN codes? (International Standard Book Number using modulus 11 with ascending weights 1, 2, 3...10 from the right-most digit.)

085 012 452 2
090 543 538 X
009 154 961 2
009 154 971 X

c) Distinguish between data verification and data validation and explain why such procedures are not sufficient to ensure the correctness of computer output. Describe briefly other checks which can be used.

NISEC 88 Paper 2 Q13

24 The following is a formal partial description in EBNF of the syntax of a simple programming language.

<program>	:: =	<line> cr { <line> cr } END
<line>	:: =	[<line no>] <statement>
<line no>	:: =	<digit> { <digit> }
<statement>	:: =	<assign> | <if> | <goto> | <read> | <print>
<assign>	:: =	<var> : <exp>
<exp>	:: =	<var> <op> <var> | <var> | <integer>
<op>	:: =	+ | - | * | /
<integer>	::=	<digit> { <digit> }
<var>	:: =	A | B | C | D | E | F | G —— | Z
<if>	:: =	IF <var> <comp> <var> THEN <line no>
<comp>	:: =	> | < | = | > | <
<goto>	:: =	GOTO <line no>

Note: [] brackets denote an optional string of symbols.
{} brackets denote repetition of a string of symbols an arbitrary number of times, including none.
Statements have the same meaning as in other languages with similar facilities; cr denotes "carriage return".

a) Draw a tree diagram or obtain a derivation to demonstrate that the following is a correctly formed < line >.

40 IF A = B THEN 8

b) Write a fragment of program in the above language, which has the same meaning as the following pseudocode:

IF A + B > 10 THEN SET X TO P + Q * (R – S)

OTHERWISE SET X TO A + B

c) Outline the function of the lexical analyser of a compiler.

NISEC 88 Paper 2 Q16

25 a) Describe the abstract structure known as a tree using a diagram to explain the terms root, subtree, node, edge (branch) and level. A strictly binary tree has exactly zero or two edges (branches) proceeding from each node. If the root is at level 0, how many nodes are there on levels 1, 2, 3, ...n?

b) Explain how a tree may be used to represent:
  i) the organisation of a disk file directory
  ii) the structure of a program to drive a multi-level menu for selection of option in an applications package.
  iii) the priorities of operators in an arithmetic expression. Illustrate your answer by drawing the tree for the expression.

$$a + b * (c - d)$$

  where the operators and symbols have their usual meanings.
c) i) A considerable improvement on ordinary sequential look-up may be achieved by distributing the data keys among the nodes of a binary tree.

  Show how the following keys should be placed on a binary tree to optimize the search time for any particular key:

$$30, \ 21, \ 2, \ 28, \ 79, \ 62, \ 91.$$

  Explain the procedure for searching for a given key.
  ii) Explain how the tree could be represented using arrays.

NISEC 89 Paper 1 Q16

26 a) Discuss the likely consequences of
  i) errors in program design.
  ii) errors in program coding.
  iii) errors in data being used
    with reference to
      – how and at what stage the error can arise,
      – how the error may be detected and eliminated,
      – what measures may be adopted to minimize the risk of the error occurring.
  b) Name one other type of error which can arise and discuss it briefly under the same headings.

NISEC 89 Paper 2 Q17

27 a) In a batch system the following file processes are usually performed by separate programs:
    – creation
    – validation
    – sorting
    – merging
    – updating
    – maintenance.
  Discuss how the situation differs for each of these processes in an interactive system.
  b) Discuss the characteristics of a suitable storage medium for large files in an interactive environment.
  c) Describe and justify one method of file organisation and an appropriate method of access for the medium chosen in part (b).

NISEC 89 Paper 2 Q13

28 A computer has a memory consisting of addressable (8-bit) bytes. The instruction register is three bytes long and may be regarded as a 24-bit word.
  a) i) If 6 bits are allocated to the instruction code, how many distinct instruction types are there and how many memory locations can be addressed, assuming that a 2-address code is used?

ii) Suggest and describe some typical 2-address instructions.

iii) If, instead the processor employs 1-address instructions, describe a typical division of the 24-bit world into instruction code and address.

State one advantage of using 1-address instruction design and explain the need to include additional instruction codes when adopting this design strategy.

iv) Describe with the aid of a diagram a feasible method of decoding the instruction bit pattern.

b) i) Explain how the principle of address modification may be used to greatly increase the number of bytes which can be addressed in an instruction word.

ii) A computer has a single accumulator, a single modifier register and used a 1-address instruction format. Mnemonic instructions for this computer include the following:

CLEAR	Set the accumulator to zero
INC	Add one to the contents of the accumulator
LD X	Load a copy of contents of address X to acc.
STO X	Store a copy of the contents of the accumulator to address X
ADD X	Add a copy of contents of address X to the contents of the acc.
SUB X	Subtract a copy of the contents of X from the contents of the acc.

M placed after X in each of the above four instructions denotes that the address X is to be modified using the contents of the modifier before execution.

SUB # n	Indicates that the decimal value n is subtracted from the contents of the acc.
LDM	Load the contents of the modifier register into the acc.
STOM	Store the contents of the acc. into the modifier register.
BN L	If the accumulator is negative branch to label L.
SL	Shift the contents of the accumulator one bit left.

All instructions may be labelled,

e.g. LAB1 STO X

Using only these instructions, produce a program which is equivalent to the following high level code:

```
(* TABLE OF SQUARES *)
        S : = 1;
        I : = 3;
        FOR K : = 1 TO 10 DO
        BEGIN
                T[K]: = S;
                S: = S + I;
                I: = I = +2
        END;
```

NISEC 89 Paper 2 Q16

29 Answer either part A or part B.

  A In order to enable better control of stock, a large retail organisation which has stores throughout the province wishes to install a central computer at the head office and terminals within each store and within the central warehouse. The store (POS) terminals would each be equipped with a keyboard, a cash drawer and a bar-code reader and would be attached to a local (in-store) control unit.

    i) Outline the benefits which the organisation might reasonably expect to obtain from installation of such a system.

    ii) Name and state the function of eight fields which you would expect to be present in the main stock-file records.

    iii) The software, which has still to be developed, may be built around <u>conventional</u> <u>files</u> using current <u>high-level</u> <u>languages</u>, or may be built around a database using a <u>Database Management System</u>.
    Outline what each of the underlined terms means to you.

    iv) By considering the arguments for and against traditional file-based systems and database systems, make a balanced recommendation to the management on which strategy offers the better facilities for the present and future data-processing needs of the organisation.

    v) Despite having point-of-sale terminals installed, the organisation still has to carry out periodic stock counts within the stores.
    Why are these considered necessary?
    Describe a suitable method of data capture for this process.

OR B Word-processing and spreadsheet packages are widely used in the office environment.

    i) Outline the features which you consider to be essential in a word-processing package, and illustrate your answer with reference to a package with which you are familiar.

    ii) a) State why a 'spreadsheet' has this name
      b) Describe the features which you would expect to find in a modern spreadsheet package, illustrating your answer with reference to a package with which you are familiar.
      c) Explain why this type of package is useful in the office/business environment.

NISEC 89 Paper 2 Q17

30 'A picture is worth a thousand words.'

  a) Explain why computers are having a more widespread use in industries using pictures.

  b) Choose one industry in which graphical information is used widely, and discuss the use of computer-aided techniques in this industry. Include in your discussion the relevance of standards for graphical information.

OLE 89 Paper 1 Q1

31 Consider the following problem: an expressline coach company wishes to program a reservation system. The data to be stored in the computer will include:

    i) All tours for the next 60 days, stored by tour number and date.

    ii) The names of all passengers holding reservations on those tours, together with a variable length character string of data about each passenger.

iii) Details of the types of unreserved seats on each tour. (This data will be continuously changing as seats are sold or cancelled and as information changes.)

Produce an outline design for the user environment required to accomplish this task. This might include the use of windows, icons, menus and pointers. You should include in your design a suitable screen display(s) showing the information required to enable queries to be answered and bookings to be made, changed or cancelled;

and also indicate how the user would:

a) move through the separate records
b) find an individual record (via tour number or date or passenger name)
c) change a record
d) enter/delete a record
e) display a passenger list for a given tour in sorted order.

Also explain the kind of facility needed within the program to update the number and class of reserved seats.

OLE 89 Paper 1 Q2

32 A skyscraper office block has a set of ten lifts controlled by a single computer.

A passenger wishing to call a lift must press one of two buttons depending on whether he wants to ascent or descend.

Each lift contains a sensor that can detect the load. If this is close to the maximum then the lift will not stop to take on any more passengers.

Data for the computer program include predictions of the number of passengers requiring lifts from each floor at different times of the day.

a) What factors will affect the variation of passenger use during the day?
b) When a lift is called for, what criteria should decide which lift should be used? Why will this not necessarily be the nearest lift?
c) Give either a structured description or a flow diagram for an algorithm to accept inputs and decide on the allocation of the ten lifts.

OLE 89 Paper 2 Q1

33 A building firm wishing to expand seeks advice on the benefits that might be achieved by the installation of a multi-user computer system.

It would hold financial details of all building jobs currently being carried out in addition to those undertaken during the current financial year. All office personnel would use the system and there would be 5 terminals, one of them allowing for remote dial-up access for placing orders with suppliers and receiving orders for jobs.

The computer system should be central to all administration functions and in particular the following applications should be included:

Management information on all jobs
Payroll
Sale and purchase details

It would also be used for word processing.

a) Why would it be necessary to give different types of access to separate users and how could this be achieved?

b) The firm needs advice before proceeding with the purchase and installation. Who might they consult and what aspects of the business will need to be taken into account?

c) Why would the firm have to take security precautions and how could this be done?

d) A consultant recommends a common database. Discuss the advantages of this.

OLE 89 Paper 2 Q2

34 a) i) When information is transmitted remotely from one computer to another it is often sent in encrypted (or scrambled) form. Why is this done?

ii) When transmitting information a certain computer sends each byte of data with the order of the bits reversed. For example, a byte containing

bit 7							bit 0
V							V
1	0	1	1	0	1	1	1

would be converted to a byte containing

1	1	1	0	1	1	0	1

and this would then be transmitted. Using a real or invented assembly language, write an annotated section of program which performs the above conversion on a single byte of data.

iii) What other information would you expect to be transmitted along with the data bytes? What purpose does each item of information serve?

b) i) What are the disadvantages of using the public telephone network for computer to computer communication?

ii) What part can modems play when transmitting data between two remote computers?

UCLES 88 Paper 1 Q7

35 A small hotel, with rooms on both the ground and first floors, has installed a lift. The doors and the movements of the lift are controlled by a microprocessor.

A person wishing to use the lift may find the doors open, in which case the lift may be operated by pressing a button inside the lift. On other occasions, the lift may be in use, or may have been left on the other floor when it was last used. The lift can then be 'called' by pressing a button next to the lift doors. When 'called' the lift always comes when it is free. For safety reasons, the lift will not operate if it is overloaded.

a) List the sensors which are required to control the lift. For each sensor, indicate why it is needed.

b) Stating any assumptions that are appropriate, describe an algorithm for a control program which operates the lift as described.

c) Outline the differences one would expect to find in an algorithm which controls a lift operating between more than two floors.

d) Machines that were in the past either controlled mechanically or electrically are nowadays often controlled by a microprocessor. What are the benefits or disadvantages of using a microprocessor for control purposes?

UCLES 88 Paper 1 Q9

36 The life expectancy of a typical mainframe multiaccess system is about 10 years. Some systems may have several hundred users, who make extensive use of all the software and hardware facilities which are available. For example, some users may use packages available for word processing, information storage and retrieval, statistical analysis and graph plotting. Sometimes, special hardware facilities such as laser printers and plotters are required. Other users may develop programs in various high-level languages, and a range of utility software, such as editors, compilers and debuggers would be available. Most large systems provide a considerable amount of on-line disk storage, and magnetic tape facilities would also be available.

a) Discuss the problems which users may face when an existing mainframe is replaced by a new mainframe system. In what ways can the computer staff help to ensure a smooth changeover from one system to the other?

b) In many organisations, mainframe computers are being replaced by several smaller computers linked together to form a computer network. Describe the advantages which such a system has over a single mainframe computer, and explain, from the users' point of view, how the network might function.

UCLES 88 Paper 2 Q3

37 An estate agent has introduced a computer in an effort to sell more houses. The system can operate both a hard disk and a floppy disk, and has a keyboard, monitor and printer. It runs a software package which maintains two files called the PROPERTIES file and the PURCHASERS file. The PROPERTIES file contains one record for each property. Each record contains some details about a property, for example, the name and address of the owner, the selling price and the number of bedrooms it has. The PURCHASERS file stores similar information about the kinds of properties being sought by potential buyers.

The agent divides much of the time during the day between interviewing potential buyers, receiving instructions to sell properties, and entering details into the PROPERTIES file. During an interview with a potential buyer, the agent keys into the computer details about the kind of property the interviewee is looking for. At the end of the interview, the agent keys in a command which asks the computer to print a list of properties which approximately meet the buyer's requirements. This list is then used to give the buyer further details about properties which may be suitable.

a) Describe suitable structures for both the PROPERTIES file and the PURCHASERS file. Indicate why the structures you have chosen are suitable for this application.

b) The agent wishes to provide an efficient mailing service for potential buyers which would supply details of newly-available properties. How could this be achieved?

c) Another facility which the agent would like the computer to provide is an interactive properties enquiry system which could be used by potential buyers. Such a facility would be used by many people who would be unfamiliar with operating a computer.

   i) Describe how such a facility could be made easy to use.

   ii) Suggest any additional hardware which the existing system does not have which would be appropriate for this facility. Indicate also how the new hardware would be used.

UCLES 88 Paper 2 Q5

38 Many city centre buildings are nowadays used as offices. Millions of people travel daily between their homes and their offices. Many office workers make extensive use of computers. Some people have already found that using a home microcomputer linked to the office computer enables them to work from home. In the future there is a possibility that the home could be the office for many people.

a) Describe the technology which would be used to bring this about.

b) Discuss the consequences which the widespread use of homes as offices would have on society. In your answer you should mention possible benefits and disadvantages to those who work in offices and their families, the companies and the organisations they work for, and others who might be affected by the changes described. Indicate also the possible effects of such changes on city centres and the rest of the environment.

UCLES 88 Paper 2 Q7

39 A sports centre offers the local community a wide range of sports activities. It requires a computer system to make the best use of its equipment and facilities, so as to provide the best possible service to members and other users. The facilities include a number of table tennis tables, snooker tables, badminton and squash courts, and a gymnasium. The centre is prepared to hire equipment to its clients and makes a charge for the hire. The computer system should be able to keep records of the bookings, and of the stock of equipment available and out on hire.

Discuss how a systems analyst would approach the task of designing and implementing such a computer system. Explain how the system could be tested.

UCLES 89 Paper 1 Q6

40 a) Use examples to show the effects of the machine code shift operations:

   i) logical,

   ii) arithmetic,

   iii) cyclic.

You may assume that no carry bit is used in shift operations.

b) An arithmetic shift operation may sometimes set the overflow flag. Explain when this would occur.

c) The machine code instruction set of an 8-bit computer includes the following instructions (in mnemonic form):

lda x	load register a with the content of x
ldc x	load register c with the content of x
clr x	set the content of x to zero
stb x	store the content of registar b in x
inc x	add 1 to the content of x

	dec x	subtract 1 from the content of x
	sll x	shift the content of x left 1 place logical
	src x	shift the content of x right 1 place cyclic
	brpz y	branch to label y if result of previous instruction was positive or zero (i.e. the most significant bit was a 0)
	brnz y	branch to label y if result of previous instruction was non-zero

The symbol % is used to indicate a register operand, for example %a represents register a. The symbol # is used to indicate an immediate operand.

The following is a program fragment:

	lda	byte
	clr	%b
	ldc	#8
loop:	sll	%b
	src	%a
	brpz	zero
	inc	%b
zero:	dec	%c
	brnz	loop
	stb	result

i) Assuming that location **byte** contains the hexadecimal value AC at the start, show the effect of executing the fragment, and write down the contents of location **result** and of register **a** after the fragment has been executed.

ii) Explain in general terms the purpose of the fragment in converting **byte** to **result**.

UCLES 89 Paper 1 Q8

41 A hospital consultant who specialises in liver disease in interested in developing an expert system to assist in diagnosis. A computer specialist is contacted with a view to developing an appropriate system.

a) i) Report on the types of issues they would need to discuss.

ii) Indicate the steps the computer specialist would need to take to design the expert system.

b) Suggest how such an expert system could be of benefits:

i) to patients

ii) to hospital doctors.

UCLES 89 Paper 2 Q6

42 The customer services manager of a large chain of supermarkets wishes to ensure that the number of available check-out points is generally adequate to avoid long queues developing. The number of check-out points which need to be staffed will vary at different times of the week. In order to help make suitable plans, a software package is to be produced to simulate the progress of customers in the queues for the check-out points. The package will need to provide information from the simulation, such as the mean and maximum queue lengths at any given period of time, the amount of time there are no queues at a check-out point, and the range of times that customers need to wait in a queue before they are checked out.

a) Explain what information would be needed to allow the simulation package to carry out these tasks, and indicate how this information could be gathered.

b) Describe the steps which could be involved in the design, implementation and testing of the simulation package.

c) Comment in the reliability and usefulness of the results obtained from a simulation package such as this.

UCLES 89 Paper 2 Q8

43 A graphic designer wishes to use a computer to assist in the design of regular patterns. These patterns may be used for tiling a floor, or for wallpaper or fabric designs.

a) Discuss suitable forms of communication between the user and the system, including examples of the different kinds of data and the devices used.

b) Describe the types of operation that the graphic designer could expect the system to perform.

c) Explain why this kind of system would normally be based on a software package.

UCLES 89 Paper 2 Q10

44 a) A certain computer has 32 bit words. Show, explaining any assumptions which you make, how the following types of data may be stored:

  i) integers
  ii) characters
  iii) binary coded decimal numbers

b) i) Explain, using an example, how the lengths of the mantissa and exponent of a floating point number determine its precision and range.

  ii) In the context of floating point arithmetic, explain what is meant by the terms normalisation, overflow and rounding.

c) In a certain computer, floating point numbers are stored in 16 bits. The exponent is stored in the six most significant bits in two's complement form, the next bit is the sign bit for the mantissa (1 for negative) and the other least significant bits represent the value of the mantissa.

  i) What is the bit pattern for the largest number that can be held in this system?
  ii) What is the smallest positive fraction that can be held?
  iii) How might zero be represented?

Explain any assumptions you have made.

UL 88 Paper 1 Q11

45 An electronics firm manufactures video recorders to order. It produces several different models using a computerised manufacturing process. As the orders are received they are input into the system and the parts for each model are placed by the automated warehouse into boxes for assembly by the workers. Each worker is responsible for assembling a small number of parts. The box of remaining parts and partially assembled video is passed on to the next worker, and so on, until the video is completed. At four separate stages it is necessary to test the video recorder electronically to check that each circuit has been correctly fitted. The testing is done by computer. The completed video

recorder is boxed and addressed ready for sending to the customer along with the account.

a) Describe the computer hardware that would need to be provided to enable the progress of a video recorder to be monitored as it is being made.

b) What are the advantages of having the completed video recorders tested by computer?

c) Describe the main files which would be required by the system.

d) What problems are the company likely to have had to solve in implementing a fully computerised system?

UL 88 Paper 1 Q12

46 A retailing company dealing mainly with prepackaged DIY products has a number of shops and warehouses sited in towns in most regions of Britain. Reports of the effectiveness of bar-code technology in the monitoring and distribution of stock has prompted the management to install suitable hardware in all of its shops, warehouses and in the head office.

a) Draw an annotated diagram of the essential hardware you would expect the company to install in its shops giving brief reasons for each item you include.

b) Discuss the advantages that such a system could provide for both the company and the customer. How might the system affect the staff?

c) Recent innovations have led to the availability of terminals that allow customer accounts to be debited when purchases are made. What are the advantages and disadvantages to the company of such technology?

UL 88 Paper 2 Q10

47 a) i) Describe briefly three methods by which a file on a direct access device may be organised. In each case suggest how a record in the file may be accessed. It is not necessary to describe how overflow is handled.

ii) What are the advantages and disadvantages of storing the records as fixed length records rather that as variable length records?

b) A hospital maintains patients' medical records on a computer. The system is to be used for the prompt on-line retrieval of a patient's medical history. Choose a suitable record structure and a suitable file structure for this application. Give detailed reasons for your choices.

UL 89 Paper 1 Q10

48 A small book-lending library has decided to install a computer system for the administration of loans. Each borrower is given a unique identification number. Each title is given a unique reference number and each copy of a book is given a unique accession number. The system keeps track of current loans and reservation requests. It immediately advises the librarian when borrowers attempt to borrow more books than they are allowed, and when reserved books have been returned. At the end of each day the system generates a recall list for newly overdue books.

The system caters for the addition, removal and amendment of records of books and borrowers.

a) Describe briefly the processing of a transaction when a book is returned.

b) List three other input transactions which the system must support, and describe the data items to be entered.

c) Design a suitable menu-driven interface for the system, providing sketches of individual menus and indicating their interrelationship. The size of the screen limits the number of choices on an individual menu to 6.

UL 89 Paper 1 Q14

49 Eezyread is a company specialising in the production of signs of shops, theatres, cinemas, etc. The company uses a microcomputer system capable of supporting a number of standard application packages. The aim of the system is to process orders and produce estimates for customers as quickly as possible.

The manager of a chain of supermarkets, who is a regular customer, telephones Eezyread to obtain an estimate for a new set of signs. The company is required to produce a range of alternative colour drawings together with an estimate of the cost of each design in a range of materials. The task is completed within a day, and the results are forwarded to the supermarket manager, together with a standard letter outlining the costs and the terms and conditions of the contract.

i) Identify the software and the peripherals that could make up a computer system capable of performing the tasks outlined above.
Point out the facilities provided by the software, and the characteristics of the peripherals, that make them both particularly suited to the task.

ii) One of the designs is acceptable subject to minor modifications. How could one of the files already created be used as part of the manufacturing process?

iii) Apart from the fast turnaround time on producing estimates, what other benefits do you imagine Eezyread would obtain from the system you have outlined? What extra features could easily be added to further improve efficiency?

UL 89 Paper 2 Q10

50 Many commentators have suggested that computers have become essential, both to maintaining, and to enhancing the quality of our lives. By describing one application and speculating on future trends, discuss critically whether you feel that these assertions are true. Your answer should reflect on whether the perceived benefits, or drawbacks, apply to society as a whole, a sector of society, a particular organization or to the "individual".

UL 89 Paper 2 Q11

51 a) An application program is to be developed in a high level language and eventually compiled. The program uses a number of pre-compiled library routines. Describe, with the aid of a diagram, how supporting utility software is used in conjunction with the compiler to produce executable code.

b) The compilation process is often viewed as being made up of a number of distinct phases. In this context:

i) what is the purpose of lexical analysis;
ii) what use is made of symbol tables;
iii) why may a compiler attempt to optimise code?

c) What is cross compilation and when might it be used?

d) Describe one diagnostic utility which can be used to locate errors in a syntactically correct program.

UL 89 Paper 2 Q13

52 a) Explain the operation of multi-access and multi-programming systems and show how one is dependent on the other.

b) Explain the role of the job scheduler in an operating system and indicate a possible strategy for an efficient scheduler.

c) What is meant by a real-time system? Give examples of two distinct real-time systems and explain why they are more complex than conventional operating systems.

WJEC 88 Paper 1 Q7

53 The term office automation has been widely used during the past few years to cover the use of computers in the office. Describe recent advances in computer hardware and software including communications and networks which have made possible this transformation of working practice within some offices. By choosing examples from various fields, such as medicine, journalism or police work, discuss how the advent of office automation has:
i) affected the nature of the work carried out;
ii) affected the tasks performed by the office worker in such offices.

Comment on how society has responded to the use of computers in the office.

WJEC 88 Paper 1 Q10

54 a) Describe, with the aid of examples, the fixed point and floating point representations of numbers. Explain why both forms are needed and show how positive and negative numbers can be catered for in each representation.

b) Choose appropriate fixed point and floating point representations to store the numbers

256 and 512.875

using a 24-bit word. Express each number in your representation in octal and hexadecimal notation. What are the largest numbers that can be stored in your representation and what is the accuracy that can be achieved in each case?

c) Summarise the processes that are involved when a computer performs floating point arithmetic. How do these differ from those used in fixed point arithmetic?

WJEC 88 Paper 2 Q5

55 a) A current area of industrial research work is concerned with the development of an automatic or robotic vehicle. The vehicle is intended to move along a number of predetermined routes or paths within a factory. The vehicle is required to carry a number of stackable objects from one loading bay to another, where it will deposit them. A computer will be used to control the movements of the robotic vehicle.

i) Explain carefully how the robotic vehicle could be designed and tested. Indicate any assumptions that you make.

ii) What are the possible benefits and drawbacks of using such a robotic vehicle rather than conventional manned vehicles in a factory?

b) Describe one other distinct use of computers in industry with which you are familiar.

WJEC 88 Paper 2 Q10

56 a) Outline the reasons that have led to the widespread use of electronic mail in business, industry and education.

b) Discuss the security problems that have arisen with electronic mail systems and indicate what steps can be taken to overcome them.

c) Describe the user interface that is provided by a system such as Telecom Gold.

d) Discuss developments to electronic mail systems which might occur in the future.

WJEC 89 Paper 1 Q9

57 The following is an algorithm for an insertion sort procedure.

procedure sort (reference A, value n)
            {insertion sort the array A, items 1 to n}
            if n > 1 then
                        sort (A, n - 1)
                        insert (A, n - 1, A[n])
            end if
end procedure

procedure insert (reference A, value i, value x)
            {the array A has items 1 to i already sorted; insert the item X
            into position to make items 1 to i + 1 sorted}
            if i = 0 then
                        A[1]:=X
            else
                        if X > A[i] then
                                    A[i + 1]:=X
                        else
                                    A[i + 1]:=A[i]
                                    insert (A, i - 1, X)
                        end if
            end if
end procedure

a) Illustrate the operation of procedure insert (A, 4, X) where

    A[1] is 'Edward'
    A[2] is 'Henry'
    A[3] is 'Julia'
    A[4] is 'Vanessa' and
    X   is 'John'

by writing down the content of the array A and the parameters each time the procedure insert is called.

b) Explain how the procedure sort works, using the initial list of the four numeric items 9, 7, 5, 8, in that order, as an example.

c) Why is the insertion sort method not always the most suitable one to use? In what circumstances would its use be sensible?

WJEC 89 Paper 2 Q10

38 Glossary of Terms

This glossary contains definitions of the technical terms introduced and used in the book. In a few cases, a word or phrase has more than one meaning depending on the context. When this occurs, the alternative meanings are marked.

absolute address an address which identifies a memory location without any modification being required.

abstract data type a data type defined in terms of its abstract properties, without regard to its representation on any particular medium.

acceptance testing testing of a newly developed hardware or software system by its intending users.

access privilege a property of a file or memory segment, indicating the extent to which the information in the file or segment may be shared.

accumulator a register storing a data item during processing.

acoustic coupler a device used for data transmission and reception which interfaces with a telephone handset.

address a number which locates a particular storage location in main store or on certain types of backing store.

address generation the process of obtaining the address of a record in a random file from the key of the record.

address modification indexed, indirect or relative addressing.

address space the set of all addressable locations in a computer memory.

addressing mode the method of addressing used in a particular machine instruction.

algorithm a description of the steps needed to carry out a task.

alphanumeric character a character which may be a letter or a digit.

American Standard Code for Information Interchange (ASCII) a code commonly used for data transmission, and becoming a standard for data representation in memory and on storage media.

analogue control system a control system which uses analogue signals.

analogue data data in the form of physical signals where the strength of the signal is proportional to the magnitude of the data.

analogue-to-digital converter (ADC) an interface which converts between analogue and digital data representations of data.

application generator a software tool which generates certain types of application programs automatically from specification.

application-specific integrated circuit (Asic) an integrated circuit designed for a particular function.

applications programmer a programmer whose work is concerned with developing applications software.

arithmetic and logic unit (ALU) the part of a processor where arithmetic and logical operations are performed.

array a fixed number of data items of identical type, stored together in memory, with each element accessible via an array index.

artificial intelligence the ability of a computer to behave in a way which, if it were the behaviour of a person, would be regarded as intelligent.

artwork the diagrams showing the layouts of the layers of an integrated circuit or printed circuit board.

assembler a program which translates from the assembly language to the machine language of a particular computer.

assembly language a programming language whose data structures correspond to the physical structure of the registers and main store of its host computer, and whose instructions are closely related to the machine instructions of the computer.

assignment the process whereby a variable takes on a value.

associative store a cache store which, when supplied with the value of a data item, returns the address of the item.

attribute a property of a data item in a file on a database system.

background processor a subsidiary processor in a multiprocessor configuration which runs modules of applications under the control of the foreground processor.

backing store permanent storage for large quantities of data, accessible to a processor.

backing store control unit a unit which controls the flow of data to and from a set of backing store devices.

Backus-Naur form (BNF) a notation for writing syntax rules.

bar code a character code in terms of patterns of thick and thin stripes.

base language the language in which a compiler is written.

base register a register which holds the start (lowest) address of the area of memory which a process is permitted to use.

baseband a technique of data transmission where the encoded data is sent directly along the communications medium, without a carrier signal.

batch processing the running of a number of programs in succession, in a batch.

batch processing system a type of data processing application where the data is processed, not as individual items or records, but in batches.

batch total the total of various numeric items in a batch of input data.

baud a rate of data transmission which is approximately equal to one bit per second.

beat the time interval for one stage of a pipelined operation.

beta test the second stage of testing a hardware or software product, by certain prospective users.

biased exponent a method of writing the exponent of a

floating point number where a fixed number, the bias, is subtracted from the exponent in order to determine the power of two.

binary   base two.

binary coded decimal (BCD)   a numeric code in which each decimal digit is coded separately in binary.

binary search   a method of searching a file involving partitioning it into successively smaller subsets, each of which is known to contain the required record.

binary tree   a tree in which each node may have at most two subtrees.

bistable   see flip-flop.

bit   a binary digit, a 0 or a 1.

bit map   an area of memory in which a screen image is stored as the set of bits which make up the image.

bit serial data transmission   the transmission of data one bit at a time.

block   (1) the unit of data transferred to or from a magnetic tape or disk in one operation, and stored as a physically separate entity.

block   (2) a structural element in programs in certain high level languages.

blocking factor   the number of records per block in a file stored on a magnetic tape or disk.

blocking strategy   the method of allocating records to physical blocks of a backing store medium.

block-structured language   a high level programming language which allows programs to be structured in blocks.

Boolean algebra   a system of notation for Boolean logic.

Boolean logic   the theory of mathematical logic, first investigated by George Boole.

Boolean operation   an operation which transforms one or more Boolean variables, producing a Boolean variable as a result.

Boolean variable   a variable which can have either of two values only.

bootstrap loader   a program which, with minimal assistance, loads itself onto a computer and then enables other programs to be loaded.

branch   a transfer of control from one part of a program to another.

breadth-first search   a search technique in which all the alternatives are considered before the detailed consequences of any one are examined; compare with depth-first search.

breakpoint   an instruction which causes the running of a program to be suspended.

broadband   a technique of data transmission in which the data is sent along the communications medium 'on top of' a carrier signal.

buffer   a storage area for data in transit to or from main store or a peripheral device.

build   to construct a program from its constituent modules.

bus   a set of connections for the transmission of data, address and control signals within a computer.

byte   a set of bits containing the code for one character, generally eight bits.

cache store   a small, fast memory acting as a buffer between a processor and a large main store.

call   to transfer control to a procedure, function or subprogram.

carry bit   a bit which is set if there is a carry out of the most significant place during addition.

carry prediction circuits   logic circuits used in fast parallel adders to determine the value of each carry directly from the inputs.

cell   (1) a storage space in a computer memory.

cell   (2) the storage space for one element in a spreadsheet.

central processing unit (CPU)   the unit of a computer system in which processing takes place.

character code   a code in which each character is coded separately as a set of binary digits.

character printer   a printer which prints one character at a time.

character set   (1) the set of characters which can be represented in a particular character code.

character set   (2) the set of all characters which may be used by a particular computer or programming language.

check digit   a character appended to a data item (generally numeric) which enables the validity of the item to be checked.

check sum   a data item appended to a transmitted block of data, containing the sum of the codes of other bytes or words in the block.

chip   a common word for integrated circuit.

circular buffer   a fixed area of store containing a queue, in which the rear of the queue 'wraps around' to the top of the area whenever it reaches the bottom.

circular list   a list in which items are linked in a closed loop.

clock cycle   the basic timing interval of a digital electronic system.

clock pulse generator   a device which generates timing pulses for an electronic system.

cluster adaptor   see multiplexer.

Codasyl   the official committee which administers the standards and upgrades of Cobol.

code generation   the production of object code during the compilation process.

command-driven interface   a user interface which operates by means of a set of commands entered by the user.

commissioning   starting up and testing a new computer.

communications processor   a processor handling the communications traffic between a main processor and a communications network.

common block   a block of data which is common to more than one segment of a program.

compact disk read-only memory (CD-ROM)   a compact optical disk used as read-only backing store.

compiler   a program which accepts a source program in a high level language and translates it into an object program in a machine language.

complex instruction set computer (Cisc)   a processor with a large set of machine instructions.

complimentary metal oxide silicon (CMOS)   a technique for fabricating integrated circuits.

compression   a technique for the reduction of the number of characters transmitted in a data communication system.

computer a collection of resources, including digital electronic processing devices, stored programs and sets of data, which, under the control of the stored programs, automatically inputs, processes, stores, retrieves and outputs data, and may also transmit and receive data.

computer-aided design (CAD) the design of buildings, engineering structures, integrated circuits and similar objects with the aid of a computer system.

computer-aided software engineering (Case) software development with the assistance of integrated software development tools.

computer architect a person responsible for the overall design of a computer.

computer-based control system a control system based on a computer.

computer operator a person who operates a computer.

computer output on microfilm (COM) reducing displayed output onto microfilm.

condition code a bit which indicates the current status of a processor.

Conference on Data Systems Languages (Codasyl) the overall steering committee for the maintenance and development of Cobol.

console log a record of all the commands to an operating system, and messages from the system, in chronological order.

constant a data item which retains the same value throughout the running of a program.

content-addressable store see associative store.

control algorithm the algorithm which determines the operation of a control system.

control character a character used in data transmission to perform some control function.

control memory memory (generally a special portion of ROM) in which microcode is stored.

control switch a solid-state switch regulates the passage of data on a bus.

control system a system which monitors and controls the behaviour of another system (the operational system).

control total see batch total.

control unit the unit which controls the step-by-step operation of a processor.

co-processor a processor which acts in parallel with another processor.

cross assembler an assembler which runs on a different computer from the one for which it is assembling programs.

cursor a character which highlights the position on the screen where the next typed character will appear.

cylinder a set of tracks, vertically above each other on magnetic disk pack, which can be accessed with the read-write head in the same position.

data information in a coded form, acceptable for input to, and processing by, a computer system.

data capture the process of obtaining data for a computer system.

data channel a pathway for the passage of data inside a computer.

data communications system a network which handles data communications.

data controller a person who controls the flow of data to a computer.

data dictionary a table giving the properties of the data files in a database system.

data driven control the control of a parallel computer architecture by the requirements of the data flowing through the system.

data encryption the representation of data in a secret code.

data entry staff people who operate data entry terminals.

data highway see data channel.

data independence the separation of the (logical) data model of a database from the (physical) structure of the stored data.

data model the logical structure of the data as it appears at a particular level of a database system.

data processing a general term describing the work done by a computer.

data processing cycle the sequence of steps of the development and maintenance of a data processing application.

data processing department the division or section of a company with direct responsibility for data processing.

data processing manager (DPM) the person in charge of a data processing department.

data security the application of safeguards to protect data from accidental or deliberate misuse.

data structure a set of data in which individual items are related in a particular way, and on which certain precisely specified operations can be performed.

data type a data item or data structure having certain properties.

database a collection of stored operational data used by all the application systems of an organisation.

database administrator (DBA) the person in charge of the overall running of a database system.

database management system (DBMS) the software responsible for all aspects of the creation, accessing and updating of a database.

database package a software package which allows a user to create, update and access files of data.

database system a computer system centred on a database.

dataflow architecture a type of parallel computer architecture in which a network of processors reflects the structure of the processing operations, and items of data flow through the network.

deadlock the situation arising when two programs prevent each other from continuing because each holds a resource needed by the other.

declaration a statement of the name and type of a variable in a program.

declarative language a programming language which expresses programs as a set of logical relationships between items of data.

decoder a logic circuit which selects one of a number of outputs according to the code of an input signal.

dedicated computer a computer designed for a specific task or narrow range of tasks.

dedicated register a register with one specific function.

default option   the menu option selected unless the user explicitly selects a different option.

default value   the value assigned to a data item unless explicitly overwritten by a user.

depth-first search   a search technique in which all the consequences of one particular alternative are considered before another alternative is examined; compare with breadth-first search.

descriptor file   a file in a database system which describes the data in another file.

descriptor register   a register which contains information about a data structure currently being accessed.

desktop   a screen representation of a desktop on which a number of icons are displayed, forming part of a user interface.

desktop publishing   the use of a desktop microcomputer to prepare, typeset and compose publications.

device   a physical unit which carries out some operation.

device driver   a software module which controls the operation of a particular device, such as a disk drive.

diagnostic error message   a message output by a compiler, indicating the location and cause of an error in a program.

diagnostics   the process of locating an error and determining its cause, carried out by a compiler.

diagnostic program   a program which examines the current state of a computer, displaying the contents of various registers and store locations.

dictionary   a set of information created and accessed during the compilation process.

diffusion   a technique for placing a precisely controlled amount of impurities on the surface of a chip wafer.

digital   the representation of data in discrete quantities.

digital control system   a control system which uses digital signals.

digital plotter   an output device which draws maps, plans, engineering drawings, etc.

digital-to-analogue converter (DAC)   an interface which converts data from digital to analogue form.

dimension   the number of indices associated with an array.

direct data entry (DDE)   data entry directly onto backing store.

direct memory access (DMA)   direct access by peripheral devices to main store, bypassing processor registers.

directive   an assembly language instruction which does not have a counterpart in machine language.

directory   a table of the files or records to be found on a particular magnetic disk or disk sector.

disable interrupts   to make a processor unreceptive to interrupts.

disk buffer   a portion of memory which holds segments of data during transfer to or from magnetic disk.

disk cartridge   an enclosure containing a single exchangeable disk.

disk crash   a read-write head coming into contact with the surface of a magnetic disk, and damaging both the disk and the read-write head.

disk drive   a device which reads from and writes to a magnetic disk.

disk pack   a set of magnetic disks on a common shaft.

distributed array processor (DAP)   a processor with parallel elements which can carry out an operation on all the elements of an array simultaneously.

DMA controller   a device which controls the direct memory access mechanism in a computer.

documentation   a written description of how a program works, how it is to be used, or how it is to be run on a computer.

doping   the process of implanting a chip wafer with carefully controlled amounts of impurities.

dump   to copy an entire file onto another storage medium, generally from a magnetic disk onto a magnetic tape.

dynamic data structure   a data structure which changes in size while in use.

dynamic memory   solid-state storage in which data 'leaks away' and must be refreshed periodically.

editor   a utility program which allows other programs or data files to be typed and edited.

electronic mail (E-mail)   a system running on a computer network which enables messages to be sent from one user to others.

electronics engineer   an engineer who specialises in the design and construction of electronic systems.

emitter coupled logic (ECL)   a technique for manufacturing high-speed integrated circuits.

emulate   to simulate the behaviour of one computer, at machine language level, on another computer.

enable   to activate a logic circuit or component.

enable interrupts   to make a processor receptive to interrupts.

enabling technology   a fundamental technology which paves the way for subsequent developments.

encryption key   a number which enables encrypted data to be decoded.

erasable programmable read-only memory (EPROM)   programmable read-only memory which can be erased and re-programmed.

etching   dissolving away the unwanted areas in a layer of a chip wafer.

even parity   see parity bit

evidential reasoning   a technique of knowledge processing based on the way in which bodies of evidence are evaluated in order to draw conclusions.

exception call   a call to an operating system from a user program when an error condition arises.

exchangeable disk pack   a set of magnetic disks which can be removed from a disk drive.

execute   to carry out a machine instruction or a program.

expert system   a computer system which automates a measure of human expertise in a particular field.

expert system shell   a software package containing the deductive aspects of an expert system without any particular knowledge base.

exponent   the power of two of a floating point number.

feasibility study   a preliminary study of a proposed

data processing application, which indicates whether or not further investigation and development should take place.

feedback   a property of a control system, when the output of the control system affects the input into the control system.

fetch   the phase of an instruction cycle in which a machine instruction is fetched from store.

field   the place allocated for a particular data item, on a data storage medium, or in a data structure such as a record.

field engineer   an engineer who commissions, maintains and upgrades computers at user sites.

fieldwidth   the number of characters in a field of a file.

FIFO   first-in-first-out, describing a queue.

fifth generation computer   a computer which applies reasoning to a knowledge base in order to solve highly complex problems.

file   a collection of related data, structured in a particular way, and used for a particular purpose.

file dump   a copy of a file on a backup medium such as magnetic tape.

file librarian   a person responsible for the magnetic tape and magnetic disk files at a computer installation.

file overflow   the situation which arises when the storage space allocated to hold a file, or a portion of a file, becomes insufficient for the data in the file.

file processing log   a record of all the processing steps carried out on a file.

file processing system   a type of data processing application where the emphasis is on the periodic updating of files.

firmware   software permanently stored on read-only memory.

fixed point number   a number in which the binary point occupies a fixed position.

flag   a single bit register used in the control and synchronisation of peripheral devices.

flip-flop   a logic circuit which has two stable output states. An input signal can cause it to 'flip' from one state to the other.

floating point number   a number expressed as the product of a fraction of magnitude between 1/2 and 1 and an integral power of two.

floppy disk   a small flexible magnetic disk.

flow soldering machine   a machine which solders all the chips on a printed circuit board in one operation.

foreground processor   the processor in a multiprocessor configuration which is in overall control, and provides external links to the background processors.

format   the layout of input, output or stored data.

fourth generation language (4GL)   a programming language which generates code from certain types of specifications.

frame   the coding area for one character on magnetic tape, being a row of bit coding positions across the width of the tape.

front panel   the front surface of a unit, generally containing switches and indicator lights.

front-end processor   a processor which controls flow of data into and out of a main processor.

full adder   a logic circuit which adds two bits, together with a previous carry, to produce a sum and a carry.

full duplex   describes data transmission in both directions simultaneously.

function   a module of a program which evaluates a function, and which is invoked from any point in the program at which the function is used.

functional decomposition   a technique of program design by expressing the operation of the program as a mathematical function, and then specifying the detailed steps as subsidiary functions.

functional specification   a document which states how an item of hardware or software, or a computer applicaiton, is intended to operate.

gate   a functional element which carries out a Boolean operation in a logic circuit.

gate array   see uncommitted logic array.

general-purpose computer   a computer capable of a wide range of applications.

gate delay   the time interval between a change in the input signals at a gate and the stabilisation of its output signal in its new state.

gateway   a link between one data communications network and another.

general-purpose language   a programming language, in most cases a high level language, suitable for a wide variety of applications.

general-purpose register   a register which can fulfil a number of functions.

generate-and-test   a process often used in artificial intelligence software, to investigate all the possible consequences of some action, and evaluate them in some way.

global variable   a variable whose scope is an entire program.

grandfather-father-son principle   a method of ensuring the security of data by keeping three generations of a file, as well as the information needed to update the generations.

graph reduction architecture   a type parallel computer architecture in which the task to be performed is represented as a graph, and processing operations are carried out in order to reduce the graph to obtain a single result.

graphics terminal   a VDU capable of graphics displays.

Gray code   a data code in which the code for each character differs in one bit position only from that for the previous character.

half adder   a logic circuit which adds two bits, producing a sum bit and a carry bit.

half duplex   describes data transmission in alternate directions, but not in both directions simultaneously.

Hamming code   a data code with sufficient built-in checking for a single bit error to be corrected and a multiple bit error to be detected.

hardware   the physical components, including the integrated circuits, printed circuit boards and connections which make up a computer.

hard-wired control   the execution of machine or control instructions directly by hardware.

hash total   the total of various numeric items within a record.

hashing an address generation technique, where the address of the first possible location of a record is generated.

hexadecimal base sixteen.

hierarchical data model a database structure based on a tree configuration.

high level language an application-oriented programming language, one which is a convenient and simple means of describing the information structures and sequences of actions required to perform a particular task.

high order digits a group of digits in a number with the highest place values.

high resolution graphics graphics displays with a fine level of detail.

icon a symbol displayed on screen as part of a user interface, representing an object such as a file.

immediate access store storage in which each location can be written to or read from immediately.

immediate operand a data item located in a machine or assembly language instruction.

implementation the putting into practice of a design or concept, under a particular set of circumstances.

implementation language the version of a programming language as implemented on a particular type of computer.

incremental dump a backup of only those files which have been updated since the last backup.

index (1) a variable which indicates the position of an element in an array.

index (2) a table storing the keys to records in a file, and their positions in the file.

indexed address an address to which the contents of an index register must be added in order to obtain an absolute address.

indexed sequential file a sequential file which includes an index relating the key of each record to its address.

indirect address an address which locates the address of a data item.

information the meaning given to data by the way it is interpreted.

information processing a general term used to describe the work done by a computer.

information storage/retrieval a type of data processing application where one or more large stores of information are continuously kept up to date, and may be accessed at any time.

input data supplied to a computer from its environment.

input device a device which supplies input to a processor.

instruction cycle the sequence of actions require to carry out one machine instruction.

instruction decoder a set of logic circuits which interpret an instruction as a sequence of control signals.

instruction register (IR) a register which contains the current program instruction.

instruction set the set of machine language instructions for a particular type of computer.

integrated circuit a single solid-state unit, containing a number of transistors and other components, which

performs one or more logic operations.

intelligent knowledge based system (IKBS) a computer system which applies techniques of artificial intelligence to sets of knowledge in order to solve problems.

intelligent terminal a terminal which incorporates a certain amount of processing capability.

intelligent user interface a user interface which is designed in accordance with the requirements and way of thinking of the user, possibly using a natural language.

interface a point of contact between one module and another, or between a module and its environment.

interpreter a program which enables a computer to run programs in a high level language, statement by statement.

interrupt an external signal causing the execution of a program to be suspended.

interrupt line a signal line used to generate an interrupt.

interrupt service routine a program module which provides the initial response of a processor to an interrupt.

inter-block gap a gap left between successive blocks on a magnetic tape.

ion implantation a technique for doping a layer of an integrated circuit, during construction.

job control language (JCL) the language in which instructions to an operating system are written.

Josephson junction a solid-state switch, working at a temperature close to absolute zero, which forms the basis of a high-speed logic circuit.

K a unit of stored data, $1K = 2^{10} = 1024$.

Karnaugh map a table used for the simplification of logic expressions.

kernel the most privileged layer of an operating system, which contains the protection mechanism and certain direct hardware interfaces.

key a data field which identifies a record.

knowledge-based system a system which draws reasoned inferences from a body of knowledge.

label a sequence of characters which identifies a program line.

large scale integration (LSI) the inclusion of thousands of transistors and other components on a single integrated circuit.

leaf a terminal node of a tree.

level of privilege a figure which determines the degree of access a program has to system resources.

lexical analysis the first stage in the analysis of a source program by a compiler.

LIFO last-in-first out, describing a stack.

limit register a register which holds the end (highest) address of the area of memory which a process is permitted to use.

line printer a printer which prints all the characters in an entire line in one operation.

linkage editor a portion of systems software which links separate modules of a program into single executable module.

linked list see list.

list a set of data items, stored in some order, where data items may be inserted or deleted at any point within the set.

load-and-go compiler a compiler which translates, links, loads and runs applications programs in a single sequence of operations.

loader a portion of systems software which copies a machine language program into the store it will occupy during execution, and adjusts any relative addresses contained in the program.

local area network a data communication system connecting a number of computers, servers and other devices in the same vicinity.

local variable a variable whose scope is limited to the block of the program in which it was declared.

location the storage space for one data item.

logic circuit a circuit connecting a number of logic elements.

loop a portion of a program which is repeated.

low level language a machine or assembly language.

M a unit of stored data, $1M = 2^{20} = 1\,048\,576$.

machine language a programming language which controls the hardware of a particular type of processor directly.

macro-instruction a single instruction in an assembly language or a system command language, which represents a group of instructions.

magnetic disk a data storage medium comprising a metal or plastic disk coated with a magnetisable substance.

magnetic ink character recognition (MICR) recognition of characters printed in a magnetic ink.

magnetic tape unit a device which reads from and writes to magnetic tape.

main store solid-state storage directly accessible to a processor.

mainframe a large computer, consisting of a number of free-standing units.

mantissa the fraction part of a floating point number.

mark sensing detection of shaded areas in a document.

mask a logic circuit which selects certain bits of a data item.

masking using a template to mark the areas of a layer on a chip wafer which are to be etched away.

medium a physical substance on which data is stored.

medium scale integration (MSI) the inclusion of hundreds of transistors and other components on a single integrated circuit.

megabyte one million bytes.

memory address register a register, connected to a main store via a decoder, which holds the address currently being accessed within the store.

memory cycle the sequence of steps to read a data item from, or write a data item to main store.

memory data register a register which holds a data item during transfer to or from a main store.

memory map a diagram showing the allocation of regions of the address space of a computer for particular purposes.

menu-driven interface a user interface which operates by the user selecting options from a set of menus.

merging the process of combining two ordered sets of data to produce a single ordered set.

message switching the routing of a message from its origin to its destination in a data communications network.

metal oxide silicon (MOS) a method of manufacturing integrated circuits.

metallisation evaporating a thin layer of a metal onto the surface of a chip wafer.

microcode instructions which carry out the steps of a machine instruction at the level of opening and closing gates.

microprocessor a single chip containing a complete processing unit.

microsecond millionth of a second.

microcomputer a computer based on a microprocessor.

mnemonic a group of letters, generally representing an operation code in an assembly language.

modem a modulator/demodulator, a device which forms the interface between a computer and a telephone line used for data transmission.

module an interchangeable unit, performing a specific function, and having a specific interface to its environment.

module library a library of procedures and functions in object code, which can be linked to other object code modules to form an executable program.

module testing testing of individual modules of a program before combining them.

most significant digit the digit in a number with the highest place value.

multiplexer a device which interleaves communication from a number of data channels onto a single data channel.

multiprogramming a method of computer operation where a number of programs are in various stages of running at any time.

multi-access the simultaneous access of a number of users, via terminals, to a computer.

multi-port memory a memory which has a number of input/output ports.

nanosecond one thousand millionth of a second.

network administrator the person in charge of the running of a computer network.

network architecture a computer configuration containing a number of communicating processors and other devices.

network data model a database structure based on a series of links between data items, forming a network.

node a data item in a tree.

noise interference in a data communication channel.

normalisation adjusting the binary point in a floating point number so that the magnitude of the fraction part is between 1/2 and 1.

n-type semiconductor a layer of semiconductor which has been doped to contain an excess of electrons.

nucleus the lowest software level of an operating system, providing a small number of essential services to higher levels.

null pointer a pointer which does not point to anything.

object language the language into which programs are translated by a compiler or assembler.

object module a program in the object language of a compiler or assembler.

octal base eight.

odd parity see parity bit.

offset the number of addresses from the start of a data structure to a particular element in the structure.

ones complements a binary code in which the most significant bit represents one less (in magnitude) than the corresponding twos complement value.

operand a data item used in a machine instruction.

operating system a program, or set of programs, driving the raw hardware of a computer, which manages the resources of the computer in accordance with certain objectives, presenting higher levels of software with a simplified virtual machine.

operation code the part of a machine instruction which determines the type of operation to be carried out.

operation table see truth table.

operational system a system which is controlled by a control system.

operations manager the person in charge of the running of a computer installation.

operator documentation an account of the operator procedures needed to run a program.

operator's console the device which enables the person operating a computer to interact with it.

optical character recognition (OCR) recognition of printed characters by a light scanning process.

optimisation producing of the most efficient object code by a compiler or assembler.

ordered list a list in which items are in numerical or alphabetical order.

original equipment manufacture (OEM) the manufacture of components such as integrated circuits, switches, casings, etc. for computers and associated devices.

output data supplied to its environment by a computer.

output device a device which supplies data from a computer to its environment.

overflow the occurrence of a numerical result which is outside the limits imposed by the number representation used.

overflow bit a status bit which is set when overflow occurs.

overlay a portion of the code of a program which is held on backing store and copied into main store when needed.

oxidation the process which forms an insulating layer of silicon dioxide on a chip wafer.

packed decimal a BCD code using four bits per decimal digit.

packet a unit of transmitted data, enclosed by strings of control characters.

packet switching the routing of data packets from their origin to their destination across a data communications network.

packing density the ratio of the amount of backing store space used by a file to the total amount available.

page a set of consecutive memory cells, the contents of which are swapped to and from backing store in order to create a virtual memory.

page table a table which associates virtual page numbers with the addresses of the corresponding pages in memory.

palette the set of colours which can be displayed on a colour screen.

parallel adder a logic circuit which adds all the bits of two numbers at the same time.

parallel data transmission the transmission of a number of data bits simultaneously, generally by means of multi-strand cable.

parallelism the performance of several actions simultaneously inside a processor.

parity a method of self-checking involving the use of a parity bit.

parity bit a bit in the code for a data item which is set to a 0 or a 1 so that the total number of 1s in the data item is even, for even parity, or odd, for odd parity.

parity check a check to determine whether the parity of a data item is correct.

parsing (1) the application of a set of rules of syntax to a source program by a compiler.

parsing (2) the application of the rules of syntax to a passage in a natural language in order to analyse its structure.

peripheral a device, linked to a processor, which performs an input, output, storage or data communication function.

photoresist a light-sensitive substance used in the process of masking and etching chip wafers.

pipelining a processing technique using an independent unit for each stage of an operation, the units being connected in sequence via buffers.

pixel a picture element - an illuminated spot which makes up a picture or character on a display screen.

place value the weighting assigned to a digit in a number, depending on its position.

plug-compatible describes items of computer equipment which can be connected together directly.

p-n junction a junction between a p-type semiconductor and an n-type semiconductor.

pointer (1) a data item which contains the address of another data item.

pointer (2) an arrow displayed on the screen which is moved by corresponding movements of a mouse, in order to select objects or menu options.

polling checking peripheral devices at regular intervals to see if they have data to transmit, or are ready to receive data.

pop to remove a data item from the top of a stack.

portable describes programs which can be run on more than one type of computer.

Postscript an industry-standard page description language in which publications are sent to printers by desktop publishing systems.

precedence the order in which operations in an expression are carried out.

precision a measure of how closely a number can

approximate its exact value.

predicate a logical relationship between two or more items.

predicate calculus the formal techniques for applying the rules of inference to predicates.

procedure see subprogram.

procedural language a programming language which expresses programs as sequences of operations to be carried out by a computer.

procedural learning a technique of knowledge processing based on the way in which experts acquire specialised knowledge.

process control the continuous monitoring and/or controlling of an operational process by a computer.

processor a unit, printed circuit board or single chip in which processing takes place.

production rule a rule which specifies how a syntactic structure or element of a knowledge base is derived from another syntactic structure or element of a knowledge base.

program a set of instructions which controls the operation of a computer.

program counter (PC) a register which stores the address of the current program instruction.

program design a method of carrying out the sequence of steps from the initial concept of a program to the final tested and accepted code.

program documentation an account of the structure and workings of a program.

program specification a document which states the objectives and main functional steps of a computer program.

program status bit see condition code

program structure the way in which a program is built up from its constituent modules.

program testing a series of tests carried out by the developers of a program or program module before passing it for system testing.

programmable control a technique of system control based on a stored program (in contrast to hard-wired control).

programmable read-only memory (PROM) read-only memory which can be loaded under program control.

programmer a person responsible for designing, writing, testing, correcting, maintaining and documenting computer programs.

prompt a message or symbol displayed by a computer system inviting input from the user.

proof of correctness a sequence of logical assertions by which the correctness of a program module is proved under stated conditions.

proposition an association between two or more items, linked by a logical relationship.

protection the prevention of unauthorised access to programs, data or areas in memory.

protocol a set of rules, used in data communication systems, which specify the packet structure and the procedures to be followed for transmission and reception.

prototype a demonstration version of a proposed computer system or program, in order to check that the initial specifications are correct.

pseudo-operation see directive.

publication language the version of a programming language used for the publication of algorithms.

push to insert a data item on the top of a stack.

push-down list see stack.

push-down stack see stack

p-type semiconductor a semiconductor which has been doped to contain a shortage of electrons.

qualifier an additional item of information entered together with a command, indicating how the command is to be carried out.

queue a data structure in which items are added at the rear and removed from the front.

quicksort a particularly efficient method of sorting data.

random access describes a data storage medium or file structure where the time taken to access a data item is independent of its position on the medium or in the file.

random access memory (RAM) solid-state storage, in which data can be accessed from any location.

random file a file in which records are not in any order, but are located by an address generation technique.

read-only memory (ROM) solid-state storage which can be read from but not written to.

read-write head a device which detects or creates magnetised areas on a disk or tape.

real-time processing processing which must keep pace with some operation which is external to the computer.

record a set of data items which are related in some way, generally forming the unit of data in a larger structure such as a file.

recursion the capability of a procedure or function to call itself.

reduced instruction set computer (Risc) a processor with a small number of machine instructions which processes them extremely rapidly.

reference language the definitive version of a programming language, independent of any implementation constraints.

register a storage element for one data item, for a particular purpose such as control, processing or data transmission.

relational data model a database structure based on a set of tables which define relationships between data items.

relative address the offset of a data item from the machine instruction containing the address.

relocatable code instructions and data which can be moved in main store without the need to change any addresses within the code.

remote job entry (RJE) the submission of programs for processing at sites remote from the computer.

report generation the process of summarising the information in a file and generating a report containing this summary information.

reserved word a word which has a defined meaning in the context of a programming language.

reset (1) the input to a flip-flop, a signal on which causes the flip-flop to change to its 0 state.

reset (2) the updating of a program counter so that it

contains the address of the next machine instruction.

resource a functional unit, portion of memory, program or set of data within a computer.

result register temporary storage for the output from logic circuits.

ring a local area network based on a closed loop of cable.

root the node at the 'top' of a tree.

root directory the top level directory in a hierarchical directory structure.

rounding error the error introduced in a number when it is rounded to a certain number of binary or decimal places.

rule of inference a general logical rule which is used in predicate calculus.

rule of precedence a rule which establishes in what order other rules are applied to data items.

run-time diagnostics a set of procedures provided by a software development system in order to check a program while it is running.

sampling frequency the frequency at which analogue signal is sampled by an analogue-to-digital converter.

scalar processor a processor based on single registers and sets of processing circuits; compare with vector processor.

scheduler part of an operating system which determines the sequence in which programs are run.

scope the part of a program in which a particular variable can be used.

searching the process of locating a record in a file or data structure, given the key of the record.

second source an alternative source of supply for a component of a computer.

sector a unit of stored data on a magnetic disk.

segment a portion of memory used for a particular purpose.

self-checking code a code which contains enough information within the coded form of the data item to determine whether the data item has been coded or transmitted correctly.

semantic network a network structure for the representation of knowledge on a computer.

semantics the meaning of a passage in a natural language.

semiconductor a material such as silicon which conducts electricity better than an insulator such as porcelain but not as well as a conductor such as copper.

sequencing the flow of control from one program instruction to the next.

sequential file a file in which the records are in order of one or more keys.

sequential search a method of searching a file by accessing each record in turn until the required record is found.

serial access describes a data storage medium where the time taken to access a data item depends on its position in the medium.

serial adder a logic circuit which adds the bits of two input numbers one pair at a time.

serial data transmission the transmission of data, using a single communications medium, one bit at a time.

serial file a file in which the records are in no particular order.

set the input to a flip-flop, a signal on which causes the flip-flop to change to its 1 state.

shell the layer of an operating system closest to the hardware of the computer.

shift register a register which enables bits of a data item to be shifted from one position to the next.

side effect the inadvertent alteration of the value of a variable by a step of a program.

sign-and-magnitude code a code in which the sign of a number and its magnitude are represented separately.

sign extension copying the sign of a low order byte into all the bits of the high order byte of a word.

simplex describes data transmission in one direction only.

single program operation a type of computer operation where only one program is run at a time.

slave store see cache store

soak test running a computer, component, chip or program for a long time in order to detect any malfunctions.

software the programs which direct the operation of a computer.

software development environment an integrated set of cross-compilers, program generators and other software development tools, used in the development of applications software.

software development tool a set of programs which assists in the development of certain types of applications software.

software engineer a person who designs and writes computer programs in accordance with the principles of software engineering.

software engineering the development of software which satisfies strict conditions of correctness and performance, in a scheduled, budgeted and cost-effective way.

software front panel software which displays the contents of processor registers on the screen of an operator's console.

software house a company whose activities are centred on the production of computer software.

software lifecycle the cycle of design, development, installation and maintenance of a software item.

software package a complete, self-contained computer program which is designed to be purchased and used by a large number of users for a particular task.

sorting the process of arranging the data items in a structure, particularly the records in a file, in some order.

source document an original document containing data for input into a computer system.

source language the programming language which is accepted for translation by a compiler of assembler.

source program a program, in a high level language, which forms the input for a compiler.

special character a character such as a punctuation mark which is not an alphanumeric character.

specification language a programming language, above the level of high level languages, for stating the specifications of a task.

spooling maintaining a queue, on backing store, of data

for output, generally by a printer.

spreadsheet a software package which stores and processes tables of numbers and other data.

stack a collection of data items which may only be accessed at one end.

stack base the fixed end of a stack.

stack pointer (SP) (1) a pointer which indicates the current address of the top of a stack.

stack pointer (SP) (2) a register which contains the current address of the top of the stack in a computer memory.

standard form a way of writing decimal numbers as the product of a fraction between 0 and 1 and an integral power of ten.

statement an instruction in a high level programming language.

static data structure a data structure which stays the same size once it has been created.

static memory solid-state storage which retains data as long as power is switched on.

status bits see condition codes.

stepwise refinement a top-down technique of program design, starting with an initial statement of the overall steps of a program, and expanding each step as a set of more detailed steps until enough detail has been added to form the basis of the code of the program.

store and forward a type of packet switching where data is stored at intermediate points while in transit.

string (1) a set of characters stored together.

string (2) a subset of a file which is small enough to be accommodated in a computer main store.

subfile a file containing a subset of the records of another file.

subprogram a portion of a program, which carries out a specific task, to which control can be transferred from any point in the program, and from which control to the point from which it was called.

subroutine see subprogram.

subsystem a part of a system which accomplishes a part of the goals of the system.

subtree a portion of a tree, itself having a tree structure.

sum of products a form of a logic expression comprising a number of product terms (linked by the AND operation) which are connected by the OR operation.

supercomputer a large mainframe computer.

symbolic address a group of characters which represent the address of a data item or instruction.

syntax (1) the rules which govern the structure of a program in a particular language.

syntax (2) the rules which govern the makeup of sentences in a natural language.

syntax analysis the determination of the structure of a source program by a compiler.

syntax error a violation of a syntax rule of a programming language by a program written in the language.

system a collection of parts working together towards some common goals.

system development the sequence of steps from the completion of the design of a system until it has been accepted for operational use.

system design the sequence of steps from the initial specification of a data processing system to the stage where the system is ready to be programmed.

system diagram see system flowchart.

system flowchart a diagram showing the overall structure of and flow of data through a system.

system implementation the process of putting a computer system to work in a particular environment.

system investigation an initial feasibility study to determine whether or not work should proceed on the design and development of a computer system.

system maintenance the periodic alteration of some aspect of a data processing system in the light of experience or changing requirements.

system manager a person in charge of the running of a computer system.

system specification an outline of a proposed data processing application, including a statement of the objectives of the system, and a summary of the overall working of the system.

system testing the testing of a data processing system as a whole.

systems analyst a person responsible for the analysis and overall design of a data processing system.

systems programmer a programmer whose work is concerned with systems software.

systems software the layers of software, generally comprising operating systems, assemblers and compilers which transform the hardware of a computer into an application-oriented machine.

target language the language into which programs are translated by a compiler.

teletype a terminal comprising a keyboard and a character printer.

terminal a general-purpose input/output device.

terminal node a node at the 'bottom' of a tree.

test data data which is specifically designed to test the working of a program.

three level memory a computer memory consisting of cache store, main store and backing store.

time sharing a method of computer operation which allows computing time to be shared among a number of users.

time slicing a scheduling policy in which each program is in turn allowed a short interval of processor time.

token a set of characters representing a syntactic object during compilation or assembly.

top-down method a technique of program design which starts with a statement of the overall steps of a program and adds detail in a systematic way.

top of stack the point at which data items may be added to or removed from a stack.

track (1) a circular path on the surface of a magnetic disk, on which consecutive bits of data are recorded.

track (2) a row of bit coding positions along the length of magnetic tape.

track (3) a thin metal conducting strip on a printed circuit board.

transaction processing (1) a type of data processing application where transactions are processed in real time.

transaction processing (2) a type of operating system

which controls the running of programs so that transactions are processed in real time.

transistor an electronic component, one or more of which can be made to carry out a logic operation.

transistor-transistor logic (TTL) a method of manufacturing integrated circuits.

transputer a single-chip processor with on-board memory designed as the processing element in a parallel computer architecture.

tree a hierarchical data structure, in which each element is linked to one element above it, and zero, one or more elements below it.

tree sort a sorting technique based on the use of a tree.

tree traversal a systematic scan of all the nodes of a tree.

truncation error an error which occurs when bits of a number are discarded, without any rounding taking place.

truth table a table which shows, for a particular logic operation, the values of the output variable(s) resulting from all possible combinations of the input variable.

turnaround document a document which is output by one stage of a computer system, and, with additional information entered on it, forms the input for another stage.

Turing Machine an abstract computer, designed by Alan Turing, having the theoretical properties of an actual computer.

turnkey contract a contract for the supply of a complete, ready-to-use computer system, including hardware and software.

two-pass assembler an assembler which scans the source code of programs twice during assembly.

twos complements a binary code, using the usual place values, except that the most significant bit represents a negative quantity.

underflow the occurrence of a numerical result which is less than the lower limit imposed by the number representation used.

uncommitted logic array (ULA) an array of identical logic gates on a chip, which are customised by suitable interconnections to dedicate the chip to a particular purpose.

uninterrupted power supply a unit which ensures a constant power supply to a computer.

updating the process of bringing a file or other collection of information up to date.

upgrade to enhance or extend the hardware or software of a computer system.

user a person who uses a computer system.

user documentation a written account of how a program is to be used.

user group a group of people or organisations which are users of the same make of computer equipment, operating system or software package.

user interface the means of communication between a computer system and the person using it.

utility programs programs for various 'housekeeping' tasks as file creation, copying files, routing messages and providing mathematical facilities.

validation the process of checking input data before storing or processing it.

variable a data item which can change its value during the running of a program.

variable wordlength the use of words of different lengths in a computer system for the representation of data.

vector describes a method of representing a screen diagram as a set of directed line elements.

vector processor a processor with a parallel architecture based on vector registers and banks of processing circuits.

vector register a bank of identical registers treated as a single unit in machine instructions, and where processing operations are carried out on all elements in the registers in parallel.

very large scale integration (VLSI) the inclusion of tens of thousands of transistors and other components on a single integrated circuit.

virtual machine the image of the hardware of a computer created by various layers of software, especially an operating system.

virtual memory the image of a computer memory presented by an operating system to higher levels of software.

visual display unit (VDU) a terminal comprising a keyboard and display screen.

volatile memory see dynamic memory.

wafer a circular slice cut from a silicon crystal on which integrated circuits are formed.

what you see is what you get (Wysiwyg) describes the user interface of a software package such as a word processing or desktop publishing system where the layout if the material on screen is the same as its layout when printed.

Winchester disk a high-capacity hard disk permanently mounted in its drive.

windows, icons, mouse, pointer (Wimp) environment a graphical user interface controlled by a mouse which moves a pointer on the screen to select objects displayed as icons.

word a set of bits which can be manipulated by a computer in one operation.

wordlength the number of bits in one word.

word processing the use of a computer system to type, edit, store and print documents.

workstation a powerful microprocessor-based computer used for applications such as computer-aided design.

wrap-around carry a carry from the most significant to the least significant bit of a number.

yield the proportion of usable chips on a wafer.

39 Teacher's Notes

These notes are intended for the guidance of a teacher of Computing following a UK GCSE Advanced Level or equivalent course. They indicate some of the ways in which this book can be used. It must be emphasised that the best preparation for the use of this book as course material is a familiarity with its contents: one of the intended uses of the book is as a 'briefing text' for teachers about to start a course in Computing at this level.

Use of the Book

Computing is a broad, many-faceted subject, with complex inter-relationships between its constituent topics. Accordingly, the structure of this book has been chosen with great care, in order to provide a logical path through the topics, and a cumulative flow of information. However, not every chapter in the book depends on all its predecessors, as shown in Figure 39.1. There is scope for selection of material, and variation in order of presentation, depending on circumstances.

Figure 39.1
Chapter dependencies of Computing Science

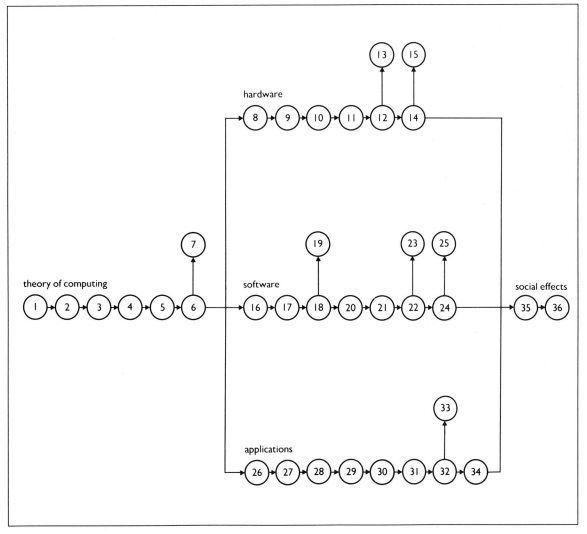

The most recent revisions of the UK GCE A Level syllabuses in Computing shift the emphasis towards computer applications. Correspondingly, there is less emphasis on the theoretical aspects of the subject. The material in the syllabuses is presented in an order which reflects this emphasis, starting with applications, and working back to the general principles of hardware and software design, and the fundamental theory of computing. The syllabuses do, however, stress that this ordering does not reflect the order in which the material should be presented to students.

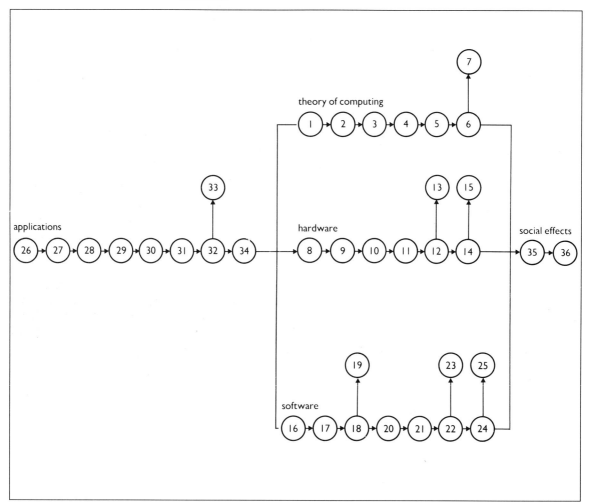

Figure 39.2
Computing Science - applications first

For the reasons stated above, Computing Science retains the traditional ordering of material, starting with the fundamental theory, and working through the hardware and software principles to applications. However, with some planning, it is possible to present the subject starting with applications. Figure 39.2 shows a possible order of presentation to achieve this aim.

Whatever the order of presentation, the following points should be borne in mind when relating the material in the book to current A Level syllabuses.

- Chapters 1 to 5 present the fundamental theory of computing, and are essential whether they are dealt with before or after the applications.
- Chapters 6 (Boolean Logic) and 8 (Logic Circuits) are no longer formal

syllabus requirements. However, it is difficult to see how Computing can be presented at this level without them, as they underpin much of what follows.

- Chapters 7 (Artificial Intelligence) and 33 (Expert and Knowledge-based Systems) are requirements of some, but not all syllabuses. They are an important indication of the general direction of the leading edge of computing.
- Chapters 9 to 15 present the hardware and machine language aspects of computing. These can be dealt with in slightly less depth with the emphasis on applications, but they are still important. The material needs to be presented so that its relevance to applications becomes apparent. The frequent use of case studies in these chapters is intended to assist in this.
- Chapters 16 to 25 present the software aspects of computing, at levels ranging from assembly language to fourth generation language. This material is essential, not only for its own sake, but as a foundation for the study of applications. The high level language case studies in Chapter 19 can be dealt with selectively, according to circumstances.
- Chapters 26 to 34 deal with computer applications, starting with the general principles of the design of information systems, and finishing with a selection of case studies. For the current A Level syllabuses, this is the central topic of the text, whether it is presented as the culmination of the theoretical development, of as an introduction to the underlying theory.
- Chapters 35 and 36 deal with the wider implications of computing, and are given increasing emphasis in the new syllabuses.

If this book is intended for a Computer Appreciation course, then the essential material is the principles of computing (in particular Chapters 1 to 5) and the applications and implications of computers (Chapters 26 to 36). The more technical chapters on hardware and software can be treated lightly or omitted.

40 Answers to Exercises

Answers to exercises have been selected for inclusion here on the basis of the following criteria:

- If a question requires a brief, specific answer then it is included. The only exceptions are 'comprehension' questions and ones which require definitions of terms; answers to the latter are to be found in the Glossary of Terms.
- Where questions require discussion, in selected cases a few relevant points are included. In most cases, conclusions are not drawn, as the merit of answer lies in the logic of its argument, and not in the 'correctness' of its conclusion.
- Answers to questions from past examination papers in Computing Science are not included.

Exercise 2

2 Systems: central and local governments, automatic pilot, any organ of the body, solar system.
Non-systems: crowd of looters, shuffled pack of cards, components of a computer before assembly.

3 Slide rule: no, not automatic or programmable.
Automatic washing machine: no, too special-purpose.
Programmable pocket calculator, television game: no, only performs part of the work of a computer, or yes, but only a dedicated computer.
Motor car electronic ignition system: no, too special-purpose.

4 In many cases, the distinction between the device and a computer is fine, based on the nature of the processing done. Examples include robots, electronically controlled cameras, multi-function digital watches.

7 Examples include many modern buildings, most electrical apparatus, plumbing systems, telephone systems, camera lens systems.

8 Advantages include:
- Ease of replacement of faulty modules
- Ease of expansion by adding more modules
- Ease of understanding of design principles
- Ease of planning for future enhancements.

Exercise 3

2 The electronic components of computers are all bistable devices. Advantages are simplicity and wide tolerances.

3 Roman numerals.

4 Each character is coded separately as a set of binary digits.

5 a) Add the binary codes of the two digits, and the carry bit
   If the sum exceeds nine (1001)
      then subtract ten (1010) from the sum
         set the carry bit to 1
      else set the carry bit to 0.

   b) Assuming that one of the numbers has been 'padded' with leading zeros if necessary, so that both numbers are of the same length:
      Set carry bit to zero
      Repeat, for each digit of the numbers from the right
         Add a pair of digits and the carry bit as in part a)
      Create an additional digit for the sum, containing the carry bit

6		four bits	six bits	eight bits
	1	0 0 0 1	0 0 0 0 0 1	0 0 0 0 0 0 0 1
	-1	1 1 1 1	1 1 1 1 1 1	1 1 1 1 1 1 1 1
	3	0 0 1 1	0 0 0 0 1 1	0 0 0 0 0 0 1 1
	-3	1 1 0 1	1 1 1 1 0 1	1 1 1 1 1 1 0 1

Duplicate the leftmost bit of the number to fill the new positions. The process is called sign extensions.

7		four bits	six bits	eight bits
	1	0 0 0 1	0 0 0 0 0 1	0 0 0 0 0 0 0 1
	-1	1 1 0 1	1 1 1 1 0 1	1 1 1 1 1 1 0 1
	3	0 0 1 1	0 0 0 0 1 1	0 0 0 0 0 0 1 1
	-3	1 1 0 0	1 1 1 1 0 0	1 1 1 1 1 1 0 0

Same process as with twos complements.

8		bits	twos complements range	ones complements range
	a)	4	–8 to 7	–7 to 7
	b)	6	–32 to 32	–31 to 31
	c)	8	–128 to 127	–127 to 127
	d)	16	–32768 to 32767	–32767 to 32767
	e)	n	$-2n-1$ to $2n-1-1$	$-(2n-1-1)$ to $2n-1-1$

9

		$\frac{-1}{2}$	$\frac{1}{4}$	$\frac{1}{8}$	$\frac{1}{16}$	$\frac{1}{32}$	1
$\frac{3}{8}$	= 0	0	1	1	0	0	
$\frac{5}{16}$	= 1	1	0	1	1	0	
$\frac{-17}{32}$	= 1	0	1	1	1	1	
$\frac{1}{5}$	= 0	0	0	1	1	0	

10

	decimal		mantissa						exponent			
			sign	$\frac{1}{2}$	$\frac{1}{4}$	$\frac{1}{8}$	$\frac{1}{16}$ ...	sign	8	4	2	1
a)	10	=	0	1	0	1	0	0	0	1	0	0
	15360	=	0	1	1	1	1	0	1	1	1	0
	1	=	1	1	0	0	0	0	0	0	0	1
	$\frac{7}{128}$	=	0	1	1	1	0	1	0	1	0	0
	$\frac{5}{1024}$	=	1	1	0	1	0	1	0	1	1	1
	240	=	1	1	1	1	1	0	1	0	0	0
b)	80	=	0	1	0	1	0	0	0	1	1	1
	3072	=	1	1	1	0	0	0	1	1	0	0
	$\frac{5}{512}$	=	0	1	0	1	0	1	0	1	1	0
	$\frac{1}{2}$	=	1	1	0	0	0	0	0	0	0	0
	1.5	=	0	1	1	0	0	0	0	0	0	1

    c) From $\frac{1}{2} \times 2^{-15}$ (= $\frac{1}{65536}$) to 2^{15} (= 32736).

11 b) First two bits must be 0 1 or 1 0 unless the number is zero.

12 a) 8   b) 16

    c) Suggestions in the region of: mantissa: 56 bits, exponent: 8 bits.

13	decimal	binary	octal	hexadecimal
	45	101101	55	2D
	21	10101	25	15
	32	100000	40	20
	4097	1000000000001	10001	1001

14 a) Parity error in 5th byte.

    b) Parity error in 7th column.

    c) 7th bit in 5th byte (should be 0).

15 a) No, the parity bit might have been copied incorrectly.
  b) No, two bits might be in error.
  c) Parity will detect that a single bit error most probably has occurred.
16 a) Computers monitoring/controlling machines, computers analysing scientific experiments.

Exercise 4

2 Data structures enable large, potentially unwieldy collections of data to be managed by relatively simple operations. Concepts associated with data structures have led to advances in computer architecture. Data structures have improved the design of programs.

3 a) Indexes in books, filing systems, maps.
  b) Casual conversations, clues in a crime.

4 There must be clear rules for the arrangement of data items, for adding and deleting items, and for the creation of an empty structure.

◆ **5** a) Array, stack, tree.
  b) Each is easy to implement in a computer memory, using pointers. Each is important for a wide range of computer applications.

6 To mark an empty stack, the end of a list and a terminal node of a tree.

7 Split the string at the point of insertion, obtaining <leftstring> and <rightstring>. Form a new string by joining <leftstring>, <newstring> and <rightstring>.

8 a) Let index I = 1
    While I <= 10 repeat
      Let Z(I) = X(I) + Y(I)
      Increase I by 1
  b) Let total T = 0
    Let index I = 1
    While I <= 10 repeat
      Let T = T + X(I)
      Increase I by 1
  c) Let product P = 0
    Let index I = 1
      While I <= 10 repeat
      Let P = P + X(I).Y(I)
      Increase I by 1

◆ **9** b) If A(I,J) goes into B(K) then K = 3(I–1) + J
  ◆ c) If A(I,J) goes into B(K) then K = 3I + J

10 a) 21 – 10 / 5:   stack 21 | 21 |

                    stack 10 | 10 |
                                       | 21 |

                    stack 5 | 5 |
                                       | 10 |
                                       | 21 |

    divide 10 by 5,   stack result | 2 |
                                             | 21 |

    subtract 2 from 21 | 19 |

  b) 6 x (4 + 5) x 3:   stack 6 | 6 |

                    stack 4 | 4 |
                                       | 6 |

                    stack 5 | 5 |
                                       | 4 |
                                       | 6 |

add 4 and 5, stack result	9
	6
multiply, stack result	54
stack 3	3
multiply, stack result	162

11 c) Disadvantage: the queue 'moves' in the memory of the computer.

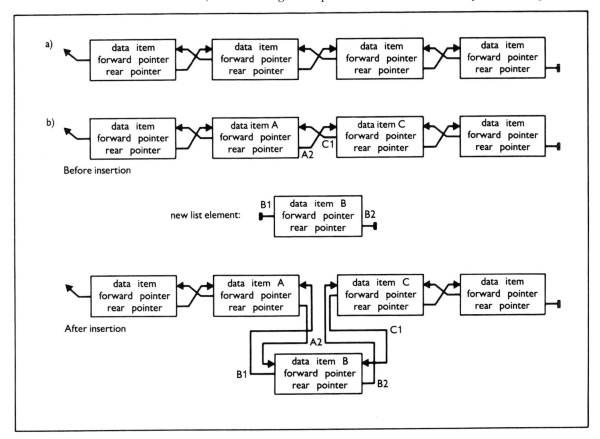

Figure 40.1
Exercise 4 Question 12

12 a) See Figure 40.1.   b) See Figure 40.1.
c) Pointers A2 and C1 point to the new data item B.
   Pointer B1 points to data item A.
   Pointer B2 points to data item C.
13 See Figure 40.2.

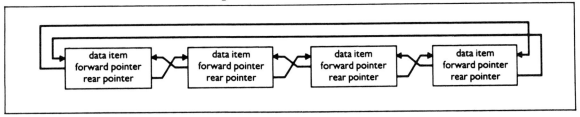

Figure 40.2
Exercise 4 Question 13

14 Insertion
   If there is at least one free element in the array
      then Repeat, from the front of the array
         Compare element to be inserted with
         current array element

Until element to be inserted is earlier in
alphabetical order than current array element
Mark current array element
Repeat, from rear of array to marked element
Move element one place down in array
Insert new element in front of marked element.
Deletion follows a similar pattern, to locate the element to be deleted,
and move remaining elements up one place. A free space is inserted at
the end.
Comment: Storing ordered data in an array involves a lot of movement
of array elements during insertion and deletion.
15 See Figure 40.3.

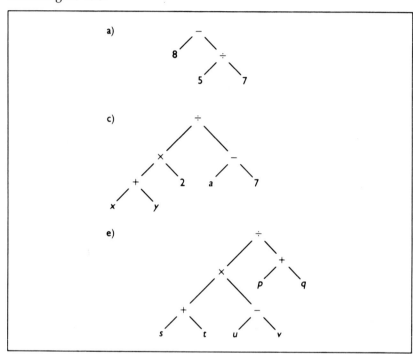

Figure 40.3
Exercise 4 Question 15

16 a) pointers array

index	item
1	1
2	6
3	8
4	12
5	0
6	2
7	0
8	3
9	14
10	16
11	0
12	4
13	0
14	5
15	0
16	6
17	0

data array

index	item
1	control module
2	input module
3	processing module
4	output module
5	calculation module
6	backing store transfer module

b)

pointers array		data array	
index	item	index	item
1	1	1	+
2	5	2	×
3	9	3	p
4	0	4	q
5	2	5	−
6	13	6	r
7	15	7	s
8	0		
9	5		
10	17		
11	19		
12	0		
13	3		
14	0		
15	4		
16	0		
17	6		
18	0		
19	7		
20	0		

Note that these are not the only correct answers.

17 a)

array	
index	item
1	+
2	×
3	−
4	p
5	q
6	r
7	s

b)

array	
index	item
1	a
2	−
3	b
4	−
5	−
6	c
7	d
8	−
9	−
10	−
11	−
12	e
13	−
14	−
15	−

c) Regular binary trees, such as Figure 4.20, are best stored by this method, but skew binary trees, such as Figure 4.21, are better stored by the method of Question 16.

◆ **18** a) Figure 4.20: p × q + r - s
Figure 4.22: a e c b d

b) Interchange lines 'output node' and 'traverse right subtree'.

c) Figure 4.17: 7 4 9 × +
Figure 4.20: p q × r s - +
Figure 4.22: e c d b a

Exercise 5 3

		−8	4	2	1
2 + 5:	2 =	0	0	1	0
	+ 5 =	0	1	0	1
	7 =	0	1	1	1
		0	0		

Carry in = 0, carry out = 0, answer correct.

$$6 + 3: \quad \begin{array}{rccccc} 6 & = & 0 & 1 & 1 & 0 \\ +3 & = & 0 & 0 & 1 & 1 \\ \hline -7 & = & 1 & 0 & 0 & 1 \\ & & & 0 & 1 & \end{array}$$

Carry in = 1, carry out = 0, answer incorrect.

$$4 - 5: \quad \begin{array}{rccccc} 4 & = & 0 & 1 & 0 & 0 \\ 5 & = & 1 & 0 & 1 & 1 \\ \hline -1 & = & 1 & 1 & 1 & 1 \\ & & & 0 & 0 & \end{array}$$

Carry in = 0, carry out = 0, answer correct.

$$2 - 7: \quad \begin{array}{rccccc} -2 & = & 1 & 1 & 1 & 0 \\ -7 & = & 1 & 0 & 0 & 1 \\ \hline 7 & = & 0 & 1 & 1 & 1 \\ & & 1 & 0 & & \end{array}$$

Carry in = 0, carry out = 1, answer incorrect.

4 Same overflow rule as for twos complements.

5 Product = 1 0 1 1 0 1 1 0

◆ **6** Use a working area layout as in Figure 5.1, except that area B is not used. The algorithm is:

Initially, B contains zeros, A the divisor and D the dividend
Repeat, for each bit of the numbers
    Shift the bits in C and D together one place to the right
    If the contents of C is greater than the divisor in A
    then Subtract A from C, placing the result in C
        Place a 1 in the least significant bit position of D
        else Place a 0 in the least significant bit position of D
When the process is complete, the quotient is in D and the remainder in C.

7

	mantissa					exponent		
	sign	$\frac{1}{2}$	$\frac{1}{4}$	$\frac{1}{8}$	$\frac{1}{16}$	sign	2	1
A + B =	0	1	0	0	1	0	1	1
B + C =	0	1	0	0	1	0	1	0
A × B =	0	1	0	0	1	0	1	1
A × C =	0	1	1	1	1	0	0	1

8 Range of positive numbers: 2^{-32} (= 2.829×10^{-10}) to 2^{31} (= 2 147 483 648).

9 a) 0 1 1 1
    1 0 0 0
    1 0 0 1 1 0

b)

	mantissa					exponent			
	sign	$\frac{1}{2}$	$\frac{1}{4}$	$\frac{1}{8}$	$\frac{1}{16}$	sign	2	1	
A + B =	0	1	0	0	1	0	1	1	no change
B + C =	0	1	0	0	1	0	1	0	no change
A × B =	0	1	0	0	1	0	1	1	more accurate
A × C =	0	1	1	1	1	0	0	1	no change

2

Inputs		Outputs				
A	B	C	AND	OR	NAND	NOR
0	0	0	0	0	1	1
0	1	0	1	1	1	0
0	1	0	0	1	1	0
0	1	1	0	1	1	0
1	0	0	0	1	1	0
1	0	1	0	1	1	0
1	1	0	0	1	1	0
1	1	1	1	1	0	0

4 a) $D = A + (B.\overline{C})$

$H = (\overline{E + F}) + (\overline{F.G})$

$L = (I.\overline{J}.K) + (\overline{I}.J.\overline{K})$

5 See Figure 40.4.

◆ **6** $A + B = \overline{(A + B).(\overline{A}.\overline{B})}$

◆ **8** $D = \overline{A}.B.C + A.\overline{B}.\overline{C}$

9 $A.B = \overline{\overline{A} + \overline{B}}$

10 a) See Figure 40.5.

b) See Figure 40.5.

c) Any combination of logic operations can be expressed in terms of the NAND operation only.

◆ **11** $x = (A \text{ AND } \overline{C}) \text{ OR } (B \text{ AND } C)$

---

2 a) and b) Most orderings can be supported by a suitable argument.

c) Only the first task.

d) The second and fourth tasks.

e) Some computer involvement in all the tasks is possible during the next ten years.

3 likes(Susan, Fred)
likes(Susan, Helen)
likes(John, Jean)
likes(Susan, Jean)

4 a) saw = (1) perceived visually
(2) realised

c) Alternative interpretations of a single word can change the meaning of an entire passage.

6 Weather forecasts
Stock market traders' dialogue
Air traffic control instructions
Operating theatre dialogue.

---

2 a) 1 0 1 0 1 0 0 0   b) 1 0 0 0 1 0 0 0

3 a) 8   b) 2^n

◆ **4** a)

Inputs			Outputs	
A	B	C	S	T
0	0	0	0	0
0	0	1	1	0
0	1	0	1	0
0	1	1	0	1
1	0	0	1	0
1	0	1	0	1
1	1	0	0	1
1	1	1	1	1

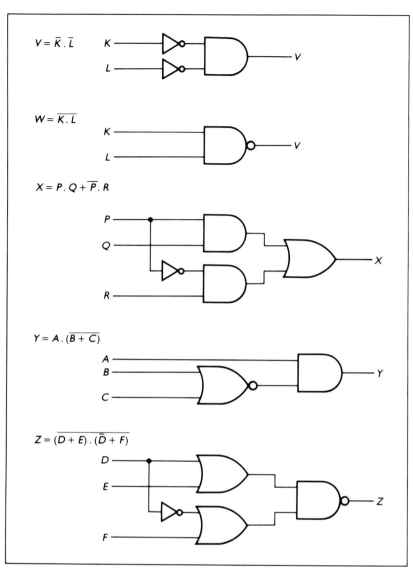

Figure 40.4
Exercise 6 Question 10 a) and b)

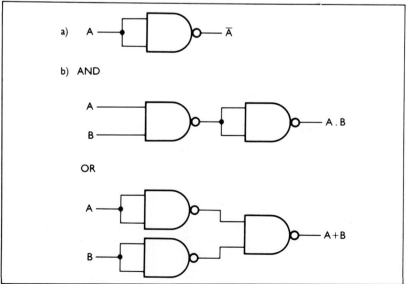

Figure 40.5
Exercise 7 Question 4 c)

440 Answers to Exercises

c) See Figure 40.6.

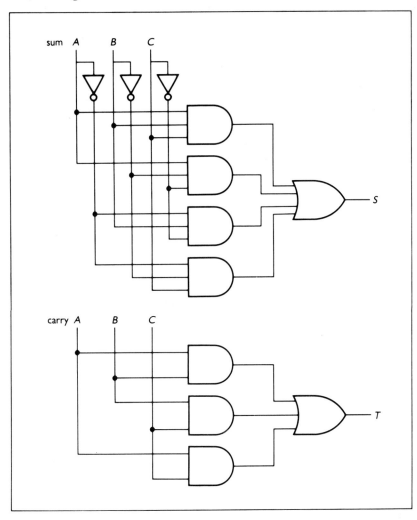

Figure 40.6
Exercise 7 Question 4 c)

Figure 40.7
Exercise 7 Question 5

◆ **5** See Figure 40.7.

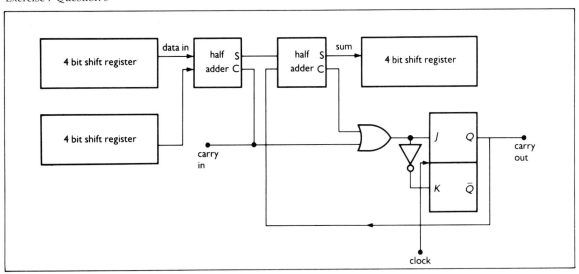

6 Relevant points:
- A logic circuit can be thought of as a module, connected to other logic circuits by inputs and outputs.
- Many logic circuit modules are constructed as integrated circuits.
- A logic circuit module can be replaced by another, with a different but equivalent arrangement of logic gates.

8 See Figure 40.8.

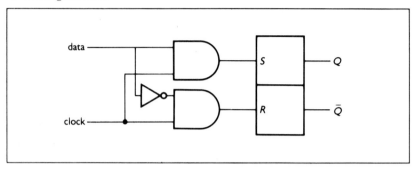

Figure 40.8
D type flip-flop

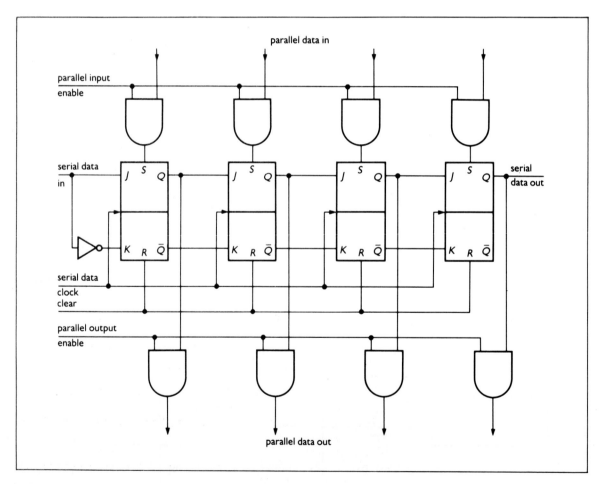

Figure 40.9
USART

9 See Figure 40.9.

Exercise 9

2 Relevant points:
- The concept of modularity enables the structure of a computer system to be expressed at a number of different levels of detail.
- Most computers are constructed as separate modules.
- Modular construction simplifies the design of processors and peripherals.
- Modular construction enables units to be interchanged, allowing systems to grow as required.
- Modularity is essential for the design of data communications equipment.

Exercise 10

3 a) $2^{24} = 16\ 777\ 216$ b) 16M
   c) $1M = 1024K$ d) $232 = 4096M$

4 Relevant points:
- The concept of modularity enables the structure of a processor to explained in relatively simple terms.
- Each module of a processor may be implemented as a single chip.
- The same processor design may be implemented by different but equivalent chips.

6 a) See Figure 40.10.

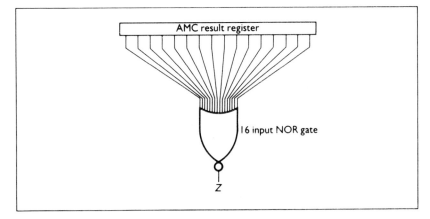

AMC result register

16 input NOR gate

Z

Figure 40.10
Exercise 10 Question 6

8 Stack overflow.

Exercise 11

2 a) Filtered air, restricted access, protective clothing, regular thorough cleansing.
   b) Even the smallest quantities of unwanted impurities will ruin a wafer.

3 Relevant points:
- Chips and PCBs are replaceable units with precisely specified physical, logical and electrical interfaces.
- The use of chips and PCBs greatly simplifies computer design and construction.

4 Relevant points:
- CAD systems are used to an increasing extent for all aspects of chip design, and most PCB design.
- CAD systems speed up the design process, and provide automated test facilities for designs.

5 Insertion of chips into PCBs.

Potential applications include most stages of computer assembly and testing.

6 Asic chips simplify designs, and reduce chip counts, power consumption and cost.

7 Beta tests are independent tests by prospective users. They provide essential feedback and lead to the rectification of most faults before volume production commences.

Exercise 12

2 Absolute address: to access individual data items at known locations.
Indexed address: to access the elements of an array.
Indirect address: to access data items from a structure such as a list or tree.
Relative address: to access relocatable data or code.
Immediate operand: to store a constant.

3 The data item whose address is located at address 49B6 is loaded into the accumulator. Since the address at location 49B6 is 3521, the data item at this address, AB02, is loaded.

4 a) For positive and negative numbers:
Arithmetic shift left has the effect of multiplication by 2.
Arithmetic shift right has the effect of division by 2.

5 0046, 0116

6 Stack: CCDD   Stack pointer: 01FC
            AABB

7 As an eight bit twos complement number, 80 = −128.
As a sixteen bit twos complement number, FF80 = −128.
The process of sign extension preserves the value of both negative and positive numbers.

8 a)

Address	Instruction	Comments
0000	08	Length of arrays, 8 bytes or 4 words.
0001		Array 1, already loaded.
to 0008		
0009		Array 2, already loaded.
to 0010		
0011		Array 3.
to 0018		
Start of program		
0019	2122 0000	Load byte at address 0000 to index register.
Start of loop to add each pair of numbers		
001D	0320	Decrease index register by 1.
001F	0320	Decrease index register by 1.
0021	670E	Branch to address 0031 if negative.
0023	1114 0001	Load first array element.
0027	1314 0009	Add second array element.
002B	1214 0011	Store total in third array.
002F	61EC	Branch to address 0010.
End of loop		
0031	8500	End of program.

b) FFFE (= −2)

c) The array length in location 0000 and the start addresses of the arrays will change, as will the location of the program. Branching instructions, being relative, are not affected.

d) The instruction at address 0027 becomes 1514 0009.

9 Address	Instruction	Comments
0000	01F	Address of first character, later of current character.

Start of program loop

0002	2113 0000	Load character at address in location 0000 to accumulator.
0006	2A11 7E	Compare with end marker 7E.
0009	6212	Branch if equal, to address 001D.
000B	7410	Signal output device to unload output register.
000F	6DFE	Branch back to this instruction if output not complete.
0011	1112 0000	Load address of current character to accumulator.
0015	0210	Increase contents of accumulator by 1.
0017	1212 0000	Store address of next character in location 0000.
001B	61E5	Branch to address 0002, to output next character.

End of program loop

001D	8500	Halt.
001F		First character.

Exercise 13

2 The functional units and buffers for the pipeline are shown in Figure 40.11. During each 'beat', data passes from a buffer, through a functional unit, to the next buffer. The hardware used by each buffer is physically separate from that used by the other buffers. Problems include:

- The duration of each 'beat' is the same. Several stages take a variable amount of time, depending on the instruction.
- Branch or jump instructions can result in the wrong instructions being loaded into the pipeline.

3 All the instructions in the loop are loaded into the cache while the loop is being executed. This increases the processing speed of the computer.

4 a) 320 microseconds.   b) 630 microseconds.
   c) $320 + 10(n - 1)$ microseconds.

5 They emphasise the shortcomings of the 'elementary' view of a computer, as an 'automatic, electronic information processing machine' (Section 1.4) and give credence to the view of a computer as a 'collection of resources' (Section 2.3). Advanced processor features do not, however, contradict either of these views.

7 Monitoring of processors in operation indicate that they spend most of the time processing a small subset of their instruction set. Risc processors have only a small set of these commonly-used instructions, whereas Cisc processors have a large set. Risc processors execute their instructions faster than Cisc processors.

8 Workstations. Common workstation applications such as CAD are well suited to Risc processing.

9 The two approaches are a small number of loosely-coupled processors, and a large number of tightly coupled processors.

Exercise 14

2 1200 characters per second.
3 a) 20 000 blocks.   b) 2 microseconds.   c) 50 microseconds.
   d) 1340 seconds, approximately 22 minutes.   e) 40 seconds.

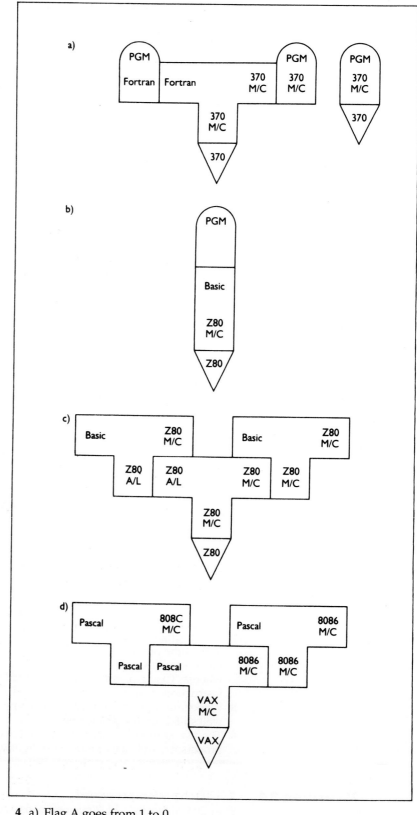

Figure 40.11
AMC instruction pipeline

4 a) Flag A goes from 1 to 0
Flag B goes from 1 to 0

Character loaded into buffer
Flag B goes from 0 to 1
Flag C goes from 0 to 1
Then
Flag C goes from 1 to 0
Flag B goes from 1 to 0
Character copied from buffer
Flag B goes from 0 to 1
Flag A goes from 0 to 1
   b) Flag A indicates that the peripheral is ready for the transfer of
      another data item.
      Flag C indicates that the processor has completed a transfer of data.
   c) Most of the delay will occur waiting for flag A to be set to 1 by the
      peripheral.
◆ 5 The program uses the index register to 'count in' the characters, and
      assign them to successive store locations. The characters are added to
      a running total as they are input. This total is then compared with the
      checksum characters.

Address	Instruction	Comments
0000	0000	Running total of characters, initially zero.
0002		Space for input characters.
to 0009		
000A		Space for checksum
000B		
Start of program		
000C	0210	Clear index register.
Start of loop to input characters		
000E	7110	Signal peripheral device to load input register.
0010	6CFE	Branch back to here if input not complete.
0012	7210	Copy character to accumulator.
0014	2214 0002	Store character at address (0002 + index).
0018	1312 0000	Add running total into accumulator.
001C	1212 0000	Store new value of total.
0020	0220	Increase index register by 1.
0022	1A21 0007	Compare index with 0007.
0026	66EG	Branch if less than or equal, to 000E.
Start of loop to input checksum		
0028	7110	Signal peripheral device to load input register.
002A	6CFE	Branch back to here if input not complete.
002C	7210	Copy character to accumulator.
002E	2214 0002	Store character at address (0002 + index).
0032	0220	Increase index register by 1.
0034	1A21 0009	Compare index register with 0009.
0038	66EE	Branch if less than or equal, to 0028.

End of input loop

003A	1112 000A	Load checksum to accumulator.
003E	1A22 0000	Compare with running total.
0042	6204	Branch if equal, to 0048.
0044	0110	Clear accumulator (check fails).
0046	6104	Branch to 004C.
0048	1111 0001	Set accumulator to 1 (check succeeds).
004C	7410	Copy to output register.
004E	7310	Signal peripheral device to output character.
0050	60FE	Branch back to here if output is not complete.
0052	8500	Halt.

8 b) 0.02 V (approx)

Exercise 15

1 A general-purpose register may be used for a number of functions, such as accumulator, index register, stack pointer, program counter. The RM Nimbus and the VAX use general-purpose registers. A special-purpose register is used for one function only. The ICL 2900 series and the Cray-2 use special-purpose registers.

2 One-address: RM Nimbus, ICL 2900 series, Cray-2. Two-address: VAX.

4 RM Nimbus, ICL 2900, Cray-2.

5 a) 7.
   b) AMC: 80 clock periods per loop cycle, 2560 for entire process.
      Cray-2: 35 clock periods.
      Comment: the AMC takes about 7000 times as long as the Cray-2.

6 ICL 2900 series. It is designed as a 'high level language processor' which makes extensive use of a stack.

7 The Cray-2 uses loosely coupled parallelism for its processor architecture, parallel processing of data in its vector registers, pipelining for most processing operations and parallel access to its multi-port memory. The other systems have some degree of parallelism through the use of pipelining and DMA.

Exercise 16

2 a)
```
    CLR A
    STO A      DT1
```
b)
```
    LOA A N    +16291
    STO A      CS1
```
c)
```
    LOB A      CTR
    NC  A
    STB A      CTR
```
d)
```
    LOA A      AB1
    CMP A      AB2
    BZE        EQU
```
e)
```
    LOA A N    /EF/
    PSH A
    LOA A N    /CD/
    PSH A
    LOA A N    /AB/
    PSH A
```

3
```
    RTA WRD
    NM1 WRD
```

Start of subprogram

```
SBP POP A
    STO A    RTA
    POP A
    STO A    NM1
    POP A
    CMP A    NM1
BGE LT2
    LOA A    NM1
LT2 PSH A
    LOA A    TRA
    PSH A
    RTS
```

End of subprogram, start of main program

```
STR LOA S N    +127
    LOA A N    +16693
    PSH A
    LOA A N    +25252
    PSH A
    JSR        SPB
    POP A
    HLT
```

5 a) HI1 WRD   +10000   High-order word of integer 1.
and LI1 WRD   +8763   Low-order word of integer 1.
  b) HI2 WRD   +20000   High-order word of integer 2.
      LI2 WRD   +14261   Low-order word of integer 2.
      HSM WRD   High-order word of sum.
      LSM WRD   Low-order word of sum.

Start of program

LOA	A	LI1	Load low-order word of integer 1.
ADD	A	LI2	Add low-order word of integer 2.
STO	A	LSM	Store in low-order word of sum.
LOA	A	HI1	Load high-order word of integer 2.
ADC	A	HI2	Add high-order word of integer 2 plus previous carry.
STO	A	HSM	Store in high-order word of sum.
HLT			Halt.
END			End of program.

c) Unless a loop is used, the program is as above, with the addition of LOA, ADC and STO instructions.

◆ d) Twos complement subtraction always results in the correct bit pattern for the low-order word, even if the low-order word of the second number is larger than that of the first. In the latter case, the high-order word of the difference is too large by 1, since this has been 'borrowed' for the low order subtraction. This situation is indicated by the overflow bit being set during low order subtraction.

Using data areas as for part a), the program is as follows:

	LOA	A	LI1	Load low-order word of integer 1.
	SUB	A	LI2	Subtract low order word of integer 2.
	STO	A	LSM	Store in low-order word of difference.
	STC			Set carry bit.
	BVS		NXT	Branch if overflow set by subtraction.
	CLC			Clear carry bit.
NXT	LOA	A	HI1	Load high-order word of integer 1.
	SBC	A	HI2	Subtract (high-order word of integer 2 + carry).

```
                    STO  A      HSM        Store in high-order word of difference.
                    HLT                    Halt
                    END                    End of program.
```

6 The program uses a subset of the instructions in Example Program .

```
PTR      WRD        LE1        Address of first item, later of
                               current list item.
```

Start of program

```
NXT      LOA  A     PTR        Load address of current list item to
                               accumulator.

         INC  A                Increment accumulator, to become
                               address of pointer part of list item.

         STO  A     PTR        Store address of pointer part of list
                               item.

         LOA  A  I  PTR        Load pointer part of list item to
                               accumulator.

         BZE        OUT        Branch out of loop if it is zero.
         STO  A     PTR        Store address of next list item.
         BRN        NXT        Branch to instruction labelled NXT to
                               continue loop.
```

End of program loop

```
         LOA  A     PTR        Load address of pointer part of last list
                               item.

         DEC  A                Decrement accumulator, to contain
                               address of last list item.

         HLT                   Halt.
LE1      BTE        /A/        First list item.
WRD                +0          Pointer part of first list item.
END                            End of program.
```

9 The version of the program written below uses a third working area,
   WA0, to allow for a possible double length product.

```
IN1      WRD        +2647      Integer 1.
IN2      WRD        +3159      Integer 2.
WA0      WRD        +0         High-order word of product.
WA1      WRD        +0         Low-order word of product.
WA2      WRD        +0         Working area.
```

Start of program

```
         LOA  A     IN2        Load integer 2 to accumulator.
         STO  A     WA2        Store integer 2 in working area.
```

Start of multiplication loop

```
NXT BZE             OUT        Branch to end of program if number in
                               accumulator is zero.

         LOA  A     WA1        Load low-order word of product.
         ADD  A     IN1        Add integer 1.
         STO  A     WA1        Store new value of low-order word of
                               product.

         LOA  A     WA0        Load high-order word of product.
         ADC  A  N  +0         Add carry from previous addition.
         STO  A     WA0        Store new value of high-order word of
                               product.

         LOA  A     WA2        Load working area to accumulator.
         DEC  A                Decrease accumulator by 1.
         STO  A     WA2        Store new value of working area.
         BRN        NXT        Branch to continue loop.
```

End of multiplication loop

```
OUT HLT                        Halt
                  END          End of program.
```
11 A store instruction with an immediate operand makes no sense.

Exercise 17

3 Checking the assembly language program for errors, and reporting the nature and position of any encountered.

4 A label can only be associated with one absolute address in the symbolic address table of an assembler.

5 An additional entry in the table of mnemonic and machine operation codes, and routines to carry out any special assembly operations required by the new instruction.

6 AMC machine language

Address	Instruction	
0000	1121	0001
0004	1A21	001B
0008	650C	
000A	1111	0064
000E	2214	0018
0012	0220	
0014	61EE	
0016	8500	

Exercise 18

2 Machine independence and problem orientation.

3 a) The inefficiency of software development using low level languages.

b) Fourth generation languages and computer-aided software engineering tools are replacing high level languages for the same reasons as high level languages replaced low level languages.

5 Similarities: use of character symbols, words and construction based on rules of syntax.

Differences: natural languages are not precisely defined. A valid program in a high level language has only one interpretation, whereas natural languages can be vague or ambiguous, or have several levels of meaning.

6 a) x: lines 2 to 19

count: lines 3 to 19

v: lines 10 to 14.

b) yes   c) No.

d) local variables: w, v, y, z

global variables: x, count.

e) line 17.

7 a) Y = 3, X = 3

b) LET T = X

LET X = Y

LET Y = T

8 a) READ (1, 200) I, J, K, L, M, N

200 FORMAT (I2, IX, I2, IX, I2, IX, I4, 1X, I4, 1X, I4)

b) 3614   2915   23   79   63725489

c) Advantages: precision, ability to check data as it is input.

Disadvantages: tedious, error-prone, difficult to program.

9 a) y = 5   b) y = 10   c) y = 10

d) y = 9   e) y = 0

f) Using 'elementary' Basic:

```
100 IF X<0 THEN 120
105 IF X>9 THEN 120
110 LET Y=9-X
115 GOTO 125
120 LET Y=10
125 REM CONTINUE
```

The logic of this program is not nearly as easy to follow as the Pascal statement.

Exercise 19

2 The three strongest reasons are the theoretical emphasis of Algol, its poor input/output facilities and the increasing popularity of Pascal and C.

4 Algol's aim of being a 'universal programming language' is rather idealistic. Pascal's aim to be a simple, well-structured teaching language which is easy to implement on a wide range of computers, is much more realistic.

5 Reasoned cases can be made for Pascal, Basic and C.

6 Possible reasons (for both languages) include their suitability for the type of work for which they are designed, and their ease of use by people working in the particular fields to which they apply.

9 Fortran, Algol: strong
Cobol, Basic, Pascal, C: moderate
Lisp, Prolog: weak

Exercise 20

3 Interpretation is simpler than compilation, and requires only one copy of the program being interpreted.

4 b) 469.31   valid   .734   valid
    4325 invalid   45.6.7   invalid
    846. invalid

  c) <decimal number>::={<number>}{<decimal point>}{<number>}

  d) <signed decimal number>::={<sign>}{<number>}
    {<decimal point>}{<number>}
    <sign>::= + | -
    All example numbers are valid.

6 The application program is compiled, with calls to the utilities regarded as unresolved external references. The utilities are copied from backing store, and the linkage editor deals with the call and return addresses. The loader places all the modules in their final positions for running, and transforms relative addresses as required.

7 a) Valid   b) Invalid   c) Invalid   d) Valid
  e) <condition>::=<variable><relation><constant> |
    <variable><relation><variable>

8 a) Valid.   b) Valid.   c) Valid.
  d) Invalid – error 2.   e) Invalid – error 2.
  f) Invalid – error 3.
  g) Error 1: No number present.
    Error 2: Duplicate sign in number.
    Error 3: No digits in number.
    Error 4: Duplicate decimal point.

◆ h)

State	Next character					
	+	-	digit	.	E	*
1	2	2	3	4	error 5	error 1
2	error 2	error 2	3	4	error	error 3
3	error 2	error 2	3	4	5	exit
4	error 2	error 2	4	error 4	5	exit
5	6	6	7	error 6	error 7	error 8
6	error 2	error 2	7	error 6	error 7	error 8
7	error 2	error 2	7	error 6	error 7	exit

Error 5: Invalid number before exponent.
Error 6: Decimal point in exponent.
Error 7: Duplicate exponent symbol.
Error 7: Incomplete exponent.

9

	Basic		AMC Assembly Language	
a)	100 LET L=J+K		LOA A	J
			ADD A	K
			STO A	L
b)	50 IF C>10 THEN 200		LOA A	C
			CMP A N	+10
			BGT	XXO
c)	100 FOR K=1 TO 20		LOA X N	+1
		NXT	CMP X N	+20
			BGT	OUT
	110 LET J(K)=J(K)+1		LOB A D	J
			INC A	
			STB A D	J
	120 NEXT K		INC X	
			BRN NXT	
		OUT		

10 One instruction is placed outside the loop, which is repeated 9 times, with three operations per repetition.

```
    LOA X N    +1
    LOA A N    +100
NXT CMP X N    +27
    BGT        OUT
    STB A D    W
    INC X
    STB A D    W
    INC X
    STB A D    W
    INC X
    BRN        NXT
OUT
```

12 See Figure 40.12.

Exercise 21

3 a) Most integrated software packages provide all the facilities of the separate ones, plus the ability to transfer data between the facilities.
b) The main benefits are the ability to transfer data, and a unified user interface.

5 a) The main benefit is the quality of the software, arising from the large development budget available to the software package developer. Additional benefits are standard data formats, for transfer of data between users or between packages, simple user interfaces, and no development cost to the user.
b) Compatibility with hardware or other software, quality, ease of use and price.

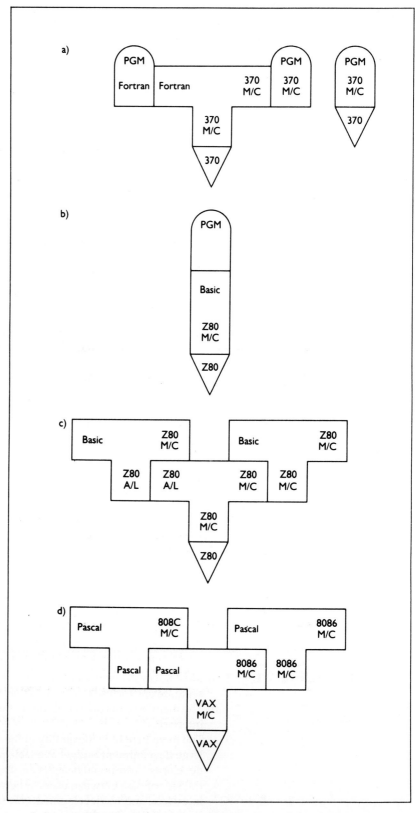

Figure 40.12
Exercise 20 Question 12

c) Successful software package producers have invested their income
  in developing improved versions of their packages, which in turn

has led to increased sales.

d) Software packages are one of the main reasons for the widespread use of microcomputers, particularly in offices.

6 Text drafted and corrected using a word processor, accounts prepared on accounting package, sales figures entered on a spreadsheet, graphics package used to produce the graphs, photographs scanned into imaging system. When all components of the report are complete, they are taken into a desktop publishing package for typesetting, layout and printing.

Exercise 22

2 The program is written for the virtual machine produced by the operating system, and not for the raw hardware of the computer.

4 Single program operation.

5 A virtual machine simplifies the programming and use of the computer, and limits the consequences of errors. It makes portability of software across types of computer a practical possibility.

6 The control and resource management of a large computer system, comprising more than one processor, large numbers of peripherals and several data communications channels is an extremely complex task.

8 a) It is the only software which has direct access to most of the 'real' resources of the computer. All requests for these resources must be channelled through it.

b) The programmer is freed from the problems of store allocation, and does not have to resort to such techniques as overlay programming.

c) No software is infallible, and only an operator can respond to unforeseen circumstances.

9 Objectives: efficient management of the resources (chiefly main store) of the computer, and simplifying the use of peripherals.

Features: a simple main store manager, controllers for each peripheral and a mechanism to allow the user to interrupt an applications program.

Exercise 23

1 a) Unix, VME/B.   b) Unix, VME/B.   c) VME/B.

2 Unix, VME/B.

6 Relevant points:

a) Computer manufacturers are obliged to develop computers which are similar to others using the same operating system.

b) Developing portable software is much easier.

c) Users have access to a wider range of software. Communication between different computers using the same operating system is easy.

Exercise 24

2 a) suitable   b) suitable   c) suitable   d) not suitable

e) not suitable   f) suitable.

3 a) The rapid production of prototypes enables users to test the consequences of their specifications at an early stage.

b) Software more suited to the needs of users.

4 Faster development of software, less revision during development, simpler maintenance.

Exercise 25

2 Similarities: both based on data dictionaries, both include application generators, both lead to cost-effective, high-quality software.
Differences:
4GLs are limited to commercial applications, software development environments are not.
Software development environments give assistance with proofs of the correctness of programs, 4GLs do not.
4GLs use a single specification language, environments use multiple programming and specification languages.
Software development environments include the program design phase, 4GLs do not.

3 Formal proofs are the only way of ensuring the correct operation of software.

4 To an increasing extent, software is being developed on computers different from the ultimate host machines.

6 Basic (in its traditional form) has no facilities for block structuring, local variables, parameter passing or linkage of separately compiled modules. It is not consistent with the philosophy of strict program structure. (Many recent versions of Basic have overcome these shortcomings.)

Exercise 26

3 a) Periodic processing.
   b) Real-time system, transaction processing.
   c) Periodic processing.
   d) Real-time system, process control.
   e) Database system, or real-time system, information storage/retrieval.

5 At almost every stage, but most common are after feasibility study, system investigation or acceptance testing.

6 Feasibility study, system investigation, system specification, evaluation of possible packages against the system specification, choice of package, package configuration and loading of data, acceptance testing.

7 They are not an adequate test of the robustness of the system.

8 Increased costs, particularly wage costs, delays and loss of business, and the computer system acquiring a bad reputation.

9 At system specification time, or when parallel running is commenced. Possibilities include: guarantee of no redundancies, inducements of free re-training of higher-paid jobs, undertakings to improve working conditions and, above all, keeping employees adequately informed about what is going on.

11 The system outlined below is one of possibilty:
   a) See Figure 40.13.
   b) One each for sale recording, updating of stock sales file, updating of cash takings file and transmission of stock sales file.
   c) Algorithm for sale recording program:
      Set sale total to zero
      Repeat, for each item sold
         Input stock number and quantity
         Access price from stock file
         Display stock number, quantity, price and amount
         Print stock number, quantity, price and amount on sales slip

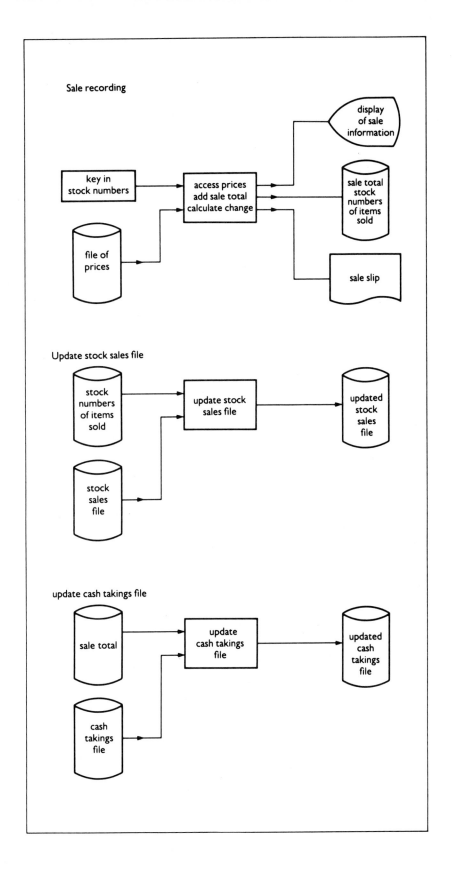

Figure 40.13
Exercise 25 Question 11

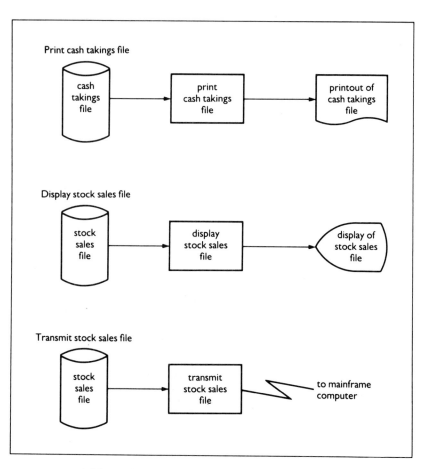

Print cash takings file

cash takings file → print cash takings file → printout of cash takings file

Display stock sales file

stock sales file → display stock sales file → display of stock sales file

Transmit stock sales file

stock sales file → transmit stock sales file → to mainframe computer

Figure 40.13
Exercise 25 Question 11
(continued)

Add amount to total
Display and print total
Input amount of cash, cheque and gift voucher tendered.
Calculate change.
Display and print amount tendered and change.
d) Training of data entry terminal operators.
Ensuring that the prices displayed on goods are always the same
as those in the price file.

Exercise 27

2 a) The index requires a different file structure from the text.
  b) Text files in word processor format.
  c) Possible keys are name and date, or reference allocated to each
     letter.
  d) One possibility is: fields for name, address, date and reference to
     the letter, which also acts as a pointer.
  e) Any medium other than disks will make editing very difficult.
3 a) Search top level index or first key greater than 132714. This
     corresponds to second level index 11.
     Search second level index 11 for first key greater than 132714. This
     corresponds to third level index 531.
     Search third level index 531 for first key greater than 132714. This
     corresponds to block 26544.
     Copy block 26544 to main store, and search it sequentially for key
     132714.

♦   b) During cylinder-surface-sector indexing, the disk drive head is
                    'homing in' on the required sector. During hierarchical indexing,
                    the location of the required block is only determined at the last
                    step.
            4 a) 412 117 503   has address   1112.
                    625 417 902   has address   1944.
                b) 462 803 906   has address   2171.
                    341 915 916   has address   2172.
                    638 702 831   has address   2173.
                    594 113 666   has address   2174.
                c) Loading in a different order will result in different addresses for
                    the records.

Exercise 28   2 b) Employee number.
                c) A check on the total of the various categories of days.
                    A check of the name against employee number on a reference file.
            3 The batch total calculated before the data was input is wrong.
            4 62973   51164
            6 String 1:   17   4   9   21,   sorted: 4   9   17   21
                String 2:   8   5   20   2,   sorted: 2   5   8   20
                String 3:   7   11   15   6,   sorted: 6   7   11   15
                String 4:   3   1   19   13,   sorted: 1   3   13   19
                Tape A: String 1 String 3
                Tape B: String 2 String 4
                Merge in pairs:
                Tape C: String 1 + String 2:   2   4   5   8   9   17 20 21
                Tape D: String 3 + String 4:   1   3   6   7   11 13 15 19
                Merge to a single string:
                Tape A: 1 2 3 4 5 6 7 8 9 11 13 15 17 19 20 21
            9 Initial situation:
                        4   7   8   10   11   19   23   31
                Select middle record (key 10) and partition set:
                       [4   7   8]   10   [11   19   23   31]
                Required key is greater than that of middle record, so search right
                subset:
                        11   19   23   31
                Select middle record (key 19) which is the required record.
           10 Re-run the backup (grandfather) copy of the tape with the previous
                transactions to re-create the current version of the tape. Then update
                the current version with the current transactions, to re-create the new
                version.
           11 The backup copy of the disk is re-run against all the transactions since
                it was backed up. The current updating is then repeated. Another
                backup copy of the disk is made before and after updating.

Exercise 29   2 a) Advantages: large number of commands, flexibility, can be used in
                    batch mode.
                        Disadvantages: difficulty of use, large amount of typing required.
                b) Advantages: ease of use, minimum use of keyboard.
                        Disadvantages: limited number of options, no batch mode.
                c) Advantages: minimal keyboard use, ease of understanding and
                    use, standardisation across programs, flexibility.

d) Disadvantage: no batch mode.

5 Possibilities include steering systems for ships and aircraft, voice activated word processor and translator.

Exercise 30 ◆ 5 Specimen answer using a relational model:

a) Table 1:   Correspondent Identities
   Identity   Name
   K347P   `John Greggorowski`
   ...

   Table 2:   Newspaper Identities
   Identity   Name
   N417W   `Washington  Star`
   ...

   Table 3:   News Items

Date Identity	Correspondent Identity	Newspaper	Text
`04/11/80`	`K007L`	`N417W`	`London experienced..`
`07/11/80`	`K347P`	`N417W`	`Strikes in Poland...`
`07/11/80`	`K347P`	`N327T`	`Strikes in Poland...`

`. . .`

Note that if an item is bought by more than one paper, then multiple entries are inserted in Table 3. A more efficient relational approach is to introduce a news item identity, and have a fourth table of this together with the text of the item. The third table would then contain the news item identity instead of the text.

b) Table 3 is used to locate the newspaper identities of all newspapers buying a news item with a given date and correspondent entry. Table 2 is then used to locate the names of the newspapers.

Exercise 31 ◆ 3 a) First row:
	binary	`1010`	`1000`	`0110`	`0000`
	hex	A	8	6	0
	ASCII	`Count = 40`			space

Second row:
	binary	`1010`	`1000`	`0010`	`1110`
	hex	A	8	2	E
	ASCII	`Count = 40`			.

Third row:
	binary	`1010`	`1000`	`0110`	`0000`
	hex	A	8	6	0
	ASCII	`Count = 40`			space

Fourth row:
	binary	`0100`	`1101`	`0100`	`0101`
	hex	4	B	4	5
	ASCII		M	E	

`... 8 characters ...`
	binary	`0100`	`0100`	`0101`	`0011`
	hex	4	4	5	3
	ASCII		D	S	

Rest of fourth to to eighteenth rows
	binary	`1111`	`1111`	`0110`	`0000`
	hex	F	F	6	0
	ASCII			`Count = 127`	space

`repeated a total of 4 times ...`
	binary	`1101`	`0000`	`0110`	`0000`
	hex	D	0	6	0
	ASCI			`Count = 80`	space

Nineteenth row: see Second row.
Twentieth row: see First row.

    b) Total characters transmitted: 28.
Total characters (including blanks) displayed: 800.

5 78 lines.

7 a)

Data:	1	0	1	1	1	0	1	
Check 1:	1		1		1		1	pass (value 0)
Check 2:		0	1			0	1	pass (value 0)
Check 3:				1	1	0	1	fail (value 1)

Error code 100: error in 4th digit.

Data:	0	1	1	1	0	0	0	
Check 1:	0		1		0		0	fail (value 1)
Check 2:		0	1			0	0	fail (value 1)
Check 3:				1	0	0	0	fail (value 1)

Error code 111: error in 7th digit.

Data:	1	1	1	1	1	0	1	
Check 1:	1		1		1		1	pass (value 0)
Check 2:		1	1			0	1	fail (value 1)
Check 3:				1	1	0	1	fail (value 1)

Error code 110: error in 6th digit.

◆ b)

	D1	D2	D3	D4	D5	D6	D7	D8	D9	D10	D11	D12
Data bits:			B1		B2	B3	B4		B5	B6	B7	B8
Check bits:	C1	C2		C3				C4				
Check 1:	*		*		*		*		*		*	
Check 2:		*	*			*	*			*	*	
Check 3:				*	*	*	*					*
Check 4:								*	*	*	*	*

Exercise 32

2 a) Cooling pump = main switch AND thermostat
    b) Radiator valve = engine thermostat
    c) Heater = main switch AND (NOT(tank thermostat))
    d) Door = time switch AND pass card AND password

3 a) Hard-wired control systems have their control algorithms permanently embedded in them; programmable control systems can have their control algorithms re-programmed; computer-based control systems have their control algorithms expressed as computer programs.
    b) Hard-wired: motor car ignition, security door lock
Programmable: factory robot, numerically controlled machine
Computer-controlled: oil refinery, nuclear power station.

4 Analysing the operation of a system, recovery from a breakdown, operator training.

5 Applications include aircraft and spacecraft control systems, a number of industrial processes such as oil refining and chemical production, control of power stations, particularly nuclear power stations, train signalling systems.

Exercise 33   2 The main processing operation of an expert system is drawing inferences: Prolog and Lisp are designed for processing of this sort.

Exercise 34   2 a) Faster response to customer orders, reduction of costs of work-in-progress, reduction of raw material costs, improved quality.
      b) Significant cost savings, reduction of assembly cycle, flexibility in delivery of orders.
      c) Loss of orders, reduced profit margins, possible business failure.
   4 Production ceases until the system has been restored to operation.
   5 Incorrect incoming data. More accurate recording equipment, more sources of weather reports.
   6 Advantages: simplification of the system, making it possible to analyse it mathematically.
      Disadvantages: errors due to inherent approximations.
   10 Reduced size and cost of device, higher operational speed, improved reliability.
   12 Silicon compilation is the automatic transformation of the logical specification of a system into an implementation as a network of transistors.
   13 a) A symbol represents the function of a lower level schematic in the hierarchy.
      b) Hierarchical design eliminates duplication of repeated functions, and simplifies a design.
   14 A simulator is an essential cross-check against the logical specification of a design.
   15 More of the objectives relate to administrative efficiency than to improved service to passengers.
   16 Most system elements can continue to operate stand-alone of there is a communications failure. There is redundancy with duplicated elements at almost every level. A transport facility of this nature cannot be closed down because of a failure in the computerised ticketing system.
   17 All the equipment below the level of station computer is special-purpose. Benefits are speed of operation, security and cost savings, because of the large number of items required.

Exercise 35   3 a) USA: a large number of highly-competitive private companies working at the leading edge of research, development and implementation. Strong collaboration between universities and corporations, significant indirect subsidies through defence grants. High corporate revenues, significant proportion devoted to research and new product development. Large and developed domestic market providing user base to fund exports.
      USSR: Centrally planned research, development and manufacture. Strong academic content, weak electronic engineering base, poorly developed domestic market outside scientific and military applications, exports limited to small number of socialist countries.
      b) Reasons include large, well-developed domestic market, enterprise culture, indirect subsidies through defence grants.
      c) Experience in manufacture and export of wide range of electrical and electronic goods, enterprise culture, government co-ordination, strong domestic demand.

8 The usual stages are: applications programmer, team leader, project manager, data processing manager; or applications programmer, systems analyst, system designer, project manager, data processing manager.

9 Other jobs include: components purchasers, technical authors, consultants, recruitment officers, training specialists, database analysts.

10 The main implication is the amount of training and re-training that is necessary if the computing industry is to absorb a significant number of the people currently unemployed.

Exercise 36

5 a) Bank, credit card company, building society, doctor, hospital, employer, inland revenue, local authority.

8 A law to prevent unauthorised access to a computer is at present before the UK parliament.

Index

absolute address 104, 112, 114, 166, 226
abstract data type 34
acceptance testing 290
access control register 263
access logic 328
access privilege 249
accounting 247
accounting module 251
accumulator 86, 105, 118, 146, 150, 154, 163, 166, 172, 174
acoustic coupler 322
Ada 184
Ada program support environment (Apse) 276
add-on RAM board 146
addition 41, 44
addition unit 67, 86
address 28, 84, 103, 116, 125, 162
address decoder 67, 84
address displacement 148
address generation 296
address modification 105
address space 84, 146, 149
address transformation 105
addressing mode 90, 104, 105, 107, 116, 118, 148, 150, 151, 153, 166
advanced integrated manufacturing system (Aims) 342, 383
advanced processor feature 122
Airbus 330, 386
A-level model computer (AMC) 10, 83, 103, 105, 161
Algol 9, 183, 195, 264
Algol-like language 199
algorithm 8, 22, 41, 43, 44, 45, 169, 183, 274, 282, 287
alphabetic character 15
alphanumeric character 15
AMC assembly language 166, 178
AMC instruction cycle 118
AMC machine language 178
American National Standards Institution (ANSI) 199
American Standard Code for Information Interchange (ASCII) 16, 21, 163, 322
analogue control system 333, 334
analogue data 22, 138
analogue input 140
analogue interfacing 140
analogue output 140
analogue signal 320
analogue-to-digital converter (ADC) 22, 140
AND 49, 67, 86, 187
ANSI 77 Fortran 192

Apple Macintosh 310
application 3, 234, 278, 299, 313
application case study 341
application generator 266, 268
application security 270
application-specific integrated circuit (Asic) 73, 335, 359, 360
applications program 251
applications programmer 379
applications software 246
applicative language 214
arithmetic 20, 187
arithmetic and logic unit (ALU) 86, 116
arithmetic error 45
arithmetic if 194
arithmetic pipeline 124
arithmetic shift 108
array 28, 122, 186
artificial intelligence 11, 32, 56, 212, 214, 216, 310, 337, 364
artwork 95, 363
ASCII character 147
assembler 178
assembly language 158, 161, 174, 178, 192
assignment 187
association 57
Association for Computing Machinery (ACM) 196, 380
associative store 125
Atlas 264
atmospheric model 353
atom 213
attribute 267
auto-decrement 210
auto-decrement address 151
auto-definition 270
auto-increment 210
auto-increment address 151
automatic control 333
automatic data conversion 163, 166, 179
automatic layout 360
automatically guided vehicle (AGV) 343
autonomous peripheral operation 123, 138

Babbage, Charles 11
background processor 156
backing store 80, 135, 156, 249, 260
backing store control unit 80
backing store device 99
backing store management 247, 249, 257, 260, 262
backup copy 235
Backus, John 192
Backus-Naur form (BNF) 185, 196
bar code 80, 129, 131, 299, 300, 349
bar code reader 80, 132

base 148
base language 219
base register 123
baseband transmission 321
baseboard 99
based address 148
based scaled index address 148
based scaled index mode with displacement 148
Basic 184, 202, 263
basic input/output system (BIOS) 255
batch file 256
batch processing 244, 261
batch processing system 279
batch processing system generator 270
batch total 299
baud 323
BCD digit 147, 153
beat 124
beta test 100
biased exponent 19, 20
binary code 11, 82, 103, 140, 322
binary coded decimal (BCD) 16, 40
binary data 321
binary number 14, 20, 40, 163
binary search 302
binary tree 33, 172
bistable 68
bit 14, 20, 82, 147, 321
bit field 147, 150
bit map 139, 239
bit serial data transmission 321
bit string 147
block 135, 137, 185, 197, 211, 223
block address 136
block-structured language 186, 206, 210
block sum 139
blocking strategy 296
bonding diagram 363
Boole, George 11
boolean algebra 48
boolean data type 186
boolean equation 334
boolean expression 53, 334
boolean logic 11, 48, 63
boolean operation 48, 63, 210
boolean variable 48, 63
bootstrap loader 252
boundary 6
branching 188
branching instruction 109
breadth of search 59
breadth-first search 304
breakpoint 227
British Computer Society (BCS) 380
British Rail (BR) 365
broadband transmission 321
bubble sort 300
buffer 123, 138, 139, 156, 257

bus 83
byte 20, 84, 107, 146, 147, 150, 166

C 158, 184, 209
C library 211
cache store 124, 153, 154, 156
call 118, 186, 249
carrier 97
carrier sense multi-access with collission detection (CSMA/CD) 326
carrier signal 321
carry 67, 88
carry flag 108
carry in 68
carry out 68
carry prediction circuit 68
cash terminal 80, 324
CD-ROM 137
cell 84, 236
central processing unit (CPU) 79, 80, 82, 324, 367
character code 15, 138, 163, 179, 322
character printer 133
character set 15, 185, 193, 196, 199, 203, 206, 210, 213, 215
character string 150, 186, 203
check bit 158
check character 324
check digit 299
check sum 139
chess 59
China 373
chip see integrated circuit
chip testing 97
circular buffer 30
circular list 32
clear 139
clock cycle 118
clock input 71
clock pulse generator 89, 91
cluster adaptor 324
coaxial cable 326
Cobol 183, 199, 199, 264, 300
code 3, 82
code generation 224, 225
code module 226
code segment 226
collision 326
Colmerauer, Alain 214
combinational logic 68
command 238
command file 308
command processor 255, 256
command-driven user interface 308
commissioning 100
commissioning software 100
common carrier cable 326
communication link 258
communications 2
communications equipment 383

communications management 262
communications network 366
communications processor 80, 355
communications system 10
compilation 219
compilation error 225
compiler 126, 158, 183, 220, 228, 276
compiler library 226
complex instruction set computer (Cisc) 125
complimentary metal oxide silicon (CMOS) 94
computer 2, 3, 6, 10, 11, 76, 82, 93, 100, 103, 118, 122, 136, 161, 244, 278, 383
computer aided design (CAD) 134, 238
computer architect 378
computer architecture 27, 35, 103, 122
computer arithmetic 14, 40, 63
computer bureau 376
computer classification 77
computer commissioning 378
computer component 99
computer construction 378
computer crime 386
computer design 97, 99, 378
computer hardware 63, 76
computer life 101
computer limitation 7
computer maintenance 100, 378
computer manufacture 97
computer media 377
computer network 325
computer operator 247, 379
computer output on microfilm (COM) 134
computer salesman 378
computer security 387
computer services 376
computer system 5, 352, 371
computer system manufacture 374, 377
computer testing 100
computer-aided design (CAD) 94, 130, 359
computer-aided software engineering (Case) 276
computer-based control system 335
computing 2, 3
computing application 341
computing industry 2, 278, 371, 374
computing industry employment 377
computing science 35
condition code 86, 105, 116
conditional branching 188, 194, 197, 200, 203, 207, 211
conditional construction 213
Conference on Data

Systems Languages (CODASYL) 199
console log 252
constant 166, 186, 223
content-addressable memory 125
control 2, 4
control algorithm 334, 336
control character 15, 322, 323
control file 238
control log 336
control memory 119
control program 335
control signal 89, 334
control structure 188
control switch 64
control system 333, 383, 386
control system cycle 334
control total 299
control unit 89
cost 12
Cray, Seymore 143
Cray Y-MP/8 356
Cray-2 154
cross-assembler 181
cross-compiler 276
cursor 130, 235
custom-designed chip (Asic) 99
cycle stealing 123
cycle time 156
cylinder 135
cylinder-surface-sector indexing 295

daisy wheel printer 133
data 5, 6, 7, 11, 14, 48, 82, 107, 135, 136, 138
data bus 64
data capture 299
data channel 64, 156
data code 14
data communication protocol 323
data communications 4, 262, 320
data communications equipment 99
data communications network 324, 353
data communications system 280
data compression 323
data consistency 313
data controller 379
data corruption 305
data dictionary 266, 267, 269, 270, 276
data division 200
data encryption 22, 305
data entry staff 379
data file 294
data file compatibility 241
data format 188
Data General 375
data independence 264, 313, 315
data item 124, 158, 200
data logger 140
data model 313, 314
data model mapping 314

data model transformation 314
data packet 323
data privacy 385
data processing 7, 57
data processing cycle 278
data processing department 378
data processing manager 379
data proliferation 313
Data Protection Act 385
data representation 63
data security 22, 305, 313, 385
data storage 14
data structure 27, 34, 35, 105, 161, 172, 184, 186, 215, 249, 274
data transmission speed 323
data transmission standardisation 322
data type 34, 147, 150, 186, 193, 197, 206, 210
database 234, 235, 265, 276, 313, 338, 353, 364
database administrator (DBA) 315, 316, 380
database concept 313
database management system (DBMS) 315, 316
database package 237, 288
database structure 316
database system 278, 279, 312, 313
deadlock 250
declaration 215
declarative programming language 184, 192, 214
decoder 65, 89
dedicated computer 11
dedicated microprocessor 368, 376
dedicated register 91
default option 310
default value 267, 270
depth of search 59
depth-first search 172, 303
descriptor file 266
descriptor register 153
design 10
desktop microcomputer 77, 139, 143, 149, 234, 240
desktop publishing (DTP) 134, 235, 240, 276
developing country 373
device 128
device controller 152
device driver 258
device independent 248
diagnostic error message 219, 226
diagnostics 226
dictionary 223, 228
dictionary security 270
differential equation 334, 354
diffusion 96
digital 3
digital code 22
digital computer 22, 122, 162

digital control system 333, 334
digital data 320
Digital Equipment Corporation (DEC) 375
digital plotter 134, 362
digital processing 140
digital telecommunications network 328, 373
digital-to-analogue converter (DAC) 140
digitising pad 129, 130, 239
dimension 28
direct access media 137
direct address 104, 148, 151
direct data entry 129
direct memory access (DMA) 123, 138
directive 166, 179
directory 249, 260
disable interrupt 119
disk block 249
disk controller 159
disk crash 137
disk directory 257
disk drive 138
disk formatting 258
disk sector 137, 249
diskette 135
displacement 148
display screen 79, 80, 129, 132, 258
distributed array processor 122
division 41, 44, 72
DMA controller 123, 146
documentation 235, 290
doping 93
dot matrix printer 79, 133
double buffering 138
duplicate processing circuit 122
dust 136
dynamic data structure 28
dynamic RAM 86

Eastern Europe 373
economic and social consequences of computerisation 383
edge connector 99
editor 222
education 384
efficiency 185
electron beam 95
electronic 3
electronic computer 122, 162
electronic control system 333
electronic exchange 328
electronic funds transfer (EFT) 386
electronic mail (E-mail) 235, 329
electronic mail incompatibility 330
electronic system 2
electronics engineer 377
emitter-coupled logic (ECL) 94
employment 3, 371, 384
emulate 119

Emycin 339
enable 91
enable interrupt 119
end-of-input marker 167
end-of-list marker 168
end-of-string marker 28
engineer 99
environment 6
environment division 199
erasable programmable read-only memory (EPROM) 86, 335
error 21, 22, 247, 251
error diagnostics 228
error handling 247, 256
error mini-packet 328
etching 96
Ethernet 326, 330
Europe 372
European Article Number (EAN) 131
European Silicon Structures (ES2) 359
even parity 21
evidential reasoning 338
exception call 152
exchangeable disk pack 135
exclusive OR 49, 67
executable module 230
execute 116
execute permission 260
execute permission bit 263
execution 118
executive program 245
expert system 61, 337
expert system shell 338
exponent 19, 20, 44
extended BNF 220

factorial 198
feasibility report 280, 291
feasibility study 280
feedback 334
fetch 116, 118
field 167, 237, 267, 294
field engineer 100, 378
field type 294
fieldwidth 294
fifth generation computer 122
file 138, 200, 206, 237, 249, 259, 265, 266, 267, 283, 294
file backup 305
file creation 283
file dump 305
file format 284
file fragmentation 297
file generation 305
file index 238, 302
file librarian 379
file log 305
file management system 269
file output 284
file overflow 304
file processing 299
file server 247, 325
file structure 294
file updating 283, 304
filing system 255
fingerprint matching 61
firmware 8, 253
firmware input/output

routine 255
first-in-first-out (FIFO) 30
fixed point code 18
fixed point operation 153
flag 87, 118, 139, 146
flat bed plotter 134
floating point multiplication 156
floating point number 19, 40, 41, 44, 147, 150, 153, 158, 186
floating point operation 153
floppy disk 135
floppy disk drive 79
flow soldering machine 100
fly-by-wire control system 386
foreground processor 156
Fortran 158, 183, 192, 264
four colour theorem 59
four-address computer 103
fourth generation language (4GL) 189, 265, 287, 304
fourth generation software development tool 317
fraction 18
frame 58, 137
front-end processor 80, 138, 156, 159, 355
full adder 67
full duplex communication 321
function 185, 203, 210, 213, 274
functional decomposition 275
functional programming language 213
functional specification 99, 282, 291

gallium arsenide 93
gallium arsenide crystal 95
game playing program 59
GAMM 196
gas turbine engine 341
gate 63, 361
gate array 73
gate delay 64
gateway 330
general-purpose computer 10, 149
general-purpose language 184, 192
general-purpose register 91, 146, 150
generate-and-test 303
gigabyte 135, 137
global telecommunications system 355
global variable 186
grandfather-father-son principle 305
graphics 125, 174, 239, 353
graphics memory 146
graphics terminal 129
Gray code 22, 24

half adder 67
half duplex communication 321

Hamming code 139, 324
hard copy 132
hard-wired control 119, 153, 335
hardware 8, 10, 41, 76, 244, 245, 246, 248, 352
hash table 296
hash total 299
hashing 296
Hewlett-Packard 375
hexadecimal number 20, 21, 105, 163
hierarchical data model 316, 317
high level language 162, 174, 183, 189, 192, 219, 220, 245, 265
high level language processor 154
high order 15
high-level language 287
high-resolution graphics 79, 129, 130, 238, 241
high-resolution graphics screen 143, 364
highlight 237
hole 93
Horn clause 215
housekeeping 305
human interface 10
hybrid control system 335

IBM PC/2 143
ICL 2900 series 143, 153, 261
icon 310
identification division 199
identifier 186, 200
image laser printer 240
image processing 61, 122, 126, 310
immediate access store 84
immediate data item 148
immediate operand 105, 112, 116, 163, 166
immediate operand mode 148
implementation 10
implementation language 196
impurity 93
incremental assembler 180
incremental dump 305
index 28, 148, 289, 295
index register 89, 90, 104, 105, 118, 150, 166, 170, 172
indexed address 104, 151, 166
indexed sequential file 294, 295
indirect address 104, 111, 112, 150, 151, 166, 169, 171, 174
industry standard 209, 260
informatics 2
information 3, 5, 7, 56, 57, 82
information processing 3, 10
information storage and retrieval 238, 279
information system 278
information systems

factory 276
information technology (IT) 2, 278, 331, 346, 371, 383
ink jet printer 133
input 3, 128, 187, 194, 197, 200, 203, 207, 211, 215, 244, 248
input device 99, 129
input register 88, 110
input/output control 246, 247, 248
input/output instruction 110
input/output system 255
insertion sort 300
instruction 82, 89, 103, 107, 148, 161, 223
instruction cache 156
instruction cycle 116, 119, 124
instruction cycle duration 117, 118
instruction decoder 67, 89
instruction pipeline 124, 153
instruction register 89, 116
instruction set 103, 119, 150, 158
instruction word 223
integer 16, 41, 147, 150, 158, 166, 186
integrated circuit (IC) 3, 12, 63, 93, 99, 335, 359
integrated circuit manufacture 377
integrated package 241, 242
integrated software environment 240
intelligence 4, 7, 56
intelligent knowledge-based system (IKBS) 338
intelligent terminal 324
intelligent user interface 310
inter-block gap 137
interactive computer system 308
interactive computing 205
interactive editor 222
interface 6, 9, 76, 128, 178, 251, 274
interfacing 321
International Business Machines (IBM) 375
International Federation for Information Processing (IFIP) 380
International Standards Organisation (ISO) 228
interpretation 219
interpreter 220, 228
interrupt 118, 138, 152, 248
interrupt handler 256
interrupt line 118
interrupt service routine 118
ion implantation 96

Japan 372
JK flip-flop 71

job control language (JCL) 251
jump 114

Kemeny, John 202
kernel 261
key 294
key field 238
keyboard 3, 79, 80, 129, 130, 235, 258
keyboard illiteracy 130
keypad 352
knowledge 56, 57
knowledge base 337, 338
knowledge model 339
knowledge representation 57, 337, 338
knowledge-based expert systems 57
knowledge-based system 57, 337
Kowalski, Robert 214
Kurtz, Thomas E 202

label 163, 179, 197
language 56
language translation 178, 219
language translation package 174, 228
language translator 230
laptop microcomputer 77
large scale integration (LSI) 63
laser beam 132, 137
laser printer 79, 132, 133, 138, 362
last-in-first-out (LIFO) 29
latency 136
layer of software 245
leaf 33
least significant bit (LSB) 15
least significant digit 15
letter-quality output 133
level of privilege 251, 263
lexical analysis 222, 228
librarian utility 229
library module 226, 228
light pen 129, 130, 239
limit register 123
line printer 132, 139
linkage editor 226
linkage program 226
linked list 31, 150
linker 228
Lisp 32, 212, 338
list 31, 168, 186, 212, 215
list head 32
list tail 32
literal data 166
load-and-go compiler 227
local area network 77, 79, 325
local variable 186, 203
locate operand 116, 118
logic 11
logic circuit 48, 53, 82, 86, 94
logic design 94
logic gate 48, 51, 335
logic operation combination 51

logic operation symbol 51
logical if 194
logical operation 187
Logo 184
London Underground 365
long integer 41, 147
long pointer 147
long-distance network 79
loop 169, 170, 194, 197, 200, 204, 207, 211, 225
loop counter 188
looping 188
low level language 161, 183, 189, 209, 245
low-resolution graphics 133

machine 3
machine code 158, 226, 226
machine dependence 184
machine independence 183, 189, 193, 196, 199, 234
machine instruction 116, 153, 158, 161
machine language 103, 162, 178, 219, 220
machine oriented language 183
macro expansion 180
macro-instruction 164, 180, 251
magnetic disk 3, 80, 129, 135
magnetic disk drive 136
magnetic ink character recognition (MICR) 129, 131
magnetic strip 129, 132
magnetic tape 3, 80, 128, 137
magnetic tape unit 137
mailbox 330
main processor 355
main program 171, 193, 210
main store see memory
mainframe 78, 100, 135, 153, 244, 347, 350, 368, 375
maintenance control console 156
maintenance engineer 100
man-machine interface 10
management 280
mantissa 19, 20, 44
manufacturing industry 384
mark sensing 131
market research 98
mask 65, 95
masking 95
massively parallel architectures 126
master-slave flip-flop 71
mathematical logic 48
mathematical model 353
mathematics 184
mathematics co-processor 143
matrix 28, 187
medium 128
medium scale integration (MSI) 63
megabyte 85, 135, 143
memory 64, 79, 82, 84, 89,

101, 103, 116, 124, 125, 136, 138, 153, 156, 157, 159, 161, 248, 251, 262
memory access 124
memory address register 84
memory cycle 85, 105, 116
memory data register (MDR) 84, 118
memory management 247, 259, 262
memory management mechanism 149
memory management module 248
memory management unit 146
memory map 85
memory port 157
memory protection 251
memory refresh 86
memory unit 84
menu 130, 235, 237, 238, 259
menu-driven interface 309
merging 301
message switching 328
metallisation 97
Meteorological Office 352
micro-instruction 119
microchannel architecture (MCA) 143
microcode 118, 119
microcomputer 7, 79, 100, 104, 128, 135, 236, 238, 244, 255, 259, 260, 310, 324, 375
micron 97
microprocessor 64, 77, 79, 82, 138, 149, 174, 335, 347, 374
microprogramming 153
microsecond 118
Microsoft 377
mid-range computer 78, 79, 100, 135, 149, 244, 260, 375
million instructions per second (mips) 146
mini-packet 328
minicomputer 78, 350
mnemonic 162
mnemonic operation code 162, 166, 179
model computer 10, 82, 83
modem 321
modular design 94
module 9, 76, 128, 180, 185, 274
module testing 290
monitor 129, 132, 139
monitor program 245
monitor station 328
Morse code 320
most significant bit (MSB) 15, 42
most significant digit 15
most significant place 41
motherboard 99
mouse 129, 130, 235, 239, 309, 310
MS Windows 258
MS-DOS 143, 228, 255, 364

multi-access 245, 250, 261
multi-layer board 99
multi-port memory 123, 126
multi-threading 245
multi-user operating system 259
multi-way branch 188, 194, 211
multiple processor 159
multiplexer 65, 324, 350
multiplication 41, 42, 45, 72, 169
multiprogramming 149, 244, 250, 259
multiprogramming environment 149
multitasking 158, 244
Mycin 339

n-type semiconductor 93
NAND 50, 73
nanoseconds (ns) 118, 362
National Computing Centre (NCC) 380
natural language 7, 60, 184, 310
negative 87
negative feedback 334
negative flag 108
negative number 16
nested loop 195
network 4, 78, 362, 128, 246, 247, 365
network administrator 380
network data model 316, 317
network station 77, 325
networking 149
Nimbus PC-386 143
no-operation 115
node 33
noise 323
non-equivalence 49
non-equivalence gate 86
NOR 50
normalisation 19
NOT 48, 86, 187
noughts and crosses 59
nuclear reactor control system 336
nucleus 247, 248, 251
null pointer 27, 31, 33, 172
number of addresses 103
numeric character 15
numeric data 186, 203
numeric string 150
numerically controlled (NC) machine 343

object code 220, 224, 225
object language 219
object program 226
octal number 20, 21, 163
odd parity 21
offset 104
one-address computer 103, 153
one-address instruction 158
one-dimensional array 28
ones complement number 17, 40

OPEC 372
operand 116, 148
operand specifier 150
operating system 118, 143, 149, 165, 174, 244, 246, 294, 310, 386
operating system call 258
operating system command 252
operation 89, 187, 193, 197, 200, 203, 206, 210, 213
operation code 103, 105, 107, 148, 150, 158
operational system 333
operations manager 379
operator 252
operator documentation 291
operator interface 247
operator's console 80, 129
optical character recognition (OCR) 129, 131, 299
optical disk 80, 137
optical disk reader 137
optimisation 220, 225, 228
OR 49, 86, 187
ordered list 32
original equipment manufacturer (OEM) 374
orthogonality 150, 153
OS/2 143, 228
output 3, 128, 187, 194, 197, 200, 203, 207, 211, 215, 244, 248
output device 99, 132
output register 88, 110
overflow 40, 41, 44, 88
overflow bit 42
overflow flag 108
oxidation 95

p-n junction 93
p-type semiconductor 93
Pacific Rim 372
package 363
packed decimal number 16, 150, 153
packet switching 329
packet switching computer 329
packet switching network 330
packing density 297
page 123, 146, 149
page table 147, 149
paging unit 146
palette 239
paper tape 129
parallel access port 159
parallel adder 67
parallel computer architecture 125
parallel data transmission 321
parallel input-output (PIO) 139
parallel module 159
parallel port 143
parallel processor 78
parallelism 122, 156, 159
parameter 172, 249

parameter passing 203
parity bit 21, 324
parity check 21, 139
Parlog 216
parsing 60, 223
part hierarchy 94
Pascal 158, 184, 205, 228, 275
password 305, 385
pathname 257
payroll system 279
PDP-11 series 149, 153
peripheral 76, 79, 80, 101, 118, 123, 128, 138, 149, 152, 153, 156, 159, 194, 246, 251, 347, 376
peripheral controller 138, 143
peripheral device selection register 88
personal identity number (PIN) 366
photoresist 95
picture clause 200
pilot running 290
pipelining 123, 146, 153, 154, 156, 159
pixel 129, 139, 239
place value 14
placement and routing 362
plotter 364
plug-compatibility 76, 376
pocket calculator 77
pointer 27, 28, 33, 58, 104, 130, 147, 150, 168, 186, 206, 310
political consequences of computerisation 387
political control 387
political pressure 388
polling 138
pollution pressure 388
pop 29, 113
popular operating system 149
population pressure 388
port 149
portability 183, 260
Postscript 240
Powerhouse 268
precision 41
predicate 57, 213, 215
price/performance ratio 12
primary key 294
print queue 30
printed circuit board (PCB) 99
printer 79, 132, 235, 258
priority 250
priority interrupt 119
problem-orientation 183, 184, 189, 265
procedural language 184, 192
procedural learning 338
procedure 185, 197, 203, 274
procedure division 200
process 153
process control 279
processing 4, 40, 215, 244
processing cell 343
processing chip 100

processing circuit 63
processing unit 99, 123
processor 79, 82, 101, 103, 118, 129, 138, 143, 153, 246
processor architecture 82, 91
processor cycle 122
processor structure 82
production plan 345
production rule 59, 339
productivity 278
professional association 380
program 6, 10, 11, 29, 35, 118, 129, 161, 245, 287
program counter (PC) 89, 114, 116, 118, 150
program design 274
program division 199
program documentation 291
program error 179, 219
program generator 276, 300
program language 34
program loader 226
program loop 112
program module 220
program paragraph 200
program section 200
program sentence 200
program specification 276
program status bit 87
program structure 178, 185, 193, 197, 203, 206, 210, 273
program testing 290
program word 200
programmable control system 335
programmable read-only memory (PROM) 86
programmed logic array (PLA) 359
programmer 228, 265, 276, 287, 379
programming 273, 276
programming language 9, 10, 32
project delay 292
project milestone 292
Prolog 57, 184, 214, 338
proposition 57
prospector 339
Prospero Software 228
protected mode 147
protection 247, 251, 260, 263
protection bit 260
protection mechanism 149, 154, 261
prototype 99, 100, 265
proving the correctness of a program 275
pseudo-code 274
pseudo-operation 163
publication language 196
punched card 129, 194
push 29, 113
push-down list 29
push-down stack 29

QTP 270
quad word 147
queue 30, 31, 150

Quick 270
quicksort 300
Quiz 270
qwerty keyboard 129

random access media 137
random access memory (RAM) 85, 143, 359, 374
random file 294, 296
range 41
range check 299
range of a number 40
read access key 263
read from store 84
read permission 260
read-after-write 139
read-only memory (ROM) 8, 85, 119, 175, 253, 359, 374
read-write head 136, 137
readability 183, 184
real address space 147
real mode 147
real number 186
real-time clock 146
real-time control system 343
real-time processing 245, 279
real-time system 278
reasoning program 59
receiving 4
reception 128
record 187, 200, 237, 267, 294
recursion 115, 186, 221, 300, 302
recursive data structure 34
recursive subprogram 172
reduced instruction set computer (Risc) 83, 125
redundancy 329, 384
reference language 196
refresh 86
register 20, 71, 84, 103, 105, 108, 116, 118, 139, 148, 150, 153, 155, 156, 161, 166
register identifier 107
register indirect address 148
register operand mode 148
relational data model 316, 317
relational database 266
relative address 104, 109, 112, 151, 179, 226
religious pressure 388
relocatable code 105, 226, 228
relocation 227
remote job entry (RJE) 244
remote-access terminal 324
report generation 266, 268, 284, 304
report writer 270
requirements specification 281, 291
research 374, 377
research engineer 377
Research Machines 376
reserved word 185, 193, 197, 199, 203, 206, 210, 213, 215

reset 70, 116, 118
reset button 253
resistance to change 292
resolution 134
resource 7, 244, 245
resource allocation 247, 250
resource allocation policy 250
resource control 246
resource pressure 388
result register 86
retrieval 3, 128
return 114
ring architecture 326
ring power supply station 328
ring station 328
Ritchie, Dennis 209
robot 57, 335
Rolls Royce 341, 383
root 33
root directory 260
rotate 108
rounding 45
RS flip-flop 68
rule 57
rule of inference 57
rule of precedence 187
rule of syntax 185, 223
run-time diagnostics 227, 229, 276

sample 22
sampling frequency 22
sampling rate 140
scalar processing 155
scaled index address 148
scanner 129, 131
scheduling 246, 247, 250, 262
scheduling policy 250
schematic 94, 359, 361
schematic hierarchy 362
scientist 377
scope 186, 193, 203, 206, 210
screen design module 266, 267
search and replace 235
searching 235, 302
second source 100
secondary key 294
sector 135
seek time 136
segment 146
segment register 146
segmentation unit 146
selection sort 300
self-checking code 21
self-modification 214
semantic error 225
semantic network 57, 339
semantics 60
semiconductor 93
sending 4
sensor 334, 350
sequencing 188, 198
sequential file 294, 295
sequential search 302
serial access medium 137
serial addition 68, 72
serial file 294, 295

serial logic 68
serial port 143
service industry 384
set 70, 139
set operation 206
shell 260
Shell sort 300
shift 42
shift register 72, 86, 328
short branch 110
side effect 274
sign extension 85
sign-and-magnitude code 16, 18, 19, 40
sign-and-modulus code 16
silicon 12, 93
silicon chip see integrated circuit
silicon compilation 359
silicon crystal 95
silicon fabrication 364
silicon layout 94
Silicon Valley 372
simplex communication 321
simplicity 185
simulation 94, 99, 352, 353, 359, 362
simulation stimuli 362
simulator 276
single-error correction, double error detection (SECDED) 140, 158
single disk cartridge 135
single program operation 244
single stepping 228
single-pass assembler 180
single-user operating system 255
slave store 124
soak test 100
software 8, 10, 27, 41, 99, 136, 161, 234, 244, 245, 246, 253, 273, 313, 350, 372
software compatibility 288
software configuration 288
software developer 246
software development 376
software development environment 276
software development system 228
software development tool 189, 202, 220, 265, 276
software engineer 278, 287, 344
software engineering 189, 273, 379, 380
software front panel 129
software house 368, 376, 380
software maintenance 265, 266
software package 149, 234, 241, 287, 308, 377
software testing 100
software virus 385
Sony Music 346
sorting 300
sorting large files 301
source code 220, 225, 273
source document 299

source language 219
source program 228
special character 15, 185
special-purpose computer 122
special-purpose language 184, 192
special-purpose microprocessor 174
specification 291
speech synthesis 134
spool file 139
spooling 249, 260
spreadsheet 234, 236
stack 29, 89, 112, 113, 114, 115, 153, 186, 262
stack base 29
stack pointer 29, 89, 90, 105, 113, 118, 150, 166
standard form number 19
standard interface 10, 246, 273
standard user interface 259, 308, 310
state table 223, 232
statement 197
static data structure 28
static RAM 86
stepwise refinement 274
storage 3, 128
storage circuit 68
store multiple access controller (SMAC) 153
strategy 57
streamer tape 137
string 28, 147, 301
structured information 27
structured programming 209
sub-directory 257
subprogram 29, 112, 114, 115, 171, 193, 203, 226
subroutine 185, 193
subsystem 6
subtraction 16, 18, 41, 45
sum 67
Sun Microsystems 375
supercomputer 78, 80, 154, 209, 244, 259, 356
supervisor program 245
Swift 329
switch 93
symbol 7, 362
symbolic address 162, 166, 179
synoptic database 355, 356
syntax 60
syntax analysis 222, 223, 228
syntax diagram 185, 222
syntax error 225
system 5, 245
system control language (SCL) 261
system cost 291
system design 281
system development 287
system failure 386
system flowchart 282
system flowchart symbol 282
system implementation 290

system maintenance 291
system manager 80, 247, 380
system security 365
system software 99
system testing 290
system troubleshooting 291
System X 329
systems analysis 265, 273, 281
systems analyst 278, 280, 379
systems house 376
systems programmer 378
systems software 174, 189, 212

T diagram 219
tape cartridge 137
tape spool 137
target language 219
team leader 287
technical author 291
technician 377
technological pressure 389
telecommunications 320, 373
telex 320
terminal 78, 80, 128, 132, 252, 299, 347, 350, 368
terminal node 33
text file 295
thermostat 334
Third World 373
three level memory 124
three-address computer 103
time allocation 246
time slicing 250
token 222, 224
top of the stack 29
top-down process 275
touch-sensitive screen 129, 130
track 99, 135, 137
training course 384
transaction processing 245, 261, 279
transaction processing application 347
transaction processing system 304, 368
transaction processing system generator 270
transistor 63, 93
transistor-transistor logic (TTL) 93
transmission 128
transnational company 371
transputer 64, 126
tree 33, 186, 211, 249, 257, 303, 317
tree search 302, 303
tree sort 300
tree traversal 34, 172, 303
truncation error 45
truth table 48, 51, 53, 361
Turing Machine 11
Turing Test 56
Turing, Alan 11
turnaround document 299

turnkey contract 376
two-address computer 103
two-address instruction 158
two-dimensional array 28
two-pass assembler 180
twos complement number 16, 18, 19, 40, 41, 108
type check 299
typeface 235, 240
typesetting equipment 240

uncommitted logic array (ULA) 73, 99
unconditional branching 109, 188, 194, 200, 204
underflow 40, 44
Underground Ticketing System (UTS) 365
unemployment 384
uninterrupted power supply (UPS) 80
Union of Soviet Socialist Republics (USSR) 373
United Kingdom (UK) 372
United States of America (USA) 372

Unix 143, 153, 209, 255, 259, 364
usage 270
USART 73
user 100, 139, 246, 251, 260, 265, 280, 290, 378, 380
user group 242, 380
user identity 330
user interface 10, 234, 241, 256, 260, 288, 290, 308, 364
user mode 270
user-defined data type 206
utility 255

vacuum column 137
validation 238, 283, 299, 353, 355, 356
validation routine 364
variable 186, 223, 223
variable declaration 186, 197
variable wordlength 20
VAX 143, 149, 268, 329, 338, 375
Vaxmail 329
Vaxmail command 330
vector 239

vector processing 155
vector processor 122
vector register 155
very high resolution graphics 154
very large scale integration (VLSI) 63, 374
video camera 131
virtual address 146, 149
virtual address space 149, 152
virtual machine 246, 261
virtual memory 123, 146, 149, 248, 249, 259, 262
visual display unit (VDU) 129
VLSI chip 143, 156, 359, 364, 372
VME/B 255, 261
voice recognition 122, 132
volatile RAM 86
Von Neumann, John 11, 122
wafer 95
waveform 94, 362
weather forecasting 352
what you see is what you

get (Wysiwyg) 235, 241, 308
wimp environment 310
Winchester disk 79, 135, 143, 241, 364
window 235, 244, 310
windows environment 129
word 20, 83, 107, 146, 156, 166
word processing 222, 234, 240, 276
wordlength 20, 153
workstation 77, 100, 125, 128, 139, 209, 234, 238, 240, 244, 252, 260, 276, 310, 375
wrap-around carry 18
write access key 263
write permission 260
write to store 85

yield 97

zero 87
zero flag 108
zero-address computer 103